─ THE ─
COUNTR
DIRECTORY

C000042372

SPHERE

THE ROYAL AGRICULTURAL SOCIETY OF ENGLAND
RASE

English
Tourist Board

STB

BWRDD CROESO CYMRU
WALES TOURIST BOARD

Northern Ireland
Tourist Board

A Sphere Book

First published in Great Britain by Sphere Books Ltd., 1991

Copyright © English Tourist Board and Royal Agricultural Society of England, 1991

The information contained in this Guide has been published in good faith on the basis of the details submitted by the proprietors of the premises listed. Whilst every effort has been made to ensure accuracy in this publication, neither the publisher nor the National Tourist Boards can guarantee the accuracy of the information in this Guide and accept no responsibility for any error or misrepresentation.

All rights reserved. No part of this publication may be reproduced, stored in a retrieval system, or transmitted, in any form or by any means without the prior permission in writing of the publisher, nor be otherwise circulated in any form of binding or cover other than that in which it is published and without a similar condition including this condition being imposed on the subsequent purchaser.

Designed and produced by the Pen and Ink Book Company Ltd, Huntingdon, Cambridgeshire

Atlas section by Lovell Johns.

Reproduced, printed and bound in Great Britain.

Cover photograph supplied by Visionbank.
All other photographs supplied by the English Tourist Board.

ISBN 0 7474 0772 X

Sphere Books Ltd
A Division of Macdonald & Co (Publishers) Ltd
Orbit House
1 New Fetter Lane
London EC4A 1AR

A member of Maxwell Macmillan Pergamon Publishing Corporation

Guide to Symbols

☎ telephone	🐕 dogs welcome (on a leash)
♿ disabled welcome	✗ dogs not welcome
🚌 coaches welcome	

CONTENTS

The Country Code
- Enjoy the countryside and respect its life and work
- Guard against all risk of fire
- Fasten all gates
- Keep your dogs under close control
- Keep to public paths across farmland
- Use gates and stiles to cross fences, hedges and walls
- Leave livestock, crops and machinery alone
- Take your litter home
- Help to keep all water clean
- Protect wildlife, plants and trees
- Take special care on country roads
- Make no unnecessary noise

Introduction

Welcome to the Countryside Directory. The first directory, published in 1989, has proven so popular and drawn such an enthusiastic response that we have produced this revised and extended edition to guide you through the rich and fascinating landscape of rural Britain. The directory is full of places and pursuits for you to see and enjoy throughout the countryside, all through the year. An invaluable guide for anyone who cares about the countryside and wishes to explore its rich patchwork of natural beauty, its cultural traditions and crafts.

Ripening corn in the open fields, parkland studded with magnificent old oaks, the rich russet reds and golds of hedgerows in autumn, the haunting silhouettes of bare trees set against a winter sky are all scenes through the seasons that never fail to evoke the longing most townspeople feel for the countryside. The more pressured our lives become as we reap the benefits and pay the price for the time saving paraphernalia of our modern lifestyle, the more we crave timeless days, windswept cliffs, cosy villages and woodland walks. This directory will guide you to whatever aspect of the countryside provides you with your heart's ease, a windswept walk along a coastal path, an opportunity to help feed the lambs and watch the pigs or perhaps the chance to taste the rich produce of the countryside, unusual cheeses, real ale, fresh fruit, English wines, cream teas with butter made on the premises. Whatever it is you'll find it in this directory and discover how easy it is for even the most urban of dwellers to reach a country corner by car, bike, horse or on foot.

The future of the British countryside has never been so high on the nation's agenda. The traditional landscape and wildlife of Britain has been under threat from the changes in the agricultural system as well as the rapid housing, commerical and industrial development that has taken place over the past 30 years. Environmental issues were once the province of a few specialist groups, today, words such as 'heritage' and 'conservation' are on everybody's lips and 'green' issues are influencing the policy-makers as we recognise our responsibility to Britain's precious rural heritage.

This increased awareness of the countryside, our natural inheritance, the 'green and pleasant land' of our dreams and the inspiration for poets and artists throughout the centuries, has awakened new interest in its traditions and ways and in the rhythms and cycles of its flora and fauna. Aroused by the possible disappearance of that cherished

countryside we are discovering its richness and diversity anew. A revival of country traditions and crafts now sees the dry stone waller and the thatcher booked up for work months in advance. The individuality of the regions and counties comes alive in the workmanship of their craftsmen; the differing techniques and materials, customs and traditions, tools and implements all contribute to the contrasts that make each twist in a country lane an exciting journey of discovery. Wandering around Leicestershire you might visit a craft workshop such as The Glass Workshop in Market Harborough where you can watch glass and pottery being made, even try your hand at it yourself, or see farming in action, whatever the weather, at the Stoughton Farm Park whilst the children meet the tame animals before they play on the adventure play island in the lake.

Over the centuries the appearance of the landscape has been fashioned by farming. The countryside, after all, is first and foremost the place where we grow the food we eat and the timber with which we build and equip our homes. The British countryside as we know and love it cannot be preserved by making it a museum of the past, it is only by actively enjoying it, by finding out what made it what it is that we can gauge the future impact of our present actions and so ensure that it remains a thriving part of our community and country. Visit one of the heavy horse centres and discover the important place shire horses once had in the rural economy, see how new machinery and traditional methods blend to make the delicious farm produce that reminds us 'small is beautiful' in the rural community, take home the attractive and useful crafts that weave, with time and care, the natural world into our everyday environments. Follow one of the woodland or country walks, an adventure for all the family and four-legged friends too. A wonderland for children, the countryside is a 'real' storybook of tractors and animals and friendly people that will enchant and enhance their days and breathe life into their bedtime reading books. Enjoy the countryside and it will live and grow in ways sympathetic to both the past and the present.

Enjoyment of the countryside must always be tempered with respect for its way of life, its industries and its possible dangers. With this in mind The Country Code has been included in this edition to inform and remind visitors of the courtesies, small and large, that will retain the goodwill of the farmers and local people, ensure the safety of the livestock and the visitor and guarantee an enjoyable country outing for everyone.

The Directory covers a wide range of rural recreation and leisure facilities in more than 2000 entries, a range of new rural attractions that will give the visitor an invaluable insight into what goes on in the countryside has also been included. You will be able to find your own special country interests or perhaps be tempted to discover some new ones from the facilities listed; there are country walks, country parks, craft centres, farm interpretation centres, farm shops, fishing, forestry centres, garden centres, herb gardens, museums, nature reserves, pick-your-own centres, picnic areas, potteries, rare breed centres, rural and agricultural archaeology sites, speciality food and drink producers, vineyards, wildlife parks, and working farms – something of interest to everyone no matter what their age.

How To Use This Book

The Directory is arranged alphabetically in county order. Within each county category, individual entries are listed under the name of the nearest town or city, again in alphabetical order. When you have found an entry that interests you, perhaps the Kitchen Garden, as listed on page 3 and included here, you will find an outline of the facilities available followed by the full address, telephone number and directions to locate it. Opening times, details of any admission charges, access for the disabled, provision for coaches, access for dogs plus any supplementary information about the place is then listed for each entry. For each locality the directory provides a comprehensive guide to what you can see and do there.

THE KITCHEN GARDEN

Speciality food producers, farm shop and pick your own

Old Down House, Tockington, Bristol, Avon BS12 4PG
☎ Thornbury (0454) 413605

Produce grain on site in a country setting. Food shop, gift shop, restaurant and garden.

At Old Down, Tockington, 3 miles north of the
  M4/M5 interchange north of Bristol
Open daily except Mondays, 9.00am–5.00pm. Closes
  7.00pm during summer
Free admission except to garden (£1.00)
& ⊞ advance notice required 🐕

The Countryside Directory is an essential handbook for anyone wanting to explore the countryside. Make it your companion, use it to plan a day out or a family holiday and you will find yourself on an unforgettable adventure through the landscapes and rural traditions that make Britain's countryside so special.

English Tourist Board
Quality Books & Guides

Where To Stay
(1991 series) Best-selling England guides to: *Hotels & Guesthouses* £6.95, *Bed & Breakfast, Farmhouses, Inns & Hostels* £5.95. *Self-Catering Holiday Homes* £4.95. *Also in the Where to Stay* series: *Camping & Caravan Parks in Britain* £4.95. With descriptions of towns, comprehensive indexes, maps and features on the English regions. (Available January 1991)

Choose Your Accommodation With Confidence.

![crown symbol] *Hotels & Guesthouses* and *Bed & Breakfast, Farmhouses, Inns & Hostels* feature the national Crown ratings. The classifications, from Listed to 👑👑👑👑👑 indicate the range of facilities and services. Those offering higher quality standards have the term APPROVED, COMMENDED or HIGHLY COMMENDED alongside the classification.

![key symbol] All the holiday homes featured in the *Self-Catering Holiday Homes* guide are inspected by the tourist boards. The classifications 🔑 to 🔑🔑🔑🔑🔑 indicate the range of facilities and equipment provided. Those offering higher quality standards have the term APPROVED, COMMENDED or HIGHLY COMMENDED alongside the classification.

![symbol] *Camping & Caravan Parks in Britain* gives details of the national British Graded Holiday Parks Scheme. Parks participating in the scheme are graded from 1-5 ✓ symbols according to the relative quality of what is offered.

![golf and holidays afloat covers]

Family Leisure Guides
(In association with Robertson McCarta)
Essential guides for anyone wanting to combine a favourite sport with a weekend break or short holiday for all the family. The first two titles in the series are Horse Racing and Golf. Each is a fully-illustrated guide to the UK with details of leisure attractions around each course. (Price £9.95)

Holidays Afloat
Your official guide to boating and watersports around Britain. (In association with Burlington Publishing and the British Marine Industries Federation.) Whatever water-based activity catches your imagination - whether a relaxing cruise or a course in powerboat handling - Holidays Afloat contains all the information you need to plan and enjoy your holiday or short break. Details of

hundreds of holiday companies - complete with entertaining and informative features. Fully illustrated, maps, glossaries, etc. (Price £4.95)

Stay On A Farm
(In association with the Farm Holiday Bureau UK and William Curtis Ltd.) Official guide to nearly 1,000 farms in membership of the Farm Holiday Bureau. All inspected and approved by the national tourist boards. Accommodation includes B&B, half-board, self-catering. Enjoy the countryside from the unique hospitality of a working farm. (Price £4.95)

The Countryside Directory
(In association with Sphere and The Royal Agricultural Society of England.) From farming museums to pick your own fruit and vegetable farms, agricultural shows to afternoon teas - whatever you need to know about countryside activities. (Price £6.99)

Let's Do It!
(In association with William Curtis Ltd.) Hundreds of ideas for holidays and breaks in England. Discover new interests or improve existing skills - from action and sport, study courses, special interests, holidays afloat and children's holidays. (Price £2.95)

Journey Through Britain
(In association with Ravensburger Fisher-Price.) Have fun getting to know Britain with this family game. A race through Britain's towns and cities answering questions based on places of interest. Beautifully illustrated. (Price £12.99 from all good toyshops)

John Hillaby's Walking in Britain
(In association with Collins). An inspirational and comprehensive guide to the great walks and walking country of Britain, with contributions from well-known enthusiasts such as Hunter Davies, Richard Mabey and Adam Nicolson. (Hardback, price £14.95, paperback, price £5.99)

For the best choice in books on England, look for the English Tourist Board logo.

Don't forget to mark your diary!

The Royal Agricultural Society of England is in the business of communication and information. In addition to managing the National Agricultural Centre, the Society organises a full programme of events throughout the year. This includes the World's No.1 international agricultural exhibition – the Royal Show. Take a look at just some of the events taking place in 1991:

Muck '91	24 – 25 April
European Poultry Fair '91	15 – 16 May
Landscape Industries '91	5 – 6 June
Cereals '91 (to be held at Toddington, Bedfordshire)	12 – 13 June
Royal Show	1 – 4 July
National Show and Sale of Registered Suffolk Sheep	17 – 18 July
Town and Country Festival	24 – 26 August
Rare Breeds Survival Trust Show and Sale	6 – 7 September
National Small Farming incorporating Goat '91	28 – 29 September

For further information on these and other events held at the NAC, or to obtain a copy of the Diary of Agricultural Show Dates, please contact the Press Office on (0203) 696969

THE ROYAL AGRICULTURAL SOCIETY OF ENGLAND

Royal Agricultural Society of England

National Agricultural Centre, Stoneleigh, Warwickshire, CV8 2LZ.
Telephone no. (0203) 696969   Fax no. (0203) 696900 Telex 31697

AVON

Avon is well watered and essentially rural, its pleasant countryside leads to the quiet charm of the Severn Estuary. Two ancient cities are contained within its boundaries, Bristol, lively and contemporary with a past that echoes its importance as a flourishing port, and Bath, a city of elegant, Georgian splendour soaked in history.

Avon's unspoilt countryside has many working farms that will give the visitor an insight into organic farming practice, cornmilling, herb farming and the conservation of rare breeds. There are several opportunities to look back to once familiar farming scenes where shire horses and horse-drawn vehicles played an important role. Traditional craftsmen can be visited and watched at work in their studios. There are many fine walks through copses, greenland, woodland and parkland which reveal the history and natural beauty of the area.

▶ **BATH** ◀

NORWOOD FARM

Working farm and rare breed centre

Bath Rd, Norton St Philip, nr Bath, Avon BA3 6LP
☎ Faulkland (037 387) 356

*Norwood is run on the principles of
sustainable agriculture, organics and the
conservation of rare breeds. Visitors can
touch and feed many of the wide variety of
native farm animals. Cafe specialising in
high quality farmhouse-made lunches and
teas. Picnic and play area. Farm shop.*

On the B3110 Bath–Frome road, 6 miles south of
Bath, just north of Norton St Philip
Open 11.00am–5.00pm 29 March–15 Sept. Parties by
appointment anytime
Admission: adult £2.00, child/OAP £1.25, party rates
available
& 🚐 advance notice required ✖

PARK FARM

Farm interpretation centre and farm visit

G E Padfield, Park Farm, Kelston, Bath, Avon BA1 9AG
☎ Bath (0225) 24139

*Groups are given a conducted tour of the
500 acre mixed farm from a tractor and
trailer. Farm cream teas available.*

From Bath take the A431 to Bristol. Kelston is on
the A431, 3 miles from Bath
Open May–Sept
Admission: £1.50 per person
& 🚐 advance notice required ✖

PRISTON MILL

Working cornmill with waterwheel

Priston Mill Farm, Priston, nr Bath, Avon BA2 9EQ
☎ Bath (0225) 423894/429894

*Once run by the monks of Bath Abbey, the
mill has been in continuous use since 931
and is now part of the Duchy of Cornwall
Estate. Milling demonstrations most
weekends. Nature trail, adventure play areas,
trailer rides and cream teas.*

Off the A39 from Marksbury, 5 miles south west of
Bath. Follow signs for Priston
Open Easter–Sept, daily 2.15–5.30pm, Sundays and Bank
Holidays 11.00am–5.30pm

Admission: adult £1.75, child/OAP £1.25, visitors in
wheelchairs admitted free
& 🚐 advance notice required ✖

RADFORD FARM & SHIRE HORSES

Farm interpretation centre and museum

Radford, Tinsbury, nr Bath, Avon BA3 1QF
☎ Tinsbury (0761) 70106

*Animals include Shire horses, hand-milked
cows, older breeds of pigs, poultry, goats and
sheep. Collection of farm implements and
horse-drawn vehicles. Nature trail, pets
corner.*

On the A367, 1½ miles from Bath, take the right
hand fork for the B3115
Open Easter–end Sept daily except Saturdays, 10.30am–
5.00pm
Admission: adult £2.00, child/OAP £1.50
& 🚐 advance notice required 🐂

RAINBOW WOOD FARM PARK

Farm interpretation centre and nature trail

Rainbow Wood Farm, Claverton Down, Bath BA2 7AR
☎ Bath (0225) 466366

*Farming bygones, farm shop, picnic area,
adventure playground, childrens farmyard
and cream teas.*

From Bath follow signs for University and American
Museum. At top of hill, farm is 150 yards on the
right
Open weekends and school holidays Easter–Sept, closed
Mondays (except Bank holidays)
Admission: adult £2.00, child £1.25, OAP/UB40 £1.25
& 🚐 ✖

▶ **BRISTOL** ◀

ARNE HERBS

Herb farm

Limeburn Nurseries, Limeburn Hill, Chew Magna, Bristol,
Avon BS18 8QW
☎ Chew Magna (0272) 333399

*Extensive collection of culinary and medical
herbs from all over the world, large plants a
speciality. No formal herb garden as such,
plants are kept in polytunnels and open
ground. Wild flower meadow.*

Turn off the A38 near Bristol Airport and rollow signposts for Winford on the B3130. 3 miles out of Winford towards Chew Magna, turn left at the Ford Garage and the entrance is 300 yards on the left
Open 9.00am–6.00pm but telephone appointment advisable
Free admission
  samples brought to disabled visitors in their cars
  advance notice required

ASHTON COURT ESTATE

Country park

Long Ashton, Bristol, Avon BS18 9JN
☎ Bristol (0272) 633518/633438 Manor House Estate

840 acres of woodland and parkland, nature trails, deer park. Ancient manor house open occasionally for guided tours – telephone ahead.

From jct 19 of the M5, head towards Bristol on the A369 for approx 4 miles. Ashton Court Estate is on the right hand side
Open all year dawn–dusk
Free admission
  advance notice required

FROME VALLEY WALKWAY

Country walk

c/o Northavon District Council, The Council Offices, Castle St, Thornbury, Bristol, Avon BS12 1HF
☎ Thornbury (0454) 416262

Footpath beside the river through copses, fields and greenways in Yate and historic Chipping Sodbury, meeting the Cotswold Way at Old Sodbury. Look for old mills, mines, kingfishers and dragonflies. A pack of 2 leaflets is available for £1.00 plus postage.

1 mile east of the B4058 at Frenchay, Bristol
Open all year – public right of way
Free admission
  access is difficult because of stiles

HARTCLIFFE COMMUNITY PARK FARM

Farm visit

Lampton Avenue, Hartcliffe, Bristol, Avon BS13 0LF
☎ Bristol (0272) 782014

A 50 acre working farm with rare cattle, traditional pigs, sheep, geese, chickens and ducks. Children may see and touch goats, lambs and 'Weenie' the pig. Refreshments available. Picnic area.

Follow signs to Bedminster, then Hartcliffe, take third left off roundabout at top of Hartcliffe Way and then first left into Lampton Avenue
Open all year daily
Free admission – donations welcome

THE KITCHEN GARDEN

Speciality food producers, farm shop and pick your own

Old Down House, Tockington, Bristol, Avon BS12 4PG
☎ Thornbury (0454) 413605

Produce grain on site in a country setting. Food shop, gift shop, restaurant and garden.

At Old Down, Tockington, 3 miles north of the M4/M5 interchange north of Bristol
Open daily except Mondays, 9.00am–5.00pm. Closes 7.00pm during summer
Free admission except to garden (£1.00)
  advance notice required

▶   *CLEVEDON*   ◀

CLEVEDON CRAFT CENTRE

Craft centre

Moor Lane, Clevedon, Avon BS21 6TD
☎ Clevedon (0272) 872149

Traditionl craftsmen at work in fourteen studios including silversmiths, woodturning, pottery, house signs, leather carving, glass engraving, re-upholstery, weaving, furniture stripping and hand-made furniture. Tea room offering home-made cakes and snacks.

Leave the M5 at exit 20, follow the signs to Clevedon Court on the B3130 Bristol road. Turn right opposite the court, proceed over the motorway and turn right into Moor Lane
Open all year Tues–Sat 11.00am–5.00pm and Sunday afternoons. Closed for lunch 1.00–2.00pm
Free admission
  some workshop access difficult
  advance notice required

BEDFORDSHIRE

Bedfordshire rests in the valley of the River Great Ouse, a broad wandering river that meanders through rolling pastureland and water-meadows, its tributaries marked by willows and lined by paths for anglers.

A peaceful region where history has been absorbed, half of Bedfordshire's population lives in Luton and Bedford leaving much of the county to the farmer. Its rural heritage is open for the visitor to enjoy at its many country parks and gardens, some of which offer excellent recreational facilities, and at its country museums, bird gardens and wild fowl parks. Rural crafts and their associated implements and tools are on show and demonstrations of pot-throwing can be booked in advance. The numerous country walks pass through ancient and modern woodland, attractive countryside and nature reserves with many species of birds to watch in their chosen habitats. A day's angling can be happily combined with a taste of the countryside as supplied by the farm shop produce.

▶ BEDFORD ◀

BROMHILL MILL

Historic mill and interpretation centre

Bromham, Bedford
☎ Bedford (0234) 228330

Restored by Bedfordshire County Council, this historic watermill with working machinery is now run as a museum with interpretative exhibitions and a natural history room. The art and craft gallery offers a varied programme throughout the season. Riverside picnic site and nature reserve.

North of the A428 Bedford–Northampton road, adjacent to Bromham bridge
Open Wed–Fri 10.30am–4.30pm, weekends and Bank Holidays 11.30am–6.00pm
Admission: adult 50p, child/OAP 25p
♿ ♨ advance notice required ✗

ELSTOW MOOT HALL

Restored mediaeval market hall managed as a museum

Elstow, Bedford
☎ Bedford (0234) 228330

A fine example of a timber framed building, originally used as a market hall, now managed as a museum containing a permanent display relating to the life of John Bunyan, which includes many editions of his works.

Sited in the centre of Elstow Village, to the south of Bedford, east of the A6
Open April–Oct, Tues–Sat and Bank Holidays 2.00–5.00pm, Sunday 2.00–5.30pm
Admission: adult 50p, child/OAP 25p
♿ no wheelchair access ♨ ✗

PRIORY COUNTRY PARK

Country park

c/o North Bedfordshire Borough Council, Barkers Lane, Bedford MK41 9SH
☎ Bedford (0234) 211182

230 acre park with lakes and river frontage. Sailing, canoeing, fishing and nature trails. Activities throughout the year.

Off the A603 from Sandy and the A428 from the A1, follow signposts
Open all year. Visitor centre open Mon–Fri 9.30am–4.30pm, Sun 2.30–4.30pm

Free admission. Telephone for details of Priory Diary
♿ ♨ advance notice required

STAGSDEN BIRD GARDENS

Bird garden and breeding centre

Stagsden, Bedfordshire MK43 8SL
☎ Oakley (02302) 2745

Bird garden and breeding centre specialising in cranes, rare pheasants, owls, waterfowl and old breeds of poultry. Collection of roses, picnic area, shop.

5 miles west of Bedford off the A422
Open daily 11.00am–6.00pm (or dusk if earlier) all year round
Admission: adult £2.00, child 80p, OAP £1.50
♿ ♨ advance notice required ✗

STEVINGTON COUNTRY WALK

Country walk

Stevington, Bedford
☎ Bedford (0234) 228321

2 mile stretch of the former Bedford to Northampton railway line giving fine views over the River Ouse valley. Developed as a nature reserve and walk, with a small car park.

West of Bedford between Bromham and Stevington
Open all year
Free admission
♿ ♨ ♨

STEWARTBY LAKE COUNTRY PARK

Country park with recreational activities

c/o Leisure Services Department, County Hall, Bedford MK42 9AP
☎ Bedford (0234) 228160

The largest expanse of water in Bedfordshire attracts many local and national bird varieties, particularly in winter. Bird watching is excellent all year round on the main walk around the 318 acre lake. Water sports are popular here too, run by the Stewartby Water Sports Club.

6 miles south west of Bedford on the A421 Bedford–M1 link road, approx 1 mile north west of Marston Moretaine
Open all year
Free admission
♿ ♨

SUMMERFIELD FRUIT FARM

Farm shop and pick your own

Rook Tree Farm, Haynes, Bedford MK45 3PT
☎ Haynes (023066) 400

Camping and caravan site. Fish and trout lake for fly fishing, fresh trout sold in farm shop.

On the A600 between Bedford and Shefford, look out for signs
Open daily all year except Christmas week
Free admission
&. 🚌 🏇

SUNDON HILLS COUNTRY PARK

Country park with recreational activities

c/o Leisure Services Department, County Hall, Bedford MK42 9AP
☎ Bedford (0234) 228160

This tranquil and unspoilt chalk downland area is one of the highest points in Bedfordshire and a Site of Special Scientific Interest. Orchids, beech hangers and heavily wooded, steep coombes distinguish the site. Sundon Hills is included in the Chiltern Hills Area of Outstanding Natural Beauty.

Approx 5 miles north of Luton on the Upper Sundon–Harlington road midway between the two villages
Open all year
Free admission
&. 🏇

WILLINGTON GARDEN CENTRE

Garden centre

Sandy Road, Willington, Bedford MK44 3QP
☎ Cardington (0234) 838777

Superb indoor plant house selling home-grown hardy stock, garden sundries shop, childrens play area, restaurant serving home-cooked meals and coffee shop.

On the A603, 6 miles from Bedford
Open Mon–Fri 9.00am–5.30pm, Sat 9.00am–5.30pm, Sun 10.00am–5.30pm, April–June open till 7.00pm Thur & Fri
Free admission
&. 🚌 advance notice required 🏇

▶ **BIGGLESWADE** ◀

THE SWISS GARDEN

Country garden

Old Warden, Bedfordshire
☎ Bedford (0234) 228330

A unique romantic landscaped garden dating from the early 19th century containing original buildings, ironwork, ponds, trees and shrubs, some of great rarity. Attractive lakeside picnic site in adjoining woodland open all year.

Approx 2 miles west of the A1 at Biggleswade
Open April–Oct Wed–Sun and Bank Holidays 1.30–6.00pm
Admission: adult £1.00, child/OAP 50p. Party rates available
&. most paths light gravel surface
🚌 advance notice required 🏇

▶ **DUNSTABLE** ◀

HARLINGTON ARMS STABLE POTTERIES

Pottery shop and studio

7 Station Road, Harlington, Bedfordshire, LU5 6LD
☎ Toddington (05255) 2582

A pottery situated in old stables attached to an ex–Public House which produces decorative and functional stoneware made and fired in a gas kiln on the premises. Demonstrations given with advanced booking.

½ mile off A5120 close to M1 jct 12, 100 yards from Harlington railway station
Open all year, Wed–Sun 10.00am–6.00pm and Bank Holiday Mondays
Free admission
&. 🚌 advance notice required 🏇

▶ **HARROLD** ◀

HARROLD-ODELL COUNTRY PARK

Country park with recreational activities

c/o Leisure Services Department, County Hall, Bedford, MK42 9AP
☎ Bedford (0234) 228330

A 144 acre site developed from former gravel workings. Riverbank, river meadows, reedbeds, nature reserve and system of lakes and islands. As may be expected this variety of habitat attracts birds ranging from kingfishers to Canada geese.

Between the villages of Harrold and Odell on the north bank of the river Ouse – vehicle entrance 100 yards north of Harrold bridge
Open all year
Free admission
&. ⚑ 🏇

► LEIGHTON BUZZARD ◄

GREENSAND RIDGE WALK

Country walk

c/o Bedfordshire County Council, Bedfordshire
☎ Bedford (0234) 228759

A fascinating mix of ancient and modern woodland, rural and town settings, and a rich animal and plant life unique to the Greensand Woods and fields can be discovered on the walk. A leaflet guide can be purchased from the above address.

Walk commences off Linslade Road, Leighton Buzzard and continues for approx 40 miles across the county to Gamlingay Cinques in Cambridgeshire
Open all year
Free admission
&. ⚑ 🏇

► LUTON ◄

STOCKWOOD CRAFT MUSEUM AND GARDENS

Craft centre and country museum

Stockwood Park, Farley Hill Entrance, Luton, Bedfordshire LU1 4BH
☎ Luton (0582) 38714

Housed in the old stable block of the former Stockwood House, the museum boasts displays illustrating rural life and trades. Objects relating to basketmaking, woodcrafts and agricultural implements stand alongside wheeled vehicles. A series of period gardens containing sculptures by Ian Hamilton Finlay.

Near M1 jct 10
Open March–Oct daily (closed Mon and Tues), 10.00am–5.00pm
Free admission
&. ⚑ 🏇

UPPER LEA VALLEY WALK

Long distance footpath

c/o Bedfordshire County Council, Bedfordshire
☎ Bedford (0234) 228759

Choose from a 9 mile walk from the river's source at Leagrave Common to East Hyde or a circular walk of 13 miles from East Hyde via Someries Castle. Leaflet guide can be purchased from the above address.

Route starts at Leagrave Common, Luton and ends at East Hyde
Open all year
Free admission
&. 🏇

WOODSIDE FARM AND WILD FOWL PARK

Farm shop, country walks, farm trails and wild fowl park

Mancroft Road, Aley Green, Nr Slip End, Luton, Bedfordshire LU1 4DG
☎ Luton (0582) 841044

Set in 7 acres of quiet countryside. Large selection of rare breeds, pets corner, adventure playground, arts and crafts, coffee shop, traditional farm shop and poultry centre. Large car park.

Borders the B4540 Luton–Markyate road, 2 miles from Luton
Open every day except Sundays, closed Christmas and Boxing Day
Admission: adult £1.00, child/OAP 80p
&. ⚑ advance notice required 🏇

► NORTH BEDFORDSHIRE ◄

THREE SHIRES WAY

Long distance bridleway/walk

c/o Bedfordshire County Council, Bedfordshire
☎ Bedford (0234) 228759

A 45 mile long distance bridleway and walk linking the Swan's Way in Buckinghamshire with a circular walk around Grafham Water in Cambridgeshire, passing through attractive countryside and villages in North Bedfordshire. Leaflet guide can be purchased from Bedfordshire County Council.

Route starts at Hanslope in Buckinghamshire and
  ends at Grafham Water in Cambridgeshire
Open all year
Admission free
♿ 🐕

Visit Britain at Work

Hundreds of interesting ideas for tours and trips

£2.95 (+ £1.00 p&p)

Visit Britain at Work is just the guide book everyone wants to read about work places to visit as a real interesting attraction.
It includes:

● Potteries, china and glass manufacturers

● Brewers, distillers and confectioners

● Power stations, candlemakers and vineyards ... and many, many more

Available from bookshops or Visitor Publications Limited, Surrey House, Surrey Street, Croydon, Surrey CR0 ISZ. ☎ 081-681 2696.

Published by Visitor Publications Limited in association with the National Tourist Boards of England, Scotland, Wales and Northern Ireland. It is also supported and recommended by the CBI.

BERKSHIRE

Berkshire is steeped in history. Ancient prehistoric tracks and pathways crisscross the downlands and the great oak, birch and beech woodlands. The Thames, now a medley of launches, skiffs, motor cruisers and punts, flows past the many historic houses that line its banks including Windsor Castle, the largest castle in England and the official residence of the Queen.

Herb gardens and vineyards, impressive country parks with outstanding landscapes and many recreational facilities, wildlife parks, windmills and shire horse centres offer the visitor a glimpse of the richness of Berkshire's countryside. It is also home to both the Museum of English Rural Life and the Council for Environment Education Information Centre, links to the past and the future of our countryside.

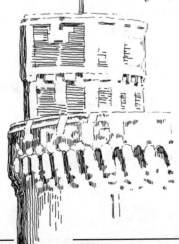

▶ *BRACKNELL* ◀

RYEHURST FARM

Bedding plants, farm shop and pick your own

Hazelwood Lane, Binfield, Bracknell, Berkshire RG12 5NG
☎ Bracknell (0344) 423819

The farm is attractively situated with land sloping gently to the river. The crops are close to the parking and picnic areas.

From Bracknell take the B3018 in the direction of Henley/Twyford. After 1 mile farm is at crossroad with the B3034
Open April, May 10.00am–6.00pm; June, July 9.00am–7.00pm; August, September Mon–Fri 2.00pm–6.00pm, Saturday, Sunday 10.00am–6.00pm
Free admission
&. 🚐 🛉

▶ *NEWBURY* ◀

HOLLINGTON NURSERIES LIMITED

Herb garden and nursery

Woolton Hill, Newbury, Berkshire RG15 9XT
☎ Highclere (0635) 253908

A beautiful 1½ acre walled garden with a fine collection of herbs, scented plants, climbers, old roses and topiary. Display gardens, herb shop, tea room overlooking the gardens open throughout the summer.

4 miles south of Newbury off the A343
Open Mar–Sept, Mon–Sat 10.00am–5.00pm, Sunday and Bank Holidays 11.00am–5.00pm. For winter hours please telephone
Free admission
&. 🚐 ✗

▶ *HUNGERFORD* ◀

COURAGE SHIRE HORSE CENTRE

Shire horse centre

Cherry Garden Lane, Maidenhead Thicket, Maidenhead, Berkshire SL6 3QD
☎ Littlewick Green (0628) 824848

Home of Courage's prize winning shire horses where up to 12 of these gentle giants can be seen. Audio visual presentation and on specific days a farrier, cooper or wheelwright can be seen at work. Souvenir shop and tea room.

On the A4, 2 miles west of Maidenhead (exit 8/9 on the M4)
Open Mar–Oct daily 11.00am–4.00pm
Admission: adult £2.00, child/OAP £1.50, special rates for groups, disabled parties and school groups
&. 🚐 🛉

HIGHCLOSE FARM ENTERPRISES & CO LIMITED

Pick your own

Highclose Farm, Bath Rd, Hungerford, Berkshire
☎ Hungerford (0488) 682973

1½ miles west of Hungerford on the A4
Open in the soft fruit season (June–July)
Free admission
&. 🚐 ✗

SNELSHORE COUNTRY PARK

Country park

Newbury Tourist Information Centre, The Wharf, Newbury, Berkshire RG14 5AS
☎ Newbury (0635) 30267

Snelshore is the largest single tract of heather remaining in Berkshire and is at its best in August and September. Nature walks are led by the warden throughout the summer.

On the B4494 Newbury–Wantage road, approx 3 miles north west of Newbury
Open all year
Free admission
&. 🚐 🛉

THATCHAN MOORS

Country walks and lakes

The Wharf, Newbury, Berkshire
☎ Newbury (0635) 30267

Walks, lakes and fishing. Contact Newbury Tourist Information Centre for more details.

Off the A4 between Reading and Newbury
Open all year
Free admission
&. 🛉

► *READING* ◄

BEALE BIRD PARK

Wildlife park

Church Farm, Lower Basildon, nr Reading, Berkshire
  RG8 9NH
☎ Upper Basildon (0491) 671325

*Part of the Child-Beale Wildlife Park
specializing in a vast collection of birdlife.
Set in beautiful gardens beside the Thames
with lakes, statues and fountains. Pets
corner, adventure playground, train rides,
paddling pools, picnic area and cafe.*

2 miles from Pangbourne on the A329 Reading–
  Oxford road
Open 2 March–Dec, 10.00am–6.00pm. Last admission
  5.00pm
Admission: adult £3.00, child (over 3 and under
  16)/OAP/disabled £1.00
& ⇔ ⋔ in car park only

BLOOMFIELD HATCH FARM SHOP

Farm shop and pick your own

Bloomfield Hatch Farm, Mortimer, Berkshire RG7 3AD
☎ Mortimer (0734) 332540

*Farm shop with summer nursery selling
home-made produce, bedding plants, hanging
baskets, free-range eggs and fresh farm
turkeys at Christmas. Pick your own
strawberries.*

From jct 11 on the M4, 2 miles towards Mortimer
Open daily except Mondays 9.00am–6.00pm. Open on
  Bank Holidays
Free admission
& ⇔ ⋔

COUNCIL FOR ENVIRONMENTAL EDUCATION INFORMATION CENTRE

Information centre

School of Education, University of Reading, London Rd,
  Reading RG1 5AQ
☎ Reading (0734) 318921

*CEE is the national co-ordinating body for
environmental education. Resources from
many organisations and publishers on
display in Information Centre. Please send a
SAE for a free publications list of resources
for teachers and youth workers.*

On the A4 (London Road), next to the Royal
  Berkshire Hospital
Open all year Mon–Fri 9.00am–5.00pm except Bank
  Holidays. Telephone first for appointment
Free admission
& ⋔

FARLEY FARMS

Farm shop

Bridge Farm, Reading Rd, Arborfield, Berkshire RG2 9HT
☎ Arborfield (0734) 760280

On the A327, 5 miles south of Reading
Open Mon, Tues, Thur, Fri, Sat 9.00am–5.30pm, Sun
  10.00am–4.00pm. Closed Wednesdays
Free admission

GARLANDS ORGANIC FARM SHOP

Farm shop

Gardeners Lane, Upper Basildon, Berkshire RG8 9NP
☎ Upper Basildon (0491) 671556

*Farm shop in rural setting selling organic
fruit, vegetables, wholefoods, meat, wine and
dairy products.*

Upper Basildon is signposted on the A329 from
  Pangbourne. Shop opposite village green
Open all year except Bank Holidays, Tues–Sat
  9.00am–4.00pm
Free admission
& ⋔

THE HERB FARM

Retail herb nursery

Peppard Rd, Sonning Common, Reading, Berkshire
  RG4 9NJ
☎ Kidmore End (0734) 724220

*Large display garden and herb shop with one
of the most extensive collections of herbs and
herbal products in the country. Interesting
collection of traditional garden sundries –
terracotta, barrels, chimney pots etc.*

5 miles north of Reading on the B481
Open 10.00am–5.00pm daily except Mondays. Guided
  tours with advance booking
Free admission
& ⇔ advance notice required ⋔

MAPLEDURHAM HOUSE AND WATERMILL

Watermill and historic house

The Estate Office, Mapledurham, Reading, Berkshire
RG4 7TR
☎ Reading (0734) 723350

*Elizabethan mansion, home of the Blounts
for 500 years and Mapledurham watermill,
the last working watermill on the Thames.
River launches leave Caversham Promenade
at 2.00pm.*

Signposted off the A4074 from Reading, through
Caversham to Woodcote and Crowmarsh
Open Easter–Sept, Sat, Sun and Bank Holidays. Watermill
1.00–5.00pm; house 2.30–5.00pm. Watermill also
open during winter, Sundays only 2.00–4.00pm.
Parties by arrangement.
Admission to house: adult £3.00, child £1.50; watermill:
adult £2.00, child £1.00
& good access but no toilets for the disabled
advance notice required
except in house grounds

MORTIMER HILL FRUIT FARM

Pick your own fresh fruit farm, and shop

Mortimer Hill, Mortimer, nr Reading, Berkshire RG7 3PG
☎ Mortimer (0734) 333157

*A small family-worked fruit farm. Pick your
own soft fruit – raspberries (July, August,
September) are the speciality. Children
welcome; play area, picnic area, farm trail
and refreshments.*

From jct 11 of the M4, take the A33 towards
Basingstoke for 200 yards. Turn right towards
Mortimer, look for yellow sign as you approach
Mortimer
Open June–Sept, telephone for recorded message giving
current opening hours, fruit availability and prices
Free admission
& no disabled toilet facilities
advance notice required
please keep *on* the lead and *off* the strawberries

MUSEUM OF ENGLISH RURAL LIFE

**Museum, information centre for history of farming
and the countryside**

University of Reading, Whiteknights, Reading, Berkshire
RG6 2AG
☎ Reading (0734) 318663

*A national collection depicting the farming,
crafts and way of life of the countryside over
the last 150 years. Special facilities available
for school parties. Extensive documentary
and photographic archives can be consulted
by appointment.*

On university campus, 2 miles south east of
Reading town centre on the A327 Aldershot road
Open all year, Tues–Sat 10.00am–1.00pm, 2.00–4.30pm
Admission: adult 50p, child free
& 🐾 🦮

WELLINGTON COUNTRY PARK

Country park with recreational activities

Riseley, Reading, Berkshire RG7 1SP
☎ (0734) 326444

*40 acre lake with 400 acres of woodland
nature trails, animal farm, windsurfing etc.*

Off the A33 between Reading and Basingstoke, 6
miles south of Reading
Open daily March–Nov (half term) 10.00am–5.30pm,
weekends only in winter.
Admission: adult £2.20, child £1.00
& 🐾 ample free parking 🦮

WESTBURY VINEYARD, WINERY AND FISHERY

Vineyard, winery, and trout fishery

Westbury Farm, Purley on Thames, nr Reading, Berkshire
RG8 8DL
☎ (0734) 843123

*Conducted tours of the vineyard with wine
tasting and food available to booked parties.
There are twenty wines on our list – Red,
Rosé and White. Also trout fishing, booking
essential.*

5 miles west of Reading, 1 mile east of
Pangbourne, down Westbury Lane
Open all year to booked parties (min 25, max 60)
Admission: tour of vineyard and winery, tea and biscuits
£3.50; tour of vineyard and winery, tasting of six wines
with lecture, vineyard meal £8.50 per head, without
food £5.50, children half price, under 5s free
& 🐾 advance notice required 🦮

► TWYFORD ◄

ROCK'S COUNTRY WINES

Winery

Loddon Park Farm, Twyford, Berkshire RG10 9RY
☎ Reading (0734) 342344

A winery specializing in the production of English country wines from English fruit, all styles available from very dry to sweet.

Off the A4 at Twyford
Open daily Jan–Easter 10.00am–4.00pm, Easter–Sept
   10.00am–5.30pm, Sundays afternoons only
Free admission
   toilet facilities awkward
🚂 advance notice required

THE THAMES VALLEY VINEYARD

Vineyard

Stanlake Park, Twyford, Reading, Berkshire RG10 0BN
☎ Twyford (0734) 340176 day, 320025 evening, Fax 320914

One of the largest vineyards in Britain set in a beautiful vale overlooked by an Elizabethan manor house. Many styles of white wine and occasional releases of red and sparkling wine available. Tastings in the 17th century barn overlooking the modern winery.

On the B3018, south of Twyford
Open Feb–Christmas. Cellar door sales weekdays
   12.00–6.00pm, Sat 10.00am–6.00pm, Sun 12.00–
   3.30pm. Other facilities by appointment.
Admission: vineyard tours with tastings and/or food from
   £3.00–£11.00 per head. Barbeques, functions and
   weddings can be accommodated
   some ramps, toilet facilities. All possible help given
🚂 advance notice required ✖

► WINDSOR ◄

ORCHARD HERBS

Farm shop and herb and soft fruit farm

Lake End Rd, Dorney, Windsor, Berkshire SL4 6QS
☎ Slough (0753) 43427 or (0860) 208845

Organic herb and soft fruit farm and farm shop – suppliers of herbs, vegetables, dried flowers, christmas trees and pick your own soft fruit in season.

Follow signs to Dorney from Eton along the B3026,

continue on this road for ½ mile to the
Pineapple public house. Orchard Herbs is 100
yards on the left
Open April–Oct, 11.30am–6.00pm daily except Mondays,
   Sunday 2.00–6.00pm
Free admission
   🚂 advance notice required 🐎

► WOKINGHAM ◄

CALIFORNIA COUNTRY PARK

Country park

Nine Mile Ride, Finchampstead, Wokingham, Berkshire
   RG11 4HT
☎ Eversley (0734) 730028

100 acres of beautiful and varied countryside. Site of Special Scientific Interest with a 6 acre coarse fishing lake, wildfowl, nature trail, guided walks, tennis courts, childrens play area and paddling pool. Cafe open at weekends and holidays.

Join Nine Mile Ride from the A321, B3016 or
   A3095. 4 miles from Wokingham
Open all year except Christmas Day, dawn–dusk
Free admission
   🚂 advance notice required 🐎

DINTON PASTURES COUNTRY PARK

Country park

Davis St, Hurst, Reading RG10 0TH
☎ Reading (0734) 342016

The park offers a variety of lakes, public coarse fishery, watersports lake, wildlife areas and visitor centre. Events and displays throughout the year. 'Tea Cosy' cafe provides home-made cooking and snacks.

Off the B3030, 2 miles north west of Wokingham, 3
   miles south east of Reading
Open all year except Christmas Day, dawn–dusk. Cafe
   Mon–Sat
Free admission. Free car parking
   admission for fishing and a bird hide. Wheelchair
available
🚂 advance notice required 🐎

GRAYS FARM

Pick your own fruit and vegetables

Heathlands Rd, Wokingham, Berkshire RG11 3AN
☎ Wokingham (0734) 785386

Strawberries, raspberries, gooseberries, rhubarb, broad beans, runner beans, calabrese, broccoli spears, carrots, courgettes, marrows, onions, peas, potatoes and sweet corn for picking. Tarmac car park near all crops, toilets and play area.

From Wokingham turn left out of Peach St, up Easthampstead Rd, right at the White Horse public house. From the south leave the B3430 at Ravenswood, signposted Heathlands

Open June–Sept, Mon–Sat 9.00am–6.00pm. Closed Sundays

Free admission

♿ assistance offered round farm and disabled customers may (with notice) drive down to the fields 🐕

Guide to Symbols

☎ telephone	🐕 dogs welcome (on a leash)
♿ disabled welcome	✖ dogs not welcome
🚌 coaches welcome	

BUCKINGHAMSHIRE

Buckinghamshire, divided by the wooded Chiltern Hills and now a major commuting area for London, has retained much of its rural character. Many villages still have their traditional Chiltern brick-and-flint houses, leafy lanes and old walkways. The Vale of Aylesbury to the north of the county is one of England's richest agricultural regions, it incorporates the 300-acre Creslow Great Field which has fattened beef for Royal households since Tudor times.

It is possible to dip into the Chiltern area's rural past at more than one museum, to visit potters at work, see furniture being restored or watch stained glass windows being designed and made. Several farms and farm interpretation centres welcome visitors and their produce is available either by 'picking your own' soft fruits and vegetables or by visiting one of the many farm shops in the area. There are many country walks and farm trails to follow and the delicious local produce can be sampled whilst sitting on a riverbank watching the ducks.

▶ **AYLESBURY** ◀

BUCKS GOAT CENTRE

Commercial farm, farm trail, speciality food producer

Bucks Goat Centre, Layby Farm Old Risborough, Stoke Rd, Stoke Mandeville HP22 5XJ
☎ Stoke Mandeville (0296) 612983

Dairy, meat and fibre goats on a commercial farm. Farm trail with sheep, poultry and rabbits, picnic area, farm shop, pine furniture shop, mini garden centre. Speciality food producer. Conducted tours available by appointment including goat cheese, English wine and cider tasting.

On the outskirts of Stoke Mandeville towards Princes Risborough on the A4010 Aylesbury–High Wycombe road
Open daily 10.00am–5.30pm (afternoon milking at 4.00pm)
Admission: adult £1.00, child/OAP 50p
& ∰ advance notice required
⊁ outdoors only

NETHER WINCHENDON HOUSE

Historic house

Nether Winchendon House, Aylesbury, Buckinghamshire HP18 0DY
☎ Haddenham (0844) 290101

Mediaeval manor house with substantial Tudor additions altered in the late 18th century in Strawberry Hill Gothic style. Good English furniture, attractive gardens, interesting church nearby, beautiful and unspoilt village.

1½ miles north of the A418 between Thame and Aylesbury
Open May–Aug, Thursday and Bank Holiday weekends 2.30–5.30pm. Parties by appointment at any time of year
Admission: adult £1.50, child £1.00, OAP (Thur only) £1.00
& ∰ advance notice required ⊁

SPRINGHILL FARM SHOP

Organic fruit, vegetables, wholefoods, meat, wine and dairy products

Cuddington Road, Dinton, nr Aylesbury, Buckinghamshire
☎ (0296) 747334

Between Thame and Aylesbury, just off the A418 on the road to Cuddington
Open Tue–Sat 9.00am–4.00pm
Free admission
& ⊁

▶ **BEACONSFIELD** ◀

THE GLASS MARKET

Glass craft centre – stained glass/blown glass

Broad Lane, Wooburn Green, High Wycombe, Buckinghamshire HP10 0LL
☎ Beaconsfield (0494) 671033

Visitors to the converted barn can see stained glass windows designed and made, purchase glass previously blown on the premises and find glass, tools, books and materials for their hobby. Weekend beginners' courses are run.

Off the A40 at Holtspur, 2 miles west of Beaconsfield old town
Open all year Mon–Sat 9.30am–5.00pm except Bank Holidays
Free admission
& ∰ advance notice required ⊁

▶ **BUCKINGHAM** ◀

GRAVEL FARM

Pick your own

Finmere, Buckingham MK18 4AQ
☎ Finmere (02804) 7986

Pick your own soft fruit and vegetables. Large car park and picnic area. Opposite a large Sunday market, easy access for those travelling east–west.

5 miles north of Buckingham on the B4031
Open mid June–mid Sept daily 10.00am–7.00pm
Free admission
& ⊁

▶ **CHALFONT ST GILES** ◀

CHILTERN OPEN AIR MUSEUM

Country walk and farming museum

Newland Park, Gorelands Lane, Chalfont St Giles, Buckinghamshire HP8 4AD
☎ Chalfont St Giles (02407) 71117

45 acres of beautiful countryside with historic buildings that have been saved from destruction by dismantling and re-erecting here. Dating from the 16th to the 19th century, the buildings house displays on Chiltern life and landscape.

Leave the M25 at jct 17, proceed via Maple Cross and follow signs to 'The Chalfonts'. Signposted from the A413 at Chalfont St Giles and Chalfont St Peter
Open Easter Sun–27 Oct, Wed, Sun and Bank Holidays 2.00–6.00pm (3 July–8 Sept Wed–Sun 2.00–6.00pm)
Admission: adult £2.00, child/OAP £1.50, reduction for parties of over 30
 ⚀ advance notice required 🐾

► CHESHAM ◄

M D HOW AND SON

Farm shop

Woodlands Farm, The Vale, Chesham, Buckinghamshire HP5 3NS
☎ Chesham (0494) 783737

Farm shop specializing in oven ready turkeys which have been reared in the traditional manner; no blanket use of antibiotics. Established in 1935, the oldest turkey farm in England.

Turn off the A416 at Nissan garage signposted Hawridge – shop is 2 miles on the right
Open Mon–Fri 9.00am–12.30pm and 2.00–5.00pm, Sat 9.00am–12.30pm. Closed on Bank Holidays
Free admission
& ⚀ 🐾

LATIMER PARK FARM

Farm shop and fly fishery

Latimer, Chesham, Buckinghamshire HP5 1TT
☎ Little Chalfont (0494) 762396

Attractive fishery with two lakes totalling 12 acres plus a stretch of the River Chess. Restocked daily. Resident keeper, fishing lodge with full facilities.

On the B485, 3½ miles east of Chesham towards Latimer
Open for the fishery Mon–Sat 9.00am–dark (advance booking required); shop Tuesday and Friday 2.00–5.30pm, Saturday 9.00am–1.00pm
Admission: full day rods £20.00, short day rods £15.00, evening rods £10.00
& 🎣

► COOKHAM ◄

COPAS BROS

Pick your own

Lower Mount Farm, Long Lane, Cookham, nr Maidenhead, Berkshire SL6 9EE
☎ Bourne End (062 85) 29511

Take the B4447 from Maidenhead to Cookham, the farm is situated on the west side
Open mid June–Oct, Wed–Sat 2.00–7.00pm, Sunday 10.00am–5.00pm
Free admission
& ⚀ 🐾

► DENHAM ◄

DENHAM PICK YOUR OWN FARM

Pick your own

Hollybush Lane, Denham, Buckinghamshire UB9 4HJ
☎ Denham (0895) 834707

Strawberries, raspberries, currants, gooseberries, logan/tayberries, also broad/green/runner beans, peas, carrots, courgettes, parsley, spinach, sweet corn, mange tout and pumpkins. Free-range eggs. Farm animals on display. Toilet.

About 1 mile down Hollybush Lane off the A40 between Denham and Gerrards Cross. Or turn into Willets Lane off the A412 Denham–Slough road about ½ mile from the Denham motorway roundabout and follow our signs
Open June–Sept, telephone for opening hours during the season
Free admission
& ⚀ 🐾 car park only

► GREAT MISSENDEN ◄

CONY CRAFTS

Craft centre

Hale-Acre Workshops, Watchet Lane, nr Great Missenden, Buckinghamshire
☎ Great Missenden (02406) 5668

Well established specialist furniture restoration business providing high standards of quality and service. All furniture from period to modern is restored and made with care and sympathy. Wood carving, chair rushing etc.

17

Off the A413, 1 mile east of Great Missenden
Open all year Mon–Fri 8.30am–5.30pm
Free admission
 ♿ 🐕

PETERLEY MANOR FARM

Pick your own

Peterley Lane, Prestwood, Great Missenden,
  Buckinghamshire HP16 0HH
☎ Great Missenden (02406) 2959

*Wide range of crops grown, from bedding
plants in May, strawberries, raspberries,
flowers, salads and vegetables in summer,
cherries, plums and apples in autumn to
Christmas trees in December.*

Off the A4128 High Wycombe–Great Missenden
  road, 5 miles north of High Wycombe
Open all year, daily (except Mondays) 9.00am–5.00pm
Free admission
♿ 🚌 🐕

► HIGH WYCOMBE ◄

THE HOME OF REST FOR HORSES

Farm visit

Speen Farm, Slad Lane, nr Lacey Green, Aylesbury,
  Buckinghamshire HP17 0PP
☎ High Wycombe (0494) 488464

*Up to 120 horses, ponies and donkeys in
retirement or on short stay rest from work or
convalescence etc. Parking and toilet
facilities, no catering. 'Tit bits' carrots,
sugar lumps, polo mints, NO apples.*

Turn off the A4010 to Bradenham, follow signs to
  Lacey Green
Open daily 2.00–4.00pm
Free admission
♿ 🚌 advance notice required, Mon–Fri only 🐕

KEEP HILL WOODS NATURE TRAIL

Nature trail

Keep Hill Woods, Wendover Way, High Wycombe,
  Buckinghamshire
☎ High Wycombe (0494) 461000 ext 3816

*Keep Hill nature trail through a 'hanging'
beechwood. Evidence of Iron Age Man on
the site. A circular trail starts at the Rye
Dyke.*

Rear of Rye, open space off the A40 to High
  Wycombe
Open all year
Free admission
♿ 🐕

► MILTON KEYNES ◄

FROSTS GARDEN CENTRE

Garden centre

Newport Road, Woburn Sands, Milton Keynes,
  Buckinghamshire MK17 8UE
☎ Milton Keynes (0908) 583511

*Frosts prides itself on home-grown trees and
shrubs, exotic houseplants and eye catching
displays of gifts. Specimen tropical plant
house. The palm house and the Garden
Room restaurant are new features.*

Situated approx 1 mile outside Woburn Sands on
  the A5130. 3 miles from exit 14 of the M1 and 5
  miles from Woburn Abbey and exit 13 of the M1.
Open daily. Winter 9.00am–5.30pm; summer 9.00am–
  6.00pm, 10.00am–6.00pm Sundays and Bank
  Holidays; April–June open until 7.00pm Thur and Fri
Free admission
♿ 🚌 advance notice required
🐕 except guide dogs

MILTON KEYNES MUSEUM OF INDUSTRY & RURAL LIFE

Museum

Stacey Hill Farm, Southern Way, Wolverton, Milton
  Keynes MK12 5EJ
☎ Milton Keynes (0908) 319148/316222

*Exhibits depicting the rural, domestic and
industrial life of North Buckinghamshire
from 1800 to the 1960s. Many exhibits
displayed in period settings – the Victorian
parlour and Edwardian kitchen. Others in
context – blacksmith's forge, wheelwright's,
printer's and cobbler's workshops.*

2 miles north of city centre, off M2 Millers Way
Open Easter–Oct Wed–Sun and Bank Holidays 1.30–
  4.30pm; special events weekends in May and Sept
Admission: adult £1.50, child/OAP £1.00, family £4.50
  (1989 prices)
♿ 🚌 🐕

▶ OLNEY ◀

THE OLNEY POTTERY

Pottery

Holes Lane, Olney, Buckinghamshire MK46 4BX
☎ Bedford (0234) 712306

Deborah Hopson-Wolpe started the Olney Pottery in 1975 after studying ceramics at Camberwell and in Tokyo. The range of functional stoneware in blues/greens/greys include inscribed commemorative pieces.

Holes Lane is at the junction of High Street, Olney and the B5388 (Northampton Road)
Open by appointment only – all year during working hours
Free admission
&. ✗

▶ SLOUGH ◀

COPAS BROS

Pick your own

Calves Lane Farm, Langley Park, Iver, Buckinghamshire
☎ Iver (0753) 652727

Pick your own strawberries, raspberries, gooseberries, plums, cherries and apples. Turkeys at Christmas. Next to Langley Park.

Take the A412 Slough–Uxbridge road, turn off at signpost to Billet Lane
Open mid June–Oct Wed–Sat 2.00–7.00pm, Sun 10.00am–5.00pm
Free admission
&. ⛟ ✗

▶ UXBRIDGE ◀

HOME COTTAGE FARM

Farm shop and pick your own

Bangors Road South, Iver, Buckinghamshire SL0 0BB
☎ Iver (0753) 653064

Pick your own raspberries, plums and apples. Free range geese, ducks, turkeys, guinea fowl and chickens – usually visible. Sheep, lambs. Children welcome. Information on local wildlife trust available from owners.

200 yards down the Iver road from the roundabout by the Black Horse public house which is on the A4007 Uxbridge–Slough road at Iver Heath
Open for pick your own – raspberries: July Tues & Thur 2.00–6.00pm, Sat & Sun 10.00am–6.00pm; plums: Sept Tues and Thur 2.00–6.00pm, Sat & Sun 10.00am–6.00pm; apples and Autumn Bliss raspberries: all day every day from third weekend Sept until end October. Farm shop 9.00am–6.00pm from end of August until stock is exhausted (usually Christmas or soon afterwards)
Free admission
&. ⛟ advance notice required ✗

▶ WENDOVER ◀

FORESTRY COMMISSION

Forest office

Upper Icknield Way, Aston Clinton, Aylesbury, Buckinghamshire HP22 5NF
☎ Aylesbury (0296) 625825

Guided walks, wayfaring and picnicking in pleasant woodland surroundings with magnificent views of the Aylesbury Vale.

Turn off the A4011 to St Leonards. Turn right after 200 yards, follow road through wood to car park
Open all year
Free admission
&. ⛟ advance notice required ✗

▶ WINSLOW ◀

BUCKINGHAMSHIRE FARMING & WILDLIFE ADVISORY GROUP 'LINK' FARM

Farm interpretation centre, country walk, farm trail and farm visit

Marstonfields Farm, North Marston, Buckingham MK18 3PG
☎ North Marston (029667) 215

1 mile north of North Marston village, off the A413 Aylesbury–Buckingham road between Whitchurch and Winslow
Open any time by prior arrangement
Admission: donations to Bucks FWAG (suggested £1.00 per head minimum)
&. very limited facilities for slighty disabled
⛟ advance notice required ✗

CAMBRIDGESHIRE

Cambridgeshire, fenland pastures with upland fringes, is crossed by three great rivers, the Cam, the Nene and the Great Ouse. Its rich farmland is predominantly arable and everywhere there are agricultural shows, flower festivals and traction-engine rallies. The rivers are busy and bright with different rivercraft in the summer. In Cambridge, punts ply the Backs, a characteristic image of that atmospheric and historic university town.

The county is rich in country parks and walks, there are sites of special scientific interest and nature reserves, rural museums and wildfowl refuge parks. It is possible to see a working windmill or visit a pottery, taste some wine from locally grown grapes or 'pick your own' soft fruit. The countryside is close at hand wherever you are in Cambridgeshire.

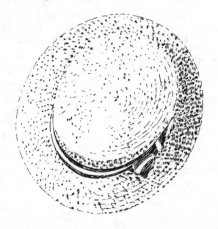

▶ *CAMBRIDGE* ◀

CAMBRIDGESHIRE WILDLIFE TRUST

Nature reserves

5 Fulbourn Manor, Fulbourn, Cambridge CB1 5BN
☎ Cambridge (0223) 880788

Diversity of habitat in 40 reserves, including the Ouse Washes (winter wildfowl), Hayley Wood (spring flowers) and Fulbourn (educational). Information boards on site, reserve booklets and events programme available. Telephone or write for further details.

Various locations
Open (office) 9.00am–5.00pm
Admission: Please check for open access
 ♿ 🚐 with advance notice, at some reserves
🐔 at some reserves

CHAPLINS FARMS (FULBOURN) LIMITED

Farm shop and pick your own soft fruit

'Bounds', 9 Doggett Lane, Fulbourn, Cambridge CB1 5BT
☎ Cambridge (0223) 880722

Farm shop and pick your own fruit and vegetables. Also a Caravan Club Certificated Location with a separate Caravan Rally field. Golf practice area, donkey rides, childrens play area, light refreshments, picnic area, walks.

Please telephone for directions
Open June–Oct daily 10.00am–6.00pm
Free admission
♿ 🚐 advance notice required 🐔

CHILFORD HUNDRED VINEYARD

Vineyard and winery shop

Chilford Hall, Balsham Rd, Linton, Cambridgeshire CB1 6LE
☎ Cambridge (0223) 892641

10 miles south east of Cambridge, via the A604. Entrance on the B1052
Open May–Sept, daily 11.00am–5.00pm
Admission: £2.50 which includes 2 tastings and a souvenir glass
♿ 🚐 advance notice required 🐔

FARM HOUSE STUDIO

Fine arts working studio

River Cam Farm House, Cambridge Rd, Wimpole, Cambridgeshire SG8 5QB
☎ Cambridge (0223) 207750

John Stapleton Arics undertakes artist impressions of development schemes and fabric design, as well as general fine art in oils, screenprints and water colours.
NB: Gardens and parking disturbed by ongoing construction work.

South west of Cambridge on the A603, 7 miles from jct 12 on the M11. Turn left by autostop cafe, down gravelled farm road. Hanging sign
Open by appointment and during working hours
Free admission to studio
♿ 💀

FARMLAND MUSEUM

Rural museum

High St, Haddenham, Cambridgeshire CB6 3XB
☎ Ely (0353) 740381

The museum, established 20 years ago, has displays of rural antiquities, a working blacksmith's forge, horse-drawn implements etc. A second 'branch' has developed at the Cambridgeshire College of Agriculture and Horticulture.

2 miles off the A10 Cambridge–Ely road
Open Easter–Sept every Wednesday 10.00am–5.00pm, and the first Sunday of every month throughout year from 2.00pm
Admission: adult £1.00, child 50p
🚐 advance notice required 💀

GIANT'S HILL (RAMPTON)

Archaeological and wildlife interest

c/o Cambridgeshire County Council, Shire Hall, Cambridge CB3 0AP
☎ Cambridge (0223) 317496

14 acre site with information boards. Leaflet available from the above address.

7 miles north from Cambridge on the B1049. Turn west from Cottenham village to Rampton
Open all year
Free admission
♿ wheelchairs impractical – kissing gates and grass meadow
🐔 cattle grazing in summer

GRAHAM–CAMERON ILLUSTRATION
Artist/Illustrator's studio

10 Church St, Willingham, Cambridge CB4 5HT
☎ Willingham (0954) 60444

As well as viewing paintings and drawings which are for sale, visitors can usually see the latest illustration projects which often include drawings for children's books.

9 miles from Cambridge. Turn off the A604 at Bar Hill – via Longstanton
Open all year by appointment
Free admission
&. some wheelchairs do not fit through the cottage door. First floor toilet
✖

M C O PAGE & SONS
Farm interpretation centre, farm shop and country walks

Birds Farm, Haslingfield Rd, Barton, Cambridgeshire CB3 7AG
☎ Cambridge (0223) 262181

3½ miles from Cambridge off the A603. M11 jct 12
Open Easter–Oct, Tues–Fri 11.00am–5.00pm, Saturdays and Sundays 2.00–5.00pm. Closed Mondays except Bank Holidays
Admission: adult £1.30, child/OAP £1.00
&. 🚌 advance notice required ✖

SHEPRETH RIVERSIDE WALK
Country walk

c/o Cambridgeshire County Council, Shire Hall, Cambridge CB3 0AP
☎ Cambridge (0223) 317496

Small car park gives access to meadows beside the River Cam. Meadows are grazed and can be muddy, creating difficulty for disabled visitors.

7 miles south west of Cambridge off the A10 on the Shepreth–Barrington road
Open all year
Free admission
&. ✖

WIMPOLE WAY
Country walk

c/o Cambridgeshire County Council, Rural Management Section, Shire Hall, Cambridge CB3 0AP
☎ Cambridge (0223) 317445

A 13 mile walk through gently rolling countryside, historic villages and small areas of ancient woodland.

Start the walk either at Wimpole Hall, 9 miles south west of Cambridge on the A14 just north of the junction with the A603 at Wimpole OR at the Backs, Queens Road, Cambridge, proceeding down Burrells Walk, across Grange Road into Adams Road
Open all year
Free admission
&. ✖

► **ELY** ◄

BISHOP'S WAY (ELY)
Country walk and ride

c/o Cambridgeshire County Council, Shire Hall, Cambridge CB3 0AP
☎ Cambridge (0223) 317445

A route through quiet country tracks following mediaeval roads formerly used by the Bishop of Ely. Includes sites of wildlife and historic interest.

Start the walk or ride at Thistle Corner on the B1382 Prickwillow road just west of Queen Adelaide near Ely or on Hurst Lane by the A10
Open all year
Free admission
&. ✖

THE HERBARY PRICKWILLOW
Herb garden, herb farm, farm shop and tea garden

Mile End, Prickwillow, Ely, Cambridgeshire CB7 4SJ
☎ Prickwillow (035 388) 456

The working farm supplies wholesale markets and has a mail order service of fresh herbs and herb plants direct to the public.

From the centre of Ely, take the B1382 through Queen Adelaide and Prickwillow. Mile End is 1 mile further on
Open every day 9.00am until dusk
Free admission to customers making a purchase
&. every assistance given
🚌 parties by appointment only ✖

▶ **HUNTINGDON** ◀

HINCHINGBROOKE COUNTRY PARK

Country park

c/o Cambridgeshire County Council, Shire Hall,
   Cambridge CB3 0AP
☎   Huntingdon (0480) 51568

60 acres of woodland, 50 acres of meadow
and 40 acres of lakes. Set in the grounds of
Hinchingbrooke House which is open to the
public on Sundays in the summer.

Just off the A141 to Brampton, beyond
   Hinchingbrooke Hospital
Open all year
Free admission, but some charge for fishing and sailing
& 🚷 🐕 restricted in certain areas

GRAYS HONEY FARM

Farm shop and bee-keeping interpretation centre

Cross Drove, Warboys, nr Huntingdon
☎   Chatteris (03543) 3798

Honey bee exhibition, observation hive, make
your own beeswax candles, find out how
bees talk. Speciality honeys and natural
beautycare products supplied. Picnic area
and refreshments including honey ice cream.

Located just off the A141 between Chatteris (2
   miles) and Warboys (5 miles) and signposted
   'Honey Farm'
Open Easter Saturday–31st Oct, Mon–Sat 10.30am–
   6.30pm
Admission: adult 70p, child 35p Small group visits by
   arrangement
& 🐕 picnic area only

RAMSEY RURAL MUSEUM

Farming museum

Wood Lane, Ramsey, Cambridgeshire
☎   Ramsey (0487) 813223

The museum covers a wide variety of
Fenland crafts & trades, agricultural
harvesters, tractors and implements, restored
cobblers shop, village shop, Victorian
bedroom and sitting room and kitchen are
displayed in restored farm buildings in a
quiet countryside setting.

Please telephone for directions
Open Apr–Sept: Sun 2.00–5.00pm, Thur 2.00–5.00pm,
   other times by appointment
Free admission
& 🚷 advance notice required 🍴

SOMERSHAM POTTERY

Hand made pottery

3 & 4 West Newlands, Somersham, Huntingdon,
   Cambridgeshire PE17 3EB
☎   Ramsey (0487) 841823

Handmade pots in either stoneware or
porcelain. House name plaques,
commemorative mugs and plates a speciality.

5 miles north of St Ives, the pottery is signposted
   on the B1089 and is on a small trading estate
Open all year Mon–Sat 9.00am–5.00pm, Sun 1.00–
   5.00pm
Free admission
& 🚷 🐕

▶ **MARCH** ◀

STAGS HOLT FARM & STUD

**Farm interpretation centre, country walk, farming
museum, farm trail and visit**

Stags Holt, March, Cambridgeshire PE14 0BJ
☎   March (0354) 52406

Opened as a breeding centre for Suffolk
Punches, Stags Holt gives an opportunity to
view them in what could be described as
their natural habitat. Complemented by
Victorian parkland with tools and
implements of that era.

4 miles from March off the B1101, signposted
Open Easter–Sept daily 10.30am–5.00pm. Closed
   Mondays except Bank Holidays
Admission: adult £1.50, child/OAP £1.00, party rates
   available (1988 prices)
& 🚷 🐕

▶ **PETERBOROUGH** ◀

COUNTRY WALKS AROUND PETERBOROUGH

Country walks

c/o Peterborough City Council, Town Hall, Bridge St,
   Peterborough PE1 1HG
☎   Peterborough (0733) 63141

Two 12 mile walks along riverside, woodland and open countryside. Please contact Peterborough City Council for details and leaflets.

Opening times, please contact Peterborough City Council for details
Free admission
  👌 🛏

FERRY MEADOWS COUNTRY PARK

Country park and country walk

Ham Lane, Peterborough PE2 0UU
☎ Peterborough (0733) 234443

Opened in 1978, the park has 500 acres of fine countryside: lakes, meadows and woodland. It is the focal point of the much larger Nene Park which runs from Peterborough to Wansford.

4 miles west of the city centre on the A605
Open all year for the park, other facilities Easter–Oct
Admission: car parking £1.50, weekends and Bank Holidays Easter–Oct
  👌 🚻 🛏

HILL FARM

Pick your own

Chesterton, Peterborough, Cambridgeshire PE7 3UH
☎ Peterborough (0733) 233270

Delightful rural surroundings on a hill overlooking Peterborough. Soft fruits and selected summer vegetables available to pick yourself or be picked for you. Grass field parking and picnic area. Ice cream, soft drinks and homemade light refreshments available.

On the A605 Oundle Road, 1 mile west of Peterborough and 200 yards from the Alwalton A1 flyover
Open June–Oct 9.00am–8.00pm weekdays, Sat–Sun 9.00am–6.00pm
Free admission
  👌 🚻 🛏

R TAYLOR, THE WOODWORKER

Workshop making specialized furniture, joinery

Eastgate Cottage, Deeping St James, Peterborough PE6 8HH
☎ Market Deeping (0778) 343381

In Deeping St James just past the church, on the B1166 Market Deeping–Crowland road
Open by appointment
Free admission
  👌 🛏

THE WILDFOWL & WETLANDS TRUST

Country park

Peakirk, Peterborough, PE6 7NP
☎ Peterborough (0733) 252271

700 captive waterfowl of 112 different species and a breeding flock of flamingoes. 17 acres of landscaped water, gardens and woodland, 30 acres of wild habitat. Special events include 'Downy Duckling Week' and 'Sweet September Days' for senior citizens.

6 miles north of Peterborough, 1 mile east of the A15 at Glinton
Open 9.30am–6.30pm or dusk, closed Christmas holiday
Admission: adult £2.50, child £1.25, OAP £1.70, party rates available
  👌 free loan wheelchairs available, special toilets
  🚻 🛏

▶   *ROYSTON*   ◀

BROOKCROFT BUNNERY

Rabbit zoo and shop

High St, Royston, Cambridgeshire SG8 0DR
☎ Cambridge (0223) 207331

Rabbits for sale at the only rabbit zoo in Europe. School trips catered for. Lectures on rabbit/angora craft available on request (25 mile radius).

8 miles north west of Royston, off the B1042 to Biggleswade. 5 miles off Bedfordshire border, nearest village Arrington
Open 10.30am–4.00pm Wed–Sun and Bank Holidays during Apr–Oct; Nov–Mar Sat and Sun only
Admission: adult £1.20, child/OAP 60p (1989 prices)
  👌 🚻 advance notice required 🛏

▶   *SOHAM*   ◀

DOWNFIELD WINDMILL

Working windmill and flour mill

Fordham Rd, Soham, Cambridgeshire
☎ Ely (0353) 720333

The mill dates from 1720, but was rebuilt in 1887. It drives 3 pairs of millstones, a dresser and corn cleaner. A commercial mill, the flours produced are sold in the Cambridge, Peterborough and East Midlands area, and are available on open days.

On the Junction of the A142 and the A1123
Open every Sunday 11.00am–5.00pm and Bank Holiday
 Mondays
Admission: adult 70p, child 30p
 ♧ ground floor only is accessible, but every assistance will be offered
🚌 advance notice required
✝ in grounds only

►   *WISBECH*   ◄

WILDFOWL & WETLANDS TRUST, WELNEY

Wildfowl refuge park

Hundred Foot Bank, Welney, Wisbech, Cambridgeshire
 PE14 9TN
☎ Ely (0353) 860711

Wetland area featuring large flocks of Bewick and Whooper swans and many species of European duck in winter, waders and other birds in summer. Nature trail and walks, original fen vegetation.

Off the A1101, 6 miles north of Littleport, 12 miles
 south of Wisbech
Open daily 10.00am–5.00pm except Christmas Eve and
 Christmas Day
Admission: adult £2.00, child £1.10, OAP £1.50,
 reductions for booked groups of 20 or more
♧ 🚌 advance notice required ✝

CHESHIRE

Cheshire consists of wooded ridges and the vast rolling countryside of the Cheshire Plain where grazing cattle and the black-and-white 'magpie' houses are typical of the county. The industrial centres have a surprisingly low impact on this rich farmland area through which the River Dee meanders to the Irish Sea.

The countryside can be appreciated from the numerous country walks including some upland hikes and forestry walks, there are canal walks and a walk along a former railway route too. Several country parks and historic houses have magnificent gardens to visit and there are exhibition centres and a heritage centre with regularly changing exhibits based on local themes. Working farms and a working watermill welcome visitors and there are dried herb specialists and craft centres with displays of country crafts. Speciality food produce will tempt the palates of the adventurous and organic farm produce is another appealing option to take to the picnic sites around the area.

▶ **ALSAGER** ◀

MERELAKE WAY

Country walk

c/o Countryside Office, Hassal, nr Sandbach, Cheshire
CW11 0XT
☎ Crewe (0270) 768835

The Merelake Way began life as a railway line carrying coal from Staffordshire to Cheshire; it's now a pleasant walk containing a wealth of diverse wildlife habitats.

From B5077 turn out of village centre towards
railway station, turn left after railway crossing
down Talke Road. Car park to Merelake Way is
½ a mile on the right
Open all year daily
Free admission
🚹 🚌 advance notice required 🐎

▶ **BOLLINGTON** ◀

GROUNDWORK DISCOVERY CENTRE

Exhibition centre and craft shop

Adelphi Mill, Gate Lodge, Grimshaw Lane, Bollington,
Macclesfield, Cheshire SK10 5JB
☎ Bollington (0625) 572681

Monthly exhibitions on the surrounding countryside and canal run by the Macclesfield and Vale Royal Groundwork Trust, housed in a Victorian cotton mill alongside the Macclesfield Canal. 'Green' shop, craft shop, canoe and bicycle hire.

1 mile north of Macclesfield on the A523. Turn
right into Grimshaw Lane in the centre of
Bollington, clearly signposted
Open 6 March–16 Dec, Tues–Sun 2.00–4.30pm. Closed
Mondays
Free admission
🚹 🐎

MACCLESFIELD CANAL

Canal and country walks

c/o Macclesfield Borough Council, Stuart House, King
Edward St, Macclesfield, Cheshire SK10 1DP
Canoe hire: ☎ Macclesfield (0625) 572681

Canal with towpath, part of the Cheshire canal ring, running through towns, villages and varied countryside. Easy walking on the improved towpath, canoes for hire.

Formal access at marina facilities at Macclesfield,
Bollington, Higher Poynton and Adlington
Open all year
Free admission
🚹 🚌 🐎

▶ **CHEADLE** ◀

W NIXON & SONS LTD

Farm shop

Outwood Farm, Bolshaw Rd, Cheadle, Cheshire SK8 3PE
☎ (061 437) 4801

Produce is all home produced and slaughtered on the premises. Wholesale prices.

Off the A34, 3 miles south of Cheadle
Open all year Tues, Wed, Thur 2.00–6.00pm, Fri
2.00–8.00pm, Sat 9.00am–1.00pm
Free admission
🚹 🚌 🐕

▶ **CHESTER** ◀

BELLE VUE FRUIT FARM

Farm shop and pick your own

H C Groom (Chester) Limited, Guilden Sutton, Chester,
Cheshire CH3 7EJ
☎ Mickle Trafford (0244) 300220

A specialist fruit farm growing a full range of soft fruits and some vegetables for pick your own. Many different varieties of strawberries and raspberries, concentrating on quality and flavour.

2 miles east of Chester, off the A55 on the A51
Open June–Aug daily 10.00am–8.00pm, Sat and Sun
10.00am–6.00pm
Free admission, minimum purchase £1.00
🚹 🚌 🐎 in car parking area only

CHESHIRE CANDLE WORKSHOPS

Craft centre

Burwardsley, nr Chester, Cheshire CH3 9PF
☎ Tattenhall (0829) 70401

Craft workshops creating hand carved candles. Located in the Peckforton Hills overlooking the Cheshire Plain. Large craftshop, glass sculpture and licensed hayloft restaurant in converted farmhouse buildings.

Signposted off the A41 Chester–Whitchurch road
and the A534 Wrexham–Nantwich road, 10 miles
from Chester
Open all year except 1–5 Jan, 10.00am–5.00pm. Evening
parties by appointment
Free admission
 ♿ 🚑 🐃

6 miles south of Chester on the A41, follow signs
for Tattenhall, then RAC and Tourist Board signs
to Cheshire Ice Cream Farm
Open daily April–Oct 10.30am–5.30pm, Nov–March
11.00am–5.00pm
Free admission
♿ 🚑 advance notice required 🐃

HAWORTHS FRUIT FARM

Fruit shop and pick your own

Eddisbury Fruit Farm, Yeld Lane, Kelsall, Cheshire
CW6 0TE
☏ Kelsall (0829) 51188

*Self pick fruit and vegetables. Farm shop
selling wide range of fruit, vegetables, apple
juice, preserves, local honey and dairy ice
cream. Good walks and views.*

On the A54, midway between Chester and
Northwich. 1 mile from Kelsall village
Open Jan–June daily 12.00–4.00 pm, July–Dec
10.00am–6.00pm
Free admission
♿ please telephone ahead
🚑 advance notice required 🐃

OAKCROFT ORGANIC GARDENS

Organic gardens

Crosso'Th'Hill, Malpas, Cheshire SY14 8DH
☏ Malpas (0948) 860213

*Organic market garden – variety of
vegetables and fruit in season, organic
cheese, eggs and herbs.*

15 miles south of Chester on the A41, turn right at
Normansheath towards Malpas, 1 mile on the left
Open 10.00am–4.00pm weekdays, but it is best to
telephone first
Free admission
♿ 🐃

TATTENHALL DAIRY PRODUCTS

Farm shop, farm visit and speciality foods

Drumlan Hall, Newton Lane, Tattenhall, nr Chester,
Cheshire CH3 9NE
☏ Tattenhall (0829) 70995

*Manufacturing of Cheshire farm ice cream
will be explained to pre-booked parties on
request. A working dairy farm with viewing
gallery to watch cows being milked (specified
times). Clotted/cream teas.*

►   *CONGLETON*   ◄

BIDDULPH VALLEY WAY

Country walk

c/o Countryside Office, County Offices, Chapel Lane,
Wilmslow, Cheshire SK9 1PU
☏ Wilmslow (0625) 534796

*Country walk which continues into
Staffordshire along the route of a former
railway.*

Off the A54, ¾ mile north east of Congleton town
centre
Open all year daily
Free admission
♿ 🐃

BRERETON HEATH PARK

Country park

Davenport Lane, Davenport, Congleton, Cheshire CW12
4SU
☏ Holmes Chapel (0477) 34115

3 miles from Holmes Chapel, 5 miles from
Congleton. Close by the village of Somerford,
just off the A54
Open all year
Free admission
♿ 🐃

TIMBERSBROOK PICNIC AREA

Country walk and picnic area

c/o Countryside Office, County Offices, Chapel Lane,
Wilmslow, Cheshire SK9 1PU
☏ Wilmslow (0625) 534796

*Picnic site close to Mow Cop Trail and
Bosley Cloud. Toilets.*

Timbersbrook, 2 miles east of Congleton
Open daily 10.00am–dusk except Christmas Day
Free admission
♿ 🚑 🐃

▶ DISLEY ◀

LYME HALL & PARK

Stately home and country park

Lyme Park, Disley, Stockport, Cheshire SK12 2NX
☎ Disley (0663) 62023

Large stately home in 1300 acres of parkland. 13 acres of formal Victorian gardens, orangery, sunken Dutch garden, red deer herd, adventure playground, pitch and putt. Visitor centre and countryside centre. National Trust owned.

On the A6 between New Mills and Hazel Grove
Open daily except Christmas Day and Boxing Day –
  gardens: 8.00am–dusk; house: varying times
  throughout the year
Admission to gardens: free to pedestrians; house: adult
  £2.50, child/OAP £1.00
&. ⟐ advance notice required for visits to
house ⊢

▶ FARNDON ◀

FARNDON PICNIC SITE

Picnic site by the river Dee

c/o Cheshire County Council, Countryside and Recreation
  Dept, Goldsmith House, Chester, Cheshire CH1 1SE
☎ Northwich (0606) 43874

At the bottom of the hill in Farndon village. Turn
  left at the bridge traffic lights when coming from
  the Chester side of the river
Open all year daily
Free admission
&. ⊢

▶ KNUTSFORD ◀

KNUTSFORD HERITAGE CENTRE

Exhibition centre and craft shop

90A King St, Knutsford, Cheshire
☎ Knutsford (0565) 50506

A restored half-timbered 17th century building housing frequently changed exhibitions on wildlife and local history. Craft shop and 'green' books. Childrens events arranged.

In Knutsford town centre, set back from King St
Open mid Jan–mid Dec, 2.00–4.30pm Sun–Fri,
  11.00am–4.00pm Saturdays
Free admission
&. ⊁

PEOVER HALL & GARDENS

Manor house and country garden

Over Peover, Knutsford, Cheshire
☎ Knutsford (0565) 812404/812135

Elizabethan manor house and gardens, home of the Mainwearing family 1066–1919. Herb, rose, lily pool and paved gardens, Elizabethan summerhouse and topiary.

Take the A50 south of Knutsford, turn left onto the
  Goosfrey–Chelford road after 2 miles
Open May–Sept Mondays only 2.00–5.00pm, excluding
  Bank Holiday Mondays
Admission charged, please telephone for details
&. majority of gardens accessible, facilitated parking

TABLEY HOUSE AND GARDENS

Country house and garden

Tabley Inferior, Knutsford, Cheshire
☎ Knutsford (0565) 3021

18th century country house, garden and wooded park. Large lake with island and ruined folly, dovecote and mirror pools. Newly-opened gallery with two of Turner's finest paintings.

On the A5033, 1½ miles east of Knutsford
Open April–Oct, Thur–Sun and Bank Holidays 2.00–
  5.00pm
&. ⟐ ⊢

TATTON PARK

Country park and gardens, farm shop and walks

Knutsford, Cheshire WA16 6QN
☎ Knutsford (0565) 54822

Furnished Georgian mansion with 60 acres of fine gardens. Japanese garden, orangery and beech maze. 1930s working farm, mediaeval Old Hall, gift shop, farm shop, restaurant.

Just off the M6, jct 19, M56 jct 7. Signposted
Open (for the park and gardens) daily except Christmas
Day; mansion closed Mondays; Old Hall and farm
Easter–October
Admission: (all-in) adult £3.75, child £1.90. Telephone
for individual attraction charges
& wheelchairs available, toilets, access to shop,
restaurant and garden (though most paths are gravelled)
🚌 🐎

▶ MACCLESFIELD ◀

ADLINGTON HALL

Historic house with gardens

Macclesfield, Cheshire SK10 4LF
☎ Prestbury (0625) 829508/829206

*Tudor Manorhouse with Elizabethan and
Georgian additions, a Royalist garrison
during the Civil War. 17th century organ
once played by Handel. Wooded gardens,
'wilderness', yew walk and lime avenue.*

5 miles north of Macclesfield, ½ mile off the A523
Open Good Friday–Oct, Sun 2.00–5.30pm, Wed and Sat
2.00–5.30pm (Aug only), Bank Holidays 2.00–5.30pm
& 🚌 advanced notice required
🐎

CAPESTHORNE HALL

Country house and gardens

Macclesfield, Cheshire SK11 9JY
☎ Chelford (0625) 861221/861439

*House and garden dating from 1719.
Georgian chapel, Mill Wood walk, chain of
lakes, herb garden, nature trail, arboretum
and childrens adventure playground.*

Off the A34, 5 miles south of Alderley Edge
Open April: Sundays only; May, Aug, Sept: Wed, Sat and
Sun; June and July: Tues–Thur, Sat and Sun; Good
Friday and Bank Holidays. Park, gardens and chapel
12.00–6.00pm; house 2.00–5.00pm
Admission: park, gardens and chapel adult £1.30, child
50p, OAP £1.00
& 🚌 advance notice required 🐎

DANEBRIDGE FISHERIES LTD

**Farm shop, country walk, speciality food producer
and smoke house**

Pingle Cottage, Danebridge, Wincle, nr Macclesfield,
Cheshire SK11 0QE
☎ Wincle (0260) 227293

On the A54 Buxton–Congleton road, turn off for
Wincle, through village 200 yards on right past
the Ship Inn
Open all year dawn until dusk for the fishing lake, shop:
9.30am–4.30pm
& 🐎

GAWSWORTH HALL

Historic house, park garden and open air theatre

Gawsworth, Macclesfield, Cheshire SK11 9RN
☎ North Rode (0260) 223456

*One of Cheshire's most beautiful half-
timbered historic houses with mediaeval
parkland, fish ponds and gardens. Open air
theatre with covered grandstand June to
August.*

2 miles south of Macclesfield off the A536
(signposted)
Open Mar–Oct 2.00–5.30pm
Admission. adult £2.50, child £1.25, special reductions
for parties
& 🚌 🎭

GRITSTONE TRAIL

Country walk

C/O Countryside Office, Remenham, Chapel Lane,
Wilmslow, Cheshire SK9 1PU
☎ Wilmslow (0625) 534796

*Upland walk, stout footwear or boots
recommended.*

Take the A6 to Disley Lyme Park for north end,
A523 to Rushton Spencer for south end, centre
Teggs Nose Country Park off the A537 nr
Macclesfield
Open all year
Free admission
& 🐎

HARE HILL GARDENS

Country park

Oak Rd, Prestbury, Macclesfield, Cheshire
☎ Prestbury (0625) 828981

Walled garden featuring formal planting with blue/white/yellow theme. Surrounding woods have colourful displays of rhododendrons and azaleas; hostas and holly trees feature in recently restored but little-known garden. (House not open to public.)

Take the B5087 north west of Macclesfield. Signposted on right after 4 miles
Open April–Oct Wed, Thur, Sat, Sun and Bank Holidays 10.00am–5.30pm; Nov–March Saturday and Sunday 10.00am–5.30pm. Special opening to see rhododendrons and azaleas 21 May–8 June daily 10.00am–5.30pm
Admission: charge made, please telephone for details
&

JODRELL BANK SCIENCE CENTRE & TREE PARK

Granada Arboretum

nr Macclesfield, Cheshire SK11 9DL
☎ Lower Withington (0477) 71571

In the shadow of the giant Radio Telescope the 35 acre arboretum contains over 2,500 varieties of native woody species, heather gardens and roses.

On the A535 between Holmes Chapel and Chelford, 8 miles west of Macclesfield, 4 miles from jct 18 on the M6
Open Easter-Oct daily 10.30am–5.30pm
Admission: adult £2.75, child £1.50, OAP £2.00
& ᕏ ✗

MACCLESFIELD FOREST

Country walk and forestry centre

Sutton, Macclesfield, Cheshire
☎ Sutton (02605) 2832 (Rangers' office)

A scenic blend of pine forest, lakes and moorland with an extensive variety of wild life, including heronry. Network of public footpaths.

Take the A523 south from Macclesfield, turn left into Langley after 1 mile. Toilets and car park are east of Langley at Trentabank Reservoir
Open all year
Free admission
& ᕏ ⵉ

MACCLESFIELD RIVERSIDE PARK (BOLLIN VALLEY)

Country park

c/o County Offices, Chapel Lane, Wilmslow, Cheshire SK9 1PU
☎ Wilmslow (0625) 534790/1

Approximately 100 acres of river valley landscape; includes walks, picnic sites, Information Centre, herd of Old English Longhorns, car parks and toilets. Full programme of guided walks and activities Easter–Oct.

On the southern fringe of Greater Manchester between Macclesfield and Warrington
Open all year
Free admission
& toilets, paths suitable for wheelchairs
ᕏ ⵉ

MELLORS GARDENS

Country garden

Hough Hole House, Rainow, nr Macclesfield, Cheshire SK10 5UW
☎ Macclesfield (0625) 72286

A restored Victorian allegorical garden featuring a stream, pool and waterfall, at its most colourful in May and June. Not flowery; the beauty lies in changing levels, water and trees giving different perspectives.

Take the A5002 north of Mace, on the left after 4 miles
Open May and August Bank Holidays. Other times by appointment only, please telephone
Admission: charge made, please telephone for details
& ✗

MIDDLEWOOD WAY

Linear recreation route, picnic areas, bridleway

Rangers Office, Adlington Road, Bollington, Cheshire
☎ Macclesfield (0625) 573998
(Macclesfield Borough Council)

The Middlewood Way provides a traffic free recreation route for pedestrians, horseriders and cyclists from Macclesfield to Marple, through the Peak District fringe. Level, well made paths, ideal for all. Toilet facilities at Adlington Road car park.

3 miles north of Macclesfield, signposted from the A523 London Road. Many entrance points along the way. Car parks at Adlington Rd (Bollington), Poynton Coppice and Higher Poynton Station (Higher Poynton)
Open all year
Free admission
& telephone for details of best access points ✝

REDESMERE LAKESIDE PICNIC AREA

Picnic area and birdwatching point

Siddington, Macclesfield, Cheshire SK11 9JY
☎ Macclesfield (0625) 21955

¹ᐟ² mile long lake with aquatic birds and gool local footpath network. Picnic area, parking and toilets.

From Alderley Edge take the A34 south towards Congleton. 2 miles from the traffic lights (Marks Heath A537) turn left, signposted
Open all year daily
Free admission
& ₪ parking limited at busy periods ✝

TEGGS NOSE COUNTRY PARK

Country park, picnic area and circular walk

Buxton Old Rd, Macclesfield, Cheshire SK1 0AP
☎ Macclesfield (0625) 614279

Teggs provides a gateway to the Peak District fringe outside Macclesfield. Scenic views, walks, either gentle or strenuous, peaceful woodland, local landmarks and industrial history. Refreshment kiosk.

2 miles east of Macclesfield, signposted from the A537 Buxton road
Open daily all year. Refreshment kiosk open at weekends in winter, daily in the afternoons in summer
Free admission
& ₪ ✝

WEST PARK

Public park and gardens, bowling green

Prestbury Road, Macclesfield, Cheshire
☎ Macclesfield (0625) 21955

One of the earliest public parks in Britain featuring ornamental gardens, picnic area, aviary, arboretum, childrens playground and the largest crown-bowling green in Europe.

½ mile from the town centre on the B5087
Open all year daily, dawn–dusk
Free admission
& ₪ advance notice required ✝

► *MALPAS* ◄

CHOLMONDELEY CASTLE GARDENS

Country gardens and farm animals

Cholmondeley Castle, Malpas, Cheshire SY14 8AH
☎ Cholmondeley (082 922) 383

Lakeside picnic area, gift shop, plants for sale. Ancient private chapel in the park.

Off the A49 Whitchurch–Tarporley road
Open Easter–14 October, Sundays and Bank Holidays only 12.00–5.30pm, weekday visits by prior arrangement
Admission: adult £2.00, child 50p, OAP £1.00
& the disabled car park is adjacent to the tearoom
₪ ✝

► *NANTWICH* ◄

DAGFIELDS FARM

Working farm and craft centre

Dagfields Farm, Walgherton, Nantwich, Cheshire CW5 7LG

Dried flower workshop, antiques, woollens, and leathercraft. Tea rooms.

4 miles out of Nantwich on the A51 Stone Road. Turn right for Audlem opposite the Boar's Head public house. 3rd farm on the left. Signposted
Open daily 11.00am–5.00pm
Free admission
& ₪ advance notice required ✝

DORFOLD HALL

Historic house and gardens

Acton, Nantwich, Cheshire CW5 8LD
☎ Nantwich (0270) 625245

Jacobean country house built in 1616 – home of Mr and Mrs Richard Roundell. Beautiful plaster ceilings and panelling, cobbled courtyard, avenue of ancient lime trees, lawns and attractive woodland garden. Guided tours.

On the A534 approx 1 mile outside Nantwich
Open April–Oct Tues and Bank Holiday Mondays
2.00–5.00pm
Admission: adult £2.00, child (over 5) £1.00 (1988
prices)
& steps in house
🚌 advance notice required; park on road at top of drive
✕

THE FIRS POTTERY

Stoneware pottery

Sheppenhall Lane, Aston, Nantwich, Cheshire CW5 8DE
☎ Crewe (0270) 780345

*See a wide variety of thrown and hand-built
functional decorative pottery. Tuition,
'making' days and longer courses by
arrangement. Send for details.*

Off the A530 Nantwich–Whitchurch road, 5 miles
south west of Nantwich
Open all year (most days)
Free admission
& ✕

THE PALMS TROPICAL OASIS AT STAPELEY WATER GARDENS

Country water gardens

The Palms, Stapeley Water Gardens, London Road,
Stapeley, Nantwich, Cheshire CW5 7LH
☎ Nantwich (0270) 628628

*Oasis featuring exotic gardens, fountains,
pirhanas and sharks set in the world's
largest water garden centre – fish, pets,
gardening supplies and display garden. Two
restaurants and a cafe, groups welcome.*

On the A51, 1 mile south of Nantwich. Signposted
from jct 16 on the M6
Open summer Mon–Fri 10.00am–6.00pm, Sat, Sun and
Bank Holidays 10.00am–7.00pm; winter 10.00am–
5.00pm all week
Admission: adult £2.00, child (4–14) £1.00, OAP £1.50,
party rates available for 20 or more
& 🚌 ✕

STRETTON MILL

Working water mill

Cheshire County Council, Cheshire Museums, Tilston,
Cheshire CW9 8AQ
☎ Northwich (0606) 41331

*A small working watermill set in beautiful
countryside only ten miles from Chester. See
the waterwheels operating the old timber
mill machinery and flour being ground.
Shop, picnic area and car park.*

Turn south off the A534 between Farndon and
Broxton (signposted)
Open March–Oct, Tues–Sat 2.00–6.00pm
Admission: adult 60p, child 30p
& ground floor only is accessible
🚌 advance notice required ✕

► *NORTHWICH* ◄

ARLEY HALL AND GARDENS

Historic house and country gardens

nr Great Budworth, Northwich, Cheshire CW9 6NA
☎ Arley (0565) 777353

*A fine hall, still a residence, set in a 14 acre
garden, one of the finest in Britain. Variety
and interest throughout the season.*

Off the B5391, 6 miles west of Knutsford
Open Easter–Oct 2.00–6.00pm daily, except Mondays
Admission: adult £1.80, child under 17 90p (under 8
free). Hall £1.00 extra
& 🚌 advance notice required ✕

ARLEY HALL WORKSHOP

**Wood furniture and turned products. Showroom
and workshop**

Back Lane, Arley, Aston-by-Budworth, Northwich,
Cheshire CW9 6LZ
☎ Arley (056 585) 432

*Watch cabinetmaker John Chalmers–Brown
making solid wood furniture in the workshop
and see the finished pieces in the showroom.
Guided tour, "From Tree to Furniture" and
the Arley Rhino sculpture by Ted Roocroft.*

In the grounds of Arley Hall gardens. Off the B5356
from Stretton or jct 10 of the M56
Open Tues–Sun and Bank Holidays. April–Oct 9.00am–
6.00pm, Sept–March 9.00am–5.00pm
Free admission to workshop
& 🚌 by appointment only ✕

BARNESBRIDGE GATES PICNIC SITE

Picnic area and forest walks

c/o Cheshire County Council, Countryside and Recreation Dept, Goldsmith House, Chester CH1 1SE

☎ Sandiway (0606) 43874

Take Delamere Forest road off the A556, midway between Hatchmere and Mouldsworth
Open all year daily
Free admission
&. ⭍

DANE'S MOSS NATURE RESERVE

Nature reserve

c/o Cheshire Conservation Trust, Marbury Country Park, Northwich, Cheshire CW9 6AT

A former peat extraction area which has been restored to provide a true peat bog environment with all the associated trees, shrubs, pools, plants and wildlife. Site of Special Scientific Interest.

Take the A536 south of Macclesfield, turn left at Gawsworth, then left again, reserve is 2 miles further on. Parking on roadside opposite right angle bend
Open all year daily
Free admission
&. ⎰ ⭍

DELAMERE FOREST PARK

Forest walks

Linmere, Delamere, Northwich, Cheshire CW8 2JD
☎ Sandiway (0606) 882167

The biggest single area of woodland in Cheshire, with conifer and broadleaf forestation. Tranquil setting.

Off the B5152, 5 miles west of Northwich
Open all year
Free admission
&. there is a specially designed trail for the disabled starting at Barnes Bridge car park on the Hatchmere–Mouldsworth road
⎰ ⭍

FOREST VISITOR CENTRE

Forestry centre

Forestry Commission, Linmere, Delamere, Northwich, Cheshire CW8 2JD
☎ Sandiway (0606) 882167

Turn west off the B5152 at Delamere station. Follow signs for approx 350 yards to centre and car park
Open all year Tues–Sun 10.30am–4.00pm
Free admission
&. ⎰ ⭍

HATCHMERE PICNIC SITE

Picnic site

c/o Cheshire County Council, Countryside and Recreation Dept, Goldsmith House, Chester CH1 1SE
☎ Sandiway (0606) 43874

Just north of Hatchmere crossroads, follow Delamere Forest signs from the A556 or A56
Open all year daily
Free admission
&. ⭍

LINMERE PICNIC SITE

Picnic area and forest walks

c/o Cheshire County Council, Countryside and Recreation Dept, Goldsmith House, Chester CH1 1SE
☎ Sandiway (0606) 43874

Take the B5152 off the A56 to Delamere Forest, the picnic site is beside Delamere station
Open all year daily
Free admission
&. ⎰ weekdays only ⭍

MARBURY COUNTRY PARK

Country park

c/o Cheshire County Council, Countryside and Recreation Dept, Goldsmith House, Chester CH1 1SE
☎ Sandiway (0606) 43874

220 acres of woodland, parkland and mere. A network of paths and picnic areas provided for recreation and relaxation.

From Northwich take the A523 towards Runcorn, then turn towards Anderton and Comberbach (signposted)
Open all year daily
Free admission
&. ⎰ ⭍

SHAKERLEY MERE COUNTRY PARK

Country park

c/o Cheshire County Council, Countryside and Recreation Dept, Goldsmith House, Chester CH1 1SE
☎ Sandiway (0606) 43874

Beside the M6 at crossroads of the B5082
(Northwich–Holmes Chapel) and the B5081
(Knutsford)
Open all year daily
Free admission
 ♿ ♫ 🏥

▶ **RUNCORN** ◀

NORTON PRIORY MUSEUM & GARDENS

Country gardens

Tudor Rd, Runcorn, Cheshire WA7 1SX

*30 acres of woodland gardens, 12th century
excavated remains of a mediaeval priory,
display telling the story of the site. Cafe,
shop, picnic area, special events and
exhibitions.*

From jct 11 on the M56, turn for Warrington and
follow signs. From other directions follow signs
for Runcorn and Norton Priory
Open March–Oct weekdays 12.00–5.00pm, weekends and
Bank Holidays 12.00–6.00pm; Nov–Feb 12.00–4.00pm
every day
Admission: adult £1.70, concession 85p
♿ ♫ 🏥 except in walled garden

NORTON PRIORY WALLED GARDEN

Kitchen garden set within attractive woodland

Gardener's Cottage, Norton Priory Walled Garden, Tudor
Road, Runcorn, Cheshire WA7 1SX
☎ Runcorn (0928) 569895

*2½ acre walled garden set in woodland.
Originally built in the 1760s to provide
fruit, vegetables and flowers for the Brooke
family of Norton Priory. Developed into a
'pleasure garden' before 1900, abandoned in
the 1920s but now restored to show a range
of gardening design. Croquet lawn,
equipment available for hire.*

Off the A558, on the eastern edge of Runcorn.
Follow signs for Norton Priory Museum
Open March–Oct weekdays 12.00–5.00pm weekends and
Bank Holidays 12.00–6.00pm
Admission: adult 60p, child/OAP 30p
♿ ♫ 🏥

▶ **SANDBACH** ◀

SALT LINE

Country walk

c/o Countryside Office, Hassall, nr Sandbach, Cheshire
CW11 0XT
☎ Crewe (0270) 768835

*The Salt Line was once a busy railway line
that carried salt from Cheshire to Stoke-
on-Trent.*

For Salt Line, turn right off the A533 by the New
Inn crossroads. Continue through Hassall Green,
under M6 to Salt Line car park, approx 2½ miles
south east of Sandbach
Open all year daily
Free admission
♿ ♫ advance notice required 🏥

WARMINGHAM CRAFT WORKSHOPS AND GALLERY

Craft centre and museum of light aviation

The Mill, Warmingham, nr Sandbach, Cheshire
CW11 9QW
☎ Warmingham (027 077) 366

*Craft gallery selling various craft items and
a museum of light aviation.*

Approx 2½ miles west of Sandbach, jct 17 of the
M6
Open most weekends, please telephone to check
Free admission
♿ ♫ by appointment only 🍽

▶ **TARPORLEY** ◀

BUNBURY WATERMILL

Restored working water-powered corn mill

Mill Lane, Off Bowes Gate Lane, Bunbury, Tarporley,
Cheshire
☎ Manchester (061) 480 6271

*The mill dates from 1844, and was restored
by N.W. Water in 1977. Literature,
bookmarks and stoneground flour for sale.*

Signposted from the A49 and A51 trunk roads, 3
miles south of Tarporley

Open Easter–Sept weekends and Bank Holidays
2.00–5.00pm, other times by appointment
Admission: adult 75p, child/OAP 50p, special party rates
  there are some narrow steep steps both inside and
outside the mill

CHESHIRE HERBS

Herb nursery with display garden

Fourfields, Forest Road, Little Budworth, nr Tarporley,
Cheshire CW6 9ES
☎   Little Budworth (082 921) 578

*A wholesale and retail herb nursery with a
display herb garden. There is also a small
shop selling herb related products. Courses
and talks are given. Cheshire Herbs exhibits
at the major horticultural shows in the
summer months.*

3½ miles north of Tarporley on the A49, next door
to the Cabbage Hall public house
Open 2 Jan–Christmas Eve 10.00am–5.00pm daily
Free admission
  advance notice required

▶   WARRINGTON   ◀

KENYON HALL FARM

Farm shop and pick your own

Winwick Lane, Croft, Warrington WA3 7ED
☎   Culcheth (092 576) 3646/3161

*Family-run farm, growing a wide range of
soft fruits and vegetables. Quality produce
and friendly service. Picnic area, tea shop
open afternoons, play area.*

½ way between Warrington and Leigh on the A579,
½ mile east of M6 jct 22
Open June–Aug daily 9.30am–8.00pm
Free admission
  advance notice required
in car park only

MOUNT PLEASANT FARM CRAFT CENTRE

Craft centre, pick your own, coffee shop

Glazebrook Lane, Glazebrook, nr Warrington, Cheshire
WA3 5BN
☎   Irlam (061 775) 2004

*A beautifully restored range of farm
buildings selling a wide selection of crafts;*

*pottery, designer knitwear, clothing, cane
furniture etc. Also a coffee shop serving
morning coffee, lunches and afternoon teas.*

M6 exit 21 – A57 towards Manchester, B5212 to
Culcheth and Leigh; or M63 exit 2 – A57 to
Warrington, B5212 to Culcheth and Leigh
Open July and December 10.00am–5.00pm daily, other
months Wed–Sun 10.00am–5.00pm, evenings by
arrangement
Free admission

RISLEY MOSS NATURE PARK

Country park

Ordance Avenue, Birchwood, Warrington, Cheshire,
WA3 6QX
☎   Padgate (0925) 824339

*Woodland walks, an educational nature
reserve, hides and an observation tower
overlooking mossland nature reserve.*

Follow signs on the A574 from Warrington or jct
11 on the M62
Open daily except Fridays and Christmas Day. Please
telephone for opening times
Free admission
  can provide wheelchairs

▶   WILMSLOW   ◀

THE CARRS (BOLLIN VALLEY)

Country park

c/o Macclesfield Borough Council, Leisure Services
Department, Stuart House, King Edward St,
Macclesfield, Cheshire SK10 1DX
☎   Macclesfield (0625) 21955

*Walks in 70 acres of riverside parkland
between Wilmslow and Styal, following the
course of the River Bollin. Picnic area.*

On the B5166, 1 mile from Wilmslow
Open all year daily
Free admission

DEAN VALLEY PICNIC SITE

Country park and country walks

c/o County Offices, Chapel Lane, Wilmslow, Cheshire
SK9 1PU
☎   Wilmslow (0625) 534790/1

Parking, picnic sites and access to the Bollin Valley via a series of footpaths. The area is particularly interesting for its bird life. Adjacent to a large garden centre, which offers a bistro, extensive garden shop and plant nursery.

Bollin Valley is on the southern fringe of Greater
   Manchester between Macclesfield and Warrington
Open all year
Free admission
 ♿ 🕴

LINDOW COMMON

Country walks

Off Altringham Rd, Wilmslow
☏ Macclesfield (0625) 573998
(Macclesfield Borough Council)

One of Cheshire's last three remaining lowland heaths with a series of easily accessible and well made up paths around the site.

1 mile north of Wilmslow, signposted from the
   Altringham Road. Car parks opposite the
   Boddington Arms on Racecourse Rd
Open all year
Free admission
♿ kissing gate access 🕴

ROSSMILL (BOLLIN VALLEY)

Country park and country walk

c/o County Offices, Chapel Lane, Wilmslow, Cheshire
   SK9 1PU
☏ Wilmslow (0625) 534790/1

Two wild flower meadows and deciduous woodland (mainly beech) with Orange Tip butterflies and a wide range of bird life. Circular pony rides, two small picnic sites.

Bollin Valley is on the southern fringe of Greater
   Manchester between Macclesfield and Warrington
Open all year
Free admission
♿ 🚊 advance notice required 🕴

SUNBANK WOOD (BOLLIN VALLEY)

Country park and country walk

c/o County Offices, Chapel Lane, Wilmslow, Cheshire
   SK9 1PU
☏ Wilmslow (0625) 534790/1

Mixed deciduous woodland with two main ponds – one stocked for fishing by permit, one used for pond dips. Large Comma butterfly colony. 2 small picnic sites, access to the Bollin Valley. Limited parking.

Follow the A538 3 miles west of Wilmslow, turn
   left into Sunbank Lane, entrance 1 mile on the
   left.
Open all year
Free admission
♿ by arrangement only 🕴

TWINNIES BRIDGE PICNIC SITE

Country park and country walk

c/o County Offices, Chapel Lane, Wilmslow, Cheshire
   SK9 1PU
☏ Wilmslow (0625) 534790/1

A riverside picnic site, providing an informal open grassland recreation area and a selection of woodland walks adjacent to the River Bollin. Access (on foot) to quarry bank mill. Toilet facilities provided (including disabled).

Take Styal Road out of Wilmslow, picnic site
   between Wilmslow and Styal village on the left
Open all year
Free admission
♿ 🕴

► WINSFORD ◄

WHITEGATE WAY

Country walk

c/o Cheshire County Council, Countryside and Recreation
   Dept, Goldsmith House, Chester CH1 1SE
☏ Northwich (0606) 43874

A 6 mile linear path following a disused railway line through fields, pasture, heath and forest. Ideal for informal recreation, horse riding and educational activites.

Take the Marton signposted road from the A556 at
   Sandiway or from the A54 west of Winsford to
   Whitegate station
Open all year daily
Free admission
♿ 🚊 🕴

CORNWALL

Cornwall is a region of farmers and fishermen with the sea never more than twenty miles away. Its dramatic coastal and moorland scenery is steeped in ancient legends and stories of shipwrecks and smuggling. Colourful fishing ports, stone-walled farmland and ruined engine-houses, reminders of Cornwall's tin-mining past are all familiar sights.

The visitor to the Cornish countryside has numerous country walks and farm trails to follow, there are several nature reserves and farm intrepretation centres and many gardens to visit, some with sub-tropical plants. There are important archaeological sites, museums and historic houses as well as a selection of art and craft workshops reflecting this county's appeal for the artisan. Cider farms and farm shops will provide a taste of Cornwall to refresh even the most weary of countryside explorers.

► BODMIN ◄

BRENEY COMMON NATURE RESERVE

Heathland nature reserve

c/o Cornwall Trust for Nature Conservation, Five Acres,
Allet, Truro, Cornwall TR4 9DJ
☎ Truro (0872) 73939

*135 acre mosaic of wet woodland, scrub,
heath, bog and ponds with superb birds,
lepidoptera and aquatic life.*

4 miles south of Bodmin, off the A391
Open daily
Free admission
&. ★

THE OLD MILL HERBARY

Country garden, country walks and herbs

Helland Bridge, Bodmin, Cornwall PL30 4QR
☎ St Mabyn (020884) 206

*Approximately 4 acres of semi-wild gardens
and woodland walks alongside the River
Camel Trail. Extensive planted display and
sale of culinary, medicinal and aromatic
herbs, shrubs and aquatics.*

Take the A30 1 mile north of Bodmin, following
signs for Helland and then on to Helland Bridge.
Or the B3266 Bodmin–Camelford road
Open most days 1 April–30 Sept 10.00am–5.00pm,
appointments advisable
Admission: adult £1.25, child 50p
★

REDMOOR MEMORIAL RESERVE

Heathland nature reserve

c/o Cornwall Trust for Nature Conservation, Five Acres,
Allet, Truro, Cornwall TR4 9DJ
☎ Truro (0872) 73939

*The reserve consists of 60 acres of mixed
heath communities, bogs, numerous small
ponds and willow carr. The ponds were
created by open-cast tin mining which
continued until the late 19th century.
Nature trail, interesting botany.*

4 miles south of Bodmin, off the B3269
Open daily, except the fourth Monday in February
Free admission
&. ★

► BOSCASTLE ◄

THE LEATHER SHOP

Craft centre and leather shop

The Old Mill, Boscastle, North Cornwall PL35 0AA

*Rob and Teresa Lloyd specialize in unusual
objects such as leather clocks and barometers,
multi coloured shoes and sandals, masks and
replicas of 11th century tankards all
produced in their workshop.*

On the B3266 nr Camelford, 6 miles south of
Boscastle
Open April–Sept daily 10.00am–9.00pm, Nov–March
daily 10.00am–6.00pm
Free admission
&. ᗑ ★

► BUDE ◄

EXEMOOR RARE BREEDS FARM

Rare breeds and nature trail

Exemoor Farm, Week-St-Mary, nr Bude, North Cornwall
EX22 6UX
☎ Canworthy Water (056681) 366

*1 mile farm trail situated in unspoilt
countryside, featuring one of the largest
collections of rare and commercial breeds
including Lundy ponies, all in their natural
habitat.*

From Bude take the A39 to Camelford, then left at
Wainhouse Corner to Canworthy Water. Take the
first Week-St-Mary turning, the farm is the first
on the right
Open May–Sept daily 10.30am–6.00pm
Admission: adult £1.50, child 75p (under 5s free)
&. ᗑ advance notice required ★

MEADS FARM GOLF RANGE & FAMILY ACTIVITY CENTRE

Golf range, farm shop and tea barn

Meads Farm, Poundstock, nr Bude, Cornwall EX23 0EE
☎ St Genny's (08403) 275/303

*Floodlit golf range, covered bays, club hire.
Farm shop selling cider, local produce and
gifts. Tea barn serving food all day,
vegetarian fayre and cream teas. Dog park
for exercising pets, toilets, telephone.*

6 miles from Bude on the A39 Atlantic Highway
   towards Tintagel
Open Easter–31 Oct daily 10.00am–7.00pm
 ♿ no toilet facilities
🚊 advance notice required 🐎

MORWENNA SHEEP'S MILK PRODUCTS

Dairy produce

Farmers Barn, Gooseham, Morwenstow, nr Bude,
   Cornwall EX23 9PG
☏ Morewenstow (028883) 481

From Bude travel north on the A39 for 8 miles,
   turn left for Morwenstow after 2 miles, right for
   Gooseham after 1 mile
Open all year by appointment only
Free admission
♿ by appointment only
🚊 advance notice required 🐔

NORTH CORNWALL HERITAGE COAST SERVICE

Heritage Coast visitor centre

The Lower Wharf, Bude Haven, Bude, Cornwall
☏ Bodmin (0208) 4121 ext 239

*Centre situated in an old warehouse on the
Bude Canal, providing information on how
best to enjoy the wildlife and unspoilt
scenery of the coast around Bude.*

Off the A39, 1 mile west of the A39 from Stratton
   Junction
Open April–Sept daily 10.00am–6.00pm
Free admission
♿ 🚊 advance notice required 🐔

PIXIELAND FUN-PARK

Tourist attraction

Pixieland Fun-Park, West Strete, Kilkhampton, Bude,
   Cornwall EX23 9QW
☏ Kilkhampton (028 882) 225

*Small family run park with ATC 4-wheel
motor bikes, bumper boats, bouncy frog,
train rides, ball pits and gym equipment for
wet or dry weather.*

On the A39, approx 6 miles north of Bude
Open daily except Saturdays. 8 April–11 May
   11.30am–4.30pm; 13 May–7 Sept 10.30am–6.00pm;
   9 Sept–5 Oct 11.30am–4.30pm; 7 Oct–2 Nov
   1.30–4.30pm
Admission: adult £2.60, child £2.10, OAP £1.90,
   wheelchair users free
♿ 🚊 advance notice required 🐎

TREWORGIE BARTON TRAILS

Woodland and farm trails, cream teas

Treworgie Barton, St Gennys, Bude, Cornwall EX23 0NL
☏ St Gennys (084 03) 233

*Treworgie Copse, through which the trail
runs, is an 'ancient woodland' in which a
management scheme is in progress in an
attempt to improve the wood as a wildlife
habitat. Cream teas.*

9 miles south of Bude, signposted off the A39 at
   Wainhouse Corner
Open Easter–Sept
Admission for the woodland walk: adult 50p, child 25p;
   guided farm walk: adult £1.25, child 50p
🚊 advance notice required 🐔

Cornish Seal Sanctuary
THE MARINE ANIMAL RESCUE CENTRE GWEEK

Your Day Out To Help A Seal ..

Exhibition and Audio-Visual Displays. Gift Shop, Cafe and
Summer Barbecue. Open 09.30 to 18.00 hrs with Free Car
Park and Facilities for Disabled People. Tel: (032 622) 361

► **CALLINGTON** ◄

KIT HILL COUNTRY PARK

Country park

Rangers Office, Delaware Road, Gunnislake, Cornwall
☎ Tavistock (0822) 833885

A rugged granite hilltop famed for its spectacular views of East Cornwall and Dartmoor. Centuries of mining and quarrying have helped shape Kit Hill and add interest for the visitor.

On the A390 between Gunnislake and Callington
Open all year
Free admission
&. ⇔ ⋔

► **CAMELFORD** ◄

ARCHAEOLOGICAL SITE

Important archaeological site, country walk and interpretation board

c/o North Cornwall Tourism Development Unit, Priory House, Bodmin, Cornwall PL31 2AD
☎ Bodmin (0208) 4471 ext 2122

Approx 3 miles north of Camelford on the A39, follow signposts to Crowdy Reservoir and Roughtor, take first right and left at next crossroads
Open all year
Free admission
&. ⇔ ⋔

► **CAMBORNE** ◄

PENDARVES WOOD RESERVE

Woodland nature reserve

c/o Cornwall Trust for Nature Conservation, Five Acres, Allet, Truro, Cornwall TR4 9DJ
☎ Truro (0872) 73939

The reserve covers 44 acres of mixed woodland, the main feature of which is the River Connor which runs into a lake created in the late 18th century.

2 miles south of Camborne, beside the B3303
Open every day except fourth Monday in February
Free admission
&. ⋔

TEHIDY COUNTRY PARK

Country park

Tehidy, Camborne, Cornwall TR14 0HA
☎ Camborne (0209) 714494

7 circular walks from 1 mile to 3 miles. Permanent orienteering course.

2 miles north of Camborne from Pool interchange on the A30 Camborne bypass. Hoppa Bus Service from Camborne
Open all year daily
Free admission
&. ⇔ advance notice required
⋔ under control around lakes for wildfowl protection

► **FALMOUTH** ◄

KENNALL VALE NATURE RESERVE

Woodland nature reserve

c/o Cornwall Trust for Nature Conservation, Five Acres, Allet, Truro, Cornwall TR4 9DJ
☎ Truro (0872) 73939

20 acre broadleaved plantation with some ancient oak wood. Site of considerable industrial archaeological interest with remains of water powered gunpowder mills.

4 miles north west of Falmouth off the A393 at Ponsanooth
Open daily except fourth Monday in February
Free admission
&. ⇔ ⋔

PENJERRICK

Country gardens

Budock, Falmouth, Cornwall

Wild valley garden featuring rhododendrons, trees, ferns, wood and pond areas.

Take the B3291 from Penryn towards Constantine and turn left at Argal Dam crossroads (3 miles south west of Falmouth)
Open March–Sept, Sun & Wed 1.30–4.30pm
Admission: 50p March, June–Sept £1.00 April–May
&. ⇔ advance notice required ⋔

TREBAH GARDEN

Country garden

Trebah Garden Trust, Trebah, Mawnan Smith, Cornwall TR11 5JZ

☎ Falmouth (0326) 250 448

Breathtaking 25 acre ravine garden with beach on Helford River. Rare sub-tropical trees and shrubs, waterfalls, water gardens and Koi carp. Garden shop, refreshments, play area.

Follow signs to Trebah from Treliever Cross. 1 mile south west of Mawnan Smith
Open all year daily 10.30am–5.00pm (last admission)
Admission: adult £2.00, child/disabled £1.00, under 5s free
 ♿ advance notice required 🦮

► HAYLE ◄

J & S CHOWN

Pottery manufacturer

Hope Farm, Gwithian Rd, Connor Downs, Hayle, Cornwall TR27 5EA

☎ Camborne (0209) 713361

Unique family pottery manufacturing the first bone china. Whole process from raw clay to tableware and giftware. Ceramic transfer printing. Bargain seconds items available for visitors to the factory.

Take the A3047 Connor Downs into Gwithian Road over the A30, right to Hope Farm
Open all year by appointment only
Admission: adult £2.00, child (5–16 years) £1.00
 🦮

► HELSTON ◄

CORNISH SEAL SANCTUARY

Marine rescue and sanctuary

Gweek, Helston, Cornwall
☎ (032622) 361

Exhibition and audio-visual centre on marine conservation, seal hospital and seal rehabilitation pools, wildlife trails, cafe, shop, car and coach park.

Off the route to the Lizard
Open daily all year 10.00am–6.00pm (4.30pm in winter)
Admission: adult £3.30, child/discount £2.60 (1990 prices)
 ♿ advance notice required 🦮

TRELOWARREN POTTERY LTD

Pottery workshop with showroom, manor house and craft centre

Trelowarren, Mawgan, Helston, Cornwall TR12 6AF
☎ Mawgan (032 622) 583

Nic Harrison and his wife Jackie established the pottery in 1981. Nic produces handthrown, domestic stoneware pottery. Jackie weaves rugs, mostly to commission. They may often be seen at work.

4 miles south east of Helston, off the B3293 St Keverne road at Garras turn left at Trelowarren sign, follow mile-long drive
Open Easter–Sept daily, Oct–Easter Mon–Fri 11.00am–5.00pm. Manor House open Easter–Oct (032 622) 366. Cornwall craft gallery, shop and various exhibitions (032 622) 567. Bistro – lunch and supper bookings (032 622) 595. Herb garden and nursery (032 622) 595. Woodland walk and shop (032 622) 595
Free admission
 ♿ advance notice required 🦮

► KILKHAMPTON ◄

NORTH CORNWALL TOURISM DEVELOPMENT UNIT

Canal and country walk, canal interpretation centre

Priory House, Bodmin, Cornwall PL31 2AD
☎ Bodmin (0208) 4471 ext 2122

3 miles east of junction of B3254 and A39 at Kilkhampton
Open April–Sept daily 10.30am–6.00pm
Free admission
 ♿ advance notice required 🦮

► LAUNCESTON ◄

ARCHAEOLOGICAL SITE

Important archaeological site and ancient monument

c/o North Cornwall Tourism Development Unit, Priory House, Bodmin, Cornwall PL31 2AD
☎ Bodmin (0208) 4471 ext 2122

Take the A395 Launceston–Camelford road, at Hallworthy take minor road to Canworthy Water, site approx ½ mile south west of Warbstow and 2 miles south west of Canworthy Water
Open all year
Free admission
 🦮

TAMAR OTTER PARK AND WILD WOOD

Branch of the Otter Trust, walks, lakes, visitor centre, tea room and shop

North Petherwin, nr Launceston, Cornwall PL15 8LW
☎ North Petherwin (056 685) 646

The only place in the West Country breeding British Otters regularly for release into the wild. Otters in semi-natural conditions, owls in 20 acres of woodland walks with 4 species of deer, pheasants, large collection of waterfowl on two lakes, wallabies, peacocks, etc. Large free car park.

Approx 6 miles north of Launceston on the B3254 to Bude
Open 1 April (or Good Friday if earlier) – 31 Oct, daily 10.30am–6.00pm or sunset.
Admission: adult £2.50, child £1.50, OAP £2.00 (1989 prices).
🚻 🚌 ✖

TRETHARNE LEISURE FARM

Leisure and interpretation farm centre, golf driving range

Kennards House, Launceston, Cornwall PL15 8QE
☎ Launceston (0566) 86324

Tretharne combines play and education. 90% of the centre is under cover, making it an ideal place to visit out of season.

3 miles south of Launceston on the A30
Open daily except Sundays 10.00am–6.00pm
Admission: adult £2.95, child/OAP £1.75
🚻 🚌 ✖

► **LISKEARD** ◄

BLISLAND HARNESS MAKERS

Saddlery workshop

Higher Harrowbridge, Bolventor, Liskeard, Cornwall
☎ Liskeard (0579) 20593

Working saddle and harness maker. Craft belts, boxes, bellows and dog equipment.

A30 Launceston–Bodmin road at Jamaica Inn (Bolventor) south on St Cleer road, 2 miles on right hand side
Open daily 9.30am–5.00pm, but please telephone to confirm
Free admission
🚻 door 29" wide ✖

► *LOOE* ◄

LANREATH FOLK AND FARM MUSEUM

Craft shop and farm museum

Churchtown, Lanreath, nr Looe, Cornwall PL13 2NX
☎ Lanreath (0503) 20349/20321

This extensive collection is housed in the village tithe barn. Wide range of farming bygones, old telephones, radios, a Bronze Age tomb, household antiques and much more. Craft demonstrations on weekdays.

5 miles from Looe, Lanreath village is situated just off the B3359 Middle Taphouse–Looe road
Open daily. Easter–June 11.00am–1.00pm, 2.00–5.00pm; June–Sept 10.00am–1.00pm, 2.00–6.00pm; Oct 11.00am–5.00pm
Admission: adult £1.50, child 75p
🚻 no disabled toilet facilities
🚌 advance notice required ✖

► *LOSTWITHIEL* ◄

PELYN WOODS RESERVE

Woodland nature reserve

c/ Cornwall Trust for Nature Conservation, Five Acres, Allet, Truro, Cornwall TR4 9DJ
☎ Truro (0872) 73939

101 acres of mixed broadleaved woodland, part of an estate once owned and managed by the Kendall family. Traces of past mining and quarrying can be seen.

2 miles west of Lostwithiel beside the A390
Open daily except fourth Monday in February
Free admission
🚻 ✖

► *MULLION* ◄

NORMAN UNDERHILL FIGURINES

Handmade ceramic figurines

Trecarne, Meaver Road, Mullion, Helston, Cornwall TR12 7DN
☎ Mullion (0326) 240667

Norman Underhill has been a sculptor for twenty five years, his figures are unique and each one is signed. They include fishermen, carpenters and musicians.

CORNWALL

7 miles from Helston, Lizard road turn right at
B3296, first building on right
Open daily 10.00am–10.00pm
Free admission
🕭 🚌 🐂

► **NEWQUAY** ◄

CUBERT STRAWBERRY FIELDS

Pick your own

Gwinear Farm, Cubert, nr Newquay, Cornwall TR8 5JX
☎ Crantock (0637) 830165

*Pick your own strawberries. Also coarse
fishing on an attractive well stocked 3 acre
lake. Large car park, toilet facilities.*

Take the A3075 out of Newquay to Redruth. On the
right hand side after 3 miles. Well signposted.
Open daily in the strawberry season 10.00am–7.00pm
Free admission
🕭 🚌 by arrangement
🐂 in the field

DAIRYLAND

**Merry-go-round milking, countrylife museum,
farm nature trail, farm park and playground**

Tresillian Barton, Summercourt, Newquay, Cornwall
TR8 5AA
☎ Mitchell (0872) 510246

*Entertainment, education and fun for all
ages. One all-in-price. Milking, lively and
informal museum with working exhibits.
Farming and nature in harmony, friendly
animals.*

On the A3058 Newquay–Truro–St Austell road
Open daily. April, Oct and Saturdays in low season
12.00–5.00pm; Easter and May–Sept 10.30am–
5.30pm. Milking approx 3.00–4.30pm
Admission: adult £3.50, child (4–15 years) £2.00,
OAP/disabled £3.20. Party rates available. (1990
prices)
🕭 🚌 by appointment
🐂 in car park only

► **PAR** ◄

LAMORNA POTTERY AND MERRY MAIDENS
BOUTIQUE

Craft centre and pottery workshop

Lamorna, nr Penzance, Cornwall TR19 6NY
☎ St Buryan (0736) 810330

*Crafts and pottery. Home-cooked food served
in tea garden or conservatory.*

Situated on the B3315 coast road from Penzance to
Lands End, 4 miles from Penzance
Open March–Oct daily 10.00am–5.30pm, extended in
peak season
Free admission
🕭 🚌 🐂

SARAH COUCH CHINA STUDIO

Craft

6 Well St, Tywardreath, Par, Cornwall PL24 2QH
☎ Par (072 681) 4160

*Studio displaying original pieces of hand-
painted china. Specializing in naturalistic
designs, Sarah Couch is established as a
leading exponent of her art in Cornwall.
Working largely on commissions, one piece
was recently presented to H.R.H. Princess
Anne.*

Off the A390, ½ mile south east of Par
Open by appointment only
Free admission
🕭 🐂

STONEYBRIDGE ORGANIC NURSERY (D B
Pascoe)

Organic nursery, farm shop and farm trails

Treesmill, Tywardreath, Par, Cornwall PL24 2TY
☎ Par (072 681) 3858

*A small family business on a 2 acre holding
growing over 40 crops, mainly on raised
beds, to Soil Association symbol
requirements. Companion planting, compost
bins, mulching and a collection of fuschias.*

1 mile off the B3269 to Fowey. Send SAE for map
showing precise location
Open Apr–Oct daily 9.00am–6.00pm, closed Sundays
from July. Winter opening Fridays only 10.00am–
4.00pm or by telephone appointment
Free admission
🕭 no disabled toilet facilities 🐂

► **PORT ISAAC** ◄

LONG CROSS HOTEL AND GARDENS

Victorian country gardens

Trelights, Port Isaac, North Cornwall, PL29 3TF
☎ Bodmin (0208) 880243

Approximately 3 acres of sheltered walks with pathways with Victorian nostalgia. Overlooking open countryside with panoramic sea views of Port Isaac and Port Quin bays. Beer garden, coffee and refreshments under cover. Cream teas 3.00–5.00pm daily.

3 miles west of Port Isaac, off the B3314
Open Easter–Oct daily 10.30am–dusk
Admission: adult 75p, accompanied child free, OAP 50p
  advance notice required

► REDRUTH ◄

SHIRE HORSE FARM AND CARRIAGE MUSEUM

Shire horse farm and museum

Lower Gryllis Farm, Treskillard, Redruth, Cornwall
  TR16 6LA
☎ Camborne (0209) 713606

All heavy English breeds of horse. Farm, agricultural and pleasure carriages. Wagon rides, guided tours, shires at work, working wheelwright and blacksmith shop. Picnic area, cream teas. Learn to work shires – courses by arrangement.

Leave Camborne bypass at Pool. Straight across traffic lights, right at railway bridge, left, then right then follow signs to Treskillard
Open Easter–Oct daily 10.00am–6.00pm
Admission: adult £2.25, child £1.25

► ST AUSTELL ◄

MID-CORNWALL GALLERIES

Art and craft gallery

Biscovey, Par, Cornwall PL24 2EG
☎ Par (072681) 2131

The Mid-Cornwall Galleries provides visitors with the opportunity to purchase or view art and crafts of the highest merit, by both national and south western artists and craftsmen.

3 miles east of St Austell at St Blazey on the A390
Open Mon–Sat 10.00am–5.00pm
Free admission

POLMASSICK VINEYARD

Vineyard and winery

Polmassick, St Ewe, St Austell, Cornwall PL26 6HA
☎ Mevagissey (0726) 842239

Steep sheltered valley producing several varieties of dry and medium dry wines, for sale by the glass or bottle in the winery. All weather wine garden, refreshments, picnic area, farm animals, vines for sale. Guided tours available by appointment.

From St Austell take the B3273 to Mevagissey and St Ewe, signposted from Polmassick crossroads. Also signposted on the B3287 from Tregony
Open end May–end Sept Tues–Sun and Bank Holiday Mondays 11.00am–5.00pm
Admission: adult 50p, child free
& access to winery only
  advance notice required

ROPEHAVEN CLIFFS RESERVE

Cliffs nature reserve

c/o Cornwall Trust for Nature Conservation, Five Acres, Allet, Truro, Cornwall TR4 9DJ
☎ Truro (0872) 73939

49 acres of cliffs and broadleaved woodland. Coastal footpath adjoins the reserve. Beautiful scenery, good for birds wintering in St Austell Bay.

2 miles south of St Austell, off the A390
Open daily
Free admission

► ST IVES ◄

ST IVES CRAFT CENTRE

Craft centre and gallery

Halsetown, St Ives, Cornwall
☎ Penzance (0736) 795078

Visitors may try their hand on the potters wheel. Evening classes and courses held.

1 mile south of St Ives on the B3311
Open April–Sept 10.00am–5.30pm except Sundays
Free admission

TREVALGAN FARM HOLIDAYS

Country walk and farm trail

Trevalgan Farm, St Ives, Cornwall TR26 3BJ
☎ Penzance (0736) 796433

Farm trail to coastal path for wonderful views of the sea and cliffs. Picnic tables. Mini golf at camping site.

Take the B3306 Lands End road from St Ives, sign after ½ mile
Open Easter–Oct
Free admission, parking 20p
&. ★

WAYSIDE MUSEUM

Museum

Zennor, nr St Ives, Cornwall TR26 3DA
☎ Penzance (0736) 796945

The oldest private museum in Cornwall, founded in 1935. Wayside Museum houses a very large collection of local artefacts: millhouse, watermill, forge, wheelwrights shop, laundry and displays on archaeology, tin mining, farming and fishing.

On the B3306 coast road, approx 4 miles west of St Ives
Open April–Oct daily 10.00am–dusk
Admission: adult £1.50, child/OAP £1.00 (1990 prices)
&. assistance available for visitors in wheelchairs to negotiate steps
🚍 advance notice required ★

▶ **ST KEVERNE** ◀

ROSKILLYS CREAM AND ICE CREAM

Speciality food producer

Tregellast Barton, St Keverne, Helston, Cornwall, TR12 6NX
☎ St Keverne (0326) 280479

A Cornish family farm following organic principles producing clotted cream, ice cream and fudges from their own Channel Island herd. Home-made jams, chutneys and mustards. Also self catering holiday cottages, ponds and woodland walk.

From St Keverne square leaving war memorial on left, turn right opposite newsagent, pass school, turn right after ¼ mile, farm is on the left
Open all year daily 9.00am–6.00pm
Free admission
&. ★

▶ **ST MARY'S** ◀

LONGSTONE HERITAGE CENTRE

Island history heritage centre

St Mary's, Isle of Scilly, Cornwall TR21 0NW
☎ Scillonia (0720) 22924

The island's visitor centre portrays the history of the Isles of Scilly with audio visual film, animated figures, artefacts and historic photographs. Restaurant. Gift shop, putting green and garden centre.

1 mile from the quay in Hugh Town, on the Telegraph Road, follow the signs from Parting Carn
Open 1 week before Easter–end Oct daily 9.30am–5.00pm
Admission: adult £2.00, child (under 14) £1.00, OAP £1.85 (1990 prices)
&. ★

TRESCO ESTATE

Sub-tropical gardens

Tresco, Isles of Scilly, Cornwall TR24 0QQ
☎ Scillonia (0720) 22849

On a private island, the sub-tropical garden at the famous Tresco Abbey has a unique collection of plants. Garden shop, cafe, heliport adjacent to the garden.

30 miles from the Cornish coast
Open daily 10.00am–4.00pm
Admission: adult £1.50, child £1.00
&. ★

▶ **TAVISTOCK** ◀

DAVID PLAGERSON

Noah's ark and other hand-made toys

5 Cliff View Terrace, Gunnislake, Cornwall PL18 9DD
☎ Tavistock (0822) 833035

Craftsman working from home makes a Noah's ark set in mixed woods using over 15 timbers, each suited to an animal and finished in beeswax. Also painted set with over 80 pairs available.

Off the A390, 5 miles west of Tavistock
Open by appointment only
Free admission
&. ★

► TORPOINT ◄

ANTONY WOODLAND GARDEN

Country garden, country walk

Antony House, Torpoint, Cornwall PL11 2QA
☎ (0752) 812364

A 50 acre woodland garden based on a Humphry Redton design, on the banks of the Lynher Estuary. Many varieties of spring flowering shrubs, camellias, rhododendrons and azaleas.

5 miles west of Plymouth via Torpoint car ferry.
  2 miles north west of Torpoint off the A374
&. ⇛ ✕

MOUNT EDGCUMBE COUNTRY PARK

Country park and historic house

Cremyll, Torpoint, Cornwall PL10 1HZ

Formal gardens and 18th century landscaped park with extensive woodland, coastal walks, flowering shrubs, unusual trees and a wealth of wildlife. The house and furniture have recently been sensitively restored.

Cremyll ferry to park entrance, or Torpoint ferry,
  the A374 to Antony then the B3247 to the park
  (8 miles)
Open all year daily for the park; for the house Easter–Oct
  Wed–Sun and Bank Holidays. Telephone for details
Admission: (house) adult £2.50, child £1.25, OAP/student
  £1.50
&. ⇛ advance notice preferable
✕ in House and Earls Garden

► TRURO ◄

CALLESTOCK CIDER FARM

Cider farm with farm shop and museum

Penhallow, Truro, Cornwall TR4 9LW
☎ Truro (0872) 573356

Learn about cider making, its history, and associated trades of coopers and blacksmiths in the museum. Friendly farm animals and tractor and trailer rides through the orchards.

Signposted from Penhallow on the A3075
  Newquay–Redruth road

Open Easter–Christmas Eve 9.00am–6.00pm Mon–Sat,
  please telephone during Jan & Feb
Free admission except to museum. Charge includes
  tractor and trailer ride through the orchards
&. ⇛ ✕

THE COUNTY DEMONSTRATION GARDEN

Garden nature reserve and demonstration gardens

Probus, Truro, Cornwall
☎ Truro (0872) 74282

A unique and much televised centre which won the Carnegie British Heritage award. 7½ acre site developed to demonstrate a whole range of gardening ideas, techniques, designs and plants. Also nature trail, historical and geological sections.

On the main A390 east of Probus, midway between
  Truro and St Austell
Open Oct–April, Mon–Fri 10.00am–5.00pm, May–Sept
  Mon–Fri 10.00am–5.00pm, Sundays 2.00–6.00pm
Admission: £1.00, summer £1.20
&. ⇛ advance notice required ✕

FIVE ACRES NATURE RESERVE

Woodland nature reserve

c/o Cornwall Trust for Nature Conservation, Five Acres,
  Allet, Truro, Cornwall TR4 9DJ

5 acres of woodland with plans to build ponds, nature trails, etc. Land bequeathed by founder member of the Trust to be used as Trust's headquarters.

5 miles north of Truro, off the B3284
Open all year daily, office weekdays only
Free admission

PARKINSON HERBS

Herb nursery

Barras Moor Farm, Perran-ar-Worthal, Truro, Cornwall,
  TR3 7PE
☎ Truro (0872) 864380

One-woman nursery. Proprietor could be delivering plants so always telephone ahead. Wholesale orders delivered in Cornwall only. Christmas herb shop open 6 weeks prior to Christmas.

Approx 7 miles from Truro, on A39 between Truro and Falmouth situated in RAC lay-by, Perran-ar-Worthal
Open daily 9.00am–5.00pm
Free admission
& very large parking area, plants can be brought to customers' cars and loaded without the customer disembarking, mail order service is also available
🏕

POLISKEN FARM SHOP & PYO

Farm shop and pick your own

Trispen, Truro, Cornwall TR4 9AU
☎ Truro (0872) 70896

Shop selling own produce in season also selection of plants and shrubs. Full range of fruit and vegetables, local cheeses, fresh milk, clotted cream etc.

2 miles from Truro on the A3076 Newquay road
Open all year Mon–Sat 9.00am–6.30pm (July–Aug daily till late)
Free admission
& 🚌 🏕

TRELISSICK GARDEN

Country park, country garden, walks and craft centre

Trelissick Garden, Feock, Truro, Cornwall TR3 6QL
☎ Truro (0872) 862090

A rare garden within 400 acres of parkland, extensive woodland walks along the shore of the Fal Estuary. Fine views over Carrick Roads. Shop, restaurant, art and craft gallery outside the admission point.

From the A39 Truro–Falmouth road take the B3289 at Playing Plake for the King Harry ferry
Open 1 April–30 Sept Mon–Sat 11.00am–6.00pm, Sun 1.00–6.00pm; March and Oct Mon–Sat 11.00am–5.00pm, Sun 1.00–5.00pm
Admission: garden adult £2.20, child £1.10; car park £1.00, refunded to garden visitors (1990 prices)
& 🚌 advance notice required
🏕 in park only

TREWITHEN GARDENS

Country garden

Grampound Rd, Truro, Cornwall TR2 4DD

30 acre garden with magnificent camellias, rhododendrons, magnolias and many rare trees and shrubs. Extensive woodland gardens surrounded by parkland landscaped in the 18th century and include an enchanting early walled garden contemporary with the house. Original water gardens; video presentation; plant centre; picnic and childrens play areas.

On the A390, between Truro and St Austell
Open 1 March–30 Sept Mon–Sat 10.00am–4.30pm
Admission: adult £1.75 (1990 prices)
& 🚌 🏕

▶ WADEBRIDGE ◀

BRIDGE BIKE HIRE

Push bike hire centre

The Camel Trail, Wadebridge, Cornwall PL27 7AL
☎ Wadebridge (020881) 3050

15 mile traffic free trail following G.W.R. line along the river bank and estuary. Open all year round. Choice of 250 bikes.

Take the Atlantic highway A39 from Bude, or the A30 to Bodmin, then the A389 to Wadebridge
Open all year
Admission: bike for a full day, adult £3.00, child £2.00, telephone for further information
& 🚌 🏕

CORNISH SHIRE HORSE CENTRE

Farm trail, visit shop and interpretation centre, craft centre and country walk

Trelow Farm, Wadebridge, Cornwall
☎ Rumford (0841) 540276

Home for over 30 Shire horses set in 120 acres. Daily parades of horses in fully seated indoor arena, blacksmith, wheelwright, restaurant, lakeside walk, shops, carriage rides.

Follow signs from the A39 Wadebridge–St Columb Major road
Open Easter–Oct daily 10.00am–5.00pm
Admission: adult £2.90, child (3–14) £1.90, OAP £2.50
& 🚌 🏕

CREAM AND CRAFTS

Farm shop, craft shop and speciality food & drink producer

Higher Farm, Trebetherick, nr Wadebridge, Cornwall
   PL27 6SB
☎   Trebetherick (020886) 3109

Farm produced clotted cream and eggs for sale, also a wide range of quality Cornish crafts. Dried flowers grown on the farm a speciality.

Off the B3314, 5 miles north of Wadebridge
   towards the coast, Trebetherick is between Rock
   and Polzeath
Open daily 8.00am–1.00pm and 4.30–6.00pm
Free admission
 ♧ 🐕

►   *WEEK ST MARY*   ◄

NORTH CORNWALL TOURISM DEVELOPMENT UNIT

Farm trail, farm visit, small visitor centre describing archaeology of parish

Priory House, Bodmin, Cornwall PL31 2AD
☎   Bodmin (0208) 4471 ext 2122

½ mile south of Week St Mary on Canworthy
   Water road
Open April–Oct daily (except Sat) 10.00am–6.00pm
Free admission
♧ 🚌 advance notice required 🐅

Guide to Symbols

☎ telephone	🐕 dogs welcome (on a leash)
♧ disabled welcome	🐅 dogs not welcome
🚌 coaches welcome	

CUMBRIA

Cumbria, tucked away in the far north-western corner of England, is renowned for its lakeland scenery. The Lake District, an area of outstanding natural beauty with high peaks, picturesque lakes, lofty fells, fertile valleys and charming villages, is ideal country for the walker, hiker or naturalist. Cumbria's coastline is rich in sandy beaches and birdlife and its many historic towns, ruined castles and remnants of Hadrian's Wall reflect the border disputes with Scotland over the centuries.

A rich area for arts and crafts, there are many studios open to the visitor where spinning and weaving, basket-making, glass work, crystal engraving and many other crafts can be seen in operation. Goats cheese, truffles and 'catch-your-own' fish will give you a taste of the area in between watching the watermills still at work, following some of the country trails and discovering more about the National Park at one of its nine information centres.

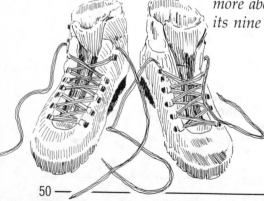

▶ ALSTON ◀

GOSSIPGATE GALLERY

Craft centre

The Butts, Alston, Cumbria CA9 3JU
☎ Alston (0434) 381806

Situated in the North Pennines, probably the biggest variety of quality regional art and craft in the North of England. Seasonal exhibitions and shop; outdoor pots; tea garden and home-baked biscuits.

Follow direction signs from the lane behind the market cross in the centre of Alston
Open Feb–Christmas/New Year daily, 10.00am–5.00pm
Free admission
& 🛉 outside only

▶ AMBLESIDE ◀

THE LANGDALE CRAFT SHOP

Craft shop

Chapel Stile, Great Langdale, Ambleside, Cumbria LA22 9JJ
☎ Langdale (096 67) 296

A wide range of traditional and contemporary crafts; local pottery, wood turning, flowercraft, Ruskin lace, slate, watercolours, knitwear, baskets and toys. Parking and refreshments.

On the B5343, 5 miles from Ambleside, nr Chapel Stile village centre
Open daily 10.30am–6.00pm, Sun 2.00–5.00pm, closed Mondays except Bank Holidays. Advisable to telephone first Nov–Jan
Free admission
🚃 & 🛉

ADRIAN SANKEY

Glass studio

Rydal Rd, Ambleside, Cumbria LA22 0EE
☎ Ambleside (05394) 33039

An open workshop, with a distinctive collection of both traditional and contemporary lead crystal studio glass. Working in front of our visitors, an attempt is made to convey some of the excitement of manipulating this molten material.

Behind the famous Bridge House over the stream, in the middle of the village
Open daily 9.00am–5.30pm
Admission: adult 30p, children free
& 🚃 advance notice required 🛉

FIBRECRAFTS AT BARNHOWE

Craft centre

Barnhowe, Elterwater, Ambleside, Cumbria LA22 9HW
☎ Langdale (096 67) 346

Individual handspun garments for sale. Extensive range of spinning wheels, fibres, yarns, dyes, books and equipment for weavers, spinners and dyers. Introductory half-day spinning tuition sessions available at short notice.

Take the B5343 from Ambleside, signposted 'Langdale' after cattle grid onto Elterwater Common, first left then first right opposite first house in village
Open Easter–Nov 10.00am–5.00pm daily except Sunday, 2.00–5.00pm; winter please telephone
Free admission
& 🛉

NATIONAL TRUST NORTH WEST – ESTATE WALKS

Country walk, farm trail and farm visit

Rothay Holme, Rothay Rd, Ambleside, Cumbria LA22 0EJ
☎ Ambleside (05394) 33883

A series of 2–3 hour countryside walks. Please telephone for details.

In the heart of the Lake District
Open throughout the summer
Admission: £1.00 per person (1990 prices)
& 🚃 advance notice required 🏌

RYDAL MOUNT

House and garden

Ambleside, Cumbria LA22 9LU
☎ Ambleside (05394) 33002

William Wordsworth's home 1813–1850.

1½ miles north of Ambleside on the A591, 2½ miles south of Grasmere. Private road from main road to house
Open Mar–Oct 9.30am–5.00pm; Nov–Feb 10.00am–4.00pm, closed first 2 weeks in Jan and Tues during winter. Evening groups by appointment
Admission: adult £1.80, child 80p, party rates available
& 🚃 🛉 garden only

▶ **APPLEBY** ◀

APPLEBY CASTLE CONSERVATION CENTRE

Conservation centre, gift shop and information centre

Appleby-in-Westmorland, Cumbria CA16 6XH
☎ Appleby (07683) 51402

Beautiful riverside setting for rare breeds of farm animals, waterfowl, pheasants, poultry, owls etc. Fine 11th century Norman Keep, Great Hall of House, gift shop, tea rooms, information centre, bird and animal quizzes.

Off the A66, 13 miles south east of Penrith, or on the B6260 11 miles from jct 38 on the M6
Open Easter–end Sept daily 10.00am–5.00pm. Great Hall closed Mon and Sat
Admission: adult £2.50, child/OAP £1.25, party rates available for groups of over 20 (1990 prices)
& ⊞ 🐕

▶ **BONESS** ◀

THE FARMSHOP

Farm shop

Gauze Rd, Boness, Cumbria
☎ Boness (0506) 822861

From the M9 driving west take slip road for Boness, 3rd turn right, first left 1½ miles turn right, farm shop is on Gauze Rd
Open Mon–Fri 8.00am–5.00pm, Sat and Sun 9.00am–5.00pm
Free admission
& ⊞ 🐕

▶ **BRAMPTON** ◀

NEW MILLS TROUT FARM

Farm shop and trout farm

Brampton, Cumbria CA8 2QS
☎ Brampton (06977) 2384

Visitors can walk out on the floating walkways and feed the fish. Lake fishing, beginners pool: fishing for all ages. Tackle for hire. Licensed farm restaurant serves home made food.

On the A69, 1 mile east of Brampton
Open all year daily 10.00am–5.00pm. Closed Mondays except Bank Holidays
Admission: adult 50p, child 30p (includes trout feed)
& ⊞ advance notice required 🐕

▶ **CARLISLE** ◀

CORBY CASTLE RIVER WALKS

Country walk

Corby Castle, Great Corby, Carlisle, Cumbria CA4 8LR
☎ Wetheral (0228) 60246

Woodland walks in the Castle grounds along the banks of the River Eden, laid out in 1730 by Thomas Howard and featuring an interesting cascade and summerhouse.

Turn off the A69 at Warwick Bridge, intersection 42 via Wetheral or 43 from the M6
Open April–Oct daily 1.00–5.00pm
Admission: adult 40p, child free, car park free
& ⊞ advance notice required 🐕

IAN LAVAL, CABINET MAKER

Craft centre and forestry centre

Meadowbank Farm, Curthwaite, Wigton, Cumbria CA7 8BG
☎ Dalston (0228) 710409

5 miles south west of Carlisle, off the A595 Carlisle–Cockermouth road
Open all year at any reasonable time
Free admission
& 🐕

PRIESTS MILL

Watermill with visitor centre, museums and craft workshops

Caldbeck, Wigton, Cumbria CA7 8DR
☎ Caldbeck (06998) 369

Restored 18th century buildings in secluded riverside setting. Shops, cafe with home cooked food, waterwheel museum, craft workshops and the Caldbeck Mining Museum.

On the B5299, 14 miles south west of Carlisle
Open mid March–Oct daily 11.00am–5.00pm. Sat and Sun only in Nov and Dec
Free admission
& ⊞ small coaches, advance notice required 🐕

▶ **EGREMONT** ◀

MUNCASTER WATERMILL

Working water-powered corn mill and speciality food producer

Ravenglass, Cumbria CA18 1ST
☎ Ravenglass (0228) 717232

This one time manorial corn mill dates from c. 1700 with early 19th century machinery in regular use. Mill worked until 1961, renovated 1976–7. Stoneground organic wheat flours and oatmeals produced and on sale. Served by the Ravenglass & Eskdale Railway, trains stop on request.

Off the A595, 11 miles south of Egremont
Open daily except Saturday April, May, Sept and Oct 11.00am–5.00pm; June–Aug 10.00am–6.00pm. Other times by appointment
Admission: adult 90p, child 40p, family £2.20, party rates available (1990 prices)
&. 🚌 🛇

▶ **ESKDALE** ◀

ESKDALE CORN MILL

Farming museum and corn mill

Boot, Cumbria CA19 1TG
☎ Eskdale (09403) 335

A 13th century corn mill driven by 12 foot diameter overshot waterwheels with original wooden machinery. Located in the picturesque village of Boot and reached by crossing a 16th century Packhorse Bridge.

On the A595 turn to Gosforth, Santon Bridge, Eskdale Green turn by George IV Inn to Boot, mill situated at the end of the road
Open Easter–Sept daily (except Saturdays apart from Bank Holiday weekends)
Admission: adult 50p, child 25p
&. 🚌 advance notice required 🛇

▶ **GILSLAND** ◀

IRTHINGSPA DAIRY GOATS

Dairy goat farm

Holme View, Gilsland, Cumbria CA6 7AJ
☎ Gilsland (06972) 481

Situated in the centre of Hadrians Wall, this small dairy produces traditionally made goats cheese, using the milk from its own herd of pedigree British Saanen goats.

Off the A69 Carlisle–Newcastle road, 8 miles east of Brampton

Open daily for cheese sales
Free admission
&. 🛇

▶ **GOSFORTH** ◀

PONSONBY FARM PARK

Farm park, working mixed farm

Cumrey Kitchen, Ponsonby, nr Seascale, Cumbria CA20 1BX
☎ Beckermet (094684) 426

Experience the sights, sounds and feel of a working farm set in the Lake District National Park. Rare breeds, pets corner, picnic area, farm walks. Winner of ICI's 'Good Relations Award' 1989.

From Gosforth north along the A595 for 1½ miles to Ponsonby turning on the right. Follow this lane to road fork, then bear right to Farm Park
Open Easter, May Day weekend, then daily (except Mondays) from beginning of May–Oct, 10.30am–5.00pm
Admission: adult £1.40, child 70p, school and party rates available (1990 prices)
&. 🚌 🛇

▶ **GRANGE-OVER-SANDS** ◀

CARTMEL CRAFT CENTRE

Craft centre

Broughton Lodge Farm, Field Broughton, Grange-over-Sands, Cumbria LA11 6HS
☎ Grange-over-Sands (05395) 36009

Craft centre featuring local craftspeople at work daily demonstrating their skills. 'Made in Cumbria' craft shop, art gallery with resident artist; licensed vegetarian wholefood restaurant.

3½ miles from Grange-over-Sands, 1½ miles north of Cartmel village. Signposted from the A590 at the top of Lindale by-pass
&. &. 🚌 advance notice required 🛇

HOLKER HALL AND GARDENS

Country garden, country park, stately home and museum

Cark-in-Cartmel, nr Grange-over-Sands, Cumbria LA11 7PL
☎ Flookburgh (05395) 58328

Former home of the Dukes of Devonshire, now home to Lord and Lady Cavendish and their family. The many attractions include magnificent gardens, motor museum, hot-air ballooning, craft & countryside exhibition, cafe, gift shop, baby animal farm, adventure playground and discovery walks.

Take jct 36 on the M6, signposted from the A590. Or the B5277 from Grange-over-Sands, or the B5278 from Newby Bridge
Open Easter Sunday – last Sunday in Oct daily except Saturdays 10.30am–6.00pm. Last admission to grounds 4.30pm; Hall closes 4.30pm. Discovery walks weekdays only, not Bank Holidays. Garden tours by appointment.
Admission: to gardens, grounds and exhibitions adult £2.20, child over 6 £1.20. Hall and Motor Museum extra. Party rates available (1990 prices)
  ♿ no lift ⊞ ✕

►   *GRASMERE*   ◄

CHRIS REEKIE & SONS LTD
Handloom weaving

The Old Coach House, Stock Lane, Grasmere, Cumbria LA22 9SL
☎   Grasmere (096 65) 221

Handloom weaving takes place Monday to Friday, usually 11.00am–1.00pm and 3.00–5.00pm. Cafe serving coffee and sandwiches, gift shop.

Off the A591, ½ mile along the B5287 into Grasmere
Open 9.00am–5.00pm all year. Closed Sundays in Dec, Jan and Feb
Free admission
♿ ⊞ ✕

THE WORDSWORTH TRUST
Dove Cottage, museum, book and gift shop

Dove Cottage, Grasmere, Cumbria LA22 9SH
☎   Grasmere (09665) 544/547

Visitors are offered guided tours of Dove Cottage, Wordsworth's Grasmere home. Garden open weather permitting. Adjacent award-winning museum presents permanent Wordsworth Exhibition and a seasonal programme of special exhibitions.

On the A591 Ambleside–Keswick road
Open daily 9.30am–5.30pm. Closed mid Jan–mid Feb 1990
Admission: to cottage and museum adult £3.00, child £1.35, family ticket and party rates available (1990 prices)
♿ ⊞ advance notice required ✕

►   *HAVERTHWAITE*   ◄

ARTCRYSTAL
Crystal hand engraving

Clock Tower Buildings, Lowwood, Haverthwaite, Cumbria LA12 8LY
☎   Newdybridge (05395) 31796

Crystal engraving studio set in an old gunpowder works steeped in history. Demonstrations – visitors may choose from a wide range of crystal available to be engraved on the spot.

½ mile from the A590. Haverthwaite Steam Railway on the Hocker, Grange Road, at Lowwood
Open all year Tues–Sun 10.30am–5.00pm, closed Mondays
Free admission
♿ ✕

►   *HAWKSHEAD*   ◄

GRIZEDALE FOREST PARK
Forest park, country walk, visitor centre and information shop

Forestry Commission, South Lake Forest District, Grizedale, Ambleside, Cumbria LA22 0QJ
☎   Satterthwaite (022 984) 373

Country walks through beautiful wooded countryside in the heart of the Lake District.

2 miles south of Hawkshead
Open all year for forest park; visitor centre and information shop April–Oct 10.00am–5.00pm
Free admission
♿ ⊞ ✕

HAWKSHEAD TROUT FARM
Farm shop and catch your own

The Boathouse, Ridding Wood, Hawkshead, Cumbria LA22 0QF
☎   Hawkshead (09666) 541

1½ miles south of Hawkshead on the Newby
Bridge road
Open daily 9.00am–5.00pm
Admission: fishing £7.50 per day, boating £6 per day and
catch your own £3.50
& ⊞ advance notice required ⅄

► **KENDAL** ◄

LEVENS HALL AND WORLD FAMOUS TOPIARY GARDEN

Topiary gardens and historic house

Levens Hall, Kendal, Cumbria LA8 0PD
☎ Sedgwick (05395) 60321

*The Elizabethan Manor has been developed
from a 13th century pele tower, offers
Jacobean furniture, panelling, plasterwork
and earliest English patchwork. World
famous topiary garden laid out in 1692.
Steam exhibition, gardens, tea room and gift
shop.*

On the A6, 5 miles south of Kendal (M6 exit 36)
Open Easter Sunday–end Sept Sun–Thurs 11.00am–
5.00pm
Admission: adult (house and garden) £3.20, child £1.60,
reductions for groups and OAPs, adult (gardens only)
£1.80, child 90p
& house is unsuitable for wheelchairs because of the
number of steps and width of doorways
⊞ ⅄ in the car park only

PETER HALL & SON

Woodcraft workshop

Danes Rd, Staveley, nr Kendal, Cumbria LA8 9PL
☎ Staveley (0539) 7821633

*Workshop produces oak and mahogany
furniture, restores antiques and turns
beautiful unusual pieces all to the highest
standards. Watch craftsmen at work. Pieces
for sale in showroom.*

Follow brown tourist signs from the A591
Kendal–Windermere road into Staveley. Next to
Staveley Autos Garage
Open Mon–Fri 9.00am–5.00pm, Sat 10.00am–4.00pm.
Showroom only all year except public holidays
& ⊞ advance notice required ⅄

SIZERGH CASTLE GARDEN – NATIONAL TRUST

Country garden

Kendal, Cumbria
☎ Sedgwick (05395) 760070

*The rock garden contains mature dwarf
conifers, Japanese maples, primula, bulbs and
a large collection of hardy ferns. Rose garden
with species roses, hydrangeas and ground
covers, herbaceous border. Native wild
flowers, a water garden, climbers and
shrubs.*

Off the A6 trunk road, 3 miles south of Kendal
Open April–Oct Sun, Mon, Wed and Thur 12.30–5.45pm,
Castle also open 2.00–5.45pm
Admission: adult £1.00, child 50p. Castle and garden:
adult £2.00, child £1.00
& wheelchair available, access is easy to most of the
garden, but after rain some grassy slopes may be
slippery ⊞ by appointment ⅄

► **KESWICK** ◄

LAKELAND RURAL INDUSTRIES

Craft centre

Grange View, Grange-in-Borrowdale, Keswick, Cumbria
CA12 5XA
☎ Borrowdale (059684) 226

*A wide selection of crafts, gifts, cards,
pictures and handbeaten stainless steel and
copper ware made in the workshops. Also
jewellery, hornware, pottery, original
watercolours and prints. Car park.*

On the B5289, 4 miles east of Keswick
Open 1 March–31 Dec daily 10.00am–5.00pm except
Nov and Dec 10.00am–4.00pm
Free admission
& ⊞ ⅄

LINGHOLM GARDENS

Formal and woodland gardens, plant centre, tea room

Lingholm, Keswick, Cumbria CA12 5UA
☎ Keswick (07687) 72003

*An impressive formal garden and an
extensive woodland garden, containing
spectacular rhododendrons, azaleas,
magnificent trees and shrubs, primulas and
meconopsis.*

On the A66 to Portinscale village via Keswick, follow garden signs
Open April–Oct daily 10.00am–5.00pm
Admission: adult £1.50, accompanied children free
&. ⟶ advance notice required
✗ except Guide dogs

SEATOLLER BARN INFORMATION CENTRE DALEHEAD BASE

Information centre, National Park, country walk

Seatoller, Borrowdale, Keswick, Cumbria CA12 5XN
☎ (059684) 294

One of 9 Information Centres run by the National Park. Special features throughout the year: craft days, farm days, slide shows, talks, bird watching, guided walks etc. Centre explains the geology, climate and history of Borrowdale.

On the B5289, 8 miles south of Keswick, 16 miles south of Cockermouth
Open mid March–Oct daily 10.00am–5.00pm
Free admission
⟶ ✗

WHINLATTER VISITOR CENTRE

Forestry centre

Braithwaite, Keswick, Cumbria CA12 5TW
☎ Braithwaite (07687 82) 469

Walks, trails and orienteering. Exhibition with computer programmes, working forest model and audio visual displays.

On the B5292 midway between Braithwaite and Lorton
Open all year except January
Free admission
&. ⟶ ✗

▶ KIRKBY STEPHEN ◀

AISGILL CRAFTS NATURE

Craft centre and trail

1 Aisgill Moor Cottages, Mallerstang, Kirkby Stephen, Cumbria CA17 4JX
☎ Kirkby Stephen (07683) 72011

Situated on top of Aisgill Summit 1,169' A.S.L. on the Settle–Carlisle Line in the lovely village of Mallerstang. 2 craft shops with homemade products; leaflets for nature trail (wellingtons for hire!), winter walking weekends, information on request.

Take road to Hawes 7 miles from Kirkby Stephen, last house in Cumbria
Open April–Oct 10.00am–6.00pm for craft shop, weekends in winter
&. help available
Coaches not allowed, but minibuses welcome. Parking restricted
✗

LANCRIGG POTTERY

Craft pottery studio

Winton, Kirkby Stephen, Cumbria CA17 4HL
☎ Kirkby Stephen (07683) 71542

Small studio producing a wide range of handthrown stoneware. Tableware, plant pots, vases, lamp bases and ornamental plates designed to look good and handle well in everyday use. Special commemorative plates incorporating lettering or other specific designs can be ordered.

Just off the A685, 1¼ miles north of Kirkby Stephen
Open most weekdays 9.00am–5.00pm, but telephone to be certain
Free admission
&. there are stairs to climb
✗

STRATA CREATIVE STONE PRODUCTS

Craft workshop

Dowgill Head, North Stainmore, Kirkby Stephen, Cumbria CA17 4EX
☎ Brough (09304) 465

Working in lakeland greenstone and unusual fossil (crinoidal) limestone we produce an attractive high quality range of clocks, barometers, lampbases, desk top items and jewellery.

Off the A66, 8 miles outside Kirkby Stephen, 3 miles east of Brough
Open April–Christmas by appointment please
Free admission
&. ✗

► KIRKOSWALD ◄

NUNNERY HOUSE AND WALKS

Forestry centre

Nunnery House, Staffield, Kirkoswald, Penrith, Cumbria
CA10 1EU
☎ Lazonby (076883) 537

Refreshments available Easter–October.

Off the A6, B6413 to Kirkoswald, 2 miles on the
Armathwaite Road
Open Feb–Oct
Admission 50p per person over the age of 11
& walks are not suitable for wheelchairs
🚌 advance notice required
🛖

► LONGTOWN ◄

HEDGEROW BASKETS

Basket workshop

Daffiestown Rigg, Longtown, nr Carlisle, Cumbria
CAG 5NN
☎ Carlisle (0228) 791187

*The cottage workshop is set in an interesting
garden of rare and unusual plants and
shrubs.*

Take the A7 from Longtown towards Langholm,
take 3rd turning left after Longtown, approx
1 mile up lane
Open daily 10.00am–5.00pm
Free admission
& 🛖

► MILLOM ◄

ASHDOWN SMOKERS

Farm shop, smoked foods

Skellerah Farm, Corney, nr Millom, Cumbria LA19 5TW
☎ Bootle (065 78) 324

1½ miles north of Bootle turn right off the A595,
farm is 1 mile on the right
Open Mon–Fri 10.00am–5.00pm, Sat 10.00am–1.00pm,
Sun 10.00am–4.00pm
Free admission
& ✗

► MILNTHORPE ◄

HERON CORN MILL

Working water mill and papermaking museum

Bettham, Milnthorpe, Cumbria LA7 7AR
☎ Lancaster (0524) 734858

*Building on the River Bela dated 1740.
Lowder Mill has 4 pairs of stones, high
breast wheel, demonstrations of milling.
Museum, mill artefacts, Paper Museum and
exhibitions. Car park, refreshments.*

1 mile south of Milnthorpe on the A6, exit 36 of
the M6
Open daily including Bank Holidays from Easter–Sept
11.00am–5.00pm or by prior booking. Closed
Mondays
Admission adult £1.40, child 90p
& 🚌 🛖

► ORTON ◄

HOLME FARMED VENISON

Farm shop and speciality food producer

Raisbeck, Penrith, Cumbria CA10 3SG
☎ Orton (05874) 618

*Commerical deer farm. Home produced
venison, pork, lamb, beef, poultry; home
cured bacon, cheeses and other speciality
Cumbrian products.*

¼ mile off jct 38 on the M6 or the A685 Kendal
road in centre of Torbay
Open 9.00am–5.00pm 6 days a week
Free admission
& 🚌 advance notice required
🛖

► PENRITH ◄

ACORN BANK GARDEN

Country garden

National Trust, Acorn Bank, Temple Sowerby, Penrith,
Cumbria CA10 1SP
☎ Kirkby Thorpe (07683) 61893

3 acre garden owned by the National Trust.

Signposted off the A66, between Penrith and
Appleby, 7 miles south east of Penrith

Open Easter–4 Nov daily, 10.00am–5.30pm
Admission: adult £1.00, child 50p, National Trust
members free
  ♿ ▥ advance notice required
  ⚑ in wild garden

EAST CUMBRIA COUNTRYSIDE PROJECT

Country walks

Unit 2c, The Old Mill, Warwick Bridge, Carlisle, Cumbria
CA4 8RR
☎ Wetheral (0228) 61601

*Guided and self-guided walks available from
this award-winning Project, which
undertakes a wide range of countryside
management work. Send s.a.e. to above
address for a free booklet order form and/or
current guided walk programme.*

Please telphone for directions
Open for guided walks all year round. 3 programmes
produced annually.
Admission for guided walks: waged adult £1.00, others
50p
♿ walks not suitable for those with ambulatory problems
or in wheelchairs (although some are planned). Guided
walk leaders are willing to adapt themselves for visually
handicapped or deaf people – prior notice appreciated
▥ advance notice required
⚑ allowed on some walks

EDEN VALLEY WOOLLEN MILL

Craft centre and small woollen mill

Armathwaite, nr Carlisle, Cumbria
☎ Armathwaite (069 12) 457 or Croglin (076 886) 406

*A woollen centre and weaving school where
production processes can be seen in
operation with a variety of products and
wools sold direct.*

Off the A6, 10 miles north of Penrith
Open Easter–Oct daily 9.30am–5.30pm; Nov and Dec
Mon–Sat; Jan–Easter Sats and 'by luck'
Free admission
♿ ▥ advance notice required
✖ in shop area

HUTTON-IN-THE-FOREST

Woodland walk, historic house and garden

Penrith, Cumbria
☎ Skelton (085 34) 449

*The home of Lord and Lady Inglewood and
their children, a beautiful historic house*

*which lies in the magnificent woodland of
the mediaeval forest of Inglewood.*

On the B5305, 3 miles west of exit 41 of the M6, 5
miles from Penrith
Open for the gardens daily except Saturdays 11.00am–
5.00pm; house June–Oct Thur, Fri, Sun and Bank
Holiday weekends 1.00–4.00pm. (Other days by
arrangment for groups).
Admission to house and gardens: adult £2.50, child
under 7 free; grounds only: £1.00 honesty box
♿ ▥ advance notice required ⚑

LOWTHER LEISURE PARK

Leisure park

Hackthorpe, nr Penrith, Cumbria CA10 2HG
☎ Hackthorpe (09312) 523

*Leisure park set in 150 acres of wooded
parkland with a variety of beautiful trees
and a deer herd. Family day out: big top
circus, rides, gift shop and restaurant.*

Off the A6, 6 miles south of Penrith
Open 2 weeks over Easter, then weekends only until 25
May, then daily until Sept, 10.00am–6.00pm
Admission: adult £3.95, child under 3 free, party rates
available
♿ toilet, ramps to restaurant and gift shop ▥ ✖

NUNNERY WALKS

Country walk

Nunnery House Hotel, Staffield, Kirkoswald, Penrith,
Cumbria CA10 1EV
☎ Lazonby (076883) 537

*Woodland walks along the River Eden laid
out in the 18th century feautring waterfalls,
conservation pond and summerhouse.*

Take the A6 Carlisle road, then the B6413 to
Kirkoswald–2 miles out on the Armathwaite road
Open daily except Christmas Day 10.00am–6.00pm
Admission: adult 50p, child under 11 free (1990 prices)
♿ ▥ advance notice required ⚑

THE OLD SMOKEHOUSE

Producer of smoked foods

Brougham Hall, Brougham, Penrith CA10 2DE
☎ Penrith (0768) 67772 (24-hour service)

*Fish, game, meat, poultry, pates and cheeses,
oak-smoked and free from artificial
preservatives and colourings. Postal service
available, send for details.*

Take the A6 Kendal road from Penrith, turn left to Brougham after leaving Eamont Bridge
Open Easter–Christmas Eve
Free admission
& ⇔ advance notice required ⋔

SOCKBRIDGE MILL TROUT FARM

'Catch your own' fishery, shop and farm trails

Tirril, Penrith, Cumbria CA10 2JT
☎ Penrith (0768) 65338

Working trout farm set in the picturesque Earmont Valley. Rainbow trout for sale or to catch; accommodation; cream teas, home baking.

Signposted from Tirril, 3 miles south west of Penrith on the B5320 to Pooley Bridge
Open all year during daylight hours
Free admission
& there are no disabled toilet facilities ⋔

SOUTHWAITE GREEN MILL FISH FARM

Farm shop and fish farm

Southwaite Green Mill, Eamont Bridge, Penrith, Cumbria CA10 2BY
☎ Penrith (0768) 62542 Fax (0768) 899011

The mill is stocked with rainbow trout and farmed on a Swedish system with 12 concrete race ways. There is also an old mill and sluice gate.

1 mile south on the A6 (Eamont Bridge), west on B5320 to Pooley Bridge, turn right 'Southwaite Green' sign, follow 'no through road' to fish farm
Open all year daily 9.00am–5.00pm
Free admission
& ⇔ advance notice required ✗

TRUFFLES

Producer of truffles

Brougham Hall, Broughton, Penrith CA10 2DE
☎ Penrith (0768) 67772 (24-hour service)

Truffles made from the finest continental chocolate and the purest ingredients: real cream, fruit and alcohol. We also have a postal service, send for details.

Take the A6 Kendal road from Penrith, turn left to Brougham after leaving Eamont Bridge
Open Easter–Christmas Eve
Free admission
& ⇔ advance notice required ⋔

THE VILLAGE BAKERY

Bakery, licensed restaurant, craft gallery

Melmerby, Penrith, Cumbria CA10 1HE
☎ (0768) 881515

Specialist bakers of wholemeal bread and confectionery with organic English wheat stoneground by waterpower and baked in a wood-fuel oven. Licensed restaurant, bakeryshop, craft gallery.

Melmerby is on the A686 Penrith–Alston road, 10 miles east of Penrith
Open Easter–Dec Tue–Sun 8.30am–5.00pm, Mon 8.30am–2.30pm for drinks and snacks, 9.30am opening on Sundays and Bank Holiday Mondays; Christmas–Easter 8.30am–2.30pm closed Sundays
Free admission
& disabled visitors can get into the restaurant, but unfortunately no wheelchair access to toilets, and the craft gallery is upstairs
⇔ advance notice required ✗

THE WATERMILL

Working traditional watermill specialising in organic British grain flours

Little Salkeld, Penrith, Cumbria CA10 1NN
☎ Langwathby (076881) 523

The Watermill at Little Salkeld is a fine example of a small 18th century country corn mill. It has been restored to full working order and it now enjoys an excellent reputation for the organic, stoneground flours produced there.

Take A686 road from Penrith (signed to Alston), turn left in Langwathby to Little Salkeld (1½ miles)
Open by appointment. Millshop open Mon–Fri 9.30am–12.30pm, 2.30–5.30pm all year except Christmas–New Year
Admission: adult £1.00, child 65p (1989 prices)
& limited access only
⇔ advance notice required ⋔

WETHERIGGS POTTERY

Working pottery, shop, restaurant and museum

Clifton Dykes, Penrith, Cumbria CA10 2DH
☎ Penrith (0768) 62946

Unique 19th century working country pottery with large beehive kiln – make your own pot. Also steam engine and machinery, children's play area, guest house, licensed restaurant and coffee shop.

Off the A6, 4 miles south of Penrith
Open daily 10.00am–6.00pm
Admission: adult £2.00, child £1.00, reduced rate for
  groups
 ♿ ✈ advance notice required 🐔

Approx 1 mile from Sedbergh on the A684 Hawes
  road
Open daily 9.30am–5.00pm, other times please telephone
Free admission
♿ there are no toilets for the disabled
✈ advance notice required ✝

▶   *RAVENGLASS*   ◀

MUNCASTER CASTLE

Country garden, art centre, nature trail and walk

Ravenglass, Cumbria CA18 1RQ
☎   Ravenglass (0229) 717203

*Run by TV ornithologist Tony Warburton,
the art centre breeds from injured stock and
releases the young into the wild.
Demonstrations and lectures.*

On the A595, 1 mile east of Ravenglass
Open April–Sept daily, closed Mondays except Bank
  Holidays. Grounds 12.00–5.00pm, castle 1.30–4.30pm
Admission to the castle and grounds: adult £3.00, child
  £1.50; grounds only: adult £1.50, child £1.00
♿ ✈ 🐔

▶   *SEDBERGH*   ◀

DENT CRAFTS CENTRE

Craft centre

Helmside, Dent, Sedbergh, Cumbria LA10 5SY
☎   Dent (05875) 400

*A good selection of pure wool products and
fabrics woven on the premises, English dried
flowers and wood turned items from British
hardwoods. Childrens play area; full catering
facilities.*

Between Sedbergh and Dent. M6 exit 37, 8 miles
Open April–Jan daily 9.30am–6.00pm, weekends in
  winter
Free admission
♿ there is one step to negotiate ✝

PENNINE TWEEDS

Working traditional wool mill

Farfield Mill, Sedbergh, Cumbria LA10 5LW
☎   Sedbergh (05396) 20558

*Using traditional flying shuttles, weavers of
exclusive short length of all wool, lambs
wool and mohair fabrics. The showroom
contains a wide range of the mill's own
products for sale.*

▶   *ULVERSTON*   ◀

FELL FOOT PARK (NATIONAL TRUST)

Country park and walks

Newby Bridge, nr Ulverston, Cumbria LA12 8NN
☎   Newby Bridge (05395) 31273

*18 acre country park on the south east shore
of Lake Windermere. ¼ mile lakeshore
frontage with Boathouse Cafe and childrens
adventure playground. Non-powered boat
launching available, row boat hire.*

At the extreme southern end of Windermere on
  east shore, entrance from the A592
Open all year for the park; information centre open
  Easter–end Oct
Free admission, car park £1.50, coaches £6.00
✈ 🐔

GLEASTON WATER MILL

Corn mill

Gleaston, Ulverston, Cumbria LA12 0QH
☎   Bardsea (0229) 869224

*Water corn mill with impressive, original
wooden machinery in working order, an 18
foot water wheel and corn drying kiln. Craft
workshops, licensed restaurant, parking and
toilets. Schools and groups welcome.*

Off the A5087, 5 miles south of Ulverston
Open all year daily 10.00am–5.00pm, winter 11.00am–
  dusk. Closed Mondays except Bank Holidays
Admission: adult £1.00, child/OAP/student 50p
♿ ✈ advance notice required ✝

▶   *WIGTON*   ◀

THE JEWELLERY WORKSHOP

Craft centre – jewellery

Oakleigh, Todd Close, Curthwaite, Wigton, Cumbria
  CA7 8BE
☎   Dalston (0228) 710756

Silver, gold and precious stones are the raw materials of the jeweller. With techniques perfected through centuries of craftsmanship the workshop produces its own individual style of jewellery.

Off the A595, 1 mile south of Thursby
Open all year, Tues–Sat 10.00am–5.30pm
Free admission
  ♿ ⛏

THORNBY MOOR DAIRY

Farm trail and visit, speciality food producer

Aikton, Wigton, Cumbria CA7 0JZ
☎ Wigton (0965) 43160

The milk from cows, goats and sheep is made into a variety of cheeses in a small dairy attached to a house and garden. 40 goats graze in an adjacent pasture.

A595 from Carlisle 6 miles to Thursby roundabout,
    the A596 Wigton direction, 3rd turning on right,
    ½ mile gateway on right
Open April–Sept, Tues–Fri 10.30am–12.30pm
Admission: adult £1.00, child free
♿ 🚌 advance notice required ⛏

►   *WINDERMERE*   ◄

LAKE DISTRICT NATIONAL PARK VISITOR CENTRE

National Park visitor centre

Brockhole, Windermere, Cumbria LA23 1LJ
☎ Windermere (096 62) 6601

On the A591, between Windermere and Ambleside
Open Easter–early Sept daily 10.00am–4.00pm
Admission: adult £1.30, child 65p (1990 prices)
♿ 🚌 ⛏

LAKELAND HORTICULTURAL SOCIETY

Country garden

Holehird, Windermere, Cumbria
☎ Windermere (096 62) 6008

A garden largely dedicated to the cultivation of plants, shrubs and trees which thrive under Lakeland conditions; large rock garden with alpines, shrubs and heathers; walled garden with herbaceous plants, herbs and climbers.

On the A592 Patterdale road, 1 mile from
  Windermere
Free admission, contributions welcome
♿ walled garden easily accessible, remainder steep
🚌 advance notice required ⛏

DERBYSHIRE

Derbyshire is a national park area, the wild high flat moorland and steep-sided dales of its Peak District invite exploration. The narrow limestone gorges and cliffs with underground quarries and caverns make it 'adventure country' for walkers, hikers, climbers and cavers.

It is possible to dedicate a tree whilst following some of the country walks and multi-purpose trails through the Derbyshire countryside. Farms and gardens including a herb garden are open to visitors and among the workshops open there is a rock shop with 'Blue John' jewellery and a wide selection of mineral specimens, there are several potteries where pots are thrown from the local clay and two engine house workshops with the old engines of the High Peak Railway.

▶ ASHBOURNE ◀

ILAM HALL AND COUNTRY PARK

Country park and walks with farm visit

The National Trust Shop and Information Centre, Ilam
  nr Ashbourne, Derbyshire
☎ Thorpe Cloud (033 529) 245

Off the A515, 4½ miles north west of Ashbourne
Open all year for the park, please telephone for more
  details
Free admission to grounds, charge for car parking
&. 🚌 🛉

R A & W K MORLEY

Heritage wood – dedicate a tree

Hall Farm, Ednaston, Brailsford, Derbyshire DE6 3AE
☎ Ashbourne (0335) 60488

*Heritage Wood presents the opportunity for
people to mark an occasion (for example the
birth of a child or the passing of a loved one)
by having a tree planted. Parking, picnic
area. Free leaflet on request.*

Off the A52, 5 miles south of Ashbourne
Open all year round, dawn to sunset
Free admission
&. 🛉

▶ BAKEWELL ◀

CHATSWORTH

Country garden with walks

Bakewell, Derbyshire DE4 1PP
☎ Baslow (0246) 582204

*Historic house with garden covering over
100 acres. It provides many delights and
surprises: a cascade, spectacular fountains
and rocks, a tropical greenhouse, herbaceous
borders, rose garden and secluded walks
among rare shrubs and forest trees.*

Off the B6012, 8 miles north of Matlock. 16 miles
  from jct 29 of the M1
Open April–Oct daily
Admission price yet to be decided
&. 🚌 🛉

HADDON HALL

Country Garden and Stately Home

Bakewell, Derbyshire DE4 1LA
☎ Bakewell (0629) 812855

*England's most perfectly preserved
Mediaeval Manor House, set amidst the
beautiful scenery of the Peak District. The
superb Medieval and Tudor interiors reflect
the unspoilt nature of this friendly house.*

On the A6, 1½ miles south of Bakewell
Open Easter–Oct daily except Mondays, 11.00am–6.00pm
Admission: adult £2.80, child £1.60 (1990 prices)
&. 🚌 🛉

▶ BUXTON ◀

BUXTON MICRARIUM

**Exhibition showing the world of nature under the
microscope**

The Crescent, Buxton, Derbyshire SK17 6BQ
☎ Buxton (0298) 78662

*The world's first micrarium – explore the
wonderful world of nature under the
microscope. Beautiful crystals; snowflakes;
flowers and delightful pond water creatures
to view at the touch of a button.*

Off the A5004
Open Easter–Oct daily 10.00am–5.00pm; weekends Nov
  and Feb (weather permitting)
Admission: adult £2.00, child £1.00
&. every assistance given but there are no toilet facilities
🚌 advance notice required 🛉

EAST VIEW AND DALE GRANGE FARMS

Farm visit

East View Farm, Chelmorton, nr Buxton, Derbyshire
  SK17 9SL
☎ Taddington (0298) 85345

*Visit farms and walk in the lovely Peak
National Park. Groups are given a guided
tour around the farms with calves, cattle and
sheep and are told some of the history of the
ancient village of Chelmorton. They can then
walk down the Dale, rich in plants and
wildlife, to the caves.*

Take the A515 or the A6 to Chelmorton. 5 miles
  from Buxton, 7 miles from Bakewell
Open all year for groups, please book in advance
Admission: £1.00 per person (teachers/tutors etc free)
&. 🚌 🛉

FOX COUNTRY FURNITURE

Cabinet makers

The Old Cheese Factory, Reapsmoor, Longnor, Buxton, Derbyshire SK17 0LG
☎ Hartington (0298) 84467

Fox Country Furniture are makers of fine furniture in English hardwoods. They will make any item of furniture to your specification, and have an attractive range of items on show.

On the B5053, via the A515, 8 miles south of Buxton
Open all year Mon–Fri 10.00am–12.30pm, 2.00–5.00pm, and most Saturdays
Free admission
&. workshop and showroom are upstairs ⛥

POOLE'S CAVERN, BUXTON COUNTRY PARK

Country park and showcave

Green Lane, Buxton, Derbyshire SK17 9DH
☎ Buxton (0298) 6978

A beautiful natural cave formed by River Wye. Visitor centre with exhibition and video; nature trail in 100 acres of woodland.

Off the A515 and A54, 15 minutes walk from town centre
Admission: adult £2.00, child £1.10, OAP/student £1.75, party rates available (1990 prices)
&. 🚌 ⛥

TIDESWELL DALE ROCK SHOP

Rock shop

Commercial Road, Tideswell, Derbyshire SK17 8NU
☎ Tideswell (0298) 871606

Jewellery in Blue John and sterling silver. The only remaining workshop producing the traditional Ashford Black Marble inlay. One of the widest selections of mineral specimens for collections available in Britain.

Take the A6 towards Bakewell, turn off at Taddington for Tideswell
Open all year Thur–Sun 10.00am–5.30pm
&. 🚌 ⛥

► CHESTERFIELD ◄

FIVE PITS TRAIL

Country walk bridleway

c/o Derbyshire County Council Countryside Centre, 23 Market Street, Clay Cross, Derbyshire S45 9JE
☎ Chesterfield (0246) 866960

7½ mile cycle route winds across rolling countryside offering pleasant picnic areas and splendid views.

Various entry points off the B6039 Holmewood-Tibshelf road
Open all year
Free admission
&. ⛥

THE HERB GARDEN

Herb Garden and plant nursery

'Hall View Cottage', Chesterfield Road, Hardstoft, Pilsley, nr Chesterfield, Derbyshire S45 8AH
☎ Chesterfield (0246) 854268

Plant nursery selling over 150 varieties of culinary, medicinal and aromatic herbs, shop selling pot pourri, gifts etc.

M1 Junction 29. Head for Clay Cross, turn left at Williamthorpe Hotel roundabout (B6039) head for Tibshelf. About 1½ miles along B6039
Open April–Oct daily 10.00am–6.00pm
Free admission
&. assistance is available and there is access to the nursery 🚌 advance notice required ⛥

ROWTHORNE TRAIL

Country walk

c/o Derbyshire County Council Countryside Centre, 23 Market Street, Clay Cross, Derbyshire S45 9JE
☎ Chesterfield (0246) 866960

1 mile country walk, part of the Pleasley trails network.

Off the A617, 1 mile south of Glapwell
Open all year
Free admission
&. a section of trail nearest to Rowthorne car park is suitable for wheelchairs 🚌 by appointment ⛥

► CLAYCROSS ◄

DERBYSHIRE COUNTY COUNCIL COUNTRYSIDE CENTRE

Countryside centre – information, exhibition and shop

23 Market Street, Clay Cross, Derbyshire S45 9JE
☎ Chesterfield (0246) 866960

Just off the High Street (A61) at Clay Cross
Open daily 11.00am–4.00pm
Free admission
& ⚑ ⚐

► CROMFORD ◄

HIGH PEAK JUNCTION WORKSHOPS

Workshops and countryside visitor centre

High Peak Junction, nr Cromford, Derbyshire
☎ Wirksworth (062982) 2831

Original workshops of the Cromford and High Peak Railway. Restored main room with forge, railway exhibition and information centre.

Signed off the A6 in Cromford
Open Jan–March, Nov–Dec Sundays only 10.30am–4.00pm; Easter–Sept daily 10.30am–5.00pm
Admission: adult 30p, child 10p (1990 prices)
& ⚑ advance notice required ⚐

► DERBY ◄

ELVASTON CASTLE COUNTRY PARK

Country park with estate museum

Borrowash Rd, Elvaston, Thurlston, nr Derby DE7 3EP
☎ Derby (0332) 571342

200 acres surrounding Elvaston Castle (not open). Extensive formal and topiary gardens, walled Old English garden, picnic areas, nature trail, information centre and shop. Museum has buildings and workshops restored to recreate life on the estate in 1910.

On the B5010, 6 miles south east of Derby. Signposted from the A6 and the A52

Open for country park: daily 9.00am–dusk; estate museum: Easter–Oct Wed–Sat 1.00–5.00pm, Sun and Bank Holidays 10.00am–6.00pm
Admission: car park 50p (£1.00 weekends and Bank Holidays); coach £5.00; estate museum: adult 75p, child 40p
& ⚑ ⚐

KEDLESTON HALL

Stately home, park and garden

National Trust, Derby DE6 4JN
☎ Derby (0332) 842191

Home of the Curzon family since the 12th century. Set within landscaped parkland this great classical palace is chiefly the work of Robert Adam. Shop and restaurant.

3 miles north of Derby, signposted from the A38 bypass
Open 1 April–end Oct, Sat–Wed 1.00–5.30pm (Hall); 11.00am–6.00pm, also Thur and Fri Nov–23 Dec, Sat and Sun 12.00–4.00pm in season (park and garden)
Admission: adult £3.50, child £1.70, party rates available please write to the Adminstrator for details
& wheelchair access difficult
⚑ advance notice required ⚐

MELBOURNE HALL

Craft centre, country garden, tea rooms, gift shop

Melbourne, Derby DE7 1EN
☎ Melbourne (0332) 862502

A beautiful historic house and formal garden. Once the home of Victorian Prime Minister William Lamb, who as 2nd Viscount Melbourne, gave his name to the Australian city.

On the A514, 8 miles south of Derby
Open for the gardens: April–Sept, Wed, Sat, Sun and Bank Holiday Mondays 2.00–6.00pm
Admission for gardens: £2.00, OAP £1.00
& ⚑ advance notice required ⚐

► HAYFIELD ◄

SETT VALLEY TRAIL

Multi-purpose trail

Hayfield Picnic Site, Hayfield, via Stockport, Cheshire
☎ New Mills (0663) 46222

A traffic-free route of 2½ miles for horse riders, walkers and cyclists between New Mills and Hayfield. Passes through attractive countryside in the 'foothills' of the Peak District. Cycle hire available Easter–Oct.

Signed off the A6 New Mills and the A624 Hayfield
Open all year for the trail
Free admission
 ♿ 🚌 🐕

▶ HEANOR ◀

SHIPLEY COUNTRY PARK

Country park, country walk and farm interpretation centre

The Visitor Centre, Shipley Country Park, Slack Lane, Heanor DE7 7GX
☎ Langley Mill (0773) 719961

600 acres of woodland, lakes, parkland and historic buildings with a full programme of events and activities for all the family. Cycle hire available.

½ mile south of Heanor town centre, signposted off A608 Heanor–Derby road and A6007 Heanor–Ilkeston road and from jct 26 on the M1
Country park open all year; visitor centre: April–Sept weekdays 12.00–4.30pm, weekend 10.00am–6.00pm. Oct–Mar, weekdays 1.00–4.30pm, weekend 10.00am–4.30pm
Free admission
 ♿ 🚌 🐕

▶ LANGLEY MILL ◀

COPPICE SIDE POTTERY

Craft centre, traditional English handmade pottery

North St, Langley Mill, Derbyshire NG16 4EU
☎ Langley Mill (0773) 716854

Fully operational working country pottery.

From jct 26 on the M1 take the A610 towards Ripley. After 3 miles take the Eastwood/Langley Mill turning, first left at the island, travel under the bridge and then turn right onto North St
Open Sat 9.00am–1.00pm please telephone ahead
Free admission
 ♿ 🍴

▶ MATLOCK ◀

CRICH POTTERY

Stoneware studio, pottery workshop

Market Place, Crich, Derbyshire DE4 5DD
☎ Ambergate (077 385) 3171

Extensive range of robust handthrown stoneware pottery, each piece richly and individually hand decorated with landscape and abstract floral images in glaze. Oven, microwave and dishwasherproof; won supreme gift award.

Off the A610, 4 miles south of Matlock, jct 28 on the M1
Open all year daily 9.00am–6.00pm except Christmas and Easter Day. If closed, please knock at the house
Free admission
 ♿ 🚌 advance notice required 🐕

HIGH TOR GROUND

Country walks

The Bungalow, High Tor, Matlock, Derbyshire DE4 3DG
☎ (0629) 583289

Woodland walks, caves, views, picnic areas, cafe bar and childrens playground.

A6 Artists Corner car park, Matlock. A6 Matlock Bath railway station car park
Open daily 10.00am–6.00pm. Closed Christmas Day
Admission: adult £1.00, child/OAP 50p, including caves, 10% reduction for parties over 10
 ♿ 🚌 🐕

▶ RIDGEWAY ◀

KENT HOUSE FARM

Craft centre

Main Road, Ridgeway, Derbyshire. All enquiries c/o North East Derbyshire District Council, Council House, Saltergate, Chesterfield S40 1LF
☎ Chesterfield (0246) 231111 ext 319

14 craft workshops, gift shop and Country Kitchen Tea Room.

Off the A616, 8 miles from Sheffield at the village of Ridgeway, nr Eckington
Open daily 10.30am–5.00pm. Closed Mondays except Bank Holidays
Free admission
 ♿ 🚌 🍴

► *WIRKSWORTH* ◄

HIGH PEAK TRAIL

Country walk

Middleton Top Visitor Centre, MIddleton, nr Wirksworth,
  Derbyshire DE4 4LS
☎ Wirksworth (0629) 823204

*17 mile multi-use trail, ex-Cromford and
High Peak Railway. Easy access from a
variety of car parks, picnic sites for walkers,
cyclists and horse riders.*

Signposted off the A6 in Cromford
Open all year for the trail
Free admission
& ⇛ advance notice required ⋔

MIDDLETON TOP ENGINE HOUSE AND VISITOR CENTRE

**Restored engine house, countryside visitor
centre, picnic site, high peak trail and cycle hire**

Middleton Top, Wirksworth, Derbyshire, DE4 4LS
☎ Wirksworth (0629) 823204

*Original beam engines built in 1829 by the
Butterley Company to haul waggons up the
Middleton Incline on the Cromford and
High Peak Railway.*

Signposted off the A6 in Cromford
Open Easter–Oct, Sundays with engines static, first
  weekend in the month with engines in motion
Admission: adult 30p, child 10p (engines static); adult
  50p, child 25p (engines in operation) (1990 prices)
& engine house is not suitable
⇛ advance notice required
✗ in engine house

Guide to Symbols

☎ telephone
& disabled welcome
⇛ coaches welcome

⋔ dogs welcome (on a leash)
✗ dogs not welcome

DEVON

Devon is well-known for its warm climate, palm trees and sub-tropical flowers, rich red-clay farmland, sandy beaches, rock headlands of its northern coast and Dartmoor. Dotted with attractive market towns and remote villages approached by sunken lanes, its richly contrasting scenery rewards any and every visitor.

Country walks, country parks and nature trails are many and varied in Devon where there are also many opportunities to see some unusual animals and birds; rare breeds that can be traced back to prehistoric times, butterflies, otters and the appealing ponies that run wild on Dartmoor. There are working farms both sheep and dairy, an organic vineyard, an orchid nursery and even a gnome reserve to visit. The craft centres of the area include potteries, a sheepskin works and the well-known Dartington Crystal glass factory, all welcome visitors to watch them at work.

► ASHBURTON ◄

THE RIVER DART COUNTRY PARK

Country park and childrens adventure playgrounds

Holne Park, Ashburton, Devon TQ13 7NP
☎ Ashburton (0364) 52511

Ideal for children offering adventure playgrounds, bathing lake, pony riding, tree and nature trails, and the exciting Anaconda run. Snack bar and country park shop.

Signposed off the A38 on Two Bridges road
Open Easter–Sept 10.00am–5.00pm
Admission: adult £2.65, child/OAP £2.00, groups of 12 or more £1.80
&. ⇔ ⵜ

► AXMINSTER ◄

BURROW FARM GARDEN

Country gardens

Dalwood, Axminster, Devon EX13 7ET
☎ Wilmington (040483) 285

5 acre garden planned for all-year interest. Devonshire cream teas served Sundays, Wednesdays and Bank Holidays. Plants for sale.

3 miles west of Axminster on the A35 turn right onto Stockland Road. Garden ½ mile on right
Open April–Sept, daily 2.00–7.00pm
Admission: adult £1.25, child 50p
&. ⇔ advance notice required ⵜ

DOLPHIN MINIATURES/DOLPHIN CANDLES

Showroom with handmade candles and miniature dolls' houses and furniture

Myrtle Cottage, Greendown, Membury, Axminister, Devon EX13 7TB
☎ Stockland (040 488) 459

Small showroom with selection of handmade candles (speciality small animal figurines) selection of one twelfth scale collectors' dolls' houses and furniture. All items made on the premises.

3½ miles from Axminster on Membury road – white cottage on left hand side 250 yards past Simons Cross

Open all year round 9.00am–6.00pm. Please telephone to confirm times
Free admission
&. ⵜ

► BARNSTAPLE ◄

EXMOOR BIRD GARDENS

Zoological gardens

Bratton Fleming, Barnstaple, Devon EX31 4SG
☎ Paracombe (05983) 352

Formal and natural gardens covering 12½ acres containing the largest collection of tropical birds in north Devon. Many waterfowl and penguins at liberty, also monkeys and other animals. Tearooms, gift shop.

Off the B3226, 3 miles from Bratton Fleming
Open all year daily except Christmas Day, April–Oct 10.00am–6.00pm, Nov–March 10.00am–4.00pm
Admission: adult £3.00, child (3-16 incl) £1.75, under 3s free, OAP £2.75
&. ⇔ ⵜ

MARWOOD HILL GARDENS

Country gardens

Marwood, Barnstaple, Devon EX31 4EB
☎ Barnstaple (0271) 42528

18 acre gardens with 3 small lakes. Rare trees, shrubs, herbaceous plants, alpines and bog plants from many parts of the world provide interest and colour throughout the year. Plants propagated from the garden for sale.

Signposed from the A361 or the B3230, 4 miles north of Barnstaple
Open all year daily dawn until dusk
Admission: adult £1.00, child 10p
&. ⇔ advance notice required ⵜ

NEWPORT POTTERY

Pottery and showroom

72 Newport Rd, Barnstaple, Devon EX32 9BG
☎ Barnstaple (0271) 72103

Craft Pottery comprising showroom and workshop producing commemorative plates, bowls, lampbases and shades and other functional pots and specialising in house name and number plates made to customers requirements.

Approaching Barnstaple on the A361/M5 link road from Tiverton. Turn left at roundabout after passing Tesco's, turn right at traffic lights into Newport Rd. Pottery 200 yards on left. Take next turning on left to Congrams Close car park (2 hours free)

&. ⋔

S SANDERS & SON LTD

Sheepskin shop, works and tannery

Pilton Bridge, Barnstaple, North Devon EX32 7AA
☎ Barnstaple (0271) 42335

One of the oldest tanneries in the south west processing raw skins to finished rugs, available at large factory shop from £14. Also sheepskin coats, slippers, gloves, leather goods; gift shop.

250 yards from Barnstaple's shopping centre, on the right hand side of the A39 Lynton road (20 yards from inner ring road
Open Mon–Fri 9.00am–5.30pm, Sat 9.15am–12.00 noon
Free admission
&. ⇔ ⋔

TARKA COUNTRY PARK

Country park

c/o Property Dept., County Hall, Exeter, Devon EX2 4QQ
☎ Exeter (0392) 77977

Follows the route of the former railway line between Barnstaple, Bideford and Meeth. The total length available for walking is 23 miles and follows parts of the trail followed by the otter described in Henry Williams book 'Tarka the Otter'. Part of it alongside the estuary for about 9 miles is a cycleway.

Signposted from the A39
Open all year
Free admission
&. ⋔

► **BIDEFORD** ◄

THE BIG SHEEP

Sheep dairy and woolcraft centre, sheepy shop, restaurant and play areas

Abbotsham, Bideford, North Devon EX39 5AP
☎ (0237) 472366

The English Tourist Board and British Tourist Authority award winning tourist attraction, combining sheep racing, sheepdog trialling, sheep milking, duck trials, woolcraft centre, sheepy shop etc. Licensed restaurant.

Signed off the A39 Bideford bypass, 2 miles west of New Bideford Bridge, Devon bus 319 Bideford–Clovelly
Open Easter–end Oct daily 10.00am–6.00pm
Admission: adult £2.50, child £1.50, families £7.50, group discount for parties
&. ⇔ ⋔

DOCTON MILL & GARDEN

Country garden, water mill

Hartland, Bideford, Devon EX39 6EA
☎ Hartland (0237) 441369

Ancient water mill in beautiful wild valley: woodlands, lawns, streams, ponds and gardens planted for all seasons and to complement natural settings near Speke's coastal waterfalls and Hartland Quay. Teas.

Take the A39 from Hartland to Stoke. 2 miles towards Elmscott
Open 1 April–30 Sept Sun–Thur 10.00am–5.00pm
Admission: £1.00 per person (July and Aug £1.50), under 16s free
&. ⋔

THE GNOME RESERVE INC. THE PIXIE KILN

Gnome reserve

West Putford, nr Bradworthy, Devon EX22 7XE
☎ Bradworthy (040924) 435

The world's first gnome reserve featuring over 1000 gnomes and pixies – 22 times on TV. 2 acre Pixies Wildflower Trail with over 150 labelled species, and the Pixie Kiln where tiny pottery pixies are created daily.

On the A386, ½ mile from Bideford. English Tourist Board signposted from the A39, the A388 and the A368
Open Easter–Oct daily 10.00am–1.00pm, 2.00–6.00pm; July, Aug and early Sept also 7.00–9.00pm. Closed Saturdays except Bank Holiday weekends
Admission: adult £1.00, child (4-15)/OAP 50p, under 4s free
&. ⇔ advance notice required ⋔

THE 'MILKY' WAY

Working dairy farm, countryside collection, shop and adventure playground

Downland Farm, Clovelly, Bideford, North Devon EX39 5RY
☎ Clovelly (02373) 255

One of largest undercover attractions in the south west. Watch hi-tech milking, handle and feed baby animals, hand milk cows. Display of old countryside machinery, farmhouse scenes of yester year, and lots more.

On the main A39 Bideford-Bude road, 2 miles from Clovelly towards Bideford
Open Easter–Oct daily (except Sat) 12.00–6.00pm
Admission: adult £2.50, child £1.50, OAP £2.00, under 3s free
♿ 🚌 🐕

BOVEY TRACEY

BECKY FALLS ESTATE

Country park, craft shop, restaurant

Manaton, Newton Abbot, Devon TQ13 9UG
☎ Manaton (064 722) 259

A private 60 acre estate with nature trails featuring a 70 foot waterfall, bridges, paths and pools. Restaurant, tea rooms, ice cream parlour, gift shop, picnic area and toilets.

On the B3344 Bovey Tracey – Manaton road
Open Easter–31 Oct 10.00am–6.00pm or dusk
Admission: £2.50 per car, no other charges
♿ 🚌 advance notice required 🐕

DARTMOOR NATIONAL PARK AUTHORITY

Information centre and main office

Parke, Haytor Road, Bovey Tracey, Devon TQ13 9JQ
☎ Bovey Tracey (0626) 832093

One of 7 information centres run by the DNPA. The assistants are friendly local people who will be pleased to help you with your enquiries. The centres have a wide selection of Dartmoor books, maps, posters postcards, T-shirts, leaflets, etc and each has its own display about the area.

Signposted from Chudleigh, Newton Abbot and the A38
Open 9.00am–1.00pm and 2.00–5.00pm throughout the year. Information centre daily early April–Oct
Free admission
♿ steep access to the information centre, disabled visitors may drive to the main office. Cars only 🚌 advance notice required 🐕

MOORHOUSE FARM CREAM TEAS

Farmhouse cream teas

Bovey Tracey, nr Newton Abbot, Devon TQ13 9NT
☎ Lustleigh (06477) 203

Cream teas on a small family farm set in beautiful countryside. The cream is made traditionally on the farm.

From Bovey Tracey take road to Chudleigh Knighton (B3344) approx 1 mile, turn left to Hennock, from village take road to reservoirs and Moretonhampstead, farm on right after 2 miles
Open Easter weekend–Sept Thurs–Sun 3.00–6.00pm
Free admission
♿ 🚌 advance notice required 🐕

PARKE RARE BREEDS FARM

Farm ship, craft centre, farm interpretation centre, country walk, farming museum, farm trail and farm visit

Parke Estate, Bovey Tracey, Newton Abbot, Devon TQ13 9JQ
☎ Bovey Tracey (0626) 833909

Rare breeds of cattle, sheep, pigs and poultry, which form part of our national heritage, displayed in a beautiful parkland setting.

Off the B3387, 300 yards from the junction with the A382 Bovey Tracey bypass
Open 1 April (or Good Friday if earlier) – 31 Oct, 10.00am–6.00pm, last admission 5.00pm
Admission: adult £2.75, child (3-14) £1.50, OAP, £2.50, party rates available (1990 prices)
♿ not suitable for wheelchairs. Toilets
🚌 advance notice required
🐕 on the estate walks but not the farm

YARNER WOOD NATIONAL NATURE RESERVE

Woodland interpretation and nature trails

Manaton Rd, Bovey Tracey, Newton Abbot, Devon
☎ Bovey Tracey (0626) 832330

Guided walks for educational purposes available by arrangement with the Reserve Warden. Also guided walks for other visitors throughout the year, programme available upon request.

2 miles west of Bovey Tracey on the B3344 Bovey Tracey-Manaton road
Open daily dawn–dusk
Free admission, small charge for the nature trail and woodlands walk leaflets
 ♿ 👤

▶ **BRIXHAM** ◀

BERRY HEAD COUNTRY PARK

Country park

Berry Head, Brixham, Devon
☎ Brixham (0803) 882619

Spectacular sea views, two Napoleonic forts, lighthouse, seabird nesting colony, conservation area, deep water fishing. Tea rooms.

Take the A3022 in the direction of Brixham, then follow signs to Berry Head
Open all year
Free admission. Car park: 1 hour 30p, 2 hours 60p, day £2.00
 👤

▶ **BUCKFAST** ◀

BUCKFAST BUTTERFLY FARM AND DARTMOOR OTTER SANCTUARY

Butterfly farm

Buckfast Steam & Leisure Park, Buckfastleigh, Devon TQ11 0DZ
☎ Buckfastleigh (0364) 42916

A tropical landscaped garden with ponds, waterfalls and bridges; the perfect environment for the exotic butterflies that live and breed here as they would in the wild. Otters can be seen at play through the special underwater viewing tunnel, elevated platforms and observation holts.

Just off the A38 Exeter–Plymouth road at Dartbridge junction, follow the brown tourist signs

Open Good Friday–Oct daily 10.00am–5.30pm or dusk, whichever earlier
Admission: adult £3.00, child £2.00, OAP £2.50
 ♿ 👤

BICTON PARK

Country Park

East Budleigh, Budleigh Salterton, Devon EX9 7DP
☎ Colaton Raleigh (0395) 68465

Over 50 acres of beautiful gardens and parkland with fascinating glasshouse displays, the James Countryside Museum, bird garden, tropical house and the magnificent 'Palm House', together with lots of exciting rides and entertainment for all ages.

2 miles north of Budleigh Salterton on the A376
Open Easter–Oct daily 10.00am–6.00pm
Admission: adult £3.25, child £2.00, OAP £2.75, (£2.00 Wed and Thur), under 3s free, party rates available
 ♿ 👤

CANONTEIGN FALLS AND COUNTRY PARK

Country park

Cantonteign, Lower Ashton, nr Exeter, Devon EX6 7RH
☎ Christow (0647) 52666

Country park featuring Britain's highest waterfall (220 feet), lakes, nature trails, junior commands assault course designed by the marines and an antique farm machinery collection. Restaurant, tea room and barbeque.

Turn off the A38 at Chudleigh and follow the brown tourist signs for 3 miles
Open Easter–Oct daily 10.00am–6.00pm; winter Sundays only 10.00am–4.00pm
Admission: One charge for all attractions, please telephone for current charge
 ♿ 👤

THE WHEEL CRAFT WORKSHOPS AND RESTAURANT

Craft centre

Clifford St, Chudleigh, South Devon
☎ Newton Abbot (0626) 852 698

Off the A38 Plymouth–Exeter road or the A380 Exeter–Torquay road

Open all year daily 10.00am–5.30pm
Free admission
 ♿ assistance offered in courtyard, workshops and ground floors, access to restaurant
🚌 advance notice required 🐕

► ◄ **CLOVELLY**

HARTLAND POTTERY

Working pottery and showroom

Hartland, Bideford, North Devon, EX39 6DE
☎ Hartland (0237) 441693

Pottery housed in an old forge, visitors can see the various processes taking place. There are several attractions in Hartland, which is 2 miles from the rugged Atlantic coast.

From Clovelly Cross and filling station on the A39 go south ¼ mile, turn right, 4 miles to Hartland
Open throughout season and most of year 9.30am–6.30pm
Free admission
♿ 🚌 🐕

► ◄ **COMBE MARTIN**

BODSTONE BARTON FARMWORLD

Working farm, country park, farm museum and nature trails

Berrydown Cross, Combe Martin, North Devon EX34 0NT
☎ Combe Martin (0271 88) 3654

160 acres with 20,000 sq feet under cover. Daily handmilking of cows and goats, bottle feeding of kids and lambs in season. Farm related videos, craft demonstrations, pony and tractor rides; shop and cafe.

Off the B3343, 2 miles south of Combe Martin. Signposted from Berrydown Cross
Open Easter–Oct daily 10.30am–6.00pm
Admission: adult £2.80, child (3-16) £1.40, OAP £2.20, disabled £1.40
♿ hilly and does not lend itself to easy access but improvements have been made for 1990 including toilets and more ramps 🚌 🍴

► ◄ **CULLOMPTON**

COLDHARBOUR MILL

Working wool museum

Uffculme, Cullompton, Devon
☎ Craddock (0884) 40960

18th century mill factory where visitors can see knitting yarn produced on turn of the century machinery, also a Carding engine, spinning mule and weaving looms. Restaurant and tea room.

2 miles from M5, jct 27 off the B3181, follow signs for Willand and then the museum at Uffculme
Open Easter–Oct, daily 11.00am–5.00pm, last tour 4.00pm. Winter Mon–Fri, please telephone to confirm
Admission: adult £2.25, child £1.50, party rates on application, family ticket (2 adults 2 children) £6.50
♿ there are quite a number of steps to be negotiated in the mill, but there is wheelchair access to the Mill Shop and knitting yarn production floor, where there is a guided tour. Lifting help available for access to weaving floor and restaurant. Visits by small groups of deaf and partially sighted people have proved very enjoyable 🚌 advance notice required 🐕 in the grounds

LOWER TURLEY FARM

Organic farm

Cullompton, Devon EX15 1NA
☎ Cullompton (0884) 32234

Coloured Friesland sheep crossed with rare blue-grey Leicester Longwool provide both milk for cheese, and attractive lustrous fleeces for spinning. Organic lamb and organic vegetables are raised.

Turn left towards Britten Bottom at Weymill Cross signpost (3 miles south of Tiverton) on the road to Cullompton
Open April–Sept
Free admission
♿ 🐕

WHITMOOR HOUSE VINEYARD AND ORCHID NURSERY

Vineyard and orchid nursery

Whitmoor House, Ashill, Cullompton, Devon EX15 3NP
☎ Craddock (0884) 40145

Wine and cider for sale; interesting collection of tropical orchids, plants and flowers for sale.

Near to the M5, jct 27 or 28, B3181, and then via Uffculme and Ashill, 4 miles from jct 27, 5 miles from jct 28
Open April–Sept, weekdays 10.00am–5.00pm, Sundays 12.00–4.00pm, closed Tuesdays. Winter months by appointment
Admission: individuals and families free, organised groups £2.00 per person (1990 prices)
♿ 🚌 🐕

► DARTMOUTH ◄

DITTISHAM FRUIT FARM

Prehistoric museum and site

Capton, nr Dartmouth TQ6 0JE
☎ Blackawton (080421) 452

Experience life inside a Neolithic Roundhouse. Flint tools and artefacts from 10,000 years of continuous habitation. Beautiful farm walk; pick your own soft fruit; pure fruit liqueurs made on the farm.

Take the B3207 from Dartmouth to Totnes, turn right at the Sportsmans Arms and follow the brown signs for the prehistoric hill settlement
Open all year 10.00am–5.00pm except Christmas and New Year
Free admission
& ⛟ small coaches with advance notice ⛨

► EXETER ◄

CHUDLEIGH VINEYARD

Organic vineyard

Farmborough House, Chudleigh, Newton Abbot, Devon
TQ13 0DR
☎ Torquay (0626) 853258

3 acre organically cultivated vineyard with Kerner, Seyval Blanc, Schonberger and Madeleine Angevine varieties; 300 newly planted shelter belt trees. Self-guided tour leaflets; guided tours for groups by arrangement.

10 miles from Exeter on the A38(T), approx 1 mile from Chudleigh along the old Exeter road
Open June–Sept daily except Thursdays 2.00–6.00pm
Admission: adult £1.50, guided tours £2.00 per head
& access limited

CREALY ADVENTURE PARK AND THE DRAGONFLY RESTAURANT

Country walk, farm interpretation centre, farm visit and restaurant

Crealy Park, Clyst St Mary, Exeter EX5 1DR
☎ Woodbury (0395) 33200

Tree Tops and Wooden Tops adventure playgrounds, crazy cable and buzzard's swoop freefall slides. Animal farm with baby and miniature animals, farm interpretation centre; lake, walks; restaurant and shop.

Nr jct 30 on the M5 (Exeter exit) on the A3052 Exeter–Sidmouth road
Open 24 March–29 Sept daily 10.00am–6.00pm, out of season by appointment. Anticipated winter opening: weekends and school holidays
Admission: adult £2.75, child (3-15) £1.75, under 3s free, OAP £2.25. Special prices for groups and parties out of season
& ⛟ ⛨

EXETER CITY COUNCIL

Countryside parks

Dept of Leisure & Tourism, Dix's Field, Exeter, Devon
EX1 1JJ
☎ Exeter (0392) 77888

Four parks – 1,000 acres total area. Leaflets available from above address. Wildlife, attractive walks, canal.

County town of Devon, exit 31 of the M5
Open all year daily
Free admission
& prior arrangment recommended so that guidance can be given ⛟ advance notice required ⛨

FURSDON HOUSE

Country walk and historic house

Cadbury, Exeter, Devon EX5 5JS
☎ Exeter (0392) 860860

700 year old house. Superb views; footpath to Cadbury Castle, an iron age and Roman hill fort said to be guarded by a dragon; picnic and play area.

Off the A3072 Tiverton/Bickleigh/Crediton signposted. Off the A396 Tiverton/Exeter signposted through Thorverton
Open: please telephone for details
Admission: house & grounds adult £2.10, child £1.00, under 10s free. Special rate for pre-booked parties over 20
& ⛟ advance notice required ⛨ except in garden

MANSTREE VINEYARD, 3.F's PICK YOUR OWN and 3 F's EVERJOY, DRIED FLOWERS

Pick your own and vineyards

Manstree Road, Shillingford St George, Alphington, Exeter
EX2 9QR
☎ Exeter (0392) 832218

Selection of own English wines. 15 different soft fruits and a wide range of dried flowers and grasses.

At double mini roundabouts in Chudleigh Road
 Alphington, take road signposted Shillingford St
 George, fork right by village hall, first farm
 beyond the village
Open June–July daily 9.00am–6.00pm; Aug–Sept
 9.00am–5.00pm Mon–Fri, Sat 9.00am–1.00pm. At
 other times of the year, dried flowers by appointment.
 Wines in licensing hours
Free admission
&. ⸺ by special arrangement ✖

STALLCOMBE HOUSE

Organic farm

Sanctuary Lane, Woodbury, Devon EX5 1EX
☎ Woodbury (0395) 32373

*This small mixed farm is run using free
range and organic husbandry. Sheep, beef
cattle, poultry and pigs can be seen as well
as organic vegetables grown on a garden and
field scale. Wild flowers, devon banks,
layered hedges and secluded ponds are all to
be seen.*

10 miles from Exeter off the Sidmouth road
Open by appointment only, letter or telephone
Admission is free, but donations are welcome
&. ⸺ ✖

▶ *EXMOUTH* ◀

WORLD OF COUNTRY LIFE

Farming museum

Sandy Bay, Exmouth, Devon
☎ Exmouth (0395) 274533

*Vintage vehicles, steam engine; craft
demonstrations; Victorian cottage, shops and
inn. Childrens play and adventure park, ball
pit, free rides, deer parks, llamas and pets
corner; restaurant, gift shop.*

Off the A376 Exmouth–Budleigh Salterton road at
 Littleham
Open 29 March–29 Sept 1991, daily 10.00am–5.00pm
Admission: adult £2.50, child (3-16)/OAP £1.50, family
 ticket £6.50. Groups of 10 or over adult £2.25,
 child/OAP £1.25
&. ⸺ advance notice required ✖

▶ *GREAT TORRINGTON* ◀

DARTINGTON CRYSTAL

Glass factory

Linden Close, Great Torrington, North Devon EX38 7AN
☎ Torrington (0805) 23797/22321

*Factory tours, award winning glass centre
with video-theatre, historic glass exhibition,
replica glass cone and studio glass blowing
demonstrations. Factory shop and licensed
restaurant.*

7 miles south east of Bideford on the A386,
 situated in Linden Close, off School Lane and is
 signposted from the parish church
Open Jan–Dec, Mon–Fri 9.00am–5.00pm, tours
 9.30am–3.30pm
Admission: Full tour: adult £1.40, child (6-16) 70p, under
 6s free. Glass centre only: adult 75p, child (6-16) 25p,
 under 6s free. Party rate (over 10) £1.00
&. can cope with limited number of wheelchairs if
 advised in advance ⸺ advance notice required ✖

ROSEMOOR GARDEN

Country gardens

Great Torrington, Devon EX38 7EG
☎ Torrington (0805) 24067

*Famous garden beautiful in all seasons,
recently featured on BBC and ITV. New for
1990: Visitors Centre with shop, restaurant,
and plant centre with many rare plants; rose
gardens and herbaceous borders. Picnic area
and cream teas available.*

On the B3220, 1 mile south of Great Torrington,
 6 miles south east of Bideford
Open daily 10.00am–6.00pm, 5.00pm in Oct
Admission: adult £1.50, child 50p, reduced rates for
 groups
&. partial access to gardens
⸺ ✖

▶ *HARTLAND* ◀

MILLTHORNE CHAIRS

Chair workshop

10 Fore Street, Hartland, nr Bideford, North Devon
☎ Hartland (0237) 441590

Take the B3248 off the A39 to Hartland (3 miles)
Open all year daily
Free admission
&. ✖

► **HATHERLEIGH** ◄

ELIZABETH AYLMER POTTERY

Pottery studio

Widgery House, 20 Market St, Hatherleigh, Devon
EX20 3JP
☎ Okehampton (0837) 810624

*A studio pottery producing a range of table
and cookware and containers for plants,
flowers and bonsai trees. All made
individually on the potter's wheel.*

Take A386 to Hatherleigh and the pottery is on the
main street near to the square and the Tally Ho
public house
Open Mon–Fri 10.00am–5.00pm. Please telephone before
calling at weekends
Free admission
& ⚕ advance notice required ⴽ

SIMPSON FARM

Coarse fishery and nature trail

Holsworthy, Devon EX22 6JW
☎ (0409 253) 593

*The nature trail is in a quiet, secluded
Devon valley past fishing lakes which have a
fine stock of Mirror Carp (many into double
figures). Also roach, tench and rudd.*

Off the A3072 Holsworthy–Hatherleigh Road, 1½
miles from Holsworthy.
Open all year dawn until dusk
Admission for trail: adult£1.00, child 50p; fishing from £2
per day, juniors and pensioners half price
⚕ advance notice required ⴽ

THORNE FARM NATURE TRAIL

Nature trail

Pancrasweek, Holsworthy, Devon EX22 7JD
☎ Holsworthy (0409) 253342

*Approx 1 hours walk in nature reserve along
part of the Old Bude Holsworth Canal. Old
pasture with lake, a good variety of flowers,
birds and insects. Leaflet available.*

Take the A3072 from Holsworthy towards Bude, 2
miles signposted 'nature trail'
Open daily April–Oct
Admission: adult 50p, child 25p
⚕ advance notice required ⴽ ✗

► **HONITON** ◄

FARWAY COUNTRYSIDE PARK

Countryside park

Nr Colyton, Devon EX13 6JL
☎ Farway (040487) 224/367

Tourist signposted off the A3052 Seaton–Sidmouth
road and the B3174 Honiton–Seaton road
Open Easter–Oct daily 10.00am–6.00pm
Admission: car park £1.00
& ⚕ ⴽ

HONITON POTTERY LTD

Pottery shop

30–34 High St, Honiton, Devon EX14 8PU
☎ Honiton (0404) 42106

*Wander through the pottery. There are no
conducted tours but leaflets and notices
explain the processes, including the special
hand painting. Have-a-go area during the
summer holidays.*

In the High Street
Open for pottery: Mon–Fri 9.00am–12.00 noon,
2.00–4.00pm. Shop: Mon–Sat 9.00am–5.00pm
Free admission
& ⚕ ⴽ

► **ILFRACOMBE** ◄

THE OLD CORN MILL

Farming museum and corn mill with waterwheel

Hele Bay, Ilfracombe, North Devon
☎ Ilfracombe (0271) 863162

*Fully restored 16th Century watermill
containing much information and many
items of machinery. Producing four grades of
wholemeal flour, also wheatflakes.*

On the A399 Ilfracombe-Combe Martin road, 1 mile
east of Ilfracombe
Open Easter Sunday–end Oct, Mon–Fri 10.00am–5.00pm,
Sun 2.00–5.00pm
Admission: adult £1.40, child 70p
& ⚕ advance notice required. Parties by
arrangement ✗

▶ INSTOW ◀

TAPELEY PARK

Country gardens, stately home and jousting centre

Instow, Bideford, North Devon EX39 4NT
☎ Instow (0271) 861200

Country gardens, stately home and jousting centre. Mediaeval costume display.

Off the A39 between Instow and Bideford
Open Easter–Oct daily except Saturdays 10.00am–6.00pm
Admission: adult £2.00, child £1.00, OAP £1.50. Groups of over 15 £1.00 each (adults). Large parties by appointment only
&. ▣ advance notice required ⊁

▶ IVYBRIDGE ◀

ERMINGTON MILL

Craft centre and trout farm, catch your own

The Mills, Ermington, Devon PL21 9NT
☎ Modbury (0548) 830172

The Craft Centre is tastefully incorporated into a 19th century water mill. A wide variety of beautiful and unusual arts, crafts and bric-a-brac is available. Adjacent is Devon's oldest trout farm.

3 miles south west of Ivybridge along the B3211
Open daily 10.00am–5.30pm
Free admission
&.
▣ advance notice required ⊁

▶ KINGSBRIDGE ◀

COOKWORTHY MUSEUM OF RURAL LIFE

Museum

108 Fore St, Kingsbridge, Devon
☎ Kingsbridge (0548) 85 3235

Complete Victorian kitchen and Edwardian pharmacy, large farm gallery in a walled garden, toys and dolls house and newly displayed costume room.

The museum is at the top of the town on the A379 from Plymouth (and Loddiswell)

Open April–Sept Mon–Sat 10.00am–5.00pm; Oct Mon–Fri 10.30am–4.00pm. Closed Nov–April
Admission: adult £1.00, child/OAP 50p, family ticket £2.75, reduced rates for groups (1990 prices)
&. there are quite difficult, twisting stairs. Wheelchair access to ground floor with use of ramps, blind people must also be accompanied, please contact the office prior to visiting for full information
▣ by arrangment
⊁ at the discretion of the steward, visitors could be requested to tie them up in the lobby

LODDISWELL VINEYARD & WINERY

Farm shop, vineyard and winery

Lilwell, Loddiswell, Kingsbridge, Devon TQ7 4EF
☎ Kingsbridge (0548) 550221

6 acre vineyard, experimental polytunnels and winery where 10-20,000 bottles of English wine are produced each year. Video of planting and harvesting. Tearoom and play area. Guided tours.

2 miles north of Loddiswell, 5 miles north of Kingsbridge and 6 miles south of the A38 Wrangaton Cross turn off
Open Easter–Oct 1.00–6.00pm Mon–Fri, and Sundays in July and Aug, and Bank Holiday weekends
Admission: guided tour of vineyard and winery (incl wine tasting) £2.50 walkabout vineyard only and wine tasting £1.50, child (accompanied by adult) 80p, under 5s free
Parties by appointment
&. ▣ advance notice required ⊁

VALLEY SPRINGS TROUT FARM

Trout farm with catch your own trout

Sherford, Kingsbridge, Devon TQ7 2BG
☎ Kingsbridge (0548) 531574

Buy or fish for trout in the peaceful setting of a delightful secluded valley in the heart of farmland. Snack bar.

From Totnes take the A381, after 7½ mies turn left and follow tourism signs. From Kingsbridge take the A379 Torcross road, at Frogmore turn left and follow signs
Open daily Easter–Oct
Admission: adult 75p, child 40p (1990 prices)
&. ▣ mini and midi coaches only ✕

► **KINGSWEAR** ◄

COLETON FISHACRE GARDEN (NATIONAL TRUST)

Country garden and country walk

Coleton, Kingswear, Dartmouth, Devon TQ6 0EQ
☎ Kingswear (080 425) 466

Unusual trees and shrubs in lush, secluded, stream-fed garden created by Lady Dorothy D'Oyly Carte of Gilbert & Sullivan fame, above small cove in glorious unspoilt coastal area.

2 miles from Kingswear. Take Lower Ferry Road and turn off at Tollhouse.
Open 1 April–end Oct, Wed, Thur, Fri and Sun 11.00am–6.00pm
Admission: adult £1.90, child half price, pre-arranged parties £1.40
&. 🚐 🐕

► **LYDFORD** ◄

RODNEY SMITH, WOODCARVER

Woodcarvers studio and workshop

Larrick Cottage, Lydford, Okehampton, Devon EX20 4BJ
☎ Lydford (082282) 288

Specialist in wild life woodcarvings and deep relief picture, his work can also be seen at the 'Walter Elliott Gallery', Braunton, near Barnstaple, and at the 'Devon Rural Skills Trust Centre', Cockington Court, Cockington, Torquay.

Off the A386 between Okehampton and Tavistock. Larrick Cottage in lane on west side of road between two entrances to the National Trust's Lydford Gorge
Open all day and evening; advisable to telephone before visiting
Free admission
&. 🐕

► **LYNTON AND LYNMOUTH** ◄

WATERSMEET

Country walks – National Trust estate

Watersmeet House, Lynmouth, Lynton, North Devon EX35 6NT
☎ (0598) 53348

Estate of 1500 acres, SSSI and area of outstanding natural beauty. Set in beautiful landscape of rivers, wooded hillsides and open moor. Restored Lime kiln. Many paths, car parks scattered around the area. House accommodates a restaurant and shop.

On the A39, 1½ miles from Lynmouth towards Barnstaple.
Open 22 March–31 Oct for refreshments: 10.30am–5.30pm, shop: 11.00am–6.00pm. Closing 1 hour earlier in Oct
Free admission
&. 🚐 🐕

WOODTURNERS (SOUTH DEVON) CRAFT CENTRE

Handmade furniture and crafts

New Road, Modbury, South Devon PL21 0RG
☎ Modbury (0548) 830405

Craft centre producing everything for the home: fruit and salad bowls, table and standard lamps, coffee tables, dressers corner units. Blanket chests, chairs, bar stools etc. made from local hardwoods and imported timbers.

On the A379 12 miles from Plymouth and 7 miles from Kingsbridge
Open all year Mon–Sat, 10.30am–6.00pm, closed on Sundays and Christmas holiday
Free admission
&. minimum requirements not complied with
🚐 park in Modbury after dropping their passengers
🐕 dogs allowed on a leash

► **MORETONHAMPSTEAD** ◄

TRADITIONAL SILVERSMITH WORKSHOP

Silversmith workshop

The Show Room, Bow Cane, Mortonhampstead, Newton Abbot, Devon TQ13 8CS
☎ Moretonhampstead (0647) 40850

Silversmith workshop incorporating craft shop and gallery.

50 yards down lane at rear of Lloyds Bank
Open all year Mon–Sat 10.00am–5.00pm
Free admission
&. 🐕

NEWTON ABBOT

DECOY COUNTRY PARK

Country park with walks

c/o Planning Dept, Forde House, Teignbridge D.C.,
Newton Abbot, Devon
☎ Newton Abbot (0626) 61101 ext 2705

100 acres of woodland walks, 13 acre lake, home to numerous waterfowl with coarse fishing, sailboard school in season, trim trail and paddling pool. Guided walks; refreshment kiosk, toilet facilities.

From the A380 take turning to Newton Abbot first left (Keyberry Road), then second right is Decoy Road, entrance to park is 100 yards on left
Open all year
Free admission
& toilets 🚐 🏕

NORTH TAWTON

GIL TREGUNNA ANIMAL SCULPTURE

Sculpture craft gallery

North Tawton Craft Gallery, 5 The Square, North Tawton, Devon EX20 2ER
☎ North Tawton (083782) 513

Life size sculptural portrait of your cat, dog or horse (head). Wildlife sculptures include badgers otters and foxes; domestic pieces include lambs, rams, sheep, bulls, geese etc.

On the A3072 between Crediton and Okehampton
Open Mon–Sat 11.00am–6.00pm
Free admission
& 🚐 🏕

OKEHAMPTON

FINCH FOUNDRY AND MUSEUM OF WATERPOWER

Working industrial museum, country walk

Sticklepath, nr Okehampton, Devon EX20 2NW
☎ Okehampton (0837) 840046

Restored 19th century factory for the manufacture of agricultural hand tools with 3 working waterwheels. Associated galleries devoted to tools and waterpower.

Off the A30, 4 miles east of Okehampton.
Signposted

Open: 4 March–21 Dec, Mon–Sat 10.00am–5.00pm
(Sundays also in April–Sept)
Admission: adult £1.50, child (5–16) 80p, OAP £1.20
& 🚐 advance notice required 🏕

GULL STUDIO

Jewellery and painting workshop

Whitehart House, 18 Market St, Hatherleigh, Devon EX20 3JP
☎ Okehampton (0837) 810049

This unspoilt 14th century Bishop's Lodging houses a Craft Studio and second hand book shop. Jewellery, painting and Dartmoor walking holiday centre, with one day courses a speciality.

On the A386, 7 miles north of Okehampton
Open all year round 10.00am–5.00pm
Free admission
& 🚐 🎣

LYDFORD FARM PARK

Farm park with cafe

Holdstrong Farm, Coryton, Okehampton, Devon EX20 4PQ
☎ Lydford (082282) 319

Farm park set in a beautiful valley on the edge of Dartmoor. Home to a wide variety of farm animals, poultry and waterfowl. Pets corner, old farming bygones; cafe.

A30 Okehampton–Launceston road 2 miles south east Coobebow towards Lydford, Okehampton–Tavistock A386 2 miles from Lydford village
Open Easter–Oct 10.00am–6.00pm
Admission: adult £1.50, child £1.00, OAP £1.00
& 🚐 advance notice required 🏕

MUSEUM OF DARTMOOR LIFE

Interpretation centre, farming museum and craft centre

The Dartmoor Centre, West St, Okehampton, Devon EX20 1HQ
☎ Okehampton (0837) 52295

Museum set in old mill with working waterwheel, reconstructions of domestic and working life and extensive displays. Also craft and gift shops, tea rooms and National Park Visitor Centre.

Signposted from the A30 Okehampton bypass, then from town centre
Open 4 March–21 Dec Mon–Sat 10.00am–5.00pm; Sundays also in July and Aug
Admission: adult 80p, child (5–16) 40p, OAP 60p (1990 prices)
& 🚌 advance notice required 🐴

▶ OTTERY ST MARY ◀

ESCOT AQUACULTURE LTD

Aquatic, pet centre and Victorian gardens

Parklands Farm, Escot, Ottery St Mary, Devon EX11 1LU
☎ Whimple (0404) 822188

Devon's largest pet and aquatic centre, set in historic Escot Park. Coldwater and tropical fish, birds, mammals, water plants and accessories. Victorian walled rose garden, rhododendron walks, otters, wild boar; croquet and trampolining. Cream teas.

Off the A30 Honiton–Exeter road, at Fairmile take the B3176 to Talaton
Open daily all year 10.00am–6.00pm
Admission: centre free; gardens and walks £1.50
& toilets 🚌 🐴

JOSHUAS HARVEST STORE

Farm shop, speciality food producer

Gostard Rd, Ottery St Mary, Devon EX11 1NU
☎ Ottery (0404) 815473

Specialist growers of organic vegetables and cut flowers with farm shop selling huge range of local produce; organic foods and meats, rare cheeses and much more.

Off the B3177, 1 mile north of Ottery or 1 mile south of the A30, turn at Pattesons Cross
Open all year daily 9.30am–6.00pm. Closed Sundays
Free admission
& 🚌

▶ PLYMOUTH ◀

LANGAGE FARM DAIRY PRODUCTS

Homemade dairy products

Higher Langage Farm, Plympton, Plymouth, South Devon PL7 5AW
☎ Plymouth (0752) 337723

Quality dairy produce made with milk from our own pedigree Jersey herd. Specializing in over 25 flavours of superb real dairy ice cream. Local country produce.

A38 Plympton exit follow signs for Langage industrial estate, sign for farm shop 300 yards past industrial estate.
Open all year (except Christmas/Boxing Day): summer 10.00am–6.00pm; winter 10.00am–5.00pm
Free admission
& 🚌 advance notice required 🐴

NATIONAL SHIRE HORSE CENTRE

Shire horse centre

Yealhampton, Plymouth PL8 2EL
☎ Plymouth (0752) 880268

One of the most popular tourist attractions in the south west with over 40 Shire horses. Falconry flying displays; childrens adventure playground; restaurants and bars.

8 miles from Plymouth on A379 to Kingsbridge
Open all year daily (except 24th–26 Dec) 10.00am–5.00pm
Admission: adult £3.95, child £2.75, OAP £3.50, party rates available
& 🚌 🐴

▶ SALCOMBE ◀

SALCOMBE DAIRY

Ice cream shop

Shadycourse Rd, Salcombe, Devon TQ8 8DX
☎ Salcombe (054884) 3228

On the A381 5 miles south of Kingsbridge
Open March–Dec, Mon–Sat 10.00am–6.00pm
Free admission
& 🚌 advance notice required 🐴

▶ SOUTH MOLTON ◀

EXMOOR TROUT

Trout farm

Mole Bridge, North Molton, Devon EX36 3JJ
☎ North Molton (059 84) 321

A working trout farm where you can see all the stages in the life history of the fish: hatchery, rearing tanks and stew ponds. Fascinating and educational – spectacular at feeding time.

Turn north in South Molton, by the bridge in North Molton village
Open all year daily 8.30am–5.00pm
Free admission
& ✗

HANCOCKS DEVON CIDER

Speciality drink producer, farm shop

Mill House, Clapworthy Mill, South Molton, North Devon EX36 4HU
☎ South Molton (07695) 2678

Mill where five generations have produced real Devon Scrumpy using traditional methods. Film show, cider presses, Museum Corner and craft shop; MIll Stream and picnic area. Full off licence where the prize-winning cider is sold.

On the B3226, 3 miles from South Molton
Open Easter–end Oct daily 9.00am–5.00pm. Closed Sundays
Admission: adult £1.50, child 75p
& ⚌ ⊢ ✗

HEAD MILL TROUT FARM LIMITED

Fish farm

Umberleigh, Devon EX37 9HA
☎ Chumleigh (0769) 80862

A working trout farm where visitors can see trout at various stages of growth. Fresh trout, smoked trout and 2 different pates made on the premises are sold in the farm shop.

On the B3226, 1 mile north of junction with the A377 Barnstaple–Exeter road at Kings Nympton station
Open daily 9.00am–5.30pm
Free admission
& access to most parts of the farm ⊢

HEAL FARM QUALITY TRADITIONAL MEATS

Farm shop and special foods

Anne Petch Heal Farm, Kings Nympton, Umberleigh, Devon EX37 9TB
☎ South Molton (07695) 4341

Ham, bacon, sausages and much more, all made from Rare Breeds using traditional recipes; English and Continental butchery. Lamb from primitive and conventional breeds, well hung Red Ruby Devon beef.

From South Molton go through Georgenympton, then turn right (no sign), until signpost on right 'Heal Farm'
Open Mon–Fri 9.00am–5.00pm, Sat 10.00am–4.00pm
Free admission
& ✗

HURSTONE FARM

Farm shop and visit

Chittlehamholt, Umberleigh, Devon EX37 9PG
☎ Chittlehamholt (076 94) 514

Farm shop and visit; home made Devon clotted cream.

From South Molton take the B3226 for 5 miles, turn right to Chittlehamholt
Open all year daily 9.00am–5.00pm
Free admission
& ⊢

QUINCE HONEY FARM

Honey farm and exhibition of bees

North Rd, South Molton, Devon EX36 3AZ
☎ South Molton (076 95) 2401

Designed for both the casual visitor and the serious student, this unique exhibition of living honey bees provides entertaining education for all the family.

On the A361 in South Molton
Open daily 9.00am–5.00pm
Admission: adult £2.45, child £1.10 (1990 prices)
& easy access to the disabled toilets, shop and cafeteria, but the exhibition is on the first floor ⚌ ✗

TWITCHEN WAGON TOURS

Horse drawn wagon trips

Higher Twitchen Mill, Twitchen, South Molton, Devon
☎ North Molton (05984) 446

Horsedrawn wagon trips. Accommodation can be organised for people wishing to stay in the area.

Take the B3226 from South Molton, through North Molton, turn right at Sandyway to Twitchen village, first left at telephone box, then second left to Twitchen Mill
Open Easter–Sept
Admission: trips adult £5-£10, half price for children
& ⊢

TAVISTOCK

THE GARDEN HOUSE

Country garden

Buckland Monachorum, Yelverton, Devon PL20 7LQ
☎ Yelverton (0822) 854769

10 miles north of Plymouth. West off the A386
Plymouth–Tavistock road
Open April–Sept daily 12.00–5.00pm
Admission: please telephone for details
 ♿ 🚩 advance notice required 🐎

MORWELLHAM QUAY

Country walks and farm trails

Tavistock, Devon PL19 8JL
☎ Tavistock (0822) 832766, information only 833808

*Mid 19th century Copper Port brought to
life with workers in period costume.
Tramway ride underground into coppermine.
Shire horse-drawn carriage ride on the
Duke's Drive.*

From the A390 Tavistock–Liskeard road bear left 2
miles west of Tavistock. Travelling from Cornwall
bear right 2 miles east of Gunnislake
Open all year daily 10.00am–5.30pm, last admission
3.30pm; winter 10.00am–4.30pm, last admission
2.30pm
Admission: adult £4.90, child (5–18 yrs) £3.40, OAP
£4.25, party rates available
♿ many surfaces are very uneven
🚩 advance notice required 🐎

S.A. WETHERBEE

Herb nursery

Devon Herbs, Thorn Cottage, Burn Lane, Brentor,
Tavistock, Devon PL19 0ND
☎ Mary Tavy (082281) 285

*A small, specialist, retail herb nursery
growing culinary, aromatic and decorative
herbs. Owner is also a Home Economist and
during winter months runs short courses
related to food and gardening.*

Take the Tavistock–Lydford road, leaving Tavistock
at Bedford Square. 1 mile past Brentor Inn turn
right, signposted N. Brentor. At sharp bend go
straight on (Burn Lane), car park ¼ mile on the
right hand side.

Open 1 April–30 Sept Fri, Sat, Sun and Bank Holidays
11.00am–5.00pm
Free admission
♿ 🐎

► TEIGNMOUTH ◄

REDDAWAYS FARM CIDER

Making of cider and scrumpy

Lower Rixdale, Luton, Ideford, Newton Abbot, South
Devon
☎ Teignmouth (0626) 775218

*The cider is traditionally made on the farm
from apples grown in the farm's own
orchards, a sideline to a working mixed
farm.*

2 miles off the A380, halfway between Exeter and
Torbay
Open all year Mon–Sat 9.00am–6.00pm
Free admission
♿ 🐍

► TIVERTON ◄

CLARKS FARM CIDER

Cider farm

Shortridge Hill, Seven Crosses, Tiverton, Devon
EX16 8HH
☎ Tiverton (0884) 252632

*Shortridge Hill is a small farm in the hills
above the Exe valley, where sheep, cattle,
ducks and chickens are reared naturally and
cider is made on an ancient cider press.*

Off the A396, 3 miles south of Tiverton, ½ mile
from Bickleigh. Follow country road for 3 miles
Open by appointment only
Free admission
♿ 🐎

DEVONSHIRE CENTRE

**Watermill, leisureland, with country walks and
farming activities**

Bickleigh Mill, nr Tiverton, Devon EX16 8RG
☎ Bickleigh (08845) 419

Restored working watermill adapted to the production and sale of craftwork. Heritage Farm, Shire horses and rare breeds; otter and fishing centres. Agricultural and Motor museums; bird gardens; childrens leisure area, picnic centre with service shop.

At Bickleigh on the A396, between Exeter (9 miles) and Tiverton (4 miles)
Open daily, April–Dec: 10.00am–6.00pm; Jan–March Sat and Sun only 10.00am–5.00pm
Free admission to shops and restaurants. To visit all attractions: adult £3.00, child £2.00, reduced rates for pre-booked parties
& 🚍 🛏

EVELEIGH JERSEY DAIRY PRODUCE

Dairy produce farm

Eveleighs, Cruwys Morchard, Tiverton, Devon EX16 8LB
☎ Tiverton (0884) 257510

Clotted cream from a pedigree Jersey herd.

5 miles west of Tiverton on the A373 South Molton road
Open all year
Free admission
& 🛏

GRAND WESTERN CANAL

Canal walk

c/o Property Dept, County Hall, Exeter, Devon EX2 4QQ
☎ Exeter (0392) 77977

Linear country park which stretches 11 miles between the Tiverton Canal Basin to Lowdeswell near Westleigh on the Somerset border and acquired by the County Council in 1974.

Well signed from the town centre
Open all year
Free admission
& 🚍 🛏

HIGHFIELD VINEYARDS

Vineyards and winery

Long Drag Hill, Tiverton, Devon EX16 5NF
☎ Tiverton (0884) 256362

The vineyard commands wonderful views across Tiverton towards Taunton Deane and the Wellington Monument. Specializing in the early ripening varieties Siegerrebe and Madeleine Angevime; the wines are made on the estate.

Clearly signposted on the road from Tiverton to Witheridge
Open all year Mon–Sat 10.00am–6.00pm. Closed Sundays
Free admission, conducted tours 50p per person
& regrettably the vineyard is not suitable for wheelchairs
🚍 only small minibuses 🛏

SOUTHWICK COUNTRY HERBS

Herb centre, garden and craft shop

Southwick Farm, Nomansland, nr Tiverton, Devon EX16 8NW
☎ Tiverton (0884) 861099

Herb centre, garden, craft shop,garden accessories and tea shop.

Off the B3137 Tiverton–Witheridge road, 2 miles before Witheridge. Turn right at Mountpleasant public house, then first left: about 400 yds at end of lane
Open Mon–Sat 10.00am–5.30pm, Sun 11.00am–5.30pm
Free admission
& 🚍 advance notice required 🛏

TIVERTON CRAFT CENTRE

Craft centre

1 Bridge St, Tiverton, Devon
☎ Tiverton (0884) 258430

The largest display of locally handmade crafts in the south west.

Take the A396 Exeter Road out of Tiverton. Craft centre on Exe bridge overlooking the river
Open all year 9.00am–5.30pm except Sundays
Free admission
& 🚍 advance notice required 🛏

▶ ## TOPSHAM ◀

THE REAL FOOD COMPANY

Farmhouse delicatessen and bakery

28 Fore St, Topsham, Exeter, Devon EX3 0HD
☎ Exeter (0392) 875556

A period shop and traditional bakery which also sells a good selection of local cheeses. All available to eat with a fine selection of teas and coffees.

In the town of Topsham
Open Mon–Sat 9.00am–5.30pm, Sun 10.00am–5.30pm
Free admission
& 🚍 🛏

► TORPOINT ◄

ANTONY WOODLAND GARDEN

Country garden and woodland walks

c/o GA Property Services, Fox House, Whimpe St,
Plymouth, Devon PL1 2DN
☎ Plymouth (0752) 260011

*100 acres of woodland gardens and natural
woodland bordering the River Lynher
Estuary, featuring extensive walks with a
variety of flowering shrubs and trees,
numerous wild flowers and birds.*

5 miles west of Plymouth via Torpoint car ferry, 2
miles north west of Torpoint, north of the A374
Open for the garden: March–June and Aug–Oct; walks:
March–Oct Mon–Sat 11.00 am–5.30pm, Sun 2.00–
5.30pm
Admission: adult £1.00, child (under 16) 50p
& ▦ ✗

► TOTNES ◄

LOTUS POTTERY

Pottery workshop

Paignton Rd, Stoke Gabriel, nr Totnes, Devon TQ9 6SL
☎ Stoke Gabriel (080 428) 303

*Michael Skipwith specializes in hand thrown
wood fired stoneware plant pots for house
and garden, together with a range of
stoneware for cooking and servng food.*

4 miles from Totnes or Paignton off the A385
Totnes–Paignton road
Open daily 9.00am–1.00pm, 2.00–5.30pm. Saturday by
appointment
Free admission
& ▦ advance notice required ✗

RIVERFORD FARM SHOP

Farm shop

Riverford Farm, Staverton, Totnes, Devon TQ9 6AF
☎ Staverton (080 426) 523

*Organic food shop; additive-free meat and
vegetable; local cheeses.*

Halfway between Totnes and Buckfastleigh on the
A384
Open Easter–Christmas Mon–Sat 9.30am–6.00pm, Sun
10.30am–4.30pm
Free admission
& ▦ ✗

► WINKLEIGH ◄

WHEATLAND FARM

Farm interpretation centre and cheese dairy

Winkleigh, Devon EX19 8DJ
☎ WInkleigh (0837) 83361

*A working dairy farm where you can watch
cheese making (some days 7.00–10.00am)
through viewing windows. A nature trail
wanders through a forgotten wetland.*

From the B3220 at Winkleigh travel from Berners
crossroads 1 mile towards Chulmleigh
Open daily for sale of cheese: 9.00am–dark. Interpretation
centre opens Easter–Sept. Wed–Sun 10.00am–6.00pm.
Guided tours for schools booking only, please
telephone
Free admission, guided tours available for schools at 50p
per pupil
& many slopes and steps
▦ No turning for coaches ✗

DORSET

Dorset has remained a quiet and rural county, its villages with their distinctive thatched and limewashed cottages, village greens and ponds remain tucked away along remote lanes, no major roads have disturbed their peace. Along the coast the unspoilt chalk cliffs have been fashioned by the sea into notable and often spectacular formations such as the natural arch at Durdle Door.

Crafts of every description from jewellery and porcelain to wood-turning and leathercraft can be seen being fashioned at many venues throughout the area, many have tea rooms too. Farm and dairy museums, a sawmill and a watermill, a working forge and a heavy horse centre, a rare breeds centre and a sea life centre, a bee breeding centre, historic houses, country parks and gardens are among the many attractions open for visits in the Dorset countryside.

▶ **ABBOTSBURY** ◀

DANSEL GALLERY

Craft centre

Rodden Row, Abbotsbury, Dorset, DT3 4JL
☎ Abbotsbury (0305) 871515

Dansel Gallery occupies a restored thatched stable block over 300 years old where it specializes in contemporary designer woodwork including desk accessories, kitchen items, one-off individual pieces and furniture.

On the B3157 Weymouth–Bridport road, 8 miles west of Weymouth
Open Jan–Dec daily 10.00am–5.00pm
Free admission and car park
& ᕫ ✦

▶ **BEAMINSTER** ◀

BROADWINDSOR CRAFT CENTRE

Craft centre and restaurant

Broadwindsor, Beaminster, Dorset DT8 3PX
☎ Broadwindsor (0308) 68362

Family-run business where old farm buildings have been converted to workshops. Gallery, restaurant and workshops where craftsmen are at work; Pottery, woodturning, upholstery, crystals and minerals.

On the B316 from Beaminster
Open April–23 Dec daily 10.00am–5.00pm
Free admission
& ᕫ advance notice required ✦

EELES FAMILY POTTERY

Ceramic showroom

The Shepherd's Well Pottery, Mosterton, Beaminster, Dorset DT8 3HN
☎ Broadwindsor (0308) 68257

Woodfired earthenware, stoneware and porcelain. Thrown, finished and decorated by hand in a wide variety of glazes and finishing techniques: large and small individual pieces.

On the A3066, 3 miles north of Beaminster
Open all year except Christmas Day, 9.00am–6.00pm
Free admission
& ✦

▶ **BERE REGIS** ◀

PAWS JEWELLERY

Craft workship

Southbrook Workshop, Bere Regis, nr Wareham, Dorset BH20 7LN
☎ Bere Regis (0929) 471808

Jewellery manufacturers. Encompassing lost-wax casting, silver and gold plating, model making; Diamond and stone setters and diamond merchants all under one roof. Commissions a speciality.

From Poole direction, first left off roundabout into Bere Regis, sharp left hand corner to Bovington, Royal Oak public house in front of you, continue for 300 yards, first right after Royal Oak into Elder Road; it is the group of wooden buildings in front of you when turning into Elder Road. Southbrook workshop on top floor of building
Open please ring first for appointment
Free admission
& ✦

▶ **BLANDFORD** ◀

FOXDALE POTTERY

Pottery

Child Okeford, Blandford, Dorset DT11 8EF
☎ Child Okeford (0258) 860039

Small pottery in pretty north Dorset village with hillforts and river. Also sells oak barels and tubs. Working cast iron village pumps and bric-a-brac; small bygones exhibited.

6 miles north of Blandford, off the A350 in centre of village
Open: Shop every day 10.00am–dusk
Admission free
& there is always someone to help (one step)
ᕫ advance notice required ✦

▶ **BRIDPORT** ◀

BRIDFISH LIMITED

Processing and selling fish

Unit 1, Sea Road North, Bridport, Dorset DT6 3BD
☎ Bridport (0308) 56306

Company producing and retailing a wide range of fish and meats naturally smoked and without additives. Wines and condiments are available to complement the smoked and fresh foods.

From Bridport take the A3066 to Beaminster, 200 yards on left
Open all year Mon–Fri, 9.00am–5.00pm Sat 9.00am–12.30pm
Free admission
  no disabled toilet facilities
  advance notice required ✖

MANGERTON MILL

17th century watermill, bygones, tea rooms, rainbow trout fishing

Mangerton, Bridport, Dorset DT6 3SG
☎ Powerstock (030885) 321/224

Historic mill in an unspoilt west Dorset hamlet. The watermill has been owned by the family for 65 years; recently restored to working order. Museum of rural bygones; tea room (light lunches & Dorset cream teas a speciality); crafts.

Turn off Bridport to Beaminster A3066, right hand tuning into West Milton/Powerstock road for 1½ miles then turn right down lane into mill.
Open 1 May–Spring Bank Holiday daily 2.30–5.30pm; Spring Bank Holiday–Sept daily 11.00am–5.30pm. Closed Mondays except Bank Holidays
Admission: £1.00
  advance notice required 🐕

S MOORES

Biscuit, bakery and retail shop

Morcombelake, Bridport, Dorset DT6 6ES
☎ Chideock (0297) 89253

The public are welcome to wander through this 110 year old bakery to see biscuits being made. There is a retail shop which also sells local foods, and a gallery of local paintings.

4 miles west of Bridport on south side of the A35 in village of Morcombelake
Open Jan–Dec Mon–Fri 9.00am–5.00pm
Free admission
  limited parking space ✖

OLD FARMING COLLECTION

Farming museum, farm visit and old sawmill

Bredy Farm, Burton Bradstock, Bridport, Dorset DT6 4ND
☎ Burton Bradstock (0308) 897229

Active dairy and arable farm, milking in the afternoons.

Between Burton Bradstock and Litton Cheney off the B3157
Open Whitsun–Sept daily 10.00am–5.30pm. Closed Sundays
Admission: adult £1.00, child 50p, OAP 70p, party rates available
    advance notice required ✖

STREATFIELD HOOD & CO LTD

Farm shop

Denhay Farm, Broadoak, Bridport, Dorset DT6 5NP
☎ Bridport (0308) 22770/22717

Farmhouse cheddar made and sold. Members of Dorset Harvest, a group promoting quality food and drink made locally, the Farm Shop stocks a range of these products as well as their own cheese and butter.

Take the B3162 out of Bridport towards Broadwindsor. After 2 miles turn left to Broadoak, and in village take second turning on the left, signposted
Open all year Mon & Thur 9.30am–5.00pm, closed Bank Holidays
Free admission
  ✖

▶ CHRISTCHURCH ◀

MAC PENNYS NURSERIES

Woodland garden with nursery

Bransgore, Christchurch, Dorset BH23 8DB
☎ Bournemouth (0425) 72348

17 acre traditional nursery (est. 1937) including 4 acre Woodland Gardens converted from gravel pits. Large selection of herbaceous plants, trees and shrubs; many rare and unusual plants on sale.

Take the B3347 north out of Christchurch, turn right at Winkton, we are approx 3½ miles on the right hand side. Approx 5 miles north east of Christchurch
Open Mon–Sat 9.00am–5.00pm, Sun 2.00–5.00pm
Free admission, but voluntary contributions to National Gardens' Scheme welcomed
    advance notice required 🐕

▶ DORCHESTER ◀

DORSET COUNTY MUSEUM

Rural museum

High West Street, Dorchester, Dorset DT1 1XA
☎ Dorchester (0305) 262735

Prize winning museum concerned with anything in Dorset. Its archaeological, geological, Natural History and literary collections have international significance and the Thomas Hardy Collection is renowned world wide.

A35 (town centre)
Open Mon–Sat 10.00am–5.00pm
Admission: adult £.1.50, child/OAP 75p
& ⛺ ♞

FLOWERS FARM TROUT LAKES

Trout farm and farm trails

Flowers Farm, Hillfield, Dorchester, Dorset DT2 7BA
☎ Cerne Abbas (03003) 351

Situated in attractive countryside with views of the Blackmore Vale with varied walks to the Bacombe Downs for non-anglers. Winner of two Nature Conservation awards.

Off the A37 midway between Dorchester and Yeovil, or off the A352 from Sherborne
Open March–Jan daily 5.30am–dusk
Admission: all day (4 fish) £15.00, half day (3 fish) £11.00, evening (2 fish) £8.00 (possible increase 1991)
& cars can park at lakeside but toilet is some way from lakes ♞

MINTERNE GARDENS

Country garden

Minterne Magna, nr Dorchester, Dorset DT2 7AU
☎ Cerne Abbas (0300) 341370

Woodland garden landscaped in the 18th century featuring lakes, cascades and streams. Spring bulbs, important collection of rhododendrons, summer flowering shrubs and autumn colouring.

On the A352, 9 miles north of Dorchester, 10 miles south of Sherborne
Open 1 April–31 Oct daily 10.00am–7.00pm
Admission: adult £2.00, accompanied children under 16 free
& paths very difficult for wheelchairs ⛺ ♞

▶ GILLINGHAM ◀

THE DORSET RARE BREEDS CENTRE

Craft centre, farming and dairy museum, tea room

Park Farm, Gillingham, Dorset SP8 5JG
☎ Gillingham (07476) 2169

At the head of the Blackmore Vale, the centre houses a unique collection of old breeds of cattle, sheep, pigs, poultry and horses. Childrens farmyard; dairy demonstrations daily. Dorset cream teas a speciality.

½ mile outside Gillingham on the B3081 Shaftesbury–Gillingham road. Clearly signposted
Open April–Sept daily 10.00am–6.00pm
Admission: adult £2.00, child/OAP £1.50
& ⛺ ♞

SUE HARVEY LEATHERWORK

Saddlery and leathercraft workshop

Four Winds, West Bourton, Gillingham, Dorset SP8 5PE
☎ Bourton (0747) 840741

As Blackmore Vale Saddlery, we provide traditional saddlery workshop services. Also belts and hand-tooled leather accessories in a coordinating range of colours; bellows made and repaired.

On the B3081, 3 miles north of Gillingham
Open Mon–Sat 9.00am–6.00pm, other times by appointment – please telephone before making a special journey
Free admission
& no toilets ⛺ by appointment ♞

▶ MILTON ABBAS ◀

PARK FARM MUSEUM

Farm shop, craft centre, country walk, farming museum and country park

Milton Abbas, Blandford, Dorset DT11 0AX
☎ Milton Abbas (0258) 880216

Friendly farm with lovely views to the coast. Many young animals to touch and feed, pony and tractor/trailer rides on Sundays and school holidays, tea room and shop. Also a collection of chimney pots by the Rev V Fletcher.

Take the A354 Blandford–Puddletown road and turn off at Winterborne Whitechurch or Milborne St Andrew
Open April–Oct daily 10.00am–6.00pm. Sundays only in winter
Admission: adult £2.00, child 50p
 ♿ 🚌 🐎

► LYME REGIS ◄

EELES FAMILY POTTERY

Ceramic showroom

The Pot Shop, 56 Broad St, Lyme Regis, Dorset.

Woodfired earthenware, stoneware and porcelain. Thrown, finished and decorated by hand in a wide variety of glazes and finishing techniques: large and small individual pieces.

In Lyme Regis
Open Mon–Sat 9.30am–5.30pm.
Free admission
 ♿ 🐎

► POOLE ◄

BROWNSEA ISLAND

Country walk

Poole Harbour, Dorset BH15 1EE
☎ Canford Cliffs (0202) 707744

500 acre heath and woodland island with magnificent views of the Dorset coast. 200 acre nature reserve with sika deer and red squirrels, managed by Dorset Trust for Nature Conservation, guided parties at fixed times.

Passenger ferry from Poole Quay and Sandbanks
Open 1 April–end Sept daily 10.00am–8.00pm or dusk if earlier (check times of last boat). Oct limited opening telephone to check
Admission: landing fee £1.50; family ticket £4.00 (2 adults, 2 children) available April, May, June and Sept. Parties £1.30 by written arrangement with Warden (1990 prices)
 ♿ 🐎

UPTON COUNTRY PARK

Country park

Upton, Poole, Dorset BH17 7BJ
☎ Poole (0202) 672625

Formal gardens lead into farmland, woodland and down to the shoreline. 3 nature trails explore the Park; displays and exhibitions in the Countryside Heritage Centre. Tea rooms.

Off the A35, 4 miles north west of Poole town centre
Open daily 9.00am–dusk
Free admission (except for special events)
♿ 🚌 advance notice required – permission may be refused at busy times 🐎

► PUDDLETOWN ◄

IVY COTTAGE GARDEN

Country garden with plants for sale

Ivy Cottage, Aller Lane, Ansty, Dorchester, Dorset, DT2 7PX
☎ Milton Abbas (0258) 880053

An informal cottage garden with a small sparkling stream running through its centre, specializing in unusual perennials and moisture-loving plants. Raised beds for alpines. Good vegetable garden.

12 miles north of Dorchester, take the A354 from Puddletown to Blandford, after Blue Vinney Inn take first left signed Dewlish/Cheselbourne. Through Cheselbourne to Ansty, first right before Fox Inn
Open April–end Oct every Thur 10.00am–5.00pm, also 4 Sundays for the National Gardens Scheme. Parties by appointment only
Admission: adult £1.00, child 20p
♿ 🚌 advance notice required 🐎

► SHAFTESBURY ◄

THE CAMELOT CRAFT GROUP

Craft centre

The Town Hall, Shaftesbury, Dorset
☎ Shaftesbury (0747) 54027

Fashion goods, needlework, clothes, quilting, jewellery, paintings, pyrography, woodturning, hand painted china, dried flowers, preserves, basket work and chair reseating, toys & dolls houses, all available at modest prices. Home made refreshments and light lunches available.

On the A30, 20 miles west of Salisbury
Open alternate Fridays only from April–Dec 10.30am–
4.30pm (extra days in Aug & Dec). 1st meeting 19
April 1991
Free admisssion
🔥 ⊞ 🏕

HAYGROVE HONEY FARM

Organic gardens and bee breeder

Twyford, Shaftesbury, Dorset, SP7 0JF
☎ Fontmell Magna (0747) 811855

*Demonstrations of organic horticulture,
beekeeping and queen bee breeding by prior
arrangement only. Royal Jelly produced to
specific order only. Those who may be
allergic to bee stings are advised that bees fly
freely in the area.*

Take the A350 south from Shaftewbury to Compton
Abbas, 100 metres south of post office turn
right, after ½ mile turn right at 'T' junction
proceed north, second farm on left after crossing
brook
Open May–Sept 10.00am–5.00pm by appointment only
Free admission
🔥 🏕

STUDIO POTTERY

Craft workshop/showroom

15 Bell St, Shaftesbury, Dorest

*Hand-crafted porcelain and stoneware
designed by Anne Chase, from the tiny and
delicate to large, fascinating forms. Unusual,
and not at all familiar, traditional
potteryware.*

Opposite town centre car park, next to the Arts
Centre
Open April–Christmas (short break late Sept/early Oct)
daily 10.00am–6.00pm except Sun. Open Bank
Holidays
Free admission
🔥 toilet in car park nearby
🏕 small and well behaved

▶ *STURMINSTER NEWTON* ◀

NEWTON FORGE

Forge

Stalbridge Lane, Sturminster Newton, Dorset DT10 2JQ
☎ Sturminster Newton (0258) 72407

*Forge making fire baskets, canopies, screens,
gates, railings and all traditionally forged
ironwork.*

On the A357 Sherborne–Blandford road. From
Sherborne go past the Red Lion public house,
first left into Stalbridge Lane, ½ mile on the right
Open all year daily 9.00am–5.00pm. Closed Sundays
Free admission
🔥 access to the workshop 🏕

▶ *SWANAGE* ◀

DURLSTON COUNTRY PARK

**Country walk, country park, farm trail and
countryside interpretation centre**

The Information Centre, Durlston Country Park, Swanage,
Dorset BH19 2SL
☎ Swanage (0929) 424443

*Over 260 acres of unspoilt countryside and
coast with clifftop and woodland trails.
Spectacular scenery, butterflies, flowers and
wild birds. Guided walks programme.*

Take the A351 to Swanage, approx 1 mile south of
town centre
Open: Information Centre April–Oct 10.30am–5.30pm,
park all year
Admission: car parking 60p per day, coaches £3.00.
Guided walks adult 80p, child 25p
🔥 ⊞ 🏕

GODLINGSTON MANOR FARM

Farm visits for schools

JC & JM Bowerman, Swanage, Dorset BH19 3DJ
☎ Swanage (0929) 422190

*477 acre rented dairy farm rising 600 feet
from the Wealdon beds to the Bagshot sands.
100 cows, 80 acres of corn and maize and
106 acre SSSI on the hills. For students of
geography up to A level.*

Take the A351 to Swanage, first left after middle
school, 1 mile due north
Open all year for school parties, 10.00am–12.00 noon
and 2.00–4.00pm. Closed Sundays
Admission: £30.00 per group
🔥 ⊞ 🗙

► **WEYMOUTH** ◄

ABBOTSBURY SWANNERY

Nature reserve, craft centre

Abbotsbury, nr Weymouth, Dorset
☎ (0305) 871684

Nature reserve featuring unique colony of Mute Swans, visitors may view nesting swans at very close quarters. Reedbed walk, working duck decoy, free guided tours available on request.

On the B3157 (coast road) between Weymouth and Bridport
Open 1 April–31 Oct daily 9.30am–5.00pm. Winter bookings for groups only, please telephone
Admission: adult £2.00, child 70p, OAP £1.80. 10% discount for pre-booked adult parties (1990 prices)
& ▨ advance notice required ✖

BENNETTS WATER LILY FARM

Country garden, farm shop

Putton Lane, Chickerell, Weymouth, Dorset DT3 4AF
☎ Weymouth (0305) 785150

7 acre site producing aquatic plants and featuring wildlife in abundance: herons, warblers, kingfishers, snipe, woodpeckers, frogs, toads and newts – and of course water lilies. At its best June–August.

3 miles west of Weymouth. Turn off the B3157 at Charlestown Post Office (Spar) – 500 yards down the lane
Open 1 April–30 July daily except Mondays and Sunday afternoons; 1 Aug–30 Aug Tues–Sat only 10.00am–5.00pm
Admission: adult £1.00, child 50p, under 5s free
& toilet door slightly too narrow
▨ advance notice required ✖

SEA LIFE CENTRE

Marine life attraction

Lodmoor Country Park, Weymouth, Dorset DT4 7SX
☎ Weymouth (0305) 788255

Multi-level viewing of exciting marine creatures including octopus and shark. 'Touch' pools featuring starfish and crabs; splashpool, sandpit and play area; picnic area, restaurant and shop.

On the A353, adjacent to the main coach and car park in Weymouth
Open all year daily from 10.00am
Admission: please telephone for details
& all displays accessible by wheelchair ▨ ✖

► **WIMBORNE** ◄

HIGHBURY GARDEN

Botanical garden

Highbury, Woodside Rd, West Moors, Wimborne, Dorset BH22 0LY
☎ Ferndown (0202)874372

Garden of ½ acre in mature setting, first opened in 1910. Many rare and unusual plants, shrubs and conifers in specialist collections. Botanical and horticultural interest with everything labelled.

6 miles east of Wimborne and 8 miles north of Bournemouth in Woodside Road, West Moors, off the B3072 Bournemouth–Vermouth road. Last road at north end of village
Open: The owners regret that due to reconstruction after gales the garden will be open in 1991 only to booked parties, and otherwise as announced
Admission: adult 65p, child 25p, OAPs and parties 45p
& given advance notice a guided tour can be provided for blind persons
▨ advance notice required ✖

KINGSTON LACY

Country walk, historic house

Wimborne Minster, Dorset BH21 4EA
☎ Wimborne (0202) 883402

17th century house with 19th century alterations; set in 13 acres of formal gardens, and woodland walks surrounded by a park of 254 acres with a find herd of Red Devon cattle.

On the B3082 Wimborne–Blandford road
Open 1 April–4 Nov daily except Thur and Fri. House 12.00–5.30pm (last admission 5.00pm); Park 11.30am–6.00pm
Admission to house: £4.00, parties of 20 or over £3.50; Park and Garden: £1.20
& ▨ advance notice required
✖ North Park only

WALFORD MILL CRAFT CENTRE

Craft centre

Stone Lane, Wimborne, Dorset BH21 INL
☎ Wimborne (0202) 841400

Home of the Dorset Craft Guild. Complex with a quality crafts shop, exhibition gallery, workshop area and licensed restaurant in an attractive riverside setting.

Off the B3078, ¼ mile from Wimborne
Open every day except Christmas and New Years Day 10.00am–5.00pm. Closed Mondays Jan–1 April
Free admission and car park
♿ 🚌 advance notice required 🐕

► *VERWOOD* ◄

DORSET HEAVY HORSE CENTRE

Six different breeds of heavy horse

☎ Verwood (0202) 824040

The horses can be seen on parade 3 times a day, or in their stables. Horse drawn farm machinery, working and show harness; pets corner, picnic and play area; gift shop and cafeteria.

Off the B3080, approx 5 miles north of Ringwood
Open Good Friday–31 Oct daily 10.00am–6.00pm. Parades at 11.30am, 2.30 and 4.15pm
Admission: adult £2.25, child (under 14)/OAP £1.75, family ticket (2 adults and 2 children) £7.00, under 3s free. Party rates available
♿ 🚌 🐕

DURHAM

Durham has at its heart Durham city itself with its superb cathedral and castle majestically situated overlooking the River Wear. It is surrounded by the spectacular and rugged scenery of the west Durham moors, the dramatic coastal cliffs to the east, many outstanding beauty spots and the reminders of its industrial and mining past and present, most noticeable in the south-east corner of the county.

Durham is magnificent walking country and there are numerous country walks and picnic areas from which to relish its fine rugged scenery. As well as these diverse walks there are country and fell parks, historic houses and gardens, old quarries and restored lead mines to explore.

► *BISHOP AUCKLAND* ◄

AUCKLAND WALK

Country walk

Director of Environment, Durham County Council, County
Hall, Durham DH1 5UF
☎ Durham (091) 3864411 ext 2355

*Disused railway reclaimed for use by horse
riders (with permits), cyclists and walkers.*

From Bishop Auckland north to Spennymoor
Open at all times
Free admission
♿ ⚞

TOYTOP PICNIC AREA

Picnic area with woodland trail

Director of Environment, Durham County Council, County
Hall, Durham DH1 5UF
☎ Durham (091) 3864411 ext 2355

Play equipment, displays and woodland trail.

Off the A68, 4 miles south of Bishop Auckland
Open at all times
Free admission
♿ ⚞ ⚞

► *CHESTER LE STREET* ◄

WALDRIDGE FELL COUNTRY PARK

Country park

Director of Environment, Durham County Council, County
Hall, Durham DH1 5UF
☎ Durham (091) 3864411 ext 2355

*County Durham's last surviving lowland
heath. A variety of car parks with views and
waymarked footpaths.*

1 mile west of the A167, 1½ miles south west of
Chester le Street
Open at all times
Free Admission
♿ ⚞ advance notice required ⚞

► *CONSETT* ◄

CARRICKS PICNIC AREA

Picnic area with riverside footpath

Director of Environment, Durham County Council, County
Hall, Durham DH1 5UF
☎ Durham (091) 3864411 ext 2355

Off the B6306, 8 miles west of Consett
Open at all times
Free admission
♿ ⚞ advance notice required ⚞

DERWENT WALK COUNTRY PARK

Country park and walks

Director of Environment, Durham County Council, County
Hall, Durham DH1 5UF
☎ Durham (091) 3864411 ext 2355

*Picnic areas and woodland linked by a 10½
mile country walk along a former railway
line.*

The Derwent walk runs alongside the A694 from
Consett to Swalwell (Tyne and Wear) via
Rowlands Gill
Open at all times
Free admission
♿ ⚞ ⚞

EBCHESTER STATION PICNIC AREA

Country walk and picnic area

Director of Environment, Durham County Council, County
Hall, Durham DH1 5UF
☎ Durham (091) 3864411 ext 2355

*Small picnic area alongside the Derwent
Walk, a former railway.*

Off the B6309, 2½ miles north of Consett
Open at all times
Free admission
♿ ⚞

POW HILL COUNTRY PARK

Country park

Director of Environment, Durham County Council, County
Hall, Durham DH1 5UF
☎ Durham (091) 3864411 ext 2355

*Overlooks the Derwent Reservoir. Features a
maze of footpaths and a bird hide.*

Off the B6306, 6 miles west of Consett
Open at all times
Free admission
♿ ⚞ ⚞

ROWLEY STATION PICNIC AREA

Country walk and picnic area

Director of Environment, Durham County Council, County
Hall, Durham DH1 5UF
☎ Durham (091) 3864411 ext 2355

Small picnic area alongside Waskerley Way, a country walk on a disused railway line.

Off the A68, 2 miles south of Consett
Open at all times
Free admission
  ♿ 🐕

SHOTLEY BRIDGE PICNIC AREA

Country walk and picnic area

Director of Environment, Durham County Council,
  County Hall, Durham DH1 5UF
☎ Durham (091) 3864411 ext 2355

Small picnic area alongside Derwent Walk.

Off the B6310, 1½ miles north of Consett
Open at all times
Free admission
  ♿ 🐕

WASKERLEY PICNIC AREA

Country walk with picnic area

Director of Environment, Durham County Council, County
  Hall, Durham DH1 5UF
☎ Durham (091) 3864411 ext 2355

Car park alongside Waskerley Way in Waskerley Village.

2½ miles west of the A68, 4½ miles south west of
  Consett
Open at all times
Free admission
  ♿ 🐕

WASKERLEY WAY

Country walk

Director of Environment, Durham County Council, County
  Hall, Durham DH1 5UF
☎ Durham (091) 3864411 ext 2355

Disused railway over the Durham moors reclaimed for use by horse riders (with permits), cyclists and walkers.

From Templetown, Consett, 6½ miles south west
  towards Stanhope
Open at all times
Free admission
  ♿ 🐕

WHITEHALL PICNIC AREA

Country walk and picnic area

Director of Environment, Durham County Council, County
  Hall, Durham DH1 5UF
☎ Durham (091) 3864411 ext 2355

A small car park alongside the Waskerley Way.

½ mile west of the A68, 2½ miles south of Consett
Open at all times
Free admission
  ♿ 🐕

► **DARLINGTON** ◄

DARLINGTON MUSEUM

Beekeeping displays and museum

Tubwell Row, Darlington, County Durham DL1 1PD
☎ Darlington (0325) 463795

Local museum with natural history, agricultural, veterinary and beekeeping displays. Observation of beehive summer only.

In town centre, 100 yards east of town clock
Open all year, Mon–Fri 10.00am–6.00pm except Thurs
  10.00am–1.00pm, Sat 10.00am–5.30pm, closed for
  lunch 1.00–2.00pm. Closed Christmas, Boxing Day,
  New Year, Good Friday and May Day Bank Holidays
Free admission
♿ suitable ground floor only
🚌 advance notice required. No museum parking
🐕 except guide dogs

► **DURHAM** ◄

BEAMISH, THE NORTH OF ENGLAND OPEN AIR MUSEUM

Museum of social, industrial and agricultural history of Northern England

Beamish, County Durham DH9 0RG
☎ (0207) 231811

An open air museum in 200 acres which vividly recreates life in the North of England around the turn of the century in The Town, The Colliery Village, The Railway station and Home Farm.

Signposted from the A1 (M) south of Newcastle
Open Nov–March daily 10.00am–5.00pm. Closed
  Mondays
Admission: adult £4.00–£4.50, child/OAP £3.00–3.50.
  Party rates available
 ♿ 🕷

BRANDON-BISHOP AUCKLAND WALK

Country walk

Director of Environment, Durham County Council, County
  Hall, Durham DH1 5UF
☎ Durham (091) 3864411 ext 2355

*Disused railway reclaimed for use by horse
riders (permit required), cyclists and
walkers.*

From Broompark picnic area, 1½ miles west of
  Durham, 9½ miles to Bishop Auckland
Open at all times
Free admission
♿ 🕷

BROOMPARK PICNIC AREA

Country walks and picnic area

Director of Environment, Durham County Council,
  County Hall, Durham DH1 5UF
☎ Durham (091) 3864411 ext 2355

*Picnic area at the junction of the three
country walks, the Lanchester valley walk,
the Deerness valley walk and the Brandon-
Bishop Auckland walk.*

Off the B6302, 1½ miles west of Durham city
  centre
Open at all times
Free admission
♿ 🕷

COCKEN WOOD PICNIC AREA

Picnic area with woodland walks

Director of Environment, Durham County Council, County
  Hall, Durham DH1 5UF
☎ Durham (091) 3864411 ext 2355

*On the riverside opposite Finchale Priory,
access to which is over a bridge.*

2 miles east of the A167, 3 miles north of Durham
Open at all times
Free admission
♿ 🕷

DEERNESS VALLEY WALK

Country walk

Director of Environment, Durham County Council, County
  Hall, Durham DH1 5UF
☎ Durham (091) 3864411 ext 2355

*Disused railway reclaimed for use by horse
riders (with permits), cyclists and walkers.*

From the B6302, 1½ miles west of Durham,
  7 miles south west towards Crook
Open at all times
Free admission
♿ at Broompark Picnic Area 🕷

HOUGALL FARM OPEN DAYS

Farm visit

Durham College of Agriculture & Horticulture, Hougall,
  Durham DH1 5UF
☎ Durham (091) 3861351

*Discovery trail always open, starts at
Shincliffe Bridge – illustrated boards explain
history. Activities in 1991 include Gardens
Open Day (12 May), Farms Open Day (2
June) and Lambing Sunday (3 March).*

On the A177, 1 mile south of Durham
Open June 24th & 25th 19??; gardens 1.30–5.00pm
  Weds
Admission: adult 60p, child 30p, Discovery Trail free
♿ ✖

LANCHESTER VALLEY WALK

Country walk

Director of Environment, Durham County Council, County
  Hall, Durham DH1 5UF
☎ Durham (091) 3864411 ext 2355

*The walk is on a former railway which
follows the River Browney.*

From Broompark picnic area, 1½ miles west of
  Durham, approx 8 miles north west beyond
  Lancaster
Open at all times
Free admission
♿ at Broompark 🕷

PLAWSWORTH SOFT FRUIT

Pick your own

Plawsworth Hall Farm, Chester le Street, Durham
  DH2 3LD
☎ Durham (091) 3710251

5 miles north of Durham just off the A167 towards
Chester le Street
Open July–Aug daily 10.00am–7.00pm
Free admission
 ♿ 🚌 advance notice required ❈

USHAW MOOR PICNIC AREA

Country walk and picnic area

Director of Environment, Durham County Council, County
Hall, Durham DH1 5UF
☏ Durham (091) 3864411 ext 2355

*Small picnic area giving access to the
Deerness Valley walk.*

Off the B6302, 3 miles west of Durham
Open at all times
Free admission
♿ ❈

▶ LANCHESTER ◀

HALL HILL FARM

Farm visit

Lanchester, Durham DH7 0TA
☏ Bishop Auckland (0388) 730300

*A working farm set in beautiful countryside
with woodland and riverside trails. Farm
animals, pets corner, trailer rides.*

On the B6296 nr village of Satley, 3½ miles from
Lanchester
Open 31 March, 1 April, 7 April, Sundays and Bank
Holidays 26 May – 26 Aug. Weekdays by appointment
Admission: adult £1.50, child 75p (1990 prices)
♿ 🚌 advance notice required ❈

MALTON PICNIC AREA

Picnic area with country walks

Director of Environment, Durham County Council, County
Hall, Durham DH1 5UF
☏ Durham (091) 3864411 ext 2355

*Alongside the River Browney and the
Lanchester Valley walk.*

Off the A691, ½ mile south east of Lanchester
Open at all times
Free admission
♿ ❈

▶ MIDDLETON IN TEESDALE ◀

BOWLEES PICNIC AREA

Picnic area, waymarked footpath

Director of Environment, Durham County Council, County
Hall, Durham DH1 5UF
☏ Durham (091) 3864411 ext 2355

Off the B6277, 3 miles west of Middleton in
Teesdale
Open all year daily
Free admission
♿ 🚌 advance notice required ❈

COW GREEN PICNIC AREA

Picnic and walkways

Director of Environment, Durham County Council, County
Hall, Durham DH1 5UF
☏ Durham (091) 3864411 ext 2355

*Overlooks Cow Green reservoir near head of
Teesdale. Walk to waterfall.*

1½ miles west off the B6277, 9 miles north west
of Middleton in Teesdale
Open at all times
Free admission
♿ 🚌 with prior permission ❈

HANGING SHAW PICNIC AREA

Picnic area

Director of Environment, Durham County Council, County
Hall, Durham DH1 5UF
☏ Durham (091) 3864411 ext 2355

Dramatic views and good base for walking.

Off the B6277, 6 miles west of Middleton in
Teesdale
Open at all times
Free admission
♿ ❈

MICKLETON STATION PICNIC AREA

Picnic area

Director of Environment, Durham County Council, County
Hall, Durham DH1 5UF
☏ Durham (091) 3864411 ext 2355

*Small picnic area alongside reclaimed
railway walk.*

Off the B6277, 2 miles south east of Middleton in
Teesdale
Open all the time
Free admission
♿ 🚌 ❈

▶ *PETERLEE* ◀

HASWELL TO HART COUNTRYSIDE WALKWAY

Country walks

Easington District Council, Council Offices, Seaside Lane, Easington, Peterlee, County Durham SR8 3TN
☎ Wearside (091) 527 0501 ext 2304

The Haswell to Hart walkway stretches 9 miles, following the old railway route designed by George Stephenson.The path is not a formally adopted footpath but public access can be gained throughout the year. Picnic tables at various points.

Access at Haswell off the B1280, 3 miles north west of Peterlee; at Castle Eden, off the A19, 1 mile south of Peterlee. Parking at the Castle Eden Masonic Hall. Disabled access at Hesleden and High Hesleden from the B1281, 1½ miles and 2 miles east respectively, from Castle Eden, adjacent to the A19
Open at all times
Free admission
& 🐂

THE ROCKS PICNIC AREA

Picnic area with coastal footpaths

Director of Environment, Durham County Council, County Hall, Durham DH1 5UF
☎ Durham (091) 3864411 ext 2355

Car park near clifftop.

Off the A1086, 3 miles south east of Peterlee
Open at all times
Free admission
& 🚌 advance notice required 🐂

WINGATE QUARRY LOCAL NATURE RESERVE

Local nature reserve

Director of Environment, Durham County Council, County Hall, Durham DH1 5UF
☎ Durham (091) 3864411 ext 2355

Disused quarry which has become a haven for limestone-loving plants. Best visited May and June.
& 🚌 advance notice required 🐂

▶ *ST JOHNS CHAPEL* ◀

WEAVERS (MICHAEL & MARY CROMPTON)

Craft centre

Forge Cottage, Ireshopeburn, Weardale, County Durham DL13 1ER
☎ Weardale (0388) 537346

Workshop, in an old Blacksmith's Forge, situated in the Upper Weardale village of Ireshopeburn. Woven tapestries and wall hangings, hand woven articles and hand decorated china for sale.

1½ miles west on A689
Open daily except Thursday 10.00am–4.00pm
Free admission
& 🚌 advance notice required 🐂

▶ *SEAHAM* ◀

THE COASTAL FOOTPATH OF COUNTY DURHAM

Country walks

Easington District Council, Council Offices, Seaside Lane, Easington, Peterlee, County Durham SR8 3TN
☎ Wearside (091) 527 0501 ext 2304

The walk is part of a coastal footpath being developed along the Durham coastline, an SSSI with spectacular Magnesian Limestone cliffs, Hawthorn Dene is a Nature Reserve managed by the Durham Wildlife Trust.

The Dawdon–Easington section may be accessed off the B1432, 2 miles south of Seaham, and at Foxholes Dene, Easington Colliery adjacent to the B1283, 4 miles south of Seaham. The shorter lengths of path at Blackhall Rocks and Crimdon may be reached from the A1086.
Open at all times
Free admission

▶ *SEDGEFIED* ◀

HARDWICK HALL COUNTRY PARK

Country park

Director of Environment, Durham County Council, County Hall, Durham DH1 5UF
☎ Durham (091) 3864411 ext 2355

18th century landscaped garden with lake. Bird hides, nature trail and arboretum.

Off the A177, ½ mile west of Sedgefield
Open at all times
Free admission
&. ᴝ ᴙ

▶ *SPENNYMOOR* ◀

BYERS GREEN PICNIC AREA

Country walk and picnic area

Director of Environment, Durham County Council, County Hall, Durham DH1 5UF
☎ Durham (091) 3864411 ext 2355

1 mile west of A6074, 1½ miles west of Spennymoor
Open at all times
Free admission
&. ᴙ

▶ *STAINDROP* ◀

RABY CASTLE & GARDENS

Historic house, walled gardens and deer park

Staindrop, Darlington, County Durham DL2 3AH
☎ Staindrop (0833) 60202

Set in a deer park – Raby offers fine furniture, pictures and china as well as a walled garden and collection of horse drawn vehicles. Game, venison, grouse, pheasant on sale as available.

On the A688, between Barnard Castle and Bishop Auckland
Opening times still to be decided
Admission: adults £2.25, child £1.20, OAP £1.75 (1990 prices)
&. ᴝ ᴙ not in castle or gardens (except guide dogs)

▶ *STANHOPE* ◀

BAYBRIDGE PICNIC AREA

Picnic area

Director of Environment, Durham County Council, County Hall, Durham DH1 5UF
☎ Durham (091) 3864411 ext 2355

A riverside site which is a good base for riverside and moorland walks.

½ mile west of B6306, 7 miles north of Stanhope, ¾ mile west of Blanchland
Open at all times
Free admission
&. ᴙ

KILLHOPE WHEEL LEAD MINING CENTRE

Restored lead mine, crushing mill, forest trail and picnic area

Director of Environment, Durham County Council, County Hall, Durham DH1 5UF
☎ Durham (091) 3864411 ext 2355

Open air museum of lead mining through the ages. Staff help visitors to participate.

Alongside the A689, 2½ miles west of Cowshill
Open Easter–Oct daily 10.30am–5.00pm
Admission: adult £1.00, child/OAP 50p, 25% discount for parties
&. ᴝ advance notice required ᴙ

THE WEARDALE MUSEUM OF HIGH HOUSE CHAPEL

Museum

High House Chapel, Ireshopeburn, Weardale, County Durham DL13 1EY
☎ Bishop Auckland (0388) 537417

Displays include The Wesley Room, Weardale Cottage and interpretations of the farms and villages, rocks, minerals and mines, landscape and wildlife, railways, water and industry of the area.

Off the A689, approx 8 miles from Stanhope
Open May–July and Sept Wed, Thur and Sat 1.00–5.00pm, Sun 1.00–4.00pm; please telephone for special appointments
Admission: adult 60p, child 30p

▶ *STANLEY* ◀

BEAMISHBURN PICNIC AREA

Picnic area

Director of Environment, Durham County Council, County Hall, Durham DH1 5UF
☎ Durham (091) 3864411 ext 2355

Picnic area within Beamish Country Park. Mature woodland with a stream running through it, woodland walks, large grassed play area.

½ mile off the A6076, 1 mile north of Stanley
Open at all times
Free admission
 ♿ 🕷

CAUSEY ARCH PICNIC AREA

Country park, picnic area with woodland walks

Director of Environment, Durham County Council, County
Hall, Durham DH1 5UF
☎   Durham (091) 3864411 ext 2355

*Walks to Causey Arch, the world's oldest
railway bridge with interpretive displays
about early wooden wagon ways. Picnic area
within Beamish Country Park.*

Off the A6076, 2 miles north of Stanley
Open at all times
Free admission
♿ 🚒 in special layby on the A6076 🕷

CAUSEY MILL PICNIC AREA

Country park with picnic area

Director of Environment, Durham County Council, County
Hall, Durham DH1 5UF
☎   Durham (091) 3864411 ext 2355

*Picnic area within Beamish Country Park in
a secluded valley alongside a stream.*

½ mile off the A6076, 1½ miles north of Stanley
Open at all times
Free admission
♿ 🕷

EDEN PLACE PICNIC AREA

Country park with picnic area

Director of Environment, Durham County Council, County
Hall, Durham DH1 5UF
☎   Durham (091) 3864411 ext 2355

Picnic area within Beamish Country Park.

Off the A693, 1 mile east of Stanley
Open at all times
Free admission
♿ 🚒 advance notice required 🕷

►   *TOW LAW*   ◄

COLLIER WOOD PICNIC AREA

Picnic area

Director of Environment, Durham County Council, County
Hall, Durham DH1 5UF
☎   Durham (091) 3864411 ext 2355

*Picnic area in an attractive woodland setting
with nature trail.*

Off the A68, 2 miles south of Tow Law
Open at all times
Free admission
♿ 🚒 🕷

HIGH HOUSELOP PICNIC AREA

Picnic area

Director of Environment, Durham County Council, County
Hall, Durham DH1 5UF
☎   Durham (091) 3864411 ext 2355

*Picnic area with a dramatic view over
Weardale and the Durham moors.*

Off the A68, 1½ miles north west of Tow Law
Open at all times
Free admission
♿ 🕷

►   *WOLSINGHAM*   ◄

DEMESNE MILL PICNIC AREA

Picnic area

Director of Environment, Durham County Council, County
Hall, Durham DH1 5UF
☎   Durham (091) 3864411 ext 2355

*Close to the centre of Wolsingham and a
good base for walking. A stream flows
through the site.*

Off the B6296, north side of Wolsingham
Open at all times
Free admission
♿ 🕷

WINDY NOOK PICNIC AREA

Picnic area

Director of Environment, Durham County Council, County
Hall, Durham DH1 5UF
☎   Durham (091) 3864411 ext 2355

Small riverside site with pleasant views.

Off the A689, 1 mile west of Wolsingham
Open at all times
Free admission
♿ 🚒 🕷

ESSEX

Essex is a deceptive county stretching inland from the north bank of the Thames estuary and the North Sea. Almost nowhere in Essex is more than 50 miles from the centre of London and the London Underground 'Tube' system runs well into the south-west of the county. Most people in this country would view Essex as a flat, uninteresting commuter extension of the capital fringed by the 'day tripper' resorts of Southend and Clacton.

The truth is that Essex is a countryside delight of a county which prides itself on maintaining its rural traditions and it offers a wide range of leisure and recreation facilities ranging from working farms and pick-your-own centres, through vineyards, potteries and craft centres to a wealth of rural and agricultural archeology sites and museums. There are many country walks including some through ancient Epping Forest, once a royal hunting reserve and now owned by the Corporation of London.

All within easy access for millions of Londoners.

▶ BILLERICAY ◀

BARLEYLANDS FARM MUSEUM

Farm museum and pick your own

Barleylands Farm, Barleylands Rd, Billericay, Essex CM11 2UD

☎ Basildon (0268) 282090

An extensive collection of vintage farm machinery, tractors and agricultural bygones illustrating the rural life of the past, including a pair of Fowler steam engines and a narrow gauge steam railway.

On the A129 past South Green towards Wickford
Open Oct–March Wed–Sat 11.00am–4.30pm, Sundays 1.00–5.00pm; April–Sept Wed–Sat 11.00am–4.00pm, Sundays 1.00–5.30pm
Admission: adult £2.00, child/OAP £1.00, people in wheelchairs half price
&. ⇔ ✝ narrow gauge railway open certain days

NORSEY WOOD

Country walk and nature reserve

Outwood Common Rd, Billericay, Essex
☎ Billericay (0277) 624553

An ancient woodland of about 164 acres of significant natural and archaeological interest with rare plants. Self guided nature trail and extensive footpath/ride system; picnic area; information centre, toilets.

Entrance off Outwood Common Road, 1 mile east of Billericay
Open all year daily 9.00am–5.00pm weekdays; 9.30am–5.00pm Saturdays; 10.00am–4.30pm Sundays
Free admission
&. although disabled access to woodland walks is restricted ✝

▶ BRAINTREE ◀

BOCKING WINDMILL

Restored windmill

Church St, Bocking, Braintree, Essex
☎ (0376) 25025

Early 18th century post mill in an historic area. Undergoing restoration; machinery in place. Guided tours and school visits by appointment.

1 mile from Braintree on the London–Cambridge road
Open by appointment and advertised open days, please telephone for details
Free admission; donations welcome
&. assistance given at all times ⇔ advance notice required ✝

BOYDELLS FARM

Farm visit and shop

Boydells Farm, Wethersfield, Braintree, Essex CM7 4AQ
☎ Gt Dunmow (0371) 850481

The milking of cows, sheep and goats with everything explained. Sheep and goat milk produce sold. Also there are pigs, poultry, a mini-stallion, a donkey and a goat cart.

On the B0153, 6 miles north of Braintree, between Wethersfield and Shalford
Open end May–Sept; Wed–Sun and Bank Holidays 2.00–5.00pm
Admission: adult £1.50, child 75p
&. ⇔ advance notice required ✗

▶ BRENTWOOD ◀

CALCOTT HALL FARM

Farm shop and pick your own

Ongar Rd, Brentwood, Essex CM15 9HS
☎ Brentwood (0272) 215279

1 mile north of town centre on the A128, on left hand side immediately after bridge over Brentwood bypass (A12)
Open all year for the farm shop: Tues–Sat 9.00am–5.30pm; June–Sept, please telephone for details
Free admission
&. ⇔ advance notice required
✝ in the car park

HARTSWOOD NATURE TRAIL

Country walk

c/o Brentwood District Council, Council Offices, Ingrave Rd, Brentwood CM15 8AY
☎ Brentwood (0277) 261111

Nature trail booklet available from golf shop.

Jct 28 on M25, take the A1023 to Brentwood town centre, followed by the A128 to King George's Playing Fields
Open all year
Free admission
&. ✝

THORNDON COUNTRY PARK (NORTH & SOUTH)

Country park, visitor centre

c/o The Ranger, Thorndon Countryside Centre, The Avenue, Brentwood, Essex CM13 3RX
☎ Brentwood (0277) 211250

The Park comprises 400 acres of ancient woodland, deer pasture, haymeadows, marshland and ponds rich in wildlife. Thorndon North Countryside Centre has informative displays, a schoolroom a coffee/gift shop, toilets and car park.

North: 1 mile south off The Avenue. South: 3 miles south on the A128
Open daily 8.00am–dusk. Countryside Centre daily except Mondays 9.00am–5.00pm
Admission: to car park 80p Sundays and Bank Holidays April–Oct
& ᗏ advance notice required ᛡ

WEALD COUNTRY PARK

Country park, visitor centre

South Weald, nr Brentwood, Essex
☎ Brentwood (0277) 216297

Extensive landscaped deer parkland offering wide variety of facilities for visitors.

1 mile west of Brentwood in South Weald village off the A1023 near A12/M25 Junction
Open daily 8.00am–dusk
Admission car park 60p Sunday and Bank Holidays April–Oct (1989 prices)
& ᗏ ᛡ

▶ *CHELMSFORD* ◀

HYDE HALL GARDEN TRUST

Country garden

Hyde Hall, ettendon, Chelmsford, Essex CM3 8ET
☎ Chelmsford (0245) 400256

A garden with colour and interest for all seasons featuring bulbs, roses old and new, flowering shrubs and trees. Two ponds; greenhouses; herbaceous borders, alpines; refreshments; plants for sale.

Signposted off the A130 Chelmsford–Southend road
Open Wednesdays, Sundays and Bank Holidays 11.00am–6.00pm
Admission: adult £1.50, child free, OAP £1.00
& ᗏ with prior booking ᛡ

KINGS FARM

Farm shop and pick your own

Ford End, Chelmsford, Essex CM3 ILN
☎ Pleshey (024537) 235

Family owned and run farm specializing in high quality soft fruits, apples and pears. Much of the crop sold in the shop or pick your own.

On the A130, 9 miles from Chelmsford, 4 miles from Great Dunmow
Open mid June–Sept daily 9.00am–6.00pm; Oct–mid June Mon–Sat 9.00am–5.00pm
Free admission
& ᗏ advance notice required
ᛡ only on the headland

NEW HALL VINEYARDS

Vineyard

Chelmsford Rd, Purleigh, Chelmsford, Essex CM3 6PN
☎ Maldon (0621) 828343

Wine Festival and Craft Fair last full weekend in September. Vineyard tours.

Off the A12 to the A414, east towards Maldon on to the B1010, 2 miles towards Burnham on Crouch in Purleigh village
Open weekdays 10.30am–5.30pm; weekends 10.30am–1.30pm. Booked tours May–Sept
Free admission for daily visitors, 2–3 hour guided tours £3.50 per person, for 20+ people (1989 prices)
& assistance given if needed
ᗏ advance notice required ᛡ

▶ *COLCHESTER* ◀

BROOK FARM

Farm shop and pick your own

Gt Bentley, nr Colchester, Essex CO7 8QP
☎ Colchester (0206) 250430

Seasonal picking in pleasant surroundings. Farm animals to see in their farmed environment. Including cattle, sheep and an outdoor pig herd. Pleasant surroundings to take a picnic.

Turn right to Great Bently off the A133 Colchester–Clacton road, turn right on the green, half a mile turn right at bottom of hill to Brook Farm Fruit, signposted in season from the A133
Open June–Sept according to fruit ripening dates, 9.00am–5.00pm
Free admission
& ᗏ ᛡ

COLCHESTER MUSEUM

Country life and crafts museum

Social History Museum, Holy Trinity Church, Trinity St,
Colchester, Essex CO1 1JN

☎ Colchester (0206) 712931

Displays illustrating the country life and crafts of the Colchester area, together with items from the town's history, housed in the 14th century church with a saxon tower built C1000 AD.

Take the A12 to Colchester, then town centre
Open Mon–Sat 10.00am–1.00pm and 2.00–5.00pm
Free admission
  🚻 advance notice required ✗

EAST MERSEA PICK YOUR OWN FARM

Farm shop and pick your own

East Mersea Hall, East Mersea, Colchester, Essex
CO5 8TJ

☎ West Mersea (0206) 383215

The farm is ¹/₂ mile from the sea. Craft shop, teas; pick your own flowers for drying a feature.

10 miles south of Colchester, turn left off the
B1025 for East Mersea, farm 2 miles on the left
Open all year daily 9.00am–6.30pm
Free admission
& doors are not wide enough for disabled toilet
facilities. Disabled are helped on PYO, and can drive cars
to crops 🚻 ✗

ESSEX NATURALISTS TRUST

Nature trails and interpretation centre

Fingringhoe Wick Nature Reserve, Fingringhoe,
Colchester, Essex CO5 7DN

☎ (0206) 729678

120 acre nature reserve beside the Colne Estuary with a wide range of wildlife habitats. 8 bird hides; seats, views of saltmarshes, binoculars for hire. Nightingale song in April and May is a highlight.

4 miles south east of Colchester, take the B1025
towards West Mersea, signposted
Open Tues–Sat and Bank Holidays 9.00am–5.00pm
Free admission but donations welcome
& there are 2 bird hides for disabled visitors
🚻 advance notice required ⊦

THE FENS – ANN LUNN

Specialist nursery

Old Mill Rd, Langham, Colchester, Essex CO4 5NU

☎ Colchester (0206) 272259

Nursery specializing in wet and woodland plants, with around 500 varieties for sale. A garden is currently being developed for visitors.

Off the A12, north of Colchester, Old Mill Rd is an
extension to Chapel Rd
Open Thur–Sun 10.00am–5.00pm, daily throughout April.
Please telephone ahead before making a special
journey
Free admission, charity box for St Helena's Hospice,
Colchester
  🚻 parking in a layby within 200 yards of
nursery ✗

NAPIERS FARM

Farm shop, pick your own and herb producers

Colchester Rd, Tiptree, Essex CO5 0EX

☎ Tiptree (0621) 815238

All produce sold is grown on the premises. Herbs are organically grown, and sold freshly cut or as plants. Strawberries and vegetables have the minimum of safe sprays with extended harvest interval.

From Colcheste on the B1022 towards Tiptree and
Maldon. Our drive is on the left on the last sharp
bend after woods on the edge of Tiptree.
Open Tues–Sat all year, daily May–July
Free admission
  🚻 by appointment only ⊦

THE NATIONAL TRUST

One of the oldest and largest timber framed buildings in the world

The Grange Barn, Grange Hill, Coggeshall, Colchester,
Essex CO6 1RE

☎ Braintree (0376) 562226

Off the A120 approx 6 miles from Braintree and 8
miles from Colchester
Open 31 Mar–31 Oct Tues, Thur, Sun & Bank Holiday
Mons 1.00–5.00pm
Admission: adult 50p, child 25p (1990 prices)
& ✗

OLIVERS ORCHARD LIMITED

Farm shop and pick your own

Olivers Lane, off Gosbecks Rd, Shrub End, Colchester, Essex CO2 0HH
☎ Colchester (0206) 330208

Roman River Valley conservation zone and countryside centre. Cream teas, barn suppers, farm tours by appointment. Cider bar, apple juice sold straight from the press in autumn; cafe; adventure playground.

From Colchester take the B1022 Maldon road and turn left after 3 miles at the Leather Bottle public house, 500 yards on the right
Open: Farm shop & PYO Jun–Dec; daily 9.00am–dusk; cafe & cider bar June–Sept daily 10.30am–5.30pm
Free admission
& personal assistance by friendly staff available 🚌 🏕

PEARTREE FARM FOODS

Farm shop and speciality food and drink producer

High Birch, Weeley Heath, nr Clacton-on-Sea, Essex CO16 9BY
☎ Weeley (0255) 830921

Peartree produce a wide range of traditional products, from prize winning sausages and hams to old style sweet pickle, bacon and crusty pork pies, from their own farm reared pork.

On leaving the A12, take the A120 then theA133 towards Clacton. Turn right at Weeley War Memorial towards Great Bentley. High Birch Road is ½ mile on the left
Open all year Thurs & Fri 9.00am–4.00pm, Sat 9.00am–12.30pm
Free admission
& parking and access to the shop can be assisted by staff
🚌 advance notice required 🏕

THE ROMAN RIVER COUNTRYSIDE CENTRE

Countryside interpretaion centre and country walks

c/o Olivers Orchard, Olivers Lane, Colchester, Essex CO2 0HH
☎ Colchester (0206) 712476/331369

5 circular walks and a small reference library.

From Colchester take the B1022 Maldon road, turn left after 3 miles at Leather Bottle public house and follow signs to 'Roman River Centre'

Open April–Sept weekends and Bank Holidays 2.00–5.00pm
Free admission
& there are no disabled toilet facilities 🚌 🏕

◄ **EPPING** ►

EPPING BURY FRUIT FARM CENTRE

Farm shop, pick your own strawberries, farm trail, farm animals, interpretation centre, country walk

Upland Rd, Epping Upland, Epping, Essex CM16 5SA
☎ Epping (0378) 78400

Rare breeds of sheep, goats, cattle, pigs, geese, ducks, turkeys, and over 20 breeds of free ranging chickens. Collect the eggs, milk a goat, feed the pigs: all friendly and approachable. Education and activity centre for school parties.

Signposted 'Fruit Farm Centre' from Epping (2½ miles)
Open daily 9.30am–6.00pm
Admission: adults £1.50, child £1.00
& 🚌 🏕

◄ **FRINTON-ON-SEA** ►

PARK FRUIT FARM

Pick your own and farm shop

Great Holland, Frinton-on-Sea, Essex CO13 0ES
☎ Frinton (0255) 674621

Over 20 varieties of apples over the season. Fresh pressed untreated apple juice differing in flavour according to season, free tasters. Also pears, PYO plums; free range eggs etc.

From Frinton, take the B1032 Clacton-on-Sea road, turn right at the Green Great Holland (where there is a farm shop sign), mile on right
Open mid Aug–Christmas daily 9.00am–5.00pm, Sunday 10.00am–12.00 noon, 2.00–4.00pm Jan daily 9.00am–5.00pm (not Sundays) until crop sold, usually March
Free admission
& 🚌 🏕

▶ **GRAYS** ◀

LORKINS FARM SHOP

Farm shop and craft centre

Lorkins Farm, Orsett, Essex RM16 3EL
☎ Grays Thurrock (0375) 891439

Elizabethan farmhouse and traditional farm buildings where children are invited to feed the chickens with poultry food supplied free. Florist and dried flower specialist; unusual gifts; fresh vegetables and home made cakes and preserves.

Off the A128, 1 mile north of Orsett village
Open all year daily (except Mondays) 9.00am–6.00pm
Free admission
& easy access to shop, but there is a step into the toilet which is not easily negotiated with a wheelchair
🚗 advance notice preferred 🐕

▶ **HALSTEAD** ◀

CASTLE HEDINGHAM POTTERY

Pottery

The Pottery, St James Street, Castle Hedingham, Essex
CO9 3EW
☎ Hedingham (0787) 60036

Small working pottery specializing in domestic stoneware, displayed in beautiful Maltings Showroom. Items to order including house signs to your design sent by post for £27.00. Talks and demonstraions to groups/schools.

Take the A604 north from Halstead, after 3 miles turn right onto the B1058 into Castle Hedingham
Open daily except Mondays 10.00am–6.00pm
Free admission
& 🚗 🐕

FULLERS DAIRY

Farm dairy

Brickwall Farm, Sible Hedingham, Halstead, Essex
CO9 3RH
☎ Hedingham (0787) 60329

60 acre dairy farm in the Colne Valley with 75 Pedigree Jersey cows (with Elite Herd Health Status) plus followers. Producing home made ice-cream, cheesecakes, Jersey cream yoghurts and soft cheeses, all available at the farm shop.

On the A604, the Braintree end of Sible Hedingham, 3 miles from Halstead, 7 miles from Braintree
Open for the farm shop: 9.00am–6.00pm daily, except Sundays 9.30am–12.30pm
Free admission
& 🐕

▬ **ILFORD** ▬

ALDBOROUGH HALL FARM SHOP

Pick your own and farm shop

Aldborough Hatch, Ilford, Essex IG2 7TD
☎ (01 597) 6540 ansaphone

Family run farm with a wide range of soft fruit and vegetables, PYO or ready picked. Pet supplies; preserves, eggs, potatoes etc available from shop. Within easy reach of London. Ample car parking.

½ mile north of the A12 at Aldborough Rd traffic lights. Farm is on the right of Aldborough Rd North next to the Dick Turpin Restaurant
Open Tues–Sat 9.00am–5.00pm, Sunday 10.00am–2.00pm (longer hours during PYO season)
Free admission
& 🚗 by appointment 🐕

▶ **MALDON** ◀

MALDON DISTRICT COUNCIL

Riverside and country walks, riverside park

Council office, Princes Rd., Maldon, Essex CM9 7DL
☎ Maldon (0621) 854477

Leaflet available from the above address for more information.

On the A414, midway between Chelmsford and Colchester on the river Blackwater
Open all year
Free admission, car parking charge
& 🚗 🐕

▶ **NAZEING** ◀

ADA COLE MEMORIAL STABLES

Rescue sanctuary for distressed equines (horses, ponies, donkeys, mules)

Broadlands, Broadley Common, nr Nazeing, Waltham Abbey, Essex EN9 2DH
☎ Nazeing (099 289) 2133

A living, serving memorial to a pioneer campaigner for legislation to protect equines. Rehabilitation and fostership is undertaken. Stableyard giftshop.

On the B181 at Broadley Common, between Nazeing and Harlow
Open daily 2.00–5.00pm
Free admission
& ⛟ advance notice required 🛉

► **ROMFORD** ◄

WELLGATE COMMUNITY FARM

Farm visit, farm shop and craft centre

Collier Row Rd, Romford, Essex RM5 2DD
☎ (01 599) 0415

Visit or become involved with this community farm: a bridge between town and country with educational facilities, animals, vegetables and herbs.

Off the A1112, 2 miles north of Chadwell Heath or the B174, 1½ miles south west of Collier Row
Open weekdays 9.00am–2.00pm, Sat 9.00am–4.00pm, Sun 9.00am–12.00 noon
Free admission for visits, donations welcomed.
& ⛟ advance notice required ✗

► **STANSTED** ◄

MOUNTFITCHET CASTLE

Re-constructed Norman castle and village

Stansted, Essex CM24 8SP
☎ Bishop's Stortford (0279) 813237

Re-constructed motte and bailey castle and village of 1066 with animals roaming freely; siege weapons; various houses; wax figures, (some animated). Free lecture tapes available, worksheets at a nominal cost.

2 miles from jct 8 of the M11
Open 17 March–10 Nov daily 10.00am–5.00pm (in 1991). Parites of over 20 must book
Admission: adult £3.00, child/OAP £2.00
& ⛟ advance notice required 🐕

► **THAXTED** ◄

GLENDALE FORGE

Forge with wrought ironwork for sale

Mond St., Thaxted, Essex CM6 2NR
☎ Thaxted (0371) 830 466

Forge with wrought ironwork for sale in showroom and a small collection of half sized vehicles which includes Stephenson's locomotive, Rocket.

Off the B184, 1½ miles south of Thaxted
Open all year (except Bank Holidays), Mon–Fri 9.00am–5.00pm; closed Saturdays; Sundays 10.00am–12.00 noon
Free admission
& ⛟ by appointment 🛉

THAXTED WINDMILL

Windmill and museum

c/o Hon Sec Mark Arman, Hanna's Bolford, Thaxted, Essex CM6 2PY
☎ Thaxted (0371) 830366

Windmill where the fantail turns the cap and sails to the wind; main machinery is intact. Rural museum on 2 floors; picnic area; sales table has cards, badges, drawings engravings etc.

200 yards from the church
Open May–Sept, weekends and Bank Holidays 2.00–6.00pm
Admission: adult 40p, child 10p
& ⛟ and school parties allowed with advance notice 🛉

► **UPMINSTER** ◄

UPMINSTER TITHE BARN AGRICULTURAL AND FOLK MUSEUM

Farming museum and shop

Hall Lane, Upminster, Essex RM14 1AU
☎ Hornchurch (04024) 47535

Domestic and other exhibits in a large 15th century barn.

Between Upminster BR underground station and the A127 (Southend arterial road)
Open from the first weekend April–Oct 1.30–6.00pm or by appointment
Free admission
& ⛟ ✗

► *WALTHAM ABBEY* ◄

EPPING FOREST DISTRICT MUSEUM

Local history museum

39/41 Sun St, Waltham Abbey, Essex EN9 1EL
☎ Lea Valley (0992) 716882

Lively local history museum in adjacent timber framed houses c.1520 and c.1760 in Waltham Abbey's Conservation Area. Special exhibitions, events, and activities; museum shop; refreshments; garden.

Easy access from M11 and M25
Open all year, Fri–Mon 2.00–5.00pm, Tues 12.00
noon–5.00pm, Wed & Thur party bookings only
Free admission
& ground floor only suitable for wheelchairs, no
disabled toilet facilities at present
🚌 coach park in town 🐕 except guide dogs

LEE VALLEY COUNTRYSIDE CENTRE

Country walk and countryside centre

Abbey Farmhouse, Crooked Mile, Waltham Abbey, Essex
EN9 1QX
☎ Waltham Abbey (0992) 713838

An information point with displays about the history, countryside, waterways, events and schools programmes at the Park which stretches 23 miles northwards from the East End of London to Ware in Hertfordshire.

At the junction of the A121 and the B194, off the
Crooked Mile roundabout
Open Easter–Sept daily 10.00am–5.00pm, check for
winter hours
Free admission
& 🚌 🐾 🐕

► *WITHAM* ◄

LODGE FARM

Pick your own

Hatfield Rd, Witham, Essex CM8 1EJ
☎ Witham (0376) 512009

Pick soft fruit and broad beans in this compact and well tended field (boxes provided or bring your own) or phone your order for freshly picked fruit. Picnic area.

South of Witham on the B1389, between Lynfield
Motors and the Jack and Jenny public house
Open daily in the summer 10.00am–6.00pm
Free admission
& 🚌 🐕

GLOUCESTERSHIRE

Gloucestershire is dominated in the east by the Cotswolds where peaceful villages of mellow, honey-coloured Cotswold stone provide inviting resting places for the weary visitor. Perfect country for touring by foot or by car, Gloucestershire is more than just the Cotswolds. The Valley of Berkeley leads down to the Severn valley in the west and the Forest of Dean beyond the Severn offers magnificent walks through its tree-covered hills. Insights into forest life are provided by a museum of forest life whilst open iron mines provide a glimpse of its iron-mining tradition.

Vineyards and wildflower nurseries, farm parks and farm trails, country parks and gardens, falconry centres and butterfly farms, arboretums and country centres, fish farms and pick-your-own centres, craft workshops and potteries, silversmiths and silk printers feature amongst the diverse pursuits that can be enjoyed in the Cotswolds countryside, perhaps whilst touring in a Romany caravan!

► BERKELEY ◄

BERKELEY CASTLE AND BUTTERFLY HOUSE

Historic castle, shops

Berkeley, Gloucestershire GL13 9BQ
☎ Dursley (0453) 810332

England's most historic home. Completed over 840 years ago by Lord Maurice Berkeley at the command of King Henry II and to this day the home of the Berkeleys.

1 mile west of the A38 midway between Bristol and Gloucester
Open April & Sept: Tues–Sun 2.00–5.00pm; May–Aug; Tues–Sat 11.00am–5.00pm, Sundays 2.00–5.00pm; October: Sundays only 2.00–4.30pm, Bank Holiday Mondays 11.00am–5.00pm
Admission: adult £2.90, child £1.45, OAP £2.60, party rates available for booked groups of over 25 (1990 prices)
&. The butterfly house has a ramp at the entrance and the house is also suitable for wheelchairs. Castle not very suitable
🚗 🐕 only in the car park and picnic area

ENGLANDS MILLS

Specialists in stoneground wholemeals

Sea Mills, Berkeley, Gloucestershire GL13 9QR
☎ Dursley (0453) 811150

Stoneground millers providing a variety of flours including organic, country seeded, malted grain, mueslis, whites, pastry and cake. We provide a range of wholefoods including our own muesli bars.

From Gloucester take the A38 south towards Bristol turn right at Berkeley Heath Motors – head into Berkeley and follow signs for Berkeley power station, take sharp left before power station
Open all year Mon–Fri 8.00am–5.00pm, Sat 8.00am–12.00 noon
Admission: £1.00 for coach parties
&. 🚗 advance notice required 🍴

SUMMERS' CIDER

Traditional cider and perry maker

Slimbridge Lane, Halmore, nr Berkeley, Gloucester GL13 9HH
☎ Dursely (0453) 311218

Cider and perry makers using traditional and modern techniques. The range of ciders and perries, matured in oak, may be blended to suit customers requirements.

1½ miles after turning west off the A38 at Prince of Wales hotel to Halmore
Open all year daily except Sundays 9.00am–5.00pm
&. 🚗 🐕

► BIBURY ◄

BIBURY TROUT FARM

Catch your own trout farm

Bibury, nr Cirencester, Gloucestershire GL7 5NL
☎ Bibury (0285 74) 215/212

A fascinating working trout farm. The fish may be fed and there is a small fishery to 'catch your own'. Lovely gifts, shrubs, perennials and herb plants, fresh and smoked trout, all available for sale at the farm shop. Picnic area. Refreshments.

On the B4425, 7 miles east of Cirencester
Open all year. Summer: Mon–Sat 9.00am–6.00pm, Sun 10.00am–6.00pm; winter: Mon–Sat 9.00am–5.00pm, Sun 10.00am–5.00pm
Admission: adult £1.30, child 70p, OAP £1.00, disabled free. Prior booking for parties (1990 prices)
&. 🚗 🐕

► BOURTON-ON-THE-WATER ◄

CHESTNUT GALLERY

Craft gallery

High St, Bourton-on-the-Water, Cheltenham, Gloucestershire GL54 2AN
☎ Cotswold (0451) 20017

Small privately owned gallery specializing in ceramics and blown glass by the country's foremost craftspeople. Also selling woodcarvings, a few prints, and watercolours of local scenes. Crafts Council recommended.

½ mile from the A429, 5 miles north of the A40 at Northleach
Open weekdays 10.00am–5.00pm, Sun & Bank Holidays 11.30am–5.00pm. Closed Mon & Wed, Nov–May
Free admission
&. no lifts or disabled toilet facilities 🚗 🐕

FOLLY FARM – DUCKPOOL VALLEY

Conservation centre, garden centre and gift/souvenir counter

Nr Bourton-on-the-Water, Cheltenham, Gloucestershire
GL54 3BY
☎ Cotswold (0451) 20285

Leading conservation centre with one of the largest collection of rare domestic waterfowl in Europe. Friendly hand-reared animals delight the children; hand feed the ducks and geese. Also well stocked garden centre.

On the A436 Bourton–Cheltenham road, 2½ miles from Bourton-on-the-Water
Open daily 10.00am–6.00pm (or dusk in the winter)
Admission: adult £2.00, child £1.00, OAP £1.30
&. 🚌 ✕

▶ **CHIPPING CAMPDEN** ◀

HART'S SILVERSMITHS

Handmade silverware

The Old Silk Mill, Sheep St, Chipping Campden,
Gloucestershire GL55 6DS
☎ Evesham (0386) 841100

This is the silversmith's workshop of C. R. Ashbees Guild of Handicraft, where the Hart family have been making silverware since 1908.

Just off the High Street.
Open all year Mon–Fri, 9.00am–5.00pm, Sat 9.00am–12.00 noon
Free admission
&. access difficult
🚌 parties welcome: maximum 12 persons ✕

R W LANGSTON & SON

Pick your own

Hoarston Farm, Charingworth, Chipping Campden,
Gloucestershire GL55 6NX
☎ Paxford (038678) 285

Small family run farm situated high in the Cotswolds with a large selection of soft fruits and fresh vegetables on sale. After picking your fruit, picnic on the large lawns with a view of four counties.

Off the B4035 in the village of Charingworth halfway between Chipping Campden and Shipston on Stour
Open June–Sept daily 9.00am till late. Telephone for prices and availability
Free admission
&. not suitable for wheelchairs
🚌 mini-coaches allowed ✕

SMITHS GARDEN CENTRE

Garden centre and farm shop

Castle Nurseries, Station Rd, Chipping Campden,
Gloucestershire GL55 6JD
☎ Evesham (0386) 840367

Family Garden Centre offering most garden requirements. Bedding plants, geraniums, fuchsias, hanging baskets, etc., wide range of tubs, terracotta, stoneware; PYO strawberries & raspberries; fresh fruit, vegetables, pet foods.

½ mile from centre on B4035 Shipton on Stour road
Open daily (except Christmas/New Year Holiday) 9.00am–6.00pm, winter: 9.00am–5.00pm
Free admission
&. toilet doors not wide enough to accommodate wheelchairs
🚌 advance notice required ✕

▶ **CINDERFORD** ◀

DEAN HERITAGE CENTRE

Museum of forest life with craft workshops and nature trails

Camp Mill, Soudley, Cinderford, Gloucestershire
GL14 7UG
☎ Dean (0594) 22170

Industrial, social & natural history of Forest of Dean; beam engine, waterwheel, reconstructed coalmine, Forester's cottage and smallholding, observational beehive & ant's nest. Cafe, picnic/barbeque area; adventure playground.

At Soudley on the B4227 between Cinderford and the A48 at Blakeney
Open daily all year, Apr–Oct, 10.00am–6.00pm; Nov–Mar 10.00am–5.00pm
Admission: adult £2.25; child £1.25, OAP/student/UB40 £1.50. Party rate: 25p reduction per person in parties of 20 or over
&. a level all-weather surface nature trial
🚌 ✕ outside Heritage Centre for Forest of Dean

▶ **CIRENCESTER** ◀

CIRENCESTER WORKSHOPS

Craft centre

Brewery Court, Cirencester, Gloucestershire GL7 1JH
☎ Cirencester (0295) 651566

Contemporary craft centre comprising craftsmen at work, gallery, shop and coffee house.

Town centre
Open Mon–Sat 10.00am–5.00pm and some Bank
   Holidays
Free admission
 ♿ 🚦 advance notice required ⚜

DENFURLONG FARM TRAIL

Farm trail

Denfurlong Farm, Chedworth, Cheltenham,
   Gloucestershire GL54 4NT
☏ (024 289) 215

Self-conducted tour on a dairy farm with parlour observation platform; ½ hour building trail and 1–1½ hour field trail; picnic sites. Booklet and data sheets available.

Leave Cirencester on the Fosse Way A429 north, 6
   miles out turn left to Chedworth, signposted
   'Farm Trail'
Open at all times
Free admission, booklet guide 50p
♿ 🚦 ⚜

KEYNES COUNTRY PARK

Country park

Shorncote, Cirencester, Gloucestershire GL7 6DF
☏ Cirencester (0285) 861459

Part of the Cotswold Water Park. Lakeside walks, trimtrail; picnic sites, barbeques; playground, childrens beach; nature reserve. Day tickets for angling and windsurfing. Toilets, information, telephone.

Off the A419, 4 miles south of Cirencester
Open all year daily 9.00am–1.00pm; children's beach
   open June–Sept 1.00–5.00pm daily
Admission: weekdays and Saturdays £1.50 per car;
   Sundays and Bank Holidays £2.50 per car; minibuses
   £5.00; coaches by arrangement only £10.00
♿ 🚦 advance notice required
⚜ except on beach and play areas

WESTERN VILLE POTTERY

Pottery workshop

Western Ville, Kemble, Cirencester, Gloucestershire
   GL7 6AW
☏ Cirencester (0285) 770651

Small workshop and showroom housed in the former Station Master's house. Domestic stoneware, terrocotta plant pots, bird feeders etc. Light refreshments, home grown produce and plants available in summer.

4 miles west of Cirencester, left off the A433
Open daily 9.00am–6.00pm please telephone before
   making special trip
Free admission
♿ ⚜

▶ COLEFORD ◀

PUZZLE WOOD

Open iron mines

Lower Perrygrove, Coleford, Gloucestershire
☏ Dean (0594) 33187

Scenic walk through open iron workings.

On the B4228 at Coleford
Open Easter–end Oct daily 11.00am–6.00pm. Closed
   Mondays except Bank Holidays
Admission: adult £1.00, child 50p
🚦 advance notice required ⚜

▶ GLOUCESTER ◀

OVER FARM MARKET

Farm shop, farm animals

Over, Gloucester GL2 8DB
☏ Gloucester (0452) 21014

Farm retail outlet selling own grown fruit and vegetables and local produce including cheese, eggs, fruit juice, bedding plants, cut flowers, conserves and pickles. Farm animals beside shop for children to see.

1 mile west of Gloucester on north side of the A40
   dual carriageway
Open daily except Christmas Day and Boxing Day
   Mon–Sat 9.00am–6.00pm, Sun 10.00am–6.00pm
Free admission
♿ 🚦 advance notice required ⚜

ROYAL SPRING FRUIT FARM

Farm shop and pick your own

Longhope, Gloucestershire GL17 0PJ
☏ Gloucester (045382) 550

A small farm growing a wide variety of high quality soft fruits. The farm is set in an attractive little valley surrounded by wooded hills. Off-road parking.

On the A4136, 9 miles west of Gloucester
Open June–Sept daily 10.00am–6.00pm
Free admission
&. **ᛏ**

ST AUGUSTINE'S FARM

Farm visit, working farm and country centre

Arlingham, Gloucester
☎ Gloucester (0452) 740277

124 acre real working farm in the horseshoe bend of the River Severn where you can get close to the animals: pigs, sheep, horses, ducks, hens and others. Farm trail, bygones; play area; shop and teas.

From jct 13 of the M5 take the A38, then the B4071 to Arlingham
Open 31 March–31 Oct daily 11.00am–5.00pm.
Prebooked school parties anytime of year by appointment
Admission: adult £1.50, child/OAP 90p, party rates available (1990 prices)
&. ᚙ advance notice required **ᛏ**

▶ **LECHLADE** ◀

BRIDGE HOUSE GALLERY

Working craft shop

Fairford Rd, Downington, Lechlade, Gloucestershire GL7 3DL
☎ Faringdon (0367) 52457

Restored 18th century barn as showroom for rocking horses, dolls houses, miniatures, pottery, jewellery and other crafts. Working crafts person(s) on premises. Tea and coffee available in barn or courtyard. Off-street parking. Children welcomed.

Just out of Lechlade, on the A417 to Cirencester. From Burford or Swindon, take the A361 through Lechalde
Open March–Dec daily 2.00pm–6.00pm. Please telephone for any other time.
Free admission
&. **ᛏ**

LECHLADE TROUT FARM

Catch your own trout, fly fishing, farm shop

Burford Rd, Lechlade, Gloucestershire GL7 3QQ
☎ Faringdon (0367) 53266

Trout farm situated in pleasant countryside. Large farm shop stocked with Minola Smoked Products, fresh trout, sea food, jams etc. 'Catch your own' trout pool great fun for beginners, 12 acre lake for serious anglers.

Off the A361, 1 mile east of Lechlade on the Burford road
Open daily 8.30am–6.00pm
Free admission
&. fishing platforms for disabled and separate parking arrangements ᚙ **ᛏ**

MINOLA SMOKED PRODUCTS

Farm shop

Kencot Hill Farmhouse, Filkins, Lechlade, Gloucestershire GL7 3QY
☎ Filkins (036 786) 391

One of only 4 traditional English smokeries specializing in quality smoked foods such as wild goose, chicken, wild boar and many other products. Smoked Scottish salmon acclaimed best by many publications.

1 mile north of Lechlade on the A361
Open daily Minola farm shop at the Lechlade Trout Farm, by appointment only to visit Minola smokery
Free admission
&. ᚙ advance notice required **ᛏ**

ROMANY CARAVANS AND COUNTRY RIDING

Riding and Romany caravan centre

Equitana Holidays, The Plough at Kelmscott, Lechlade GL7 3HG
☎ Southrop (036 785) 489

Tour the Cotswolds in a gypsy caravan, horse drawn Jersey wagon or on a fit hunter, starting from a 17th century inn set in attractive countryside. Evening stops at coaching inns or farmhouses with good home cooking.

Turn off the A40 Cheltenham–Oxford road at Burford to Lechdale. After 5 miles left to Kelmscott, after 2 miles left and then right to Kelmscott village
Open April–Sept, please telephone
Admission for riding: £5.00 per hour; caravan & horse £60.00 per day, £300–£380 per week.
&. **ᛏ**

► LYDNEY ◄

DENE RISE FRUIT FARM

Fruit farm

Blakeney, Gloucestershire GL15 4AQ
☎ Dean (0594) 510322

Farm situated close to the Forest of Dean with views of the River Severn and Cotswold Hills. Strawberries, raspberries, tayberries, gooseberries, black/red currants, plums, apples and pears for PYO.

Adjacent to A48 Chepstow–Gloucester road, 4 miles north of Lydney
Open for farm shop March–Dec 9.00am–6.00pm; June–Oct PYO
Free admission and car parking
&. 🚌 🐾

LYDNEY PARK GARDENS

Rhododendron and azalea gardens, farm shop

Lydney Park Estate office, old Park, Lydney, Gloucestershire GL15 6BU
☎ Dean (0594) 832844

Beautiful gardens set in a lakeland valley. Magnolias, daffodils, primroses and bluebells bloom in profusion in spring. Deer park, Roman Temple site, Roman and New Zealand Museums. Picnic area, shop, teas.

Entrance off the A48 Gloucester–Chepstow road between Lydney and Aylburton
Open April–June, Wednesdays, Sundays and Bank Holidays 11.00am–6.00pm Parties welcome by appointment
Admission: £1.50 per person, parties of 25 or more £1.25 per person. Accompanied children and car parking free
&. steep slopes difficult for wheelchairs
🚌 advance notice required 🐾

► MICKLETON ◄

KIFTSGATE COURT GARDENS

Country garden

Kiftsgate Court, Chipping Campden, Gloucestershire, GL55 6LW
☎ (0386) 438 777

Magnificently situated house with a garden created over three generations. Fine views; unusual plants and shrubs including Rosa, filipes 'Kiftsgate', the largest rose in England.

1 mile east of the A46 and the B4081, adjacent to Hidcote National Trust Garden
Open 1 April–30 Sept Wed, Thur & Sun and Bank Holiday Mondays 2.00–6.00pm
Admission: adult £1.90, child 70p (1990 prices)
&. 🚌 advance notice required ✗

► MORETON-IN-MARSH ◄

BATSFORD ARBORETUM

Arboretum

Estate Office, Batsford, Moreton-in-Marsh, Gloucestedrshire GL56 9QF
☎ Moreton-in-Marsh (0608) 50722

50 acres containing over 1200 different species of trees, many rare. Superb views; carpets of bulbs, magnificent magnolias, flowering cherries, spectacular 'Handkerchief' tree. Maples and sorbus provide wonderful autumn colour.

1½ miles out of Moreton on the A44 to Evesham
Open April–Oct daily 10.00am–5.00pm
Admission: adult £2.00, child/OAP £1.00
&. no special toilet facilities. Not suitable for wheelchairs as steps and steep hill
🚌 advance notice required 🐾

COTSWOLD FALCONRY CENTRE

Falconry centre

Batsford Park, Moreton-in-Marsh, Gloucestershire GL56 9QB
☎ Blockley (0386) 701043

Daily demonstrations in the ancient art of falconry with free flying Eagles, Hawks, Owls and Falcons (weather permitting). Great importance is placed on their breeding and conservation.

Off the A44, 1 mile west of Moreton-in-Marsh
Open 9 March–end Nov daily 10.30am–5.30pm
Admission: adult £2.00, child £1.00, OAP £1.50
&. 🚌 ✗

EVENLODE POTTERY

Pottery

Evenlode, nr Moreton-in-Marsh, Gloucestershire
  GL56 0NX
☎ Moreton-in-Marsh (0608) 50804

'Slipware' pottery (decorated with liquid clay) in brown, green, yellow and blue; oven-to-tableware. Visitors welcome to see potter at work; individual orders taken.

Evenlode village – between Moreton-in-Marsh and
  Stow-on-the-Wold
Open daily, anytime
Free admission
& ⛺ ☂

▶ NEWENT ◀

THE FALCONRY CENTRE

Falconry centre

Newent, Gloucestershire GL18 1JJ
☎ Newent (0531) 820286

One of the largest collections of birds of prey in the world set in beautiful Gloucestershire countryside. An education in conservation. 4 flying demonstrations per day, cafe, gift and book shop.

From the centre of Newent (off B4215) follow the
  signs leading towards Cliffords Mesne
Open Feb–Nov daily 10.30am–5.30pm
Admission: adult £3.00, child £1.95, party rates available
& ⛺ ☂

NEWENT BUTTERFLY AND NATURAL WORLD CENTRE

Butterfly centre and natural world centre

Springbank, Birches Lane, Newent, Gloucestershire
  GL18 1DN
☎ Newent (0531) 821 800

One of the most interesting natural history tourist attractions in England. Displays and collections of many interesting live creatures from ornamental pheasants to insects and reptiles, also large static displays.

From Newent head for Ledbury, ample road signs
Open Easter–Christmas (closed Christmas Day) daily
  10.00am–5.00pm
Admission: adult £2.75, child £1.85, OAP £2.30, group
  rates on request (1990 prices)
& no toilet facilities ⛺ ☂

ST ANNES VINEYARD

Speciality food & drink producer, vineyard, shop, speciality marmalades

Wain House, Oxenhall, Newent, Gloucestershire
  GL18 1RW
☎ Gorsley (098982) 313

The largest outdoor vine collection in the UK. Many varieties of wine both from own grapes, and fruit, all made at the vineyard; free tasting. Also speciality marmalades.

Off the B4215 Gloucester–Ross road. Take first
  right past Newent (sign at bottom of road), 2
  miles down road
Open Tues–Fri 2.00–7.00pm, weekends & Bank Holidays
  10.00am–7.00pm
Free admission
& assistance available ☂

▶ NORTHLEACH ◀

COTSWOLD COUNTRYSIDE COLLECTION

Countryside museum and tourist information centre

Northleach, Cheltenham, Gloucestershire GL54 3JH
☎ Cotswold (0451) 60715

Gallery, audio and visual exhibitions. Contains Lloyd-Baker Collection of Agricultural History in an 18th century country prison. Free car parking and picnic area; refreshments and shop.

On A429 Foss Way west of Northleach in the heart
  of the Cotswolds signposted from A40
  Northleach bypass. Nearest BR station:
  Moreton-in-Marsh
Open daily Apr–Oct 10.00am–5.30pm, Sundays 2.00–
  5.30pm
Admission: adult 80p, child 40p, OAP/Student/parties 50p
& ⛺ ☂

▶ PAINSWICK ◀

PAINSWICK ROCOCO GARDEN

Country garden

The Stables, Painswick House, Painswick, Gloucestershire
  GL6 6TH
☎ Painswick (0452) 813204

Unique restoration of an 18th century garden set in a hidden Cotswold valley. Combines period buildings, formal vistas and winding woodland walks. Licensed restaurant.

On the B4073, ½ mile from Painswick on the Gloucester road
Open Feb–Dec, Wed–Sun and Bank Holidays 11.00am–5.00pm
Admission: adult £2.00, child £1.00, OAP £1.75 (1990 prices)
& certain paths are too steep for wheelchairs
🚌 advance notice required 🐴

▶ *STOW-ON-THE-WOLD* ◀

COTSWOLD FARM PARK

Farm park and education centre

Guiting Power, Stow-on-the-Wold, Cheltenham, Gloucestershire GL54 5UG
☎ (04515) 307

One of the most comprehensive collections of rare breeds of British Farm animals in the country. Pets corner, adventure playground, picnic area, education facilities, cafe, gift shop. Lambing and shearing exhibitions in season.

From Stow take the B4077 for 6 miles, turn left at Farm Park signs
Open 1 April–30 Sept 10.30am–6.00pm
Admission: adult £2.40, Child £1.20, OAP £1.75. Free parking and drive in picnic area.
& 🚌 🐴 on the farm trial, but not in animal exhibition area

DONNINGTON FISH FARM

Fish farm

Condicote Lane, Upper Swell, Stow-on-the-Wold, Gloucestershire GL54 1EP
☎ Cotswold (0451) 30873

Working trout farm with fish of all sizes on display. Farm shop selling top quality fresh trout and smoked trout prepared ;in our own smokery. Small, day-ticket, fly fishery.

3 miles north west of Stow-on-the-Wold, off the A434 towards Condicote
Open April–Oct daily 10.00am–5.30pm; Nov–March daily (except Mondays) 10.00am–5.00pm
Free admission
& 🚌 advance notice required 🐴

WYE ORGANIC FOODS

Organic retail shop

The Square, Stow-on-the-Wold, Gloucestershire GL54 1AB
☎ (0451) 31004

First privately owned shop in the UK selling Soil Association standard produce: meat, vegetables, fruit, wine, pet food; homeopathic remedies. No smoking allowed.

The A429 from Cirencester and Stratford upon Avon, A40 & A436 from Cheltenham
Open all year Mon–Sat 9.00am–5.30pm
Free admission
& 🚌 🐴

▶ *STROUD* ◀

COWCOMBE FARM HERBS

Herb and wildflower nursery

Gipsy Lane, Chalford, nr Stroud, Gloucestershire GL6 8HP
☎ (0285 76) 544

Herb and wildflower nursery also specializing in cottage garden species.

Between Stroud and Cirencester, just off the A419 at Aston Down, signposted 'Herb Nursery'
Open Easter–Sept, Wed–Sat 10.00am–5.00pm, Sun 2.00–5.00pm
Free admission
& 🚌 🐴

DENNIS FRENCH WOODWARE

Wood craftsman and workshop

The Craft Shop, Brimscombe Hill, Brimscombe, nr Stroud, Gloucestershire GL5 2QR
☎ Brimscombe (0453) 883054

Craft shop selling own woodwork. A good variety of well-finished products is always available. Great care is taken in the selection and drying of timber, English ash being widely used.

Turn right off the A419 Stroud–Cirencester road at Brimscombe, 2 miles east of Stroud. ¼ mile up hill on left hand side
Open for the shop: Tues–Fri 9.00am–5.00pm, Sat 8.00am–4.00pm. Mondays by appointment. Workshop strictly by appointment only
Admission for woodturning demonstrations in the workshop (appointment only) maximum 2 persons: £5.00 per person per hour
& 🐴

SELSLEY HERB & GOAT FARM

Herb and goat farm

Stroud, Gloucestershire GL5 5LW
☎ Stroud (04536) 6682

Selsley Herb Farm covers 4 acres laid out with several herb gardens and a paddock for the goats and other animals. Refreshments available daily with special cream teas on Sundays and Bank Holidays.

Take the B4066 to Dursley out of Stroud through village of Selsley, over cattle grid, onto Selsley Common and first turn left marked Waterlane (also marked unsuitable for motors, but this is beyond the herb farm)
Open April–Sept, daily 10.00am–5.30pm
Free admission to the herb farm and animals. Gardens: adult 50p, child under 16/OAP 25p
&. ⬛ with advance notice (150 yard walk)
🐾

◀ **TETBURY** ▶

SHIPTONS STONEGROUND FLOOR

Working flour mill

Tetbury, Gloucestershire GL8 8RP
☎ Tetbury (0666) 505050

Situated on the upper reaches of the River Avon, the mill is first recorded in the Domesday Book. A unique waterwheel to be seen and flour can be bought.

Take the B4014 Tetbury–Malmesbury road, after 2 miles turn right into track in layby
Open 10.00am–4.00pm by appointment
Free admission
&. 🐾

WESTONBIRT ARBORETUM

Arboretum with walks, visitor centre, cafeteria, book shop & exhibition

Forestry Commission, Research Division, Westonbirt Arboretum, Westonbirt, Tetbury, Gloucestershire GL8 8QS
☎ Westonbirt (066688)220

A landscaped collection of trees and shrubs from around the world. 17 miles of paths, picnic area, snack bar and a visitor centre housing an exhibition and shop. Best in spring and autumn.

3 miles south west of Tetbury, on the north side of the A433 Bath road
Open daily 10.00am–8.00pm or sunset
Admission: adult £1.50, child/OAP 50p (1989 prices)
&. ⬛ 🐾

▶ **TEWKESBURY** ◀

BECKFORD SILK LTD

Hand printers of silk – workshop and millshop

Beckford, nr Tewkesbury, Gloucestershire GL20 7AD
☎ Evesham (0386) 881507

Visitors may watch hand-printing, dye making and other processes in the manufacture of silk scarves and silk ties. Pre-booked parties of up to 25 people in evening. Coffee shop.

6 miles north of Tewkesbury, on the B4080
Open throughout the year (except 24 Dec–2 Jan), Mon–Sat 9.00am–1.00pm and 2.00pm–5.30pm
Free admission
&. ⬛ for pre-booked evening events only 🐾

CONDERTON POTTERY

Pottery

The Old Forge, Conderton, nr Tewkesbury, Gloucestershire GL20 7PP
☎ Overbury (0386) 89387

Handmade domestic ware pottery using a special saltglazing technique to create subtle textures and colours. Set amidst its own orchard the pottery is situated in a delightfully unspoilt village.

Take the A438 Tewkesbury–Stow-on-the-Wold road for 5 miles, at Teddington Hands roundabout take first left to Conderton (signposted), follow road to T-junction. Turn right and the pottery is the first building on your left
Open Mon–Sat 9.00am–5.00pm. Closed Christmas Day, Boxing Day and New Years Day
Free admission
&. 🐾

THE JOHN MOORE COUNTRYSIDE MUSEUM

Museum, farm interpretation centre, country garden, forestry centre

41 Church St, Tewkesbury, Gloucestershire GL20 5SW
☎ Tewkesbury (0684) 297174

Opened in 1980, in a heavily timbered mediaeval house built in 1450. Three galleries exhibit aspects of nature conservation related to farming, forestry, and wetlands management

On the A38 Gloucester road in Tewkesbury, adjacent to Abbey
Open Good Friday–31 Oct 10.00am–1.00pm and 2.00–5.00pm. Winter months by telephone to Tewkesbury (0684) 296335
Admission: adult 40p, child/OAP 20p, Party bookings 30p each.
   ♿ no facilities, but partly disabled visitors welcome
🚌 preferably with advance notice 🐴

From Wotton take the B4060 to Dursley after 2 miles to Nibley turn right at Black Horse then keep left ½ mile to entrance
Open for the nursery: all day Tues–Sat all year except August. Garden: 2.00–6.00pm Tues–Sat, May–Sept (except August, last 3 Sundays in June & first 2 Sundays in July)
Admission: adult £1.00, child over 15/OAP 60p
   ♿ 🚌 advance notice required 🐴

► **WINCHCOMBE** ◄

WINCHCOMBE POTTERY LTD

Handmade pottery

Becketts Lane, Greet, Winchcombe, Cheltenham, Gloucestershire GL54 5NU
☎   Cheltenham (0242) 602462

Ray Finch and team of five potters continue making a complete range of traditional hand-made, practical, wood-fired pottery of the highest standard that justifies its world-wide reputation.

1 mile north of Winchcombe, turn off the B4632˝ towards Greet. The pottery is at this junction
Open all year Mon–Fri 8.00am–4.00pm, Sat 9.00am–4.00pm, Sundays May–Sept 12.00 noon–4.00pm
Free admission unless conducted tour required. Please telephone for details
   ♿ 🚌 advance notice required 🐴

► **WOTTON** ◄

HUNTS COURT GARDEN AND NURSERY

Nursery garden

Hunts Court, North Nibley, Dursley, Gloucestershire GL11 6DZ
☎   Dursley (0453) 47440

Hunts Court is surrounded by a peaceful and largely informal garden with a wide range of shrubs and perennials that give year round interest. Main attraction is the collection of over 400 varieties of old roses.

GREATER LONDON AND MIDDLESEX

Even the huge suburban sprawl that comprises Greater London retains its country connections – there are a wealth of open spaces, parks and heathland with expanses of countryside preserved around its boundaries as the Green Belt.

You can walk from the town into the country when you visit one of the farm interpretation centres or the nature and wildlife centres listed. Milking cows and tending sheep become a reality and there are even sheep dog trials featured at open weekends. For the horticulturalist there are special interest gardens and pick-your-own fresh produce, including vegetables and soft fruits, allowing you to take the taste of the countryside home.

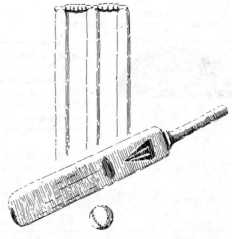

▶ **ENFIELD** ◀

CAPEL MANOR ENVIRONMENTAL CENTRE

Farm interpretation centre, farm trail and farm visit

c/o Capel Manor, Bullsmoor Lane, Enfield, Middlesex
 EN1 4RQ
☎ Lea Valley (0992) 763849

Guided tours and coach parties by prior arrangement. Special events throughout the season. Centre and farm based on adjacent site.

Adjacent to jct 25 of the M25
Open weekends and school holidays April–Oct 1.00–
 6.00pm
Admission to the gardens: adult £1.25, child 60p; farm:
 adult £1.00, child 50p (1990 prices)
ૐ ⟭ advance notice required
🐕 except on farm

CAPEL MANOR HORTICULTURAL CENTRE

Gardens

Bullsmoor Lane, Enfield, Middlesex EN1 4RQ
☎ Lea Valley (0992) 763849

Special interest gardens including rock, historical and modern theme gardens and a sensory garden for the blind.

Adjacent to jct 25 of the M25
Open all year except Christmas, Boxing and New Year
 Days, weekdays 10.00am–4.30pm, weekends April–Oct
 10.00am–5.30pm
Admission: weekdays & normal weekends adult £1.25,
 concessions 60p. Special rates for special events and
 guided tours (1990 prices)
ૐ limited access to some buildings. 2 wheelchairs
available. Sensory garden for the blind ⟭ 🐕

PARKSIDE FARM

Pick your own

Hadley Rd, Enfield, Middlesex EN2 8LA
☎ Enfield (081) 367 2035 (24 hours)

Strawberries, raspberries, gooseberries, black/redcurrants, blackberries and Autumn raspberries. Also courgettes, broad beans, sweetcorn, french beans, onions and runner beans. Containers available. Toilets.

Hadley Road runs between the A1005 (Enfield
 Ridgeway) and the A11 (Cockfosters Road)
Open June–Oct daily. Telephone for daily bulletin
Free admission and parking. No school parties. Children
 welcome with parents
ૐ ⟭ advance notice preferred 🐕

▶ **STROUD GREEN** ◀

PARKLAND WALK WILDLIFE CENTRE

Nature reserve and wildlife interpretation centre

Station House, 73c Stapleton Hall Rd, Stroud Green,
 London N4
☎ (081) 341 3582

Disused railway now nature reserve and footpath with wildlife interpretation centre. Walk links Finsbury Park to the well known and historic Alexandra Palace and park.

London Underground to Finsbury Park station –
 access opposite station at Stroud Green Road.
 W3 bus from Finsbury Park bus station to
 junction of Stapleton Hall Road and Ferme Park
 Road

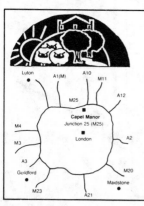

Capel Manor

where the country comes to town.
Educational farm open April-
October, weekends & school
holidays, 1-5pm.
Gardens open April-October daily,
November-March, weekdays
1-4.30pm.
Special events and activities!
For more details and costs, contact:
**Capel Manor Horticultural and
Environmental Centre.**
Bullsmoor Lane, Enfield, EN1 4RQ.
By J25/M25. Tel: 0992 763849

Open Mon & Thur 10.00am–4.00pm; Sun Nov–Feb
   12.00–4.00pm, March–Oct 12.00–5.00pm; Bank
   Holidays as Sundays. Closed Christmas, New Year and
   Good Friday
Free admission
&. except for toilets. Ramped access to Interpretation
Centre and onto Walk
▰▰ advance notice required ⟙

► **UXBRIDGE** ◄

PARK LODGE FARM CENTRE

Farm centre

London Borough of Hillingdon, Park Lodge Farm, Harvil
   Rd, Harefield, Uxbridge UB9 6JW
☎   Harefield (089 582) 4425

*Demonstrates the reality of agriculture to
schools – 200 cows, rotary parlour, 200
ewes, young stock and lambs on 600 acres.
Teacher tuition, lectures; two trails. Open
weekends feature sheep dog trials, crafts and
trailer rides.*

A40/M40 jct 1 to A412 (Watford) turn to Harefield
   at Denham Green ¾ mile
Open by appointment for school parties, weekends for the
   public, telephone for details
Admission (1988 prices): schools £27.00 per group of
   50, June Open Weekend £1.50, September Open
   Weekend £1.00
&. ✖

Guide to Symbols

☎   telephone
&.   disabled welcome
▰▰   coaches welcome

⟙ dogs welcome (on a leash)
✖ dogs not welcome

HAMPSHIRE

Hampshire is a diverse county with sharp country and town divisions. It is largely chalkland but is also rich in trees, for many people Hampshire is synonymous with the New Forest. The forest, planted over 1000 years ago, became a royal hunting ground for William the Conqueror and it still has an extremely rich selection of trees.

The attractions of Hampshire are as diverse as its character, the visitor can enjoy the wide selection of country parks and walks, or visit several farms and follow the farm trails, see birds of prey in a woodland setting or butterflies in an indoor tropical jungle, wander round the country gardens or watch the painting and restoration of gypsy caravans whilst refreshing themselves with a sample of award winning wines made from locally grown grapes or a tankard of 'Old Thumper', a traditional local brew!

▶ ## ALRESFORD ◀

WIELD WOOD SHEEP DAIRY

Sale of own products and farm visit

Wield Wood, Alresford, Hampshire SO24 9RU
☎ Alton (0420) 63151

This was the first commercial sheep dairy to be set up in Britain in modern times, thus continuing a tradition well established in the early Middle Ages on this farm. Watch sheep being milked; sample and buy produce.

The farm is on the Preston Candover side of Upper Wield, ½ mile north of the village
Open March–Oct 2.30–5.00pm
Admission: adult £1.00, child under 14 free
& ⇌ advance notice required 🐴

▶ ## ALTON ◀

THE OATES MEMORIAL MUSEUM & THE GILBERT WHITE MUSEUM

Museum, historic house and garden

The Wakes, Selborne, Alton, Hampshire GU34 3JH
☎ Selborne (042050) 275

Museum in the home of Rev Gilbert White, author of 'The Natural History of Selborne' (1789) with original manuscript on display. Also exhibits relating to Captain Lawrence Oates, Frank Oates and Scott's expedition to the South Pole. 5 acre garden.

On the B3006, 4 miles from Alton, 8 miles from Petersfield
Open 27 March–27 Oct (1990): Wed–Sun 1.00am–5.30pm; closed Mondays and Tuesdays
Admission: adult £1.25, child 50p, OAP £1.00, discount for parties
& arrangements can be made to use a side entrance without steps. Most of the garden and some of the museum accessible by wheelchair ⇌ 🐴

THE ROMANY FOLKLORE MUSEUM & WORKSHOP

Museum of Romany folklore and workshop

Limes End Yard, High St, Selborne, nr Alton, Hampshire GU34 3JW
☎ Selbourne (042050) 486

Workshop, museum and shop. Building, painting and restoring of gypsy caravans. The only working museum of its type in Great Britain.

4 miles from Alton and 6 miles from Petersfield on the B3006
Open Easter–Oct 10.30am–5.30pm
Admission: adult 75p, child 35p. Parties by arrangement
& ⇌ parking in village car park 🐴

STUBBS FARM TRAIL

Farm trail

Stubbs Farm, Kingsley, Bordon, Hampshire GU35 9NR
☎ Bordon (0420) 474906

Family farm with trail: observe farm animals and wildlife whilst enjoying panoramic views over unspoilt countryside. Woodland walk, conservation lakes, farming display; picnic area, home made teas.

Off the B3004 at South Hay. 5 miles east of Alton, 1 mile north of Kingsley
Open May–Sept Sundays and Bank Holidays (also Tuesdays and Wednesdays during August) 1.00–5.30pm
Admision: adult £1.75, child £1.25 (1990 prices)
& ⇌ advance notice required 🐴

▶ ## ANDOVER ◀

FINKLEY DOWN FARM PARK

Farm visit and museum

Andover, Hampshire SP11 6NF
☎ Andover (0264) 52195

A comprehensive selection of rare and not so rare breeds of all farm animals; many rearing their young in a natural environment. Playground, pets corner; barn of bygones.

1½ miles east of Andover, signposted from the A303
Open April–Sept daily, 10.30am–6.00pm
Admission: adult £2.00, child/OAP £1.00, reduced rates for parties (1989 prices)
& ⇌ advance notice required 🐴

THE HAWK CONSERVANCY

Specialist bird of prey centre

Weyhill, nr Andover, Hampshire SP11 8DY
☎ Andover (0264 77) 2252

10 acres of aviaries in a woodland setting. Breeeding pairs of eagles, hawks and falcons together with the largest collection of owls on view to the public in this country. Daily flying demonstrations at 12 noon, 2.00pm, 3.00pm and 4.00pm (weather permitting).

Just off the A303, 3½ miles west of Andover
Open 1 March–last Sunday in Oct 10.30am–4.00pm
    Spring and Autumn, 5.00pm in Summer
Admission: reduced rates for parties by prior arrangement. School parties catered for by arrangement. Free car park. Under 16s must be accompanied by an adult
& ♿ advance notice required ✗

► **ASHURST** ◄

LONGDOWN DAIRY FARM

Farm visit, shop and interpretation centre

Longdown, Ashurst, nr Southampton, Hampshire
SO4 4UH
☎ Southampton (0703) 293326

A combination of a busy dairy unit and a children's farm. Visitors can watch the milking, feed the young animals and try the computer quiz. Adventure playground and shop

Off the A35 between Totton and Ashurst
Open 7 April–28 Oct (1990), daily 11.00am–5.00pm
Admission: adult £2.50, child £1.50, OAP £2.30
& ♿ advance notice required ✗

NEW FOREST BUTTERFLY FARM

Butterfly farm, countrywalk, country garden and farm shop

Longdown, Ashurst, nr Southampton, Hampshire
SO4 4UH
☎ Southampton (0703) 292166

An indoor tropical jungle where butterflies and moths from all over the world live and breed. Plus insectarium, dragonfly ponds, aviaries, woodland walk, adventure playground, 2 shops and a restaurant.

Off the A35 between Totton and Ashurst
Open 7 April–28 Oct daily 10.00am–5.00pm (1990)
Admission: adult £3.00, child £2.00, OAP £2.80
& ♿ advance notice required ✗

► **BEAULIEU** ◄

EXBURY GARDENS

Woodland gardens, plant centre and gift shop

The Estate Office, Exbury, Southampton, Hampshire
SO4 1AZ
☎ Fawley (0703) 891203

200 acre woodland garden comprising the world famous Rothschild collection of rhododendrons, azaleas, camellias and magnolias as well as rock, water and iris gardens, ponds, cascades etc. 2 licensed cafeterias.

M27 jct 3, or from New Forest via Beaulieu on the
    B3054, turn south to Exbury, follow RAC signs
Open March–July; 10.00am–5.30pm; Sept–Oct;
    10.00am–5.00pm daily
Admission: Spring – adult £2.50, OAP/party £2.00 (Bank
    Holiday weekends 50p extra an all prices; Autumn –
    £1.50
& ♿ ample free parking for coaches and cars ✗

► **FAREHAM** ◄

HOLLY HILL WOODLAND PARK

Woodland park

Barns Lane, Locks Heath, Southampton

89 acre woodland park with lakes, woodland walks, picnic areas and toilets.

Off the A27 near Sarisbury Green, 7 miles west of
    Fareham (near river Hamble)
Open all year
Free admission
& toilets ✗

► **FLEET** ◄

FLEET POND

Local nature reserve

c/o Hart District Council, Civic Office, Harlington Way,
    Fleet, Hampshire GU13 8AE
☎ Fleet (0252) 622122

A network of paths through the reserve offers varied walks through woodland, heathland and views across open water. The 68 acre pond is a regionally important site for the wintering birds it attracts.

Adjacent to the B3014, 1 mile from Fleet town centre
Open all year
Free admission
& ➡ advance notice required ⊀

▶ FORDINGBRIDGE ◀

ALDERHOLT MILL

Craft centre and working watermill producing stoneground flour, art exhibitions

Sandleheath Rd, Alderholt, Fordingbridge, Hampshire SP6 1PU
☎ Fordingbridge (0425) 53130

On the border of Hampshire and Dorset, this picturesque watermill has been restored to full working order over the past eight years; three-weekly art and craft exhibitions. Teas and ices, confectionery, handmade fudge and biscuits.

2 miles west, off the B3078, signposted Alderholt from Sandleheath
Open Good Friday–1st Oct & 18 Nov–24 Dec, Tues–Fri & Sun 2.00–6.00pm, Sat & Bank Holidays 10.00am–6.00pm. Closed Mondays (1989 dates)
Free admission
& cars may be parked in drive, access to ground floor
➡ advance notice required. Small admission charge ⊀

CRANBORNE FARMS PICK YOUR OWN

Farm shop, country walk and pick your own

Daggons Rd, Alderholt, Fordingbridge, Hampshire SP6 3DN
☎ Fordingbridge (0425) 55003

Wide variety of fruit and vegetable crops set amid woods with lakeside walks and picnic area.

3 miles west of Fordingbridge near St James Church, Alderholt which is halfway between Fordingbridge and Cranborne
Open June–Dec daily 10.00am–7.00pm
Free admission
& ➡ ⊀ not in PYO and shop

▶ LIPHOOK ◀

BOHUNT MANOR

Country garden with large waterfowl collection

Liphook, Hampshire GU3 0DU
☎ Liphook (0428) 722208

Medium sized gardens featuring herbaceous borders, flowering shrubs and specimen trees. Woodland walk with replanted trees; collection of waterfowl.

On the A3 London–Portsmouth road, in centre of village opposite Jet Petrol Station
Open all year daily 9.00am–5.00pm
Admission: adult £1.50, child free, OAP £1.00
& ➡ ⊀

▶ LYMINGTON ◀

LYMINGTON VINEYARD

Vineyard and winery

Wainsford Rd, Pennington, Lymington, Hampshire SO41 8LB
☎ Lymington (0590) 72112

A vineyard set in peaceful surroundings producing award winning wines. Walk at leisure around the vineyard and herb garden with a map, see the winery and slide show.

Take the A337 west from Lymington ½ mile turn right to Pennington village, turn left in village
Open May–Oct, weekdays 10.30am–4.30pm; Sundays 11.30am–4.30pm, closed Saturdays
Admission: adult £1.50, child 80p
& ➡ advance notice required ⊀

SPINNERS

Country garden and nursery

Boldre, Lymington, Hampshire SO41 5QE
☎ Lymington (0590) 673347

Rhododendrons, azalea, magnolias and hydrangeas interplanted with a wide variety of choice plants. The nursery for less common plants, trees and shrubs. Visited by people from all over the temperate world.

Take the A337 from Brockenhurst. Follow signs for Boldre and Pilley, turning right at signpost for Vicars Hill, 150 yds on the right.
Open daily April–Sept 10.00am–6.00pm , at other times by appointment only. Nursery open all year
Admission: £1.00 per person
🚌 advance notice required ✕

▶ **LYNDHURST** ◀

FURZEY GARDENS

Country gardens

Minstead, nr Lyndhurst, Hampshire SO43 7GL
☎ Southampton (0703) 812464

8 acres of peaceful, informal landscape in the heart of the New Forest. Within the grounds is a 16th century cottage and gallery displaying work of local craftspeople.

Follow signs to Minstead from the A31 or the A35 from Cadnam
Open all year except Christmas Day and Boxing Day, daily 10.00am–5.00pm
Admission: Nov–Feb adult £1.00, child 50p; March–Oct adult £1.75, child 90p
👤 🚌 by arrangement ✕

THE NEW FOREST

Forest park and forestry centre

Forestry Commission, The Queens House, Lyndhurst, Hampshire SO43 7NH
☎ Lyndhurst (0703) 283141

The New Forest is a mediaeval hunting forest surviving to the present day partly because of the continuing exercise of common grazing rights and partly through the value of its woodland as a source of timber during several centuries.

Open all year, daylight hours
Free admission (except campsites)
👤 🚌 not allowed on some roads 🐎

NEW FOREST MUSEUM AND VISITOR CENTRE

Museum relating to the history, customs and wildlife of the New Forest

High St, Lyndhurst Hampshire SO43 7NY
☎ Lyndhurst (042 128) 3914

Exhibition telling the history, traditions and wildlife of the New Forest. Includes 'The changing forest' audio visual show and the New Forest embroidery. Gift shop and Tourist Information.

Just off the High Street, Lyndhurst. In the visitors car park
Open daily from 10.00am
Admission on application
👤 🚌 ✕

▶ **PETERSFIELD** ◀

GREATHAM MILL GARDEN

Country garden and nursery garden

Greatham Mill, Greatham, Liss, Hampshire, GU33 6HH
☎ Blackmoor (04207) 219

Attractive garden of about 2 acres, intersected by waterways, with many unusual plants. Subject of BBC Television 'Gardeners World' 1989.

From Petersfield towards Farnham on the A325, turn at Greatham to the B3006 towards Selborne. After 500 yards fork left into No Through Road. Lane to garden
Open Mid April–Sept, Sun & Bank Holidays 2.00–6.00pm weekdays by appointment only
Admission: adult £1.00, child free
👤 🚌 advance notice required ✕

QUEEN ELIZABETH COUNTRY PARK

Farm interpretation centre, country walk, country park and forestry centre

Gravel Hill, Horndean, Portsmouth, Hampshire PO8 0QE
☎ Horndean (0705) 595040

1400 acres of forest and downland, providing many recreational opportunities and events. Ranger staff available for walks, talks and activities. Park centre, shop, cafe, forest drive, picnic area.

Astride the A3, 4 miles south of Petersfield
Open all year for the park; centre open March–Oct 10.00am–6.00pm; Nov–Feb, Sundays only 10.00am–6.00pm
Admission: centre car park £1.20, Butser Hill car park 60p (1990 prices)
👤 🚌 advance notice required 🐎

RINGWOOD

HOCKEYS

Farm shop

South Gorley, Fordingbridge, Hampshire SP6 2PW
☎ (0425) 52542

Hockeys is a unique farm dating from the 16th century, specializing in the production of chemical free farm produce.

A338 Ringwood–Fordingbridge road, right at Old Beams restaurant, left at 'T' junction, farm on right down that road
Open Mon–Sat 9.00am–6.00pm
Free admission
&. ∞ advance notice required 🐎

RINGWOOD BREWERY

Traditional brewers

138 Christchurch Rd, Ringwood, Hampshire BH24 3AP
☎ Ringwood (0425) 471177

Small, independent family firm famous for its real ale – notably 'Old Thumper' voted champion beer of Britain 1988. Brewery shop sells party packs of draught ale, from 4 to 72 pints.

A few minutes drive from Ringwood centre on the Christchurch Road
Open for tours around brewhouse: Jan–March & Sept–Nov, please telephone for appointment; brewery shop open all year weekdays 10.00am–5.00pm (6.00pm on Thursdays), Sat 9.30am–12.00 noon
Admission: on application
&. ∞ advance notice required 🐎

ROMSEY

THE HILLIER GARDENS AND ARBORETUM

Country gardens

Jermyns Lane, Ampfield, nr Romsey, Hampshire SO51 0QA
☎ Braishfield (0794) 68787

The 160 acre gardens are home to one of the largest collections of trees and shrubs anywhere, with something of interest to enjoy always, 'A garden for all seasons'.

Between the village of Ampfield and Braishfield, 3 miles north east of Romsey and 9 miles south

west of Winchester. ½ mile west of the A31 along Jermyns Lane
Open Mon–Fri all year round 10.30am–5.00pm; weekends and Bank Holidays March–second Sunday in Nov 10.30am–6.00pm
Admission: adult £1.50, child free weekdays (50p weekends), reduced rates for parties
&. toilets
∞ advance notice required 🐎

PAULTONS PARK

Family leisure park

Ower, nr Romsey, Hampshire SO51 6AL
☎ (0703) 814442

Family entertainment in beautiful garden setting. Exotic birds, animals; lake; miniature railway; museums; kids kingdom, Bumper Boats, Astroglide, Magic Forest, Pets Corner. Restaurant, tearooms, refreshment kiosks; picnic area and gift shops.

Just off exit 2 of the M27. 1 mile off motorway, follow signs
Open March–Oct daily 10.00am–6.30pm
Admission: charge includes all main attractions. Special rates for groups.
&. all paths are flat, most are tarmaced
∞ 🐎

SALISBURY

BREAMORE COUNTRYSIDE MUSEUM

Country park and walks with a farming museum

Breamore, nr Fordingbridge, Hampshire SP6 2DB
☎ Downton (0725) 22488

Designed to show the visitor village life when it was self sufficient and self supporting. History of agriculture and rural life; workshops with rural industries; tractors, implements and steam engines.

Off the A338, 9 miles south of Salisbury
Open April: Tues, Wed, Sun and Easter holiday; May–July & Sept: Tues, Wed, Thurs, Sat Sun and all Bank Holidays; August: every day. 2.00pm–5.30pm
Admission: adult £3.00, child £1.50, reduced rates for parties and OAPs, combined ticket for house and 2 museums (1989 prices)
&. ∞ 🐎

▶ SOUTHAMPTON ◀

CALSHOT CRAFTS

Craft centre and country walk

Badminton Farm, Calshot Rd, Fawley, nr Southampton, Hampshire SO4 1BB
☎ Fawley (0703) 898846

Set in 7 acres overlooking the Solent and the Isle of Wight. Wide range of craftswork for sale, exhibitions; nature trail, picnic area. Licensed tea rooms seat 70, pizzas and cream teas a speciality.

On the A326 Fawley Road. ½ mile on left from Fawley village towards Calshot
Open all year except Christmas Day and New Years day, daily 10.00am–5.00pm
Free admission, free parking
&. entrance & doors suitable, no toilet
🚻 advance notice required
🐕 outside only

ELING TIDE MILL

Working flour mill

The Toll Bridge, Eling, Totton, nr Southampton SO4 4HF
☎ Southampton (0703) 869575

Restored in 1980, and now the only surviving tide mill in the world to harness tidal power for the regular production of wholemeal flour. Video interpretation, museum, shop.

4 miles west of Southampton, off the A35
Open all year Wed–Sun 10.00am–4.00pm, closed Mon & Tues
Admission: adult 95p, child 50p, OAP 75p
&. 🚻 🐕

LEPE COUNTRY PARK

Country park

Lepe, Exbury, Southampton, Hampshire
☎ Fawley (0703) 899108

Lepe Country Park lies south of the New Forest on the Solent coast. Country walks, beaches and coastal views; refreshments available.

Take the A35 to Totton, then the A326 towards Fawley, follow signs
Open at all times
Admission: car parking charges apply all year
&. 🚻 advance notice required 🐕

THE MEON VALLEY VINEYARD

Speciality drink producer, vineyard with wine tasting

Hill Grove, Swanmore, Southampton, Hampshire SO3 2PZ
☎ Droxford (0489) 877435

Vineyard, established 1977, specializing in production of red wines and sparkling wines (methode champenoise) as well as white. Also a range of country wines and farmhouse cider. Bar facilities for visitors.

6 miles north of Fareham, 1 mile west of A32 on unclassified road marked 'Cott St' signposted Swanmore. Vineyard is on eastern outskirts of village, next to Hunters Inn
Open Easter–Sept, please telephone for appointment
Admission: £2.00 per person for parties of 15 or more (including free wine tasting)
&. we will be pleased to give details of facilities to the individuals concerned
🚻 advance notice required 🐕

▶ WINCHESTER ◀

THE ANCHORAGE

Farm shop and organically grown vegetables and fruit

Salisbury Rd, Broughton, nr Stockbridge, Hampshire SO20 8BX
☎ Romsey (0794) 301234

Home grown organic fruit and vegetables to Soil Association standard, also organically grown whole foods, bio-degradeable cleaning

Off the A30, 4 miles west of Stockbridge on the B3084
Open daily 10.30am–6.00pm except Sundays
Free admission
&. 🐕

WINNAL MOORS NATURE RESERVE

Nature reserve

c/o Hampshire & Isle of Wight Naturalists Trust Ltd, 71 The Hundred, Romsey, Hampshire SO51 8BZ
☎ Romsey (0794) 513786

Nature reserve featuring wet meadows with hide, hard footpath. Leaflet available from the above address, 10p and SAE.

Park in Winchester Recreation Centre car park,
  follow signs for Winnall Moors Nature Reserve
Open daily
Free admission
♿ by arrangement 🚌 advance notice required ✈

Journey Through Britain

Have Fun Getting To Know Britain

An exciting race through the towns and cities of Britain by Ravensburger games.

Be first to reach each of the twelve destinations and answer one of the many fascinating questions.

A beautifully illustrated and presented game, price £12.99. Endorsed by the National Tourist Boards.

English Tourist Board

HEREFORDSHIRE

Herefordshire, the land of the cider apple, combines the fine scenery of the Wye valley with a gentle landscape of blossom covered orchards, old timbered houses and rolling farmland grazed by red-and-white cattle – peaceful countryside tucked away from the main tourist routes.

A cider museum and several cider mills, not surprisingly, feature amongst the opportunities for the visitor to sample the country flavour of Herefordshire. There are also various speciality food producers, a vineyard with a long history, and a choice of gardens including an Edwardian garden and a 'garden for all seasons' to enjoy before exploring the countryside by following one of the country walks or farm trails.

► *BROMYARD* ◄

THE HYDE FARM

Speciality food producer

The Hyde, Stoke Bliss, Tenbury Wells, Herefordshire
WR15 8RS
☎ Kyre (0885) 410408

Cheese made from goats' milk in a recently restored 16th century barn. Herd and creamery may be viewed.

Turn left off the B4214 Bromyard–Tenbury Wells
road, 6 miles north of Bromyard
Open: cheesemaking 2.00–4.00pm Mondays and Fridays,
goats milked every afternoon
Admission: £1.00 per person
&. ⛟

► *HEREFORD* ◄

ABBEY DORE COURT GARDEN

Country garden and nursery

Abbey Dore, South West Hereford, HR2 0AD
☎ Golden Valley (0981) 240419

4 acre mixed garden featuring wooded area, pond, rock garden, shrub and hardy perennial borders. Old walled garden for unusual plants. Also conservatory serving home made lunches and teas; country gift gallery.

11 miles south west of Hereford, from the A465 –
mid way between Hereford–Abergavenny – turn
left, signed Abbey Dore, then 2½ miles
Open 3rd Sat in March–3rd Sun in Oct daily except
Wednesdays 11.00am–6.00pm
Admission: adult £1.25, child 50p
&. toilet
⛟ advanced notice required ✖

BULMERS CIDER MILL VISITORS CENTRE

Speciality drink producer

The Cider Mills, Plough Lane, Herefordshire HR4 0LE
☎ Hereford (0432) 352000

The 2 hour tour includes video, factory tour, and cider sampling. Opportunity to buy cider and souvenirs from the Visitors Shop. Morning cofee, afternoon tea, evening snack included in admission.

Close to the city centre, on Whitecross Road
Open Jan–Dec, 3 organised tours per day Mon–Fri, by
appointment only
Admission: adult £2.50 to include cider tasting, student
£1.75, child £1.00
&. may find it difficult to complete the full tour
⛟ advance notice required ✖

CIDER MUSEUM AND KING OFFA DISTILLERY

Museum and distillery

Pomona Place, Whitecross Rd, Herefordshire HR4 0LW
☎ Hereford (0432) 354207

Displays include enormous 17th century French beam press, coopers shop, farm ciderhouse, travelling cidermaker's 'tack', original champagne cider cellars, huge oak vats, 1920s hydraulic presses and cider brandy distillery.

½ mile from city ring road, on the A438 to Brecon
Open April–Oct daily 10.00am–5.30pm; Nov–March
Mon–Sat 1.00–5.00pm
Admission: adult £1.50, child/OAP 90p, reduced rates for
parties
&. ⛟ ✇

DINMORE MANOR

Country garden, chapel, music room and cloisters

Wellington, Herefordshire HR4 8EE
☎ Canon Pyon (043271) 322

Beautiful gardens in a glorious setting with easterly aspect towards the Malvern Hills. Commandery of St John of Jerusalem dating from the 12th century with a fascinating Music Room and cloisters.

On the A49, 6½ miles north of Hereford
Open daily 10.00am–6.00pm
Admission: adult £2.00, child free when accompanied
&. ⛟ advance notice required ✖

MOCCAS COURT

Country walk, country garden and stately home

Moccas, Herefordshire HR2 9LH
☎ Moccas (098 17) 381

A fine Georgian house by Anthony Keck, decoration designed by Robert Adam. Situated in Capability Brown parkland on the banks of the River Wye.

From Hereford take the A465 3 miles, turn right on the Hay-on-Wye road (B4352) to Moccas, turn right to court

Open first Thur in April–last Thur in Sept, 2.00–6.00pm. Party bookings by appointment at other times.
Admission: adult £1.50, child 75p
 ♿ advance notice required
♐ in garden and park

► *KINGTON* ◄

HERGEST CROFT GARDENS

Country garden and country walks

Kington, Herefordshire HR5 3EG
☏ Kington (0544) 230160

One of the finest collections of trees and flowering shrubs in Britain in a garden for all seasons. An old fashioned kitchen garden has spring and summer borders. Park Wood is a hidden valley with rhododendrons up to 30 feet tall.

Turn left off the A44 at west side of Kington
Open May–Oct
Admission: adult £1.50 child 70p
 ♿♐

► *LEOMINSTER* ◄

BERRINGTON HALL – NATIONAL TRUST

Country mansion and garden

Leominster, Herefordshire HR6 0DW
☏ Leominster (0568) 5721

An elegant late 18th century mansion by Henry Holland set in a landscaped park by 'Capability' Brown. Richly decorated interior with fine furniture; Nursery, Dairy, & Victorian laundry. Interesting garden including historic apple orchard.

Signposted off the A49, 3 miles north of Leominster, 7 miles south of Ludlow
Open April: Sat, Sun and Bank Holiday Monday 1.30–5.30pm (closed Good Friday); May–Sept Wed–Sun and Bank Holiday Mondays 1.30–5.30pm; Oct weekends 1.30–4.30pm
Admission: adult £2.50, child £1.25, parties £2.10 National Trust Members free
 ♿

BROADFIELD GARDENS AND VINEYARDS

Country gardens, vineyard and shop

Broadfield Court Estate, Bodenham, Herefordshire HR1 3LG
☏ Bodenham (056 884) 483

Old English gardens and 15 acre vineyard at Broadfield which was mentioned in the Domesday Book. Open for guided tours for parties, wine tasting and light refreshments, tea/supper by arrangement.

From Leominster take the A49 for 4 miles, left onto the A417, take signs for broadfield after 2½ miles
Open Easter Monday–31 Oct daily 11.00am–4.30pm. Closed Mondays except Bank Holidays
Admission: adult £2.00, child 50p, OAP £1.50 (1990 prices)
 ♿ advance notice required ⚑

CROFT CASTLE – NATIONAL TRUST

Country park, walk and garden

Leominster, Herefordshire HR6 9PW
☏ Yarpole (0568 85) 246

The four round corner towers and ancient walls date from the 14th or 15th century; inside, the fine Georgian Gothic staircase and ceilings were added in the 18th century. Park contains avenues of Spanish Chestnut 400 years old.

5 miles north west of Leominster signposted off the A49 and the A4110
Open April: weekends 2.00–5.00pm, Easter Sat, Sun & Mon 2.00–6.00pm; May–Sept Wed–Sun & Bank Holiday Monday 2.00–6.00pm; Oct weekends 2.00–5.00pm
Admission: adult £2.40, family ticket £6.30, parties by prior arrangement
  some parts accessible by wheelchair. Wheelchair available
♿ by appointment only
♐ in the park

THE ELMS

Country garden, speciality food producer

Eardisland, Leominster, Herefordshire HR6 9BN
☏ Pembridge (05447) 405

House set in 32 acres of grassland in the heart of the English Marches serving

*traditional cream and farmhouse teas in a
no-smoking tearoom. Home made lemonade,
scones and cakes served on bone china. Egon
Ronay recommended.*

¾ mile off the A44 at west end of village. 5 miles
from Leominster
Open Easter week, Spring Bank Holiday 25 May–31 Aug
2.30–5.30pm. Other times by appointment
Free admission
& no toilets ∰ advance notice preferred
✝ not in tearoom

LUGG VALLEY FIELD CENTRE

Country walk and garden

Pipes Trow Farm, Byton, nr Presteigne, Herefordshire
LD8 2HS
☎ Presteigne (0544) 267968

*Field Centre and wildlife sanctuary in
setting of a working farm; wildflower
gardens, wetlands and walks. Also indoor
audio-visual nature and countryside
exhibition.*

Just off the B4362, which can be reached from
Leominster via the A44 or the A4110 (20
minutes)
Open 1 April–31 Oct, Tue, Wed, Thur, Sat & Sun
11.00am–6.00pm. Closed Mon & Fri except Bank
Holidays
Admission: adult £2.50, child £1.50, family ticket (2
adults and up to 3 children) £7.50. Party rates
available on application
& ∰ advance notice required ✗

WILLOWS NURSERIES

Garden nursery

Newtown Lane, Leominster, Herefordshire HR6 8QD
☎ Leominster (0568) 4041

*Specialist garden nursery selling herbaceous
plants.*

2 miles west of town centre, first lane left from
Barons Cross A44 junction
Open most days throughout the year, 11.00am–5.00pm.
Please telephone first
Free admission
& there are no disabled toilet facilities ✝

▶ **MUCH MARCLE** ◀

H WESTON & SONS LIMITED

Cider and perry makers

The Bounds, Much Marcle, Ledbury, Herefordshire
HR8 2NQ
☎ Much Marcle (053 184) 233

Situated between Ledbury and Ross-on-Wye on the
A449, on entering Much Marcle turn between
Westons garage and post office and proceed
uphill for ¼ mile
Open weekdays 9.00am–5.00pm, tours Easter–Dec, Tues
& Thur 2.30pm
Free admission
& ∰ advance notice required ✗

▶ **PEMBRIDGE** ◀

DUNKERTONS CIDER COMPANY

Cider mill

Luntley, Pembridge, nr Leominster, Herefordshire
HR6 9ED
☎ Pembridge (05447) 653

*Only unsprayed genuine cider apples like
Foxwhelp and Dabinett are pressed. We
bottle blends, single varieties and organic
perry. All are still, strong and delicious.
Come and taste from the oak cask.
Production area can be seen on request.*

From Leominster on the A44, turn left in
Pembridge at the New Inn, follow our signs for 1
mile, on the left
Open all year Mon–Sat 10.00am–6.00pm; May–Sept Sun
12.00 noon–3.00pm, Oct–April closed Sunday
Free admission
& we go out to disabled visitors to talk to them in their
car, take them samples and serve them ∰ ✗

▶ **PONTRILAS** ◀

ROWLSTONE POTTERY

Craft centre

Rowlstone, Pontrilas, Herefordshire HR2 0DW
☎ Golden Valley (0981) 240759

*A small country pottery by an interesting
church making domestic stoneware for sale
in a variety of styles and sizes. You may ask
to see the potter at work*

12 miles south west of Hereford. Rowlstone is
signposted off the A465 at Pontrilas
Open: please telephone for details
Free admission
&. there is a ramp entrance to showroom and working
area 🚌 🛏

► *ROSS-ON-WYE* ◄

HOW CAPLE COURT

Edwardian gardens, fabric shop, plant nursery

How Caple, Herefordshire HR1 4SX
☎ How Caple (098 986) 626

*11 acres of Edwardian gardens overlooking
the River Wye featuring formal terraces,
pools, herbaceous borders; mature trees and
woodland; sunken Florentine garden under
restoration. Nursery specializing in old roses
and unusual herbaceous plants.*

Off the B4224, 5 miles from Ross on the
Ross–Fownhope–Hereford road
Open for the garden & nursery: Mon–Sat 9.30am–
4.30pm, Sun (1 May–1 Oct) 10.00am–5.00pm. Shop:
Mon–Sat 9.30am–4.30pm
Free admission but gardens £1.75 (1990 prices)
&. access to shop only
🚌 advance notice required 🛏

MSF COUNTRY SUPERSTORE

Farm shop

Overross, Ross-on-Wye, Herefordshire HR9 7QJ
☎ Ross-on-Wye (0989) 62264

*Country clothing and fashion, saddlery and
tack, garden centre, giftware and cafe.
Delicatessen and fine wines.*

On the A40, just outside Ross-on-Wye
Open Mon–Fri 8.30am–6.00pm, Sat 8.30am–5.30pm,
Sundays 10.00am–5.00pm March–Aug only
Free admission
&. 🚌 ✗

ROSS-ON-WYE CANDLEMAKERS

Craft centre

Old Gloucester Rd, Ross-on-Wye, Herefordshire HR9 5PB
☎ Ross-on-Wye (0989) 63697

*One of Britain's leading candlemakers,
manufacturing all types of table, party,
perfumed and souvenir candles using
modern and traditional methods. Shop and
workshop open to the public.*

200 yards from the Market House
Open Mon–Sat 9.00am–5.00pm. Evening demonstrations
by arrangement
Free admission to shop and workshop. Small charge for
evening visits
&. 🚌 advance notice required ✗

WYE VALLEY FARM PARK

**Farm interpretation centre, country walk, farm
trail and visit**

Goodrich, Ross-on-Wye, Herefordshire HR9 6JN
☎ Symonds Yat (0600) 890296

*Farm park where children are encouraged to
get close to and touch, wherever possible, a
collection of animals from a bygone era.
Lovely riverside and woodland walk.*

Follow signs from Goodrich
Open Easter–end Oct daily 10.00am–5.00pm
Admission: adult £2.00, child £1.00, party rates available
(1990 prices)
&. no toilets 🚌 🛏 but not near the animals

► *WEOBLEY* ◄

THE DAIRY HOUSE

Speciality food or drink producer

Whitehill Park, Weobley, Herefordshire HR4 8QE
☎ Weobley (0544) 318815

*This small Herefordshire dairy specializes in
the production of fresh soft cheeses,
yoghurts, cream and cheesecakes. Suppliers
to high quality retailers throughout the
villages and county towns.*

On the B4230, just off the A4112, ½ mile north
west of Weobley
Open all year Mon–Fri 8.30am–4.00pm
&. ✗

HERTFORDSHIRE

Hertfordshire, one of the Home Counties, is criss-crossed by ancient footpaths. It is a landscape of leafy lanes and unspoilt villages – a typically English rural scene.

Its proximity to London has encouraged the building of many fine houses and stately homes over the centuries and several of these are now open for everyone to enjoy their very diverse attractions. There are also country parks and a wild wood, nature reserves and a RSPB reserve, working farms and a rare breeds centre, woodturning workshops and a stained glass studio to explore. For those interested in the local produce there are fish farms and venison producers, farm shops that also include organic produce, vineyards and pick-your-own, all within easy reach of central London.

► BALDOCK ◄

RADWELL MILL

Riverside walk, wildfowl collection

Lake Caravan Site, Radwell Mill, Baldock, Hertfordshire
☎ Hitchin (0462) 730253

Wildlife and birdwatching £2.50 per night for members.

Turn off the A1(M) at exit 10 then on the A507 towards Baldock, ½ mile just turn right through village to lake
Open March–Nov
Free admission to lake viewing point
&. 🛉

► BERKHAMSTED ◄

ASHRIDGE MANAGEMENT COLLEGE

Country garden

Berkhamsted, Hertfordshire HP4 1NS
☎ Little Gaddesden (044284) 3491

The gardens at Ashridge, influenced by Humphrey Repton, enjoy a spectacular natural setting. 150 acres with many interesting and unusual plants, surrounded by woodlands.

Past the railway station (off A41) first left under bridge, turn left at next major junction. Proceed to next junction, turn left, follow road straight on to Ashridge (approx 4 miles from station)
Open every weekend April–Oct
Admission: adult £1.50 child/OAP 75p for gardens
&. 🚌 advance notice required 🛉

FRITHSDEN VINEYARD

Vineyard

38 Crouchfield, Boxmoor, Hemel Hempstead, Hertfordshire HP1 1PA
☎ Hemel Hempstead (0442) 57902

From Hemel Hempstead take the A4146 to Leighton Buzzard, signposted most of the way
Open Sunday 11.15am–2.00pm for tours of vineyard, winery and wine tasting, other visits by appointment
Admission: adult £2.50. child free
&. however some surfaces are not suitable for wheelchairs
🚌 advance notice required 🛉

► BISHOP'S STORTFORD ◄

CAMMAS HALL FRUIT FARM

Pick your own

Cammas Hall, Hatfield Broad Oak, nr Bishop's Stortford, Hertfordshire CM22 7JT
☎ Hatfield (027970) 777

Specialist strawberry and raspberry growers situated in lovely countryside – offering top quality produce and a genuine welcome to all our visitors – young and old.

Take the M11 to Bishop's Stortford, A120 east to Takeley, B183 to Hatfield Broad Oak and follow signs
Open June–July
Free admission
&. 🚌 🛉

HATFIELD FOREST – NATIONAL TRUST

Country park and walks, forest and nature reserve

Hatfield Forest, nr Bishop's Stortford, Hertfordshire
☎ Bishop's Stortford (0279) 870678

Widely considered the last of the small mediaeval forests in complete working condition, Hatfield Forest has a depth of historical and biological interests almost unrivalled in this country.

3 miles from jct 8 on the M11
Open all year
Admission: car park £2.00, coach £20.00, school £10.00
&. 🚌 🛉

► BOREHAMWOOD ◄

ALDENHAM COUNTRY PARK

Country park, farm interpretation centre, country walk & farm trail

The Park Office, Dagger Lane, Elstree, Borehamwood, Hertfordshire WD6 3AT
☎ (081) 953 9602

Home of the Aldenham herd of rare breed longhorn cattle, the Country Park provides the perfect setting for an enjoyable day out. Adventure playground, angling and countryside events.

Off the A411, 2 miles west of Borehamwood
Open all year (except Christmas Day) 9.00am until 1 hour before dusk
Free admission car park 50p per car (1988 prices)
&. 🚌 advance notice required 🛉

▶ BUNTINGFORD ◀

THE PELHAM VENISON COMPANY LIMITED

Farm shop

Estate Office, Furneaux Pelham Hall, Buntingford,
Hertfordshire SG9 0JP
☎ (027 978 348

Full range of prime farmed venison. Orders can be prepared in advance or posted.

Via Hare Street, Lt. Hormead, Furneaux Pelham
Open Mon–Fri 9.00am–6.00pm
Free admission
&. ━ advance notice required ✘

▶ CUFFLEY ◀

NORTHAW GREAT WOOD

Country walk, country park and wild wood

The Ridgeway, Cuffley, nr Potters Bar, Hertfordshire
EN6 4BH
☎ (0707) 872213

This Site of Special Scientific Interest comprises 290 acres of ancient forest with marked paths, interesting flora and fauna and now has a visitor information centre.

Off the B157, 2 miles west of Cuffley
Open all year (except Christmas Day) 8.00am–6.00pm for
cars 8.00am–dusk for pedestrians. Dec–Feb closed
4.30pm for cars
Admission Mon–Fri (trust box) cars 20p. Sat & Sun 50p
(1990 prices)
&. ✝ in car park, off leash in wood provided under
control

▶ HARPENDEN ◀

THRALES END QUALITY FRUIT FARM

Pick your own

Thrales End, Harpenden, Hertfordshire AL5 3NS
☎ Harpenden (0582) 460919

Pick your own strawberries, raspberries, gooseberries and tayberries. Cream and ice cream available in caravan.

Adjoining north Harpenden on the A1081
Open June–Aug daily except Mondays, 9.30am–7.00pm
Free admission
&. ━ advance notice required
✝ in car park only

▶ HATFIELD ◀

HATFIELD HOUSE

Historic home, park and gardens

Hatfield, Hertfordshire AL9 5NQ
☎ Hatfield (07072) 62823

Historic Jacobean house (1611), Old Palace (1497); Great Park with nature trail and venture play area; formal knot, scented and wilderness gardens. Model soldiers, kitchen exhibitions, gift and garden shops, licensed restaurant.

On the A1000, signposted from the A1(M) and the
A414. Entrance opposite BR station
Open 25 March–13 Oct (1991): Tue–Sat 12.00
noon–5.00pm, Sun 1.30–5.00pm. Closed Mondays
except Bank Holidays
Admission for house/park/gardens/exhibitions: adult
£3.85, child £2.65, OAP £3.30; park/
gardens/exhibitions: adult £2.15, child £1.60, OAP
£2.00
&. ━ ✝

▶ HODDESDON ◀

RYE HOUSE MARSH

RSPB wildlife reserve

Hertfordshire

Opposite Rye House station, east of Hoddesdon
Open daily 10.00am–5.00pm
Admission: adult £1.00, child 50p
&. ━ ✘

▶ LETCHWORTH ◀

MANOR FARM SHOP

Farm shop

Manor Farm, Wilwan, Letchworth, Hertfordshire
☎ Letchworth (0462) 480828

General farm shop with a good range of fruit and vegetables, goats and sheeps milk and a selection of honey. Also English wine.

On the Wilwan-Wymondley road, south of
Letchworth
Open Mon–Thur 8.30am–5.00pm, Friday 8.30am–
6.00pm, Saturday 8.30am–5.00pm, Sunday 10.00am–
1.00pm
Free admission
&. ━ ✘

NORTH HERTFORDSHIRE MUSEUMS

Museum

The Letchworth Museum, Broadway, Letchworth,
Hertfordshire SG6 3PF
☎ Letchworth (0462) 685647

*Letchworth Museum has galleries reflecting
the natural history and archaeology of North
Hertfordshire. A third gallery houses
temporary art exhibitions which are changed
monthly. Other regular events include the
Craftsmen of the Month, and Collectors
Corner show cases.*

In town centre, 1½ miles from the A1(M)
Open Mon–Sat 10.00am–5.00pm
Free admission
♿ reasonable access to ground floor (Natural History)
only. Entry assistance available
🚌 ✗

STANDALONE FARM

Working farm, museum, wildlife area

Wilbury Rd, Letchworth Garden City, Hertfordshire
SG6 4JN
☎ Letchworth (0462) 686775

*Working farm with cattle, sheep, pigs and
poultry including Warrant the Shire horse
and Rodey the donkey. Wildfowl area,
museum, daily milking demo; inside/outside
picnic area, refreshments, shop.*

Signposted from all entrances to Letchworth
Open end March–end Oct daily, 10.00am–5.00pm
Admission: adult £1.80, child/OAP 90p, under 3s free.
Special rates for booked groups and schools
♿ wheelchair available
🚌 advance notice required
✗ except guide dogs

◄ ### RADLETT ►

PA & GM HAWORTH

Farm shop

Battlers Green Farm Shop, Common Lane, Radlett,
Hertfordshire WD7 8PH
☎ Radlett (0923) 856551

*Fresh table poultry and eggs, fruit,
vegetables and groceries. Comprehensive
cheese counter, Organic Free Range Meats,
Fresh Fish (Tue–Sun only). Also a pet shop
and a florist.*

Take the B462 from Radlett towards Watford, take
the third left turn (New Road) and the farm shop
is 750 yards on the right hand side
Open daily, Mon–Fri 9.00am–5.45pm, Sat 9.00am–
5.30pm, Sundays and Bank Holidays 9.00am–1.00pm
Free admission
♿ no toilets 🚌 ✗

◄ ### RICKMANSWORTH ►

CHERRY TREES FARM

**Organic farm shop, craft centre, farm trail and
visit, speciality food producer**

Olleberrie Lane, Belsize, Sarratt, Rickmansworth,
Hertfordshire WD3 4NU
☎ (0923) 268289

*Visitors can wander amongst rare breeds of
poultry and livestock in a traditional setting,
join in egg collecting or romp in the straw
barn. Also wholefood tearooms.*

From the M25 at Chorleywood take the A404 (to
Amersham) take right hand turn to Sarratt, go
through Church End. Turn left at Sarratt for
Belsize, to the left of the Plough public house,
turn down Flaunden Lane. Turn right after 100
yards into Olleberris Lane. Cherry Trees Farm is
½ mile on the left
Open all year Wed–Sun and Bank Holiday Mondays,
11.00am–5.00pm
Admission: adult/child £1.50
♿ 🚌 advance notice required ✗

◄ ### ROYSTON ►

DOCWRA'S MANOR GARDEN & NURSERY

Country garden

Shepreth, Royston, Hertfordshire
☎ Royston (0763) 260235/261557

*A 2½ acres garden in which choice plants
are grown in informal settings. Many of
these plants are offered for sale in the small
nursery.*

8 miles south west of Cambridge, ½ mile off the
A10 between Royston and Cambridge
Open 1 March–31 Oct: Wed and Fri 10.00am–5.00pm;
first Sunday of the month 2.00–5.00pm; Bank Holiday
Mondays 10.00am–5.00pm
Admission: £1.00 (1990 prices)
♿ 🚌 advance notice required ✗

THE CROSSING HOUSE

Country garden

78 Meldreth Road, Shepreth, Royston, Hertfordshire
SG8 6PS
☎ Royston (0763) 261071

*Small cottage garden with many old
fashioned plants grown in mixed beds in
company with modern varieties, shrubs,
bulbs etc. Many alpines in rock beds and
alpine house.*

8 miles south west of Cambridge, ½ mile west of
the A10
Open all year daily any time
Free admission
♿ 🚐 advance notice required 🐄 🐂

FOXHALL STUDIO

Stained glass studio

Kelshall, nr Royston, Hertfordshire SG8 9SE
☎ Kelshall (076387) 209

*A wide range of stained glass creations on
display and for sale, from small gifts to
larger items. Unusual and unique
lampshades, terrariums, jewel boxes,
windows and suncatchers. Commissions
undertaken.*

From Royston take the A505 towards Baldock, turn
left after ¾ mile. Follow signposts to Kelshall
Open all year daily but telephone first before making a
special journey
Free admission
🐂

THE MALTINGS STUDIO

**Studio and workshops making furniture and
domestic woodware**

The Maltings, 99 North End, Meldreth, nr Royston,
Hertfordshire SG8 6NY
☎ Royston (0763) 61615

*The Maltings Studio is full of hand-turned
wooden bowls, platters, fruit bowls etc. and
exclusive furniture in solid English
hardwoods made to order in the Maltings
workshop.*

Off the A10 8 miles south of Cambridge
Open Mon–Fri 8.30am–1.00pm, 2.00–5.30pm. Always
by prior appointment
Free admission
♿ 🚐 advance notice required

SHEPRETH MILL FISH FARM

Farm shop and fishing

Shepreth Mill, nr Royston, Hertfordshire SG8 6OZ
☎ Royston (0763) 260351

*Brown, rainbow and American Brook trout
in the fishery. Also ornamental fish section,
herb garden and tea garden.*

On main A10 Royston–Cambridge road 5 miles
from Royston, 7 from Cambridge
Open all year Mon–Sat 9.00am–5.30pm, Sunday
11.00am–4.00pm
Free admission
♿ 🚐 advance notice required

WILLERS MILL

Wildlife sanctuary and fish farm

Station Rd, Shepreth, nr Royston, Hertfordshire SG8 6PZ
☎ Royston (0763) 261832

*Set in natural grounds and lakes with a
large collection of birds, animals and fish
including large carp that will eat from your
hand. Cafeteria, pets corner, sandpit,
dodgems, play fort. Farm shop selling pond
fish and accessories.*

Just off the A10, 5 miles north of Royston
Open 1 Nov–1 March 10.30am–5.00pm; 2 March–31 Oct
10.30am–6.00pm
Admission: Mon–Sat adult £2.50, child £1.25, OAP
£1.75; Sundays and Bank Holidays adult £3.00, Child
£1.50, OAP £2.25, under 2s free
♿ 🚐 ✗

WIMPOLE HOME FARM – NATIONAL TRUST

Farm visit, rare breeds centre

The National Trust, Arrington, nr Royston, Hertfordshire
SG8 0BW
☎ Cambridge (0223) 207257

*Wimpole Home Farm was built in 1794 to
demonstrate new agricultural techniques and
breeding stock. Now it is a rare breeds centre
with fascinating varieties of farm animals,
such as Hebridean sheep, Tamworth pigs
and longhorn cattle.*

Signposted from the M11, A603 and A14
Open April–Oct, Sat, Sun, Tue, Wed, Thur and Bank
Holiday Mondays 10.30am–5.00pm
Admisssion: adult £2.50, child £1.25 (1990 prices)
♿ 🚐 ✗

▶ **ST ALBANS** ◀

THE HERTS & MIDDLESEX WILDLIFE TRUST

Country walk, local countryside and wildlife information centre

Grebe House, St Michael's Street, St Albans, Hertfordshire AL3 4SN
☎ St Albans (0727) 58901

Local countryside and wildlife information centre consisting of displays, a wildlife garden, children's games and details of 49 nature reserves.

The centre is situated in Verulamium park, next to the Verulamium museum
Open March–Dec weekdays 10.00am–4.30pm, Sat 10.00am–4.30pm, Sun 2.00–4.30pm
Free admission
& toilet facilities are available a short distance away
🚌 🐕

THE GARDENS OF THE ROSE

Country gardens

Chiswell Green Lane, Chiswell Green, St Albans, Hertfordshire AL2 3NR
☎ St Albans (0727) 50461

12 acres of gardens of the Royal National Rose Society with over 30,000 roses – species, historic, modern and roses of the future in the international trial ground. Some 1650 different varieties in a peaceful and beautiful English garden.

Off the B4630 St Albans–Watford road, 2 miles south of St Albans
Open June–Oct, Mon–Sat 9.00am–5.00pm, Sunday and Bank Holidays 10.00am–6.00pm
Admission: adult £2.00, child accompanied and under 16 free, parties of 20+ £1.50 per person, disabled £1.00 (1990 prices)
& 🚌 🐕

▶ **STEVENAGE** ◀

KNEBWORTH HOUSE, GARDENS & COUNTRY PARK

Country park, country garden, stately home, deer park & adventure playground

Knebworth, Hertfordshire SG3 6PY
☎ Stevenage (0438) 812661

Home of the Lytton family for 500 years, set in 250 acres of parkland. Gardens by

Lutyens, British Raj exhibition, large adventure playground, licensed restaurant in 16th century tythe barn.

Direct access from the A1(M) at jct 7 (Stevenage South)
Open Easter–Sept. Park: 11.00am–5.30pm. House and gardens: 12 noon–5.00pm
Admission: house/park/gardens adult £3.50, child/OAP £3.00 park & playground only £2.00 special party rates available (1990 prices)
& 🚌 🐕

ROGER HARVEY GARDEN WORLD

Garden centre

The Farm House, Bragbury Lane, Stevenange, Hertfordshire SG2 8TJ
☎ Stevenage (0483) 811777

Unique garden centre house in old farm buildings with seasonal displays of plants, bulbs and Christmas decorations. Adventure playground, pets corner; tropical fish; coffee house specializing in cream teas.

Take Exit 7 off the A1, 2 miles east on the A602 Hertford road
Open all year daily 9.00am–5.30pm in winter, 9.00am–6.00pm in summer. Late night opening, Wed, Thur & Fri April–June until 8.00pm
Free admission
& 🚌 advance notice preferred 🐕

▶ **TRING** ◀

THE ASHRIDGE ESTATE

Country walk

Ringshall, Berkhamsted, Hertfordshire
☎ Aldbury Common (044 285) 227

At Northchurch just off B4506, 3 miles north of the A41 approaching from the B4506 Northchurch–Ringshall road, visitors will find a car park and facilities near the monument
Open all year for estate. Monument shop & Information Centre April–Oct, Mon–Thur 2.00–5.00pm, Sat Sun & Bank Holiday Monday 2.00–5.30pm
Admission: free to estate, monument 50p parking facilities 50p on summer weekends (1990 prices)
& access for disabled visitors in monument area, on monument drive and Information Centre, special parking near Information Centre, Disabled toilet. Self-drive battery powered vehicles available free of charge from Information Centre: advance booking advisable
🚌 advance notice required 🐕

► *WATFORD* ◄

BLACKBIRDS COUNTRY FARE

Farm shop, pick your own, country walks, plant centre, farm animals

Oakridge Farms Limited, Blackbirds Farm, Aldenham,
    Watford, Hertfordshire WD2 8BS
☎ (0923) 853771

A range of activities and country interests: nature trail, farm animals and birds, PYO produce, farm shop, bonsai and garden centre and caravan park.

Just off the B462 between Radlett and Watford.
    2 miles from jct 5 of the M1
Open all year
Free admission
& ⇌ advance notice required ✘

Guide to Symbols

☎	telephone	⋈	dogs welcome (on a leash)
&	disabled welcome	✘	dogs not welcome
⇌	coaches welcome		

KENT

Kent has been not only the 'gateway to England' but also the 'garden of England' through the centuries. Narrow winding lanes twist around the fruit orchards, the hop gardens, the eye-catching conical oast houses, past the many great houses and through the neat villages.

Kent has more than its share of historic houses and converted castles, several welcome visitors to their gardens and attractions. The fertile land supports many vineyards that offer samples of their produce to refresh the country wanderer as they tour the country parks, enjoy the animals, see the working watermills and windmills in action, visit the model museum or watch locally grown rush being woven into seats.

► ASHFORD ◄

GODINTON PARK

Country garden, historic house and park

Godinton Park, Ashford, Kent TN23 3BW
☎ Ashford (0233) 20773

Mainly Stuart house, the interior contains a wealth of very fine panelling and carving, portraits, furniture and china. Set in gardens originally laid out in the 18th century.

2½ miles from Ashford
Open June–Sept Sundays and Bank Holidays
Admission: adult £1.50, child 70p, parties over 20 £1.20 each
&. 🚐 🏌

SWANTON MILL

Country garden, working water mill

Lower Mersham, Ashford, Kent TN25 7HS
☎ Aldington (023372) 223 or 071 937 0931

Working water mill with 3 acre garden. Organically grown wheat used; milled flour on sale.

Turn off the A20 to Mersham. From Mersham, mill is marked with brown tourist signs
Open April–Sept weekends 2.00–6.00pm, or by appointment
Admission: £1.00 per person
&. access to garden but mill not suitable 🚐 🎍

► BIDDENDEN ◄

BIDDENDEN VINEYARDS

Vineyard, winery and cider works

Little Whatmans, Biddenden, Ashford, Kent TN27 8DH
☎ Biddenden (0580) 291726

Kent's oldest established commercial vineyard with 22 acres of vines. Enjoy a leisurely stroll round our vineyard walks and winery, then taste our range of wines, ciders and apple juice.

1½ miles south on the Benenden road, follow signs from village
Open all year daily, please telephone to check opening times
Free admission
&. 🚐 advance notice required 🏌

► CANTERBURY ◄

BADGERS HILL FARM

Cider farm and craft centre

Chilham, nr Canterbury, Kent
☎ Canterbury (0227) 730573

Largest selection in the south east for oak barrels. Picnic area, childrens play area, herbaceous plant centre. Pick your own, free range poultry and animals.

Off the A252, 5 miles from Canterbury in the Charing direction
Open daily 9.00am–5.30pm
Free admission
&. 🚐 🏌

CHILHAM CASTLE GARDENS

Country garden

Chilham, Canterbury, Kent CT4 8DB
☎ Canterbury (0227) 730319

A peaceful and scenic garden of old terraces, fine lawns and topiary overlooking the lake, with a rock garden and lakeside walk. Magnificent views over the Stour River valley. Birds of prey flying free.

On the A252, 6 miles south west of Canterbury
Open April–mid Oct daily 11.00am–5.00pm
Admission: Mon–Fri (no birds of prey), adult £2.00, child £1.00; other days adult £2.30, child £1.15. Events as advertised
&. 🚐 🏌

ELHAM VALLEY VINEYARDS

Vineyards, winery, shop and picnic area

Breach, Barham, nr Canterbury, Kent CT4 6LN
☎ Canterbury (0227) 831266

Small, commercial vineyard planted by the resident owners. Purpose built winery has the latest wine making equipment in pursuit of ever higher quality wines.

8 miles south west of Canterbury on the B2065, well signposted
Open 1 May–31 Dec wine sales only; 1 June–30 Sept self guided tours and wine sales, Wed–Sun and Bank Holiday Mondays 11.00am–5.00pm. Telephone first to ensure open
Admission: for self guided tours £1.00
&. 🎍

THE MASTER MAKERS

Craft centre with coffee shop and workshops

Howfield Lane, Chartham, Canterbury, Kent CT4 7HQ
☎ Canterbury (0227) 730183

Wander around and see master craftsmen producing highly original work. Assistance readily given with enquiries and purchases.

2 miles west of Canterbury, on the A28 towards Ashford
Open all year Mon–Sat 9.30am–6.00pm including Bank Holidays
Free admission
& ⛟ advance notice required
🐕 only in the grounds

PARSONAGE FARM RURAL HERITAGE CENTRE

Farm visit, museum and interpretation centre

North Elham, nr Canterbury, Kent CT4 6UY
☎ Elham (0303) 840766/840356

Old and rare breeds, particularly sheep on a family run working farm displaying its history and present-day work. Trail, museum, crafts, tea room and shop.

Just off the B2065, 10 miles south of Canterbury
Open 29 March–30 Sept. Closed Mondays except for Bank Holidays
Admission: adult £1.90, child £1.10, OAP £1.20. Special rates for pre–booked parties of 12 or more people
& 🐕

SARRE WINDMILL

Working mill, shop and tearooms

Canterbury Rd, Sarre, Kent CT7 0JU
☎ Thanet (0843) 47573

19th century smock mill undergoing complete restoration, powered by 1922 gas engine and producing wholemeal flour. Craft shop, tearooms, toilets. Agricultural bygones displayed in mill yard.

Just off the A253 Canterbury–Ramsgate road. Lane to the mill on left leaving Sarre village towards Ramsgate. Signposted
Open all year daily 10.00am–5.00pm
Admission: adult 50p, child 25p
& ⛟ advance notice required 🐕

STAPLE VINEYARDS

Vineyards

Church Farm, Staple, Canterbury, Kent CT3 1LN
☎ Ash (0304) 812571

Attractive vineyard trail around 7 acres of vines; a small collection of old farm implements, a walk through the winery followed by a tasting of Staple St James wines.

From Canterbury take the A257 to Wingham, then off the B2046 to Staple, vineyard opposite the church
Open Easter, then May–Sept 10.00am–5.00pm (Sun 12.00 noon–4.00pm). Rest of year irregular opening hours for wine sales only
Admission for self guided tours £1.20 (includes wine tasting and tour of vineyards and winery)
& ⛟ advance notice required 🐕

ST NICHOLAS OF ASH VINEYARD AND WINERY

Vineyard

Moat Farm House, Ash, Canterbury, Kent CT3 2DG
☎ Ash (0304) 812670

Vineyard trail between St Nicholas and 2 vineyards in adjoining villages. Thatched shop, picnic area and gardens around a 15th century farmhouse (not open) run by the Wilkinson family who personally welcome visitors.

On A257 Canterbury–Sandwich road, signposted opposite Lion Hotel in heart of village. (2 mins from main road on south side of Ash)
Open April–Oct daily 10.00am–6.00pm. Nov–March 10.00am–dusk, weekends. Any other time by appointment
Free admission. Group tours of vineyard and winery with wine tasting: £1.25 per adult. Vineyard walkabout with informative leaflet, incl wine tasing: £1.25 per adult (1990 prices)
& ⛟ advance notice required 🐕

THEOBALDS BARN CIDER

Farm shop and cider producer

Heronsgate Farm, Stourmouth, nr Canterbury, Kent CT3 1HZ
☎ Canterbury (0227) 722275

We grow and press our own fruit for making natural cider and pure apple juice.

Take the B2046 Wingham–Thanet road and approx 5 miles from Wingham on the left hand side; or from Thanet take the B2046 direction Plucks Gutter, on the right hand side after 5 minutes
Open Jan–June 10.00am–4.30pm, Tues, Thur & Sat; June–Dec 10.00am–5.00pm Tues–Sat, Sundays 10.30am–1.00pm, 2.30–5.00pm
Free admission
&. ￼ advance notice required ￼

THREE CORNERS VINEYARD

Vineyards

Beacon Lane, Woodnesborough, Kent CT13 0PA
☎ Ash (0304) 812025

Family run vineyard with superb views to the white cliffs of Pegwell Bay. Free tastings of 3 elegant white wines. Free parking for walkers using the vineyard trail to 2 other vineyards.

10 miles from Canterbury off the A257 Canterbury–Sandwich road via Ash and Woodnesborough
Open daily 10.00am–6.00pm
Free admission to vineyard, off licence and vineyard trail, £2.00 for guided tour and wine tasting
&. ￼ advance notice required, max 30 people ￼

▶ CHATHAM ◀

CAPSTONE FARM COUNTRY PARK

Country park

Capstone Road, Gillingham, Kent ME7 3JG
☎ Medway (0634) 812196

Guided walks can be arranged at this country park which has picnic areas and a lake where coarse fishing is available during open season. Cafe/kiosk open March–Oct.

From the east on the A2 to Chatham, directional signs for Sittingbourne. Park signposted right at Luton Arches. From the M2 (Gillingham exit), park signposted left at roundabout
Open dawn until dusk daily all year. Visitor centre open by appointment to organised parties through Warden
Free admission
&. ￼ advance notice required ￼

▶ DEAL ◀

NORTHBOURNE COURT GARDEN

Country garden

c/o Court Cottages, Northbourne, Deal, Kent CT14 0LF
☎ Deal (0304) 360813

A fine example of a Tudor terraced garden, with 3 tiers of terraces and high flanking walls. Plants of the old fashioned variety predominate in these fine gardens.

Turn east off the A256 or west off the A258 following signs to Northbourne, in village follow 'Northbourne Court Garden' signs
Open several Sundays 2.00–6.00pm, and every Wednesday 2.00–5.00pm, in June, July and August. At other times by appointment
Admission: adult £1.50, child/OAP 50p, party rates available if booked in advance (1990 prices)
&. no disabled toilet facilities
￼ advance notice required ￼

▶ DOVER ◀

SUTTON COURT FARM

Riding school

'Cornilo Partners', Sutton Court, Sutton by Dover, Kent CT15 5DF
☎ Deal (0304) 375033

Riding school with livery facilities, RDA centre, escorted trail riding, dressage, show jumping and cross country courses for public events and for hire.

From roundabout at Whitfield on the A2, take Archers Court Road for 4 miles – do not turn off the road until you reach Sutton
Open all year for riding, caravans and camping
Free admission
&. recognised by the RDA as the 'Cornilo Group' ￼ advance notice required

WALMER COURT FARM

Farm shop and pick your own

Dover Rd, Walmer, Kent CT14 7PQ
☎ Deal (0304) 375033

Pick your own strawberries, farm shop and pine furniture shop.

From the roundabout at Whitfield on the A2, take the A258 towards Deal for 4 miles. Pass through Ringwould, farm on right at brow of hill
Open all year for shops, June and July for strawberries
Free admission
🛧 banned in strawberry fields

▶ EAST GRINSTEAD ◀

LOWER BASING FARM

Goat farm and farm shop

Furnace Lane, Cowden, Edenbridge, Kent TN8 7JU
☎ Cowden (0342) 850251

Goat farm on the Sussex/Surrey/Kent borders. Animals free-range, chickens and ducks also kept. Basing cheese, yoghurt, cream, meat, meat products, milk and ice cream, home made cakes and pastries. Farm shop.

Off the A264 Tunbridge Wells road, 4 miles east of East Grinstead, turn left towards Lingfield then first right
Open all year 8.00am–8.00pm
Free admission
♿ ➡ advance notice required 🛧

▶ EDENBRIDGE ◀

CHIDDINGSTONE VINEYARDS LIMITED

Vineyards

Vexour Farm, Chiddingstone, Edenbridge, Kent TN8 7BB
☎ Penshurst (0892) 870277

Winery and 28 acres of vines. No tours, but lovers of wine are always made welcome, and can taste estate bottled wines in the French style and buy at case prices.

8 miles south of Sevenoaks. Turn south off the B2027, 1 mile west of Chiddingstone Causeway village. Iron gates at river bridge approx 1 mile along this road
Open at any time to visitors who have first telephoned, even at short notice
Free admission
♿ 🛧

HEVER CASTLE AND GARDENS

Country garden

Hever, nr Edenbridge, Kent TN8 7NG
☎ Edenbridge (0732) 865224

Moated 13th century castle, home of Anne Boleyn, with lovely gardens, yew maze, topiary, Italian garden, lake, wooded walks, cascades and fountains. Garden shop, gift shop, licensed self-service restaurant.

3 miles south east of Edenbridge off the B2026, M25 jcts 5 & 6, 20 minutes
Open Easter–1st Sun in Nov daily, gardens open 11.00am
Admission to gardens: adult £2.70, child £1.60, family ticket (2 adults & 2 children 5–16) £7.00 (1990 prices). Additional charge for castle
♿ ➡ free parking 🛧 in gardens and grounds only

▶ FAVERSHAM ◀

DODDINGTON PLACE GARDEN

Landscaped Edwardian garden

Doddington Place, Doddington, nr Sittingbourne, Kent ME9 0BB
☎ Doddington (079 586) 385

10 acres of tranquil landscaped gardens. Fine trees, yew hedges and lawns; woodland rhododendron and azalea garden, formal terraces and sunken garden, extensive rock garden. Tea room and gift shop.

Off the A20, 4 miles north east of Lenham, or off the A2, 4 miles south west of Faversham
Open Easter Monday, then May–Sept, Wed & Bank Holiday Mondays 11.00am–6.00pm, groups by appointment
Admission: adult £1.50, child 25p
♿ 80% of gardens accessible, but limited access to tea room ➡ advance notice required
🛧 dogs allowed

RICKY HOLDSTOCK, SEAT WEAVER

Workshop

Hillside Cottage, The Forstal, Hernhill, Faversham, Kent ME13 9JQ
☎ Canterbury (0227) 751204

Seat weaving in rush, cane, seagrass, cord, etc. Member of the Guild of Master Craftsmen and the Basket Makers'

Association. Writer, lecturer and demonstrator of the craft.

Off the A299 (M2 jct 7), 3½ miles east of Faversham; or off the A2, 8 miles west of Canterbury
Open throughout the year, weekdays 9.00am–5.30pm. Phone call necessary in advance. Visitors limited to 6 people at any one time due to limited space
Free admission
 ♧ ♧

MOUNT EPHRAIM GARDENS

Craft centre, country gardens and vineyards

Hernhill, nr Faversham, Kent ME13 9TX
☎ Canterbury (0227) 751496

Terraced garden with beautiful views leading to small lake. Herbaceous borders, topiary, extensive Japanese rock garden, woodland area with rhododendrons, water garden, many fine trees, shrubs and rose terraces. Cream teas and lunches.

3 miles from end of the M2, 6 miles west of Canterbury, ½ mile north of the A2 at Boughton
Open May, June, Aug, Sept, Sundays and Bank Holidays only or weekdays by arrangement. Also in July by arrangement
Admission: adult £1.50, child 25p, group rate £1.25
♧ 🚐 advance notice required 🐼

▶ HERNE BAY ◀

HERNE MILL

Working windmill

Mill Lane, Herne Bay, Kent
☎ Herne Bay (0227) 368511/364660

Kentish smock mill built in 1789, successor to mills dating to 1400. Much original machinery, some in working order, and many exhibits. Maintained and operated by local volunteers.

From the A291 Canterbury–Herne Bay road, proceed via Mill View Road to junction with Mill Lane, turn left, Herne Mill is on left hand side
Open April–Sept Sundays and Bank Holidays 2.00–5.00pm also Thurs 2.00–6.00pm in peak holiday period
Admission: adult 50p, child 25p
♧ wheelchair access to ground floor. Steep stairs but may be accessible to some types of disabled
🚐 advance notice required 🐼

▶ HORSMONDEN ◀

MARLE PLACE GARDENS AND HERB NURSERY

Country garden and herb nursery

Marle Place, Brenchley, Kent TN12 7HS
☎ Brenchley (089272) 2304

Plantsmans garden with interesting trees and shrubs, featuring a Victorian gazebo, an Edwardian rockery, now planted with herbs, a walled fragrant garden and ornamental ponds. Woodland walks; teas.

On the B2162, 1 mile south of Horsmonden and 1½ miles north west of Lamberhurst, turn west on Marle Place Road
Open for the herb nursery: April–Oct Mon–Sat 10.00am–5.00pm. Gardens: April–Oct Weds only, or telephone for an appointment
Admission gardens: adult £1.50, child/OAP £1.00, nursery: no charge
♧ 🚐 advance notice required 🐼

▶ LAMBERHURST ◀

MR HEAVERS NOTED MODEL MUSEUM AND CRAFT CENTRE

Craft centre and museum

Forstal Farm, Tunbridge Wells, Kent
☎ Lamberhurst (0892) 890711

Converted oast complex housing Dickensian village street with crafts and other silly things of interest, model of 1920s fairground; Model Museum covers nursery themes, Victoriana, science and fantasy, and more.

From the A21 Hastings–Tunbridge Wells road take the A262 (near Lamberhurst), centre is approx ½ mile down the A262 on the right
Open all year daily 10.00am–6.00pm summer, 10.00am–dusk winter
Admission: adult £1.75, child/OAP 95p
♧ 🚐 advance notice required 🐼

▶ MAIDSTONE ◀

BEARSTED VINEYARD

Vineyard

24 Caring Lane, Bearsted, Maidstone, Kent ME14 4NJ
☎ Maidstone (0622) 36974

4 acres of vines. Bearsted wines, which range from dry to medium sweet, are bottled on the premises. Guided tours of winery and vineyard can be arranged for groups of 5 to 20 adults.

½ mile south of the A20, between Maidstone and Leeds Castle
Visitors by appointment only, please telephone
Self guided tour free of charge
&. ✗

BOUGHTON MONCHELSEA PLACE

Country gardens and farm museum

Nr Maidstone, Kent ME17 4BU
☎ Maidstone (0622) 43120

Battlemented Elizabethan manor with breathtaking views. Beautiful interior, still an intimate and inhabited 'home'. Walled gardens with unusual plants. Displays of dresses, carriages and early farm implements; tea rooms.

On the B2163, 4½ miles south of Boughton Monchelsea
Open Easter–Oct 9.00am–5.00pm, Wed, Sun and Bank Holidays; Sat in July and Aug 2.15–6.00pm
Admission to grounds: adult £1.20, child (under 14) 60p; house and grounds: £2.00 and £1.00 (1990 prices)
&. ⊞ ✗

BRATTLE FARM MUSEUM

Farm museum and craft centre

Brattle Farm, Staplehurst, Kent TN12 0HE
☎ (0580) 891222

Country museum featuring vintage cars, motorcycles, bikes, tractors, and wagons housed on a farm. Resident potter and saddler; animals including 2 oxen.

Off the A229, 9 miles south of Maidstone
Open Easter–Oct, Sundays and Bank Holidays 9.30am–6.30pm, groups by appointment
Admission: adult £1.00, child/OAP 50p, reduced rates for groups
&. ⊞ ✗

COBTREE – MUSEUM OF KENT LIFE

Farm shop, museum and country garden

Lock Lane, Sandling, Maidstone, Kent ME14 3AU
☎ Maidstone (0622) 63936

The history of Kent illustrated with inside displays and outside live exhibits on 27 acres of land; rare breeds and farm animals, hop gardens, market and herb gardens. Childrens play area; craft demonstrations and special events.

Off jct 6 of the M20, at intersection with the A229, 1 mile north of Maidstone
Open March–Oct, Mon–Fri 10.00am–5.00pm, Sat 12.00 noon–5.00pm, Sun 12.00 noon–6.00pm
Admission: adult £1.00, child 50p, events £1.50, 75p
&. ⊞ advance notice required ✗

DOWNINGBURY FARM SHOP AND PYO

Farm shop and pick your own

Downingbury Farm, Maidstone Rd, Pembury, Kent TN2 4AD
☎ Pembury (089282) 4282

An excellent selection of fruit and vegetables for pick your own, also a wide selection of farm produce in a farm shop open all year.

From Tunbridge Wells take Pembury and Maidstone road, 3 miles, farm shop 300 metres off the B2015 Maidstone road
Open daily except Christmas and Mondays in winter
Free admission
⊞ ✗

HEADCORN VINEYARD & FLOWER NURSERY

Vineyard and nursery

Grigg Lane, Headcorn, Kent TN27 9LX
☎ (0622) 890561

Tours offer a fascinating insight to the production of over 45,000 bottles of fine English wine and 4 million chrysanthemums and alstroemeria. Guided tours, refreshments, flower and gift shop.

Off the A274, 8 miles south of Maidstone. Follow signs from Headcorn High St
Open all year Mon–Sat 11.00am–4.30pm, Sun 11.30am–4.30pm
Admission for self guided tour including wine tasting, adult £1.00 (includes voucher worth 50p off one bottle of wine); guided tour £1.00 extra, as above
&. ⊞

KENT GARDEN COUNTRY WINES

Vineyard, country garden and craft centre

Yew Tree House, Upper St, Leeds, nr Maidstone, Kent
ME17 1SO
☎ Maidstone (0622) 861638

*Vineyard producing country wines where
visitors may look around the vineyard,
vinehouse, and winery. Wine sales etc.*

Turn off the M20 onto the B2163 for Leeds village
Open all year Thur–Sun and Bank Holidays 10.00am–
4.00pm
Free admission
& ⛟ advance notice required 🐾

LEEDS CASTLE

**Castle, maze, grotto, gardens, aviary, duckery
and vineyard**

Maidstone, Kent ME17 1PL
☎ Maidstone (0622) 765400

*Castle in an unforgettable setting on two
islands in a lake. Allow several hours to
enjoy the castle, park, superb gardens and
attractions. Also 17th century tithe barn
restaurant. Telephone the sales office for
details of special events.*

4 miles east of Maidstone at jct 8 of the M20/A20
Open 1 April–31 Oct daily 11.00am–5.00pm; Nov–March
weekends 11.00am–4.00pm
Admission to castle and park: adult £5.20, child £3.70,
OAP/student £4.20, reduced rate for groups
& ⛟ advance notice required 🐾

► MEOPHAM ◄

MEOPHAM WINDMILL

Restored windmill

Meopham Green, Meopham, Kent
☎ (0474) 813218

*A smock mill built in the early 19th century
by the Killick brothers, and sold to the
Norton family in the 1890s. Restored by the
KCC and Meopham Windmill Trust.*

On the A227, 6 miles south of Gravesend
Open June–Sept Sundays and Bank Holidays, Easter and
May Bank Holidays 2.30–4.30pm
Admission: adult 50p, child/OAP 25p. Parties by prior
arrangement including guided tour 30p all classes
(1990 prices)
& ⛟ advance notice required 🐾 in grounds only

► SEVENOAKS ◄

BOUGH BEECH CENTRE

**Countryside interpretative centre and information
centre**

Winkhurst Green, nr Ide Hill, Sevenoaks, Kent TN14 6LD
☎ Ide Hill (073275) 624

*The centre lies adjacent to the Kent Trust for
Nature Conservation's Bough Beech Nature
Reserve, with excellent bird watching across
the reservoir.*

2 miles south of Ide Hill off the B2042
Open Easter–Oct, Wed, Sat and Sun 11.00am–4.30pm
Free admission
& ⛟ 🐾

GREAT COMP GARDEN

Country garden

Borough Green, Sevenoaks, Kent TN15 8QS
☎ Borough Green (0732) 883889

*7 acres of formal gardens near the house,
then surrounded by informal planting with
woodland glades and winding paths. Wide
variety of plants, many for sale.*

Take the A20/A25 to Wrotham Heath, then the
B2016 for ½ mile, Great Comp signposted at
crossroads
Open April–Oct daily 11.00am–6.00pm
Admission: adult £2.00, child £1.00
& ⛟ 🐾

GREAT HOLLANDEN

Farm park, rare farm animals

Great Hollanden Farm, Mill Lane, Hildenborough,
nr Sevenoaks, Kent TN15 0SG
☎ (0732) 832276

*A survival centre for endangered species of
farm animals, with a coffee shop, play areas,
gift and farm shop.*

Hildenborough, nr Sevenoaks
Open Easter–mid Sept daily and most weekends in
winter, 10.30am–5.00pm
Admission: adult £2.50, child/OAP £1.50, disabled £1.20
(1990 prices)
&

THE HOP SHOP

Dried flower shop, pick your own

Castle Farm, Shoreham, Sevenoaks, Kent TN14 7UB
☎ Otford (09592) 3219

A wide and unusual range of English dried flowers grown on a family farm in the picturesque Darenth Valley. Pick your own apples available in September and October.

On the A225, halfway between the villages of Shoreham and Eynsford
Open Saturdays all year 10.00am–5.00pm; pyo apples mid Sept–mid Oct every afternoon
Free admission
&. ✗

KNOLE

Historic house set in deer park

Sevenoaks, Kent TN15 0RP
☎ Sevenoaks (0732) 450608

Built in 1456 and extended in next 200 years. Contains pictures, silver, and one of the most important collections of 17th century furniture in the world.

At the Tonbridge end of Sevenoaks, just east of the A225
Open April–Oct Wed–Sat, Bank Holiday Mondays and Good Friday 11.00am–5.00pm, Sunday 2.00–5.00pm
Admission: adult £2.50, child £1.30, special party rates on selected days (1990 prices)
🚌 🐕 in park only

SEPHAM FARM

Farm shop and pick your own

Filston Lane, Otford, Kent TN14 5JT
☎ Otford (09592) 3626

Nick and Ros Chard specialise in growing soft fruits (strawberries, raspberries, etc.), apples and pears. They press their own delicious apple juice, and also sell locally made real dairy ice cream.

2 miles north of Sevenoaks on the A225 to Otford, 1 mile west of Otford
Open June–Dec daily (except Mondays) 10.00am–5.00pm
Free admission
&. 🚌 advance notice required 🐕

► SITTINGBOURNE ◄

GORE FARM

Farm shop, pick your own and country walks

Upchurch, Sittingbourne, Kent ME9 7BE
☎ Medway (0634) 388856

17th century barn and cattle sheds have been converted to farm shops, coffee shop and dairy selling 60 different British cheeses. Farm trail includes traditional wild flower meadow and wildfowl.

North off the A2, approx ½ mile towards Upchurch
Open June–Aug daily 10.00am–6.00pm; Sept–May daily except Mondays 10.00am–5.00pm
Free admission
&. 🚌 advance notice required ✗

SYNDALE VALLEY VINEYARDS

Farm shop, vineyards and winery

Newnham, nr Sittingbourne, Kent ME9 0NA
☎ Eastling (079589) 711/693

Situated in an area of outstanding natural beauty, producing red and white wines, also fruit wines processed in a modern winery. Visitors tea room, shop, also guided tours with meal and wine tasting.

Take left hand turn 2 miles west from Faversham on the A2 for Newnham
Open Easter–Christmas daily 10.00am–5.30pm
Free admission. Guided tours, wine tasting and meal £4.00
&. 🚌 advance notice required 🐕

► STAPLEHURST ◄

IDEN CROFT HERBS

Farm shop, craft centre and country gardens

Frittenden Rd, Staplehurst, Kent TN12 0DH
☎ Staplehurst (0580) 891432

Acres of growing herbs. Large herb gardens, suitable for blind and disabled visitors. Plenty of seats, shop full of interesting herbal products, light refreshments. Herb plants available – culinary, aromatic, medicinal, cosmetic, bee and butterfly.

Off the A229 south of village, signposted 'Iden
  Croft Herbs', from main road and on Frittenden
  Road
Open April–Sept daily 9.00am–5.00pm, Sundays
  11.00am–5.00pm; Oct–March daily 9.00am–5.00pm.
  Closed Sundays
Free admission, donations welcome
& wheelchairs available
🚌 advance notice required 🐴

▶ ST MARGARET'S BAY ◀

THE PINES GARDEN

Country garden

St Margaret's Bay, nr Dover, Kent CT15 6DZ
☎ Dover (0304) 852764

*Garden features a large lake with a waterfall,
many fine trees and shrubs, a Romany
caravan and Oscar Nemon's famous statue
of Sir Winston Churchill. Bay museum
opposite has a tea room and shop.*

Off the B258 Dover–Deal road, signposted Pines
  Garden
Open daily all year, winter 10.00am–4.00pm, summer
  10.00am–6.00pm, closed in bad weather
Admission: adult 50p, child under 14 free, child 14–18
  20p, OAP 25p
& 🚌 access not easy for large coaches 🐴

▶ TENTERDEN ◀

HARBOURNE VINEYARD

Vineyard and winery

Wittersham, Tenterden, Kent TN30 7NP
☎ Wittersham (0797) 270420

*A small family run vineyard, where
everything from planting to bottling is done
in the cottage tradition. We produce 3 wines:
dry, medium and rose, also medium apple
wine and our own honey. Free wine tasting.*

On the B2082 Tenterden–Rye road, 3 miles from
  Tenterden, 6 miles from Rye
Open for the shop: Mon–Fri 2.00–7.00pm, Sat
  8.30am–7.00pm, Sun 12.00 noon–5.00pm or by
  appointment at any time; vineyard anytime by
  arrangement
Free admission, although a small charge may be made
  for special requirements
& we can serve people from their cars if required,
  vineyard can be muddy 🐴

TENTERDEN & DISTRICT MUSEUM

Museum

Station Rd, Tenterden, Kent TN30 6HN
☎ Tenterden (05806) 3350/4310

*Museum illustrates the local connection
with the Cinque Ports, life in Victorian
rural England, hop–growing and
agriculture, Wealden architecture, and the
light railways of Col. Stephens.*

Off the A28, near town centre in Station Road
Open Easter–Oct daily 2.00–5.00pm, August 11.00am–
  5.00pm
Admission: adult 50p, child/OAP 25p, 20% discount for
  booked parties
& 🚌 advance notice required 🐴

▶ TONBRIDGE ◀

BADSELL PARK FARM

Farm shop, pick your own and animal park

Crittenden Rd, Matfield, Tonbridge, Kent TN12 7EW
☎ Paddock Wood (0892 83) 2549

*Badsell Park is an open farm with rare
breeds of farm animals, and a pet area. There
is a cafe, fruit and gift shop, pick your own
fruit and vegetables, and nature trails.*

Going south on the A21, turn left just before
  Pembury, drive 3 miles on the B2015, farm is on
  the first right
Open April–Nov daily 10.00am–6.00pm
Admission: adult £2.00, child/OAP £1.50
& 🚌 🐴

PENSHURST VINEYARDS

Farm shop, trails and vineyards, farm animals

Grove Rd, Penshurst, Tonbridge, Kent TN11 8DU
☎ Tunbridge Wells (0892) 870255

*Visitors are welcome to walk among the
vines, visit the winery and taste the various
wines. In the grounds are wallabies,
waterfowl, and rare breed sheep. Ample
parking space.*

3½ miles west of the Tonbridge–Tunbridge Wells
  road, off the B3188 Penshurst–Fordcombe road

Open daily 10.00am–4.00pm, May–Sept 10.00am–6.00pm. Closed Christmas week and weekends in Jan and Feb
Admission for guided tours, which must be booked in advance: adult £2.50, child free. Otherwise free admission – no guide
  ♿ advance notice required ✖

Wide range of hand-made stoneware and porcelain. Delightful 18th century farmhouse set in large garden overlooking wooded farmland.

On the B2169, 6 miles south east of Tunbridge Wells, 1 mile west of Lamberhurst
Open all year, but telephone before visiting
Free admission
  ♿ ✦

▶ TUNBRIDGE WELLS ◀

BEDGEBURY PINETUM

Forestry centre and national pinetum

Forestry Commission R & D, Goudhurst, Kent TN17 2SL
☎ Goudhurst (0580) 211044

International collection of coniferous specimen trees. Established as the National Pinetum in 1925, currently holds 3 NCCPG collections and affords peace, tranquility and panoramic vistas for the visitor. Refreshments available.

2½ miles south of Goudhurst on the B2079 and 1 mile off the A21
Open daily 10.00am–dusk
Admission: adult £1.00, child 50p
  ♿ advance notice required ✦

CHERRY GARDENS FARM SHOP

Farm shop, pick your own, pets corner

Groombridge, Tunbridge Wells, Kent TN3 9NY
☎ Langton (0892) 864348

We aim to produce high quality fruit and vegetables using organic based manures and as few chemicals as practicable. In the family business tradition, you will be made personally welcome. Panoramic views.

On the B2188, between Groombridge and Crowborough
Open May–Oct 9.00am–6.00pm
Free admission
  ♿ advance notice required ✦

HOOK GREEN POTTERY

Pottery

Hook Green House, Hook Green, Lamberhurst, Tunbridge Wells, Kent TN3 8LR
☎ Lamberhurst (0892) 890504

PIPPINS FRUIT FARM

Pick your own

Maidstone Road, Pembury, Tunbridge Wells, Kent TN2 4AB
☎ Pembury (0892 82) 4569

From the A21 London–Hastings road, 1 mile north of Pembury off the B2015 to Maidstone
Open June–Oct Fri–Sun 10.00am–5.00pm, Mon–Thur 2.00–5.00pm (9.00am–6.00pm in the soft fruit season)
Free admission
  ♿ ✖

▶ WEST MALLING ◀

HAYSDEN COUNTRY PARK

Country park

c/o Tonbridge & Malling Borough Council, West Malling, Kent
☎ West Malling (0732) 844522

2 large lakes, the 160 acre park provides scope for walking, nature watching, and quiet relaxation in unspoiled woods and grassland. Nature and industrial heritage trails, club arrangements for sailing and canoeing, childrens play area

Approx 1 mile from town centre, off the A26 in a south west direction of the town centre (signposted)
Open all year round, 8.30am–dusk
Free admission
  ♿ by arrangement ✦

MILL YARD CRAFT CENTRE

Craft workshops with tea room

Swan St, West Malling, Kent ME19 6LP
☎ West Malling (0732) 841111

Tea room, ceramics, cards, gents and ladies tailor, wedding gowns, beadcraft, craft kits,

goldsmith – jeweller, gallery and gifts,
designer knitwear, florist, dolls and gifts,
towels, cushions and toys and cakecrafts.
Tourist Information Centre.

Take the A228 south from jct 4 on the M20, into
   centre of village, 40 yards into the B2014
   towards East Malling
Open daily all year, summer Sundays, (not Bank
   Holidays)
Free admission
& 🚌 advance notice required (free parking
nearby) 🐕

▶   **WYE**   ◀

THE WOODEN SPOON PRESERVING CO LTD

Preserving company

Wye, nr Ashford, Kent TN25 5BZ
☎   Wye (0233) 812251 Fax (0233) 813326

A family run company founded in 1975
manufacturing handmade high quality
preserves and other food products at a
Kentish oast house. Visitors can see the
process being carried out. Tea room.

Ashford, Kent, then take the A28 Canterbury road.
   Take road to Wye from Kempes Corner. Wye is 4
   miles from Ashford, 11 miles from Canterbury
Open by appointment only
Free admission
& would find the factory difficult to negotiate
🚌 advance notice required 🐕

Guide to Symbols

☎   telephone
&   disabled welcome
🚌 coaches welcome

🐕 dogs welcome (on a leash)
🐕 dogs not welcome

LANCASHIRE

Lancashire combines a fertile, sheltered, wooded plain with windy moorland and the rugged fell country that leads up to the Pennines. The Lancashire coastline was once the home of one of Britain's largest fishing fleets, it is now the most popular resort in the north of England.

An area rich in craft centres, it is possible to watch dolls houses and rocking horses being made, chess pieces being fashioned or stoneware and pottery being thrown. There are country parks and farm interpretation centres to visit, country walks to follow, an RSPB reserve to enjoy and boats to hire to see another 'face' of the Lancashire countryside.

► BARNOLDSWICK ◄

DOUG MOORE (BOATBUILDERS) LTD

Day boat hire, canalside shop selling canal art and gifts

Lower Park Marina, Kelbrook Rd, Barnoldswick, Lancashire BB8 5TB
☎ Barnoldswick (0282) 815883

Please telephone for directions
Open Mon–Fri 9.00am–5.00pm, Sun 10.00am–5.00pm.
 Day boats 9.30am–4.30pm daily
Free admission
&. ⋒ advance notice required ☂

► BARROWFORD ◄

PENDLE HERITAGE CENTRE

Farm interpretation centre with country walks

Park Hill, Barrowford, Nelson, Lancashire BB9 6JQ
☎ Nelson (0282) 695366

1 mile from centre of Nelson, off the A682 in
 direction of Gisburn
Open Easter to Nov Tues–Thur, weekends and Bank
 Holiday Mondays 2.00–4.30pm, guided tours at other
 times by arrangement
Admission charged
&. assistance available, advance telephone call
appreciated
&. ⋒ ✖

► BENTHAM ◄

BENTHAM POTTERY

Craft centre – pottery

Oysterber Farm, Low Bentham, Lancashire LA2 7ET
☎ (05242) 61567

A wide range of hand thrown pottery in a variety of colours for sale in the well stocked showroom. Commissions undertaken; wholesale enquiries welcome; pottery courses from half day upwards.

From the A65 Skipton–Kendal road, turn off
 through Burton–in–Lonsdale, straight on over
 bridge, up the hill and through crossroads. On
 the right, signposted Bentham Pottery
Open Mon–Fri 8.30am–4.00pm and Sun 1.00–5.00pm
 during season
Free admission
&. ✖

► BLACKBURN ◄

WITTON COUNTRY PARK

Country park and walks

The Visitor Centre, Preston Old Rd, Blackburn, Lancashire
 BB2 2TP
☎ Blackburn (0254) 55423

Nature trail, treasure trail, childrens play area and picnic sites, horse drawn carriage display, crafts shop, wayfaring course, natural history display, British mammal display and cafe.

2 miles west of Blackburn, just off the A674
 Chorley road
Open at all times for the country park. Visitor centre:
 Thur, Fri & Sat 1.00–5.00pm, Sundays and Bank
 Holidays 11.00am–5.00pm
Free admission
&. ⋒ ☂

► BURNLEY ◄

VILLAGE OF HOLME VALLEY & CLIVIGER VALLEY

Country walk

Burnley Tourist Information Centre, Burnley Mechanics,
 Manchester Rd, Burnley, Lancashire BB11 1JA
☎ Burnley (0282) 35411

Walk in the Cliviger Gorge, with its farmland, woods and streams. 2 hours for the 5 miles. Can be walked in two sections. A brochure is available from the above address.

Approximately 5 miles from Burnley town centre on
 the A646 bus route
Open all year
Free admission
&. ☂

WORSTHORNE MOORE & HURSTWOOD VILLAGE

Country walk

Burnley Tourist Information Centre, Burnley Mechanics,
 Manchester Rd, Burnley, Lancashire BB11 1JA
☎ Burnley (0282) 35411

Walk through diverse Pennine scenery. The extended circuit of 7 miles can be walked in

2 sections. Allow 4 hours for the extended walk. A brochure is available from the above address.

Approx 4 miles from Burnley town centre along Red Lees Rd, left down Salterfood Lane, right down Hurstwood Lane
Open all year
Free admission
 ♿ 🐕

Picture frames and fine art gallery with a display of a collection of fine art prints, limited editions and original paintings. Bespoke picture framing; picture restoration.

On the main A680 in the town centre
Open Mon–Fri 9.00am–5.30pm, Saturdays 9.00am–5.00pm, closed Sundays
Free admission
 ♿ ✱

► **CARNFORTH** ◄

ROBIN & NELL DALE

Craft workshop

Bank House Farm, Holme Mills, Via Carnforth, Lancashire LA6 1RE
☎ Burton (0524) 781646

Robin and Nell's painted figures and chess sets have been widely collected. They are now also creating beautiful little icons and batik pictures. Prices: figures from £15, chess sets from £350, icons and batik from £40.

Please telephone for directions
Open by appointment
Free admission
 ♿ 🐕

► **FENCE** ◄

SLATE AGE (FENCE) LIMITED

Craft centre and workshops

Fence Gate, Fence, nr Burnley, Lancashire BB12 9EG
☎ Nelson (0282) 66952

At the junction of the A6068 and Greenhead Lane leading to Burnley
Open all year daily (except Sundays), 9.00am–4.30pm
Free admission
 ♿ 🚌 advance notice required 🐕

► **HASLINGDEN** ◄

ANN BELSHAW GALLERY

Craft centre

40–42 Manchester Rd, Haslingden, Rossendale, Lancashire BB4 5ST
☎ Rossendale (0706) 220540

► **INGLETON** ◄

INGLETON POTTERY

Craft centre and pottery

Ingleton, Via Carnforth, Lancashire LA6 3HB
☎ Ingleton (05242) 41363

Small family pottery producing high quality handmade stoneware, including tableware, goblets, lamps, vases and planters. Potters may be seen working (and heard arguing) from the showroom.

Situated under the viaduct by the riverside
Open daily 9.00am–5.00pm
Admission: shop free, workshop and demonstrations £4.00 per group (up to 10 visitors)
 ♿ 🚌 🐕

► **KIRKBY LONSDALE** ◄

SELLET HALL HERBS

Herb garden

Whittington, Via Carnforth, Lancashire LA6 2QF
☎ Kirkby Lonsdale (05242) 71865

Various gardens planted with herbs, shrubs and herbaceous plants, set in beautiful countryside with extensive views.

Off the A65, through Biggins village, for about 1 mile on the road to Hutton Roof and Burton
Garden open Apr–Sept, daily 10.00am–5.00pm. Shop and plant nursery open all year
Admission: 50p to view gardens, guided tour round herb garden by appointment in summer
 ♿ 🚌 advance notice required ✱

▶ **LEYLAND** ◀

WORDEN HALL ARTS AND CRAFT CENTRE

Craft centre, country walk, woodland park, picnic areas & miniature railway on special weekends

Worden Park, Leyland, Lancashire
☎ Leyland (0772) 455908

Surrounded by 157 acres of parkland, the centre houses a fully equipped theatre, 8 craft workshops, a coffee shop and an exhibition room.

Off the M6 at Leyland junction
Open all year except Christmas and New Year's Day
Free admission for car parks and craft workshops
& 🚌 🐕

▶ **ORMSKIRK** ◀

CEDAR FARM GALLERY

Craft centre and tea room

Back Lane, Mawdesley, Ormskirk, Lancashire L40 3SY
☎ Rufford (0704) 822038

Quality crafts, bespoke picture framing, prints, interior designs, clothing, coffee and tea specialists, fashion designs, lingerie and 'Piggies' tea room.

At crossroads in Mawdesley village, turn into Gorsey Lane, at the top of Gorsey Lane turn right into Back Lane, then first on left
Open Tues–Sun 10.00am–5.00pm, closed Mondays (except Bank Holidays)
Free admission
& 🚌 advance notice required 🐕

K & R CUNLIFFE WOODEN TOYS & CRAFTS

Craft centre

'The Old Post Office', School Lane, Haskayne, nr Ormskirk, Lancashire L39 7JE
☎ Halsall (0704) 841066

Craft centre selling locally made crafts including rocking horses, doll houses and work produced in the 4 workshops; wooden toys, wood turnery, hand-painted silks, pyrography and dried flower arrangements.

Off the A5147, 4 miles west of Ormskirk
Open all year Thur, Fri & Sat 9.30am–4.30pm, some Sundays, other times by appointment
Free admission
🐕

ECCLES FARM CRAFT CENTRE

Craft centre

Eccles Lane, Bispham Green, nr Ormskirk, Lancashire L40 3SD
☎ Parbold (02576) 3113/2075

Housed in a 17th century converted barn, we offer a vast range of supplies for all aspects of needlecraft. We also have a selection of carefully chosen jewellery, pottery and gifts.

Follow the A59 from Ormskirk, approx 2 miles north take the A5209 signed to Parbold and the M6 – 3 miles on turn left on to the B5246 – follow for approx 2 miles
Open all year Wed–Sun and Bank Holiday Mondays 10.00am–5.00pm
Free admission
& 🚌 advance notice required 🐕

▶ **SILVERDALE** ◀

LEIGHTON MOSS

RSPB wildlife reserve

c/o Myers Farm, Silverdale, Carnforth LA5 0SW
☎ (0524) 701601

A 320 acre reserve with reed beds and open water set in a small undeveloped valley. Famous for the north west's only bitterns, marsh harriers and bearded tits. 7 large observation hides, displays, shop and tea room.

Off Yealand Redmayne–Silverdale road, just short of station
Open daily (except Tuesdays), 9.00am–9.00pm or sunset
Admission £2.50, guide 50p
& 🚌 advance notice required 🐕

► *SKELMERSDALE* ◄

BEACON COUNTRY PARK

Country park, walks and recreational activities

Beacon Lane, Dalton, Up Holland, nr Skelmersdale,
  Lancashire WN8 7RU
☎ (0695) 622794

*Public golf course and country pub within
the Visitors Centre. Horse riding permits
and orienteering maps sold.*

From jct 26 off the M6/M58 to Orrell, take the
  A577 for 2 miles towards Up Holland/
  Skelmersdale, round severe bend on Cenotaph,
  upwards to brow of road, turn right between
  Barory and Victoria public house onto Mill Lane,
  1½ miles turn left – follow brown tourist signs
Open: centre 9.00am–5.00pm and 7.00–11.00pm. Park
  access 24 hrs
Free admission
♿ 🚌 🐕 except in centre

► *SOUTHPORT* ◄

LANCASHIRE FRUIT GROWERS

Farm shop and pick your own

Mere Brow Fruit Farm, The Gravel, Mere Brow, Tarleton,
  nr Preston, Lancashire
☎ Hesketh Bank (0772) 814804

*Situated close to Southport, at the entrance
to Leisure Lakes which is popular for
boating, fishing and windsurfing.*

6 miles from Southport on the A565 Preston route
Open June–Aug 10.00am–8.00pm
Free admission
♿ 🚌 🗡

LEICESTERSHIRE

The Leicestershire countryside is notable for its red-brick villages rich grazing land, tall church spires and largely unspoilt rural landscapes. The tranquil countryside is traversed by canals, used extensively by narrow boats for commercial purposes in the last century, they are now used by pleasure craft. The towpaths offer peaceful walks through the county's countryside.

Farm life can be experienced at various farm parks where there are Shire horses and rare breeds, farm trails and special event weekends. The countryside can be explored and enjoyed along the country walks and two wildfowl sanctuaries invite the bird watcher. Rural life is displayed in the Rutland County Museum and crafts from glass making to clock and cabinet making can be watched at the workshops. A collection of historic motorcycles and a replica of the 1898 Flying Machine are also on show in the area.

▶ ASHBY-DE-LA-ZOUCH ◀

DICK BASS CABINET MAKER AND WOODTURNER

Craft centre and country park

Old Stables, Staunton Harold, nr Ashby-de-la-Zouch,
Leicestershire LE6 5RU
☎ Melbourne (03316) 4617

*Oak furniture hand made to customers
requirements, traditionally finished. Also a
range of clocks from bracket to grandfather
(to order), antique restorations and
polishing. Large and small wood turnery.*

Off the A453, 4 miles east of Ashby-de-la-Zouch,
craft centre situated in Staunton Harold Park
Open all year, Tues–Sat 7.00am–5.00pm, Sunday
1.00–4.30pm, closed Mondays except Bank Holidays
Free admission
&. ⟪⟫ advance notice required ⟨

▶ BOROUGH OF CHARNWOOD ◀

WHATOFF LODGE FARM

Farm visit

Woodhouse Rd, Quorn, Leicestershire LE12 8AI
☎ Quorn (0509) 412127

*Farm trail with guide, small animal section,
farm shop, special event weekends (shoeing,
lambing, etc.).*

Off the B591, Quorn–Woodhouse road, 2 miles
south of Loughborough
Open Easter–Nov daily
Admission: adult £1.50, child 75p (1989 prices)
&. ⟪⟫ ⟨

▶ CORBY ◀

THE GLASS WORKSHOP

Country park, walks and craft centre

Unit 1, The Old Coach House, East Carlton Countryside
Park, Market Harborough, Leicestershire LE16 8YF
☎ Rockingham (0536) 770977

*Watch glass figures being made at close
quarters in safety. You can sit inches away,
protected by a glass screen, and see the glass
melted and shaped into many varied forms
from miniature animals to galleons.*

On the A427; Market Harborough 8 miles, Corby 3
miles
Open all year, Mon–Fri 9.00am–5.00pm, Saturdays by
appointment only, Sun 1.00–5.00pm
Free admission
&. ⟪⟫ ⟨

▶ EGLETON ◀

RUTLAND WATER NATURE RESERVE

Wildfowl sanctuary and nature reserve

c/o The Warden, Fishponds Cottage, Stamford Rd,
Oakham, Leicestershire LE15 8AB
☎ Oakham (0572) 724101

*At Egleton, birdwatching hides overlook 3
lagoons and open water, which attract many
species of wildfowl and waders. The
meadows, mature hedges and woodland
abound with birds, butterflies and
wildflowers.*

Entrance is in Egleton village, which is off the
A6003 Oakham–Uppingham road
Open all year, Sat, Sun, Wed, Fri and Bank Holidays
10.00am–5.00pm
Admission: adult £2.00, accompanied child (under 16)
50p (1990 prices)
&. one birdwatching hide has wheelchair access from
the car park and there is a toilet designed for disabled,
we welcome disabled birdwatchers – £1.00 permit
⟪⟫ advance notice required ⟨

▶ LEICESTER ◀

FARMWORLD LEICESTER

Stoughton Farm Park

Gartree Rd, Oadby, Leicestershire LE2 2FB
☎ Leicester (0533) 710355

*Experience the world of farm life at
Farmworld. Shire horses, cart rides, rare
farm animals, nature trails, childrens
farmyard, milking parlour with viewing
gallery.*

3 miles south east of Leicester (signposted from
the A6 and the A47). 6 miles east of the M1/M69
(jct21). Follow southerly ring road
Open daily 10.00am–5.30pm
Admission: adult £2.75, child £1.50, reduced rates for
OAP and pre–paid parties. Free parking and
admission to craft shops, farm produce and gift shop,
Wheatsheaf cafe and garden centre
&. ⟪⟫ ⟨

HALSTEAD HOUSE FARM SHOP AND TEA ROOM

Farm shop, country gardens, walks, lakes and tea rooms

Halstead House Farm, Tilton-on-the-Hill, Leicestershire LE7 9DJ

☎ Tilton (053754) 239

Our tea room provides light lunches and cream teas through the summer, and the farm shop provides home produced poultry, game and venison. We are constructing a poultry demonstration unit.

Approx 1 mile off the B6047 at Tilton-on-the-Hill, 10 miles east of Leicester
Open daily May–Sept, closed Mondays other than Bank Holidays, open weekends Oct–April
Free admission
&. ⇛ advance notice required
⋔ but not in the shop or tea room

▶ *LUTTERWORTH* ◀

EAGLESFIELD FARM

Farm shop and pick your own

Main St, Leire, Lutterworth, Leicestershire LE17 5HF

☎ Leire (0455) 209647/202158

Eaglesfield has pick your own strawberries, raspberries, blackcurrants, redcurrants, gooseberries, beans, calebrese and cauliflowers. In addition the farmshop sells fresh chickens, turkeys, eggs, game, cream, trout, potatoes and a variety of smoked products.

From the A426 Lutterworth–Leicester road, turn off to Dunton Bassett, follow signposts to Leire 1½ miles
Open for the farm shop Mon–Fri 9.00am–5.00pm, Sat 9.00am–12.00 noon, pick your own 9.00am–8.00pm
Free admission
&. ⇛ advance notice required ⋔

FOSSE WAY FOOTPATH

Country walk

Harborough District Council Offices, Adam and Eve St, Market Harborough, Leicestershire LE16 7AG

☎ Market Harborough (0858) 410000

Historic linear walk of 3½ miles, following the line of the Roman Fosse Way, through the attractive countryside of south Leicestershire. Limited parking space at High Cross (A5/B577) and near Sapcote (lay-by on B4114).

4 miles north west of Lutterworth, on the A5/B577 intersection
Open at all times
Free admission
&. ⋔

ORGANICHIC

Free range poultry

Top House Farm, North Kilworth, Lutterworth, Leicestershire LE17 6NG

☎ Market Harborough (0858) 880279

Our poultry are reared outside and fed on grain produced on the farm with no added antibiotics or additives. The birds are sold traditionally prepared ready for the oven.

On the B5415, 2½ miles off the A427, 6 miles east of Lutterworth
Open, please telephone for enquiries or advance orders
Free admission
&. ⋔

STANFORD HALL

Craft centre and country walk

Lutterworth, Leicestershire LE17 6DH

☎ Rugby (0788) 860250

The hall contains antique furniture, fine pictures including the Stuart Collection and family costumes. Replica of 1898 Flying Machine, outstanding collection of historic and unique motorcycles in the stables.

Off the B5414, 7 miles north east of Rugby, jcts 18/20 on M1, jct 1 on M6
Open Easter–Sept, Sat, Sun, Bank Holiday Mondays and Tues (Thur in July/Aug) 2.30–6.00pm
Admission: grounds, adult £1.20, child 60p; house and grounds, adult £2.30, child £1.10; motorcycle museum, adult £1.00, child 25p
&. the front door of the hall is not on ground level. Wide steps enable wheelchairs to be carried up. The tea room is upstairs but teas can be carried down by arrangement. Disabled toilet facilities
⇛ advance notice required ⋔

► **LYNDON** ◄

RUTLAND WATER NATURE RESERVE
Wildfowl sanctuary and nature reserve

c/o Fishponds Cottage, Stamford Rd, Oakham,
Leicestershire LE15 8AB
☎ Manton (057 285) 378

*At Lyndon, deep and shallow water attracts
many wildfowl and waders. Nature trails
lead through wildflower meadows to Gibbet
Gorse wood, or to three birdwatching hides.
Visitor centre and shop.*

The reserve is situated on Rutland Water's southern
shoreline in east Leicestershire, turn north off
road between Manton and Edith Weston villages
Open Easter–Oct daily except Monday and Friday, but
including Bank Holidays, 10.00am–4.00pm, Nov–
Easter open weekends only 10.00am–4.00pm
Admission: adult £1.00, child 30p, OAP 75p, school
groups by arrangement (1990 prices)
& ⛟ advance notice required 🐾

► **MARKET BOSWORTH** ◄

MIDDLEWAY
Clock and furniture makers

Old Village Hall, Shenton, Leicestershire CV13 6DA
☎ Hinckley (0455) 212372

*Individually hand made longcase and other
clocks. Commissions for furniture
undertaken. Cane chairs and rush seating
service available. Restoration of clocks and
furniture. Selection of work on show.*

2 miles from Market Bosworth, close to Battlefield,
midway between the A447 and the A444
Open all year (except Christmas) including Bank
Holidays, Sat–Sun 10.00am–5.00pm
Free admission
& ⛟ advance notice required 🐾

► **MARKET HARBOROUGH** ◄

FRANK HAYNES GALLERY
Art and craft gallery

50 Station Rd, Great Bowden, Market Harborough,
Leicestershire LE16 7HN
☎ Market Harborough (0858) 64862

*The gallery shows and sells original
paintings, drawings, ceramics and other
crafts, together with Frank Haynes' own
pottery. The display changes monthly. All
exhibits are from Leicestershire and
neighbouring counties.*

Approx 1 mile from Market Harborough station, via
Bowden/Station roads
Open Tues, Thur, Fri & Sat 2.00–5.00pm, Sun
10.00am–5.00pm, closed July/Aug
Free admission
& 🦮

► **OAKHAM** ◄

MILLHOUSE GALLERY
Hand made gifts in silk

Millhouse, Melton Rd, Tilton-on-the-Hill, Leicestershire
LE7 9LG
☎ Tilton (053754) 242

*On a hill in the heart of Leicestershire with
50-mile views. Groups are catered for with
refreshments, talk and film on the history of
silk. Items include jackets, scarves, jewellery,
cushions, bags, ties and pictures.*

10 miles west of Oakham, on the B6047 in village
of Tilton-on-the-Hill
Open daily (except Mon & Thur) 10.00am–6.00pm
Free admission
& ⛟ advance notice required 🐾

► **RUTLAND** ◄

RUTLAND COUNTY MUSEUM
Rural life museum

Catmos St, Oakham, Rutland, Leicestershire LE15 6HW
☎ Oakham (0572) 723654

*The museum of Rutland life, including
agricultural equipment, implements and
waggons, local tradesmen's tools and
domestic items. Local archaeology. Special
gallery on the Volunteer Soldier in
Leicestershire and Rutland. Housed in late
18th century riding school.*

Approx ½ mile south of town centre on the A6003
Open Tues–Sat and Bank Holiday Mondays 10.00am–
1.00pm, 2.00–5.00pm, Sun (April–Oct) 2.00–5.00pm
Free admission
& ⛟ advance notice required 🦮 except guide dogs

► *WOODHOUSE EAVES* ◄

BROOMBRIGGS FARM COUNTRY PARK

Country park with farm trail

Woodhouse Eaves, Loughborough, Leicestershire
☎ (0509) 890048

*130 acre typical Charnwood Forest Hill
Farm with approx 2 miles illustrated farm
trail. Extensive system of paths for walkers
and riders. Windmill Hill – adjoining
wooded area with the remains of a windmill.*

On the B591, beyond Woodhouse Eaves village
Open all year (daylight hours)
Free admission, car parking 20p
& ∰ ⊧

Stay on a Farm

Official guide of Farm Holiday
Bureau UK

Enjoy the unique hospitality of a
working farm. Over 950 properties,
between them offering bed and
breakfast, half-board, self-catering
and camping and caravanning.

All inspected and approved by the
National Tourist Boards. Published
by William Curtis.

.£4.95. Available from all good
bookshops.

LINCOLNSHIRE

Lincolnshire on the North Sea coast is made up of flat, fertile fenland and rich rolling hills that make up the Wolds. It is famous for the bulb fields that cover it in glorious colours in the springtime and also for its rich agriculture.

A unique working windmill, a listed watermill, and a large tropical butterfly house feature among the countryside attractions. There are also country gardens, a heritage centre, a herb nursery, a rest home for horses and a selection of craft workshops with a wide range of crafts to visit.

▶ *ALFORD* ◀

ALFORD POTTERY

Craft centre – pottery

Commercial Rd, Alford, Lincolnshire LN13 9DJ
☎ Alford (0507) 463342

*Stoneware pottery made on the premises.
Full domestic range and decorative giftware.
Specialised in pierced and cut away
decoration. Many 'one off' pieces available.*

On the A1104, off the A16
Open weekdays 9.00am–5.00pm
Free admission
♿ no disabled toilet facilities
🚌 advance notice required 🐕

CLAYTHORPE WATERMILL & WILDFOWL GARDENS

Watermill

Aby, Alford, Lincolnshire LN13 0DU
☎ Alford (0507) 450687

*18th century listed watermill with grounds
full of birds and animals. Also a restaurant,
tea rooms, gardens and craft shop.*

Follow the brown tourist signs
Open daily through season 10.00am–7.00pm
Admission: adult £1.20, child 60p, OAP 80p
🚌 advance notice required

LINCOLNSHIRE SCULPTURE PROJECT

Country garden

Buttercup Farm, Mawthorpe, nr Alford, Lincolnshire
LN13 9LY
☎ Alford (0507) 462793

*Converted farm buildings set in 24 acres of
woodland. Facilities include exhibition area,
gift shop, restaurant and workshop.
Sculpting and drawing workshops arranged.
Further details can be obtained by mail or
telephone.*

Off the B1196, 2 miles south of Alford towards
Willoughby
Open all year
Free admission, although a small charge for exhibition
and tour of studios will apply. Exhibition: adult 50p,
child 25p, OAP 65p. Tour of studio: adult 75p, child
30p
♿ 🚌 advance notice required 🐕

▶ *BOSTON* ◀

JACK O'LANTERN

Village tea room and art gallery

Orchard House, High St, Swineshead, nr Boston,
Lincolnshire PE20 3LH
☎ Boston (0205) 820647

*Gallery – prints plus many originals, all at
reasonable prices. Home bakery, tea room –
take away service or eat on premises.*

6 miles south west of Boston off the A52
Open daily 9.00am–5.00pm, closed Wednesdays
Free admission
♿ 🐕

▶ *GAINSBOROUGH* ◀

CANDLESBY HERBS

**Craft centre, country garden, herb nursery and
workshop**

Cross Keys Cottage, Candlesby, nr Spilsby, Lincolnshire
PE23 5SI
☎ Scremby (075485) 211

*A small cottage garden industry, growing
and selling 300 varieties of herbs, wild
flowers and herbal products, retail, wholesale
and mail order (s.a.e. please).*

Off the A1028, 1 mile west of Gunby roundabout
Open daily, except Mondays although open Bank Holiday
Mondays, 10.00am–5.00pm
Free admission
♿ 🚌 advance notice required 🐕

KIRTON POTTERY

Craft shop – pottery

36 High St, Kirton-in-Lindsey, Gainsborough,
Lincolnshire DN21 4LX
☎ (0652) 648867

*We make both domestic ware and individual
items ranging from commemorative plates to
garden sculpture. Most of the pottery is sold
from our own well stocked shop.*

18 miles north of Lincoln off the A15
Open all year, Mon–Sat 9.30am–5.30pm, Sun 2.30–
5.00pm, closed Tuesdays
Free admission
♿ 🚌 advance notice required 🐕

▶ # GRANTHAM ◀

BELVOIR FRUIT FARMS

Pick your own

Belvoir, Grantham, Lincolnshire NG32 1PB
☎ Grantham (0476) 870286

We produce fresh fruit cordials which make delicious drinks, ice creams, sorbets, fruit salads and salad dressings.

8 miles west of Grantham, 3 miles off the A52, ½ mile north west of Belvoir Castle
Open daily during soft fruit season June–Aug
 10.00am–8.00pm
Free admission
♿ 🚌 🐎 but only in car park

MANOR STABLES CRAFT WORKSHOPS

Craft centre

Manor Stables, Fulbeck, Grantham, Lincolnshire
 NG34 8EY
☎ Lovedon (0400) 72779

The craft workshops are in stone built stables in one of Lincolnshire's most attractive villages. The units are home to weaving, furniture making, jewellery, sewing, dried and fresh flowers.

12 miles north of Grantham on the A607 to Lincoln
Open Tues–Sun and Bank Holiday Mondays 10.30am–
 4.30pm
Free admission
♿ 🚌 advance notice required 🐎

▶ # HECKINGTON ◀

HECKINGTON WINDMILL

Working windmill

Hale Road, Heckington, Sleaford NG34 0JW
☎ Sleaford (0529) 60088

Unique as the only 8 sailed working mill in the country. Built around 1830, the mill is extremely powerful and capable of driving 5 pairs of stones as well as a number of wood-working machines.

Village on the A17, 5 miles east of Sleaford
Open: access to mill Mon–Sat and Bank Holidays
 10.00am–5.00pm, Sun 12.00 noon–5.00pm; working
 times: Easter–Sept, Sat, Sun and Bank Holidays
 2.00–4.30pm. Enquire at Tourist Information Centre,
 Pearoom, Station Yard
Admission: small charge when mill working. Catering available at the Pearoom Craft & Heritage Centre at weekends, and for groups if booked in advance
🚌 advance notice required

THE PEAROOM CRAFT & HERITAGE CENTRE

Craft centre and heritage centre

Station Yard, Heckington, Lincolnshire NG34 9JJ
☎ Sleaford (0529) 60765

The Pearoom is home to a lively group of craft workers who include a wood carver, potter, weaver and felt maker, musical instrument restorer and stained glass maker. Workshops take place regularly.

Please telephone for directions
Open Tues–Sat 10.00am–5.00pm, Sun 12.00 noon–
 5.00pm and Bank Holidays 12.00 noon–5.00pm. Cafe
 open at weekends – catering arranged with advance
 notice
Free admission
♿ 🚌 advance notice required 🐎

▶ # HORNCASTLE ◀

ALISON BELL FABRIC DESIGNS

Craft workshop

Gravel Pit Cottages, High Toynton, Horncastle,
 Lincolnshire LN9 6NW
☎ Horncastle (06582) 6591

Alison designs and handprints a range of leisurewear from casual sweatshirts to silk outfits.

1 mile east of Horncastle on the A158, situated on the crossroads at High Toynton, opposite the church and the garage
Open most days 10.00am–5.00pm, but please telephone to confirm
Free admission
♿ 🚌 advance notice required 🐎

▶ # LINCOLN ◀

BRANSBY HOME OF REST FOR HORSES

Rest home for horses

Bransby, Saxilby, Lincolnshire LN1 2PH
☎ Gainsborough (0427) 788464

140 rescued horses, ponies and donkeys.

Turn off the A57 at Saxilby to the B1241, 8 miles from Lincoln
Open daily, daylight hours
Free admission
 🚌 ⛟

HARTSHOLME COUNTRY PARK

Country park and information centre

Skellingthorpe Rd, Lincoln
☎ Lincoln (0522) 688264

96 acres of beautiful and tranquil parkland within the city boundary offering space for informal recreation and countryside walks. Contact a Ranger for further information.

Signposted from the A46 bypass south west of the city
Park open daily, information centre open March–Oct, Fri–Tues 11.00am–5.00pm
Free admission
& 🚌 advance notice required ⛟

► LONG SUTTON ◄

BUTTERFLY PARK

Country park with farm shop and butterfly house

Long Sutton, nr Spalding, Lincolnshire PE12 9LE
☎ Holbeach (0406) 363833

One of the largest landscaped tropical butterfly houses in the British Isles with hundreds of the world's most colourful butterflies flying freely around. Also has a gift shop, tea room, outdoor gardens, farm animals/pets corner, adventure playground and picnic areas.

1 mile off the A17 in Long Sutton (signposted)
Open daily March–Sept 10.00am–6.00pm, Oct 10.00am–5.00pm
Admission: adult £2.50, child (under 16) £1.50, OAP £2.20, special party rates available
& 🚌 advance notice required
⛟ in car park

► LOUTH ◄

HARVEST POTTERY

Craft workshop

Brinkhill, nr Louth, Lincolnshire
☎ Swaby (05216) 702

Specialists in hand thrown terracotta garden planters and kitchen ware. All pottery is made and decorated in our workshop.

From the A16 Louth–Boston road, turn off at Burwell or off main Lincoln–Skegness road, then turn off at Hagworthingham
Open daily except Mondays 9.00am–9.00pm
Free admission
& ⛟

► NEWARK ◄

COUNTRY CRAFTSMAN

Craft centre – hand–made wooden furniture

Brook Cottage, Newark Rd, Stapleford, Lincolnshire LN6 9LD
☎ Bassingham (052285) 640

Handmade English oak furniture made in the traditional manner, i.e. hand cut dove tails, staining and polishing, comprising of dressers, side boards, tables and chairs, corner cupboards, bedroom furniture, all made to clients specifications.

Off the A46, 7 miles north of Newark
Open all year by appointment
Free admission
& ⛟

► NORTH SCARLE ◄

F A & J JONES & SON

Farm butcher's shop and trout lake

Red House Farm, Spalford Lane, North Scarle, Lincolnshire LN6 9HB
☎ Spalford (052277) 224

Delicious pork pies, sausage rolls, pasties, pates and Lincolnshire sausages are all made on the premises. All meat is additive free, from animals kept traditionally. Trout lake, rainbow and brown in season, fishing by appointment; telephone for price.

Off the A1 take the A46, signposted Lincoln, at first roundabout take the A1133 signposted Gainsborough, at Besthorpe turn right, straight on at first crossroads, at second crossroads turn left, and immediately right into farm shop yard
Open Wed–Sat 9.00am–5.00pm, Fri open till 7.00pm, closed lunch 12.30–1.30pm. Trout fishing all year by appointment please
Free admission to the shop. Trout fishing prices (1990) full day – 4 fish bag £12, ½ day – 2 fish bag £7.00
&. ✗

▶ SKEGNESS ◀

GEORGE MARRIOTT THREEWAYS POTTERY

Craft centre – pottery

Common Lane, Burgh-le-Marsh, Lincolnshire PE24 5HH
☎ Skegness (0754) 810756

Hand thrown, high fired domestic stoneware. Special orders taken. Classes on Wednesdays.

Burgh-le-Marsh is 5 miles from Skegness on the A158 Lincoln road
Open all year daily, if making a special journey please telephone first
Free admission
&. ➠ advance notice required ✗

MILLSTONE CRAFT CENTRE

Craft centre

Mill House, West End, Hogsthorpe, Skegness, Lincolnshire PE24 5PA
☎ Skegness (0754) 72977

Stuart MacDonald makes stoneware pottery on the premises – castles, dragons, vases, mugs and individual pots of all kinds. Other craft work is also stocked, including ships in bottles. Bed & breakfast available.

On the A52, 8 miles from Skegness, 10 miles from Mablethorpe, next to telephone box
Open daily May–Sept 9.00am–8.00pm; Oct–April 10.00am–5.30pm, closed Wednesday in winter
Free admission
&. ➠ advance notice required ★

▶ SPALDING ◀

SPRINGFIELDS GARDENS

Country show gardens

Camelgate, Spalding, Lincolnshire PE12 6ET
☎ Spalding (0775) 4843

Spring – tulips, daffodils, hyacinths, woodlands, sunken garden, maze and greenhouses. Summer – over 150,000 summer bedding plants. Famous Spalding flower parade 4–7 May 1991

Follow brown and white tourist signs – Springfields
Open April–Sept daily 10.00am–6.00pm
Admission: adult £2.00, accompanied children free, special events £2.50 (1990 prices)
&. ➠ ✗

▶ SPILSBY ◀

ATKIN & FARROW LIMITED

Pick your own

Glebe Farm, Main Rd, East Keal, Spilsby, Lincolnshire PE23 4BB
☎ Spilsby (0790) 53300

Attractive view of fens, good picnic area.

3 miles south of Spilsby, 400 yards north of jct A155 with the A16
Open July–Aug daily 10.00am–7.00pm, caravan club open all year
Free admission
★ allowed on leash

MERSEYSIDE

Merseyside incorporates the busy, colourful city of Liverpool, a busy Atlantic seaport, and the scenery and resorts of the Wirral peninsula where there are miles of beaches, dunes and parks. The mythical 'Liver' bird gave Liverpool its name, it sits on one of the two towers of the Royal Liver building dominating the waterfront in Liverpool.

A 500-acre country park at Croxteth offers a wide range of countryside pursuits which include a rare breeds farm and a local nature reserve. The country visitor can also pick-their-own taste of the Merseyside countryside.

► *LIVERPOOL* ◄

CROXTETH HALL AND COUNTRY PARK

Historic house, rare breeds farm, walled gardens, country park with local nature reserve

Liverpool, Merseyside L12 0HB
☎ (051) 228 5311

Croxteth Hall and Country Park is situated amidst 500 acres of woodland and gardens. Adventure playground, picnic areas, gift shop, special events held throughout the main season. Entry to parkland free most days.

5 miles north east of city centre on the Liverpool side of the M57, signposted from the A580 (East Lancs Road) and the A5058 (ring road)
Open: park all year except Christmas. Main facilities daily 11.00am–5.00pm mid April–Sept
Admission to country park: free; hall, farm and garden £2.00
  ♻ 🐎 🐕

LYDIATE FRUIT FARMS

Farm shop and pick your own

Lydiate, Liverpool, Merseyside L31 4HB
☎ (051) 526 0638

The farm shop in Pilling Lane is situated in an old stone building (early 18th century coach house and stables listed grade II). It has an interesting oak timbered roof.

Midway between Liverpool and Southport on the A5147, signposted by RAC
Open daily, late June–mid Aug (soft fruit season)
Free admission
♻ regret no facilities for wheelchairs, other handicapped are welcome including organised parties with prior notice
🚌 advance notice required 🐕

Step off the earth for a while...

Where can a narrowboat 'fly' at over 300 feet?
What are the seven Wonders of the Waterways?
How do you get a place on a sea training vessel?
How easy is it to learn to drive a canal cruiser?

Why keep your feet on the ground when there's a water-based activity to suit you?
A new FREE leaflet, produced by the British Marine Industries Federation and the National Tourist Boards, will give you all the answers - whether you are interested in inland waterways, yacht charter, sailing schools, powerboating, waterskiing, canoeing, surfing, diving, sea training, learning courses... With hints and tips, ideas for holidays and short breaks, a round-up of what's available, plus a handy reference guide to such things as classic craft, sail marks, types of boat.

For your FREE leaflet, send off the coupon, or write to Holidays Afloat Offer, Harrington Dock, Liverpool X, L70 1AX.

Please send me your FREE leaflet on holidays afloat
Name: ————————————————————————
Address: ——————————————————————
————————————————————————
Post Code: ——————————————————————
Send to: Holidays Afloat Offer, Harrington Dock, Liverpool X, L70 1AX.

NORFOLK

Norfolk remains a predominantly agricultural landscape with small rural communities. It is well-known for its reed-fringed Broads, a network of slow-moving rivers and man-made lakes; for its miles of coastline and coastal marshes and its fragrant lavender fields.

Fine opportunities exist for birdwatching, country walks, both short and long, and woodland walks. There are working wind and watermills, country parks and gardens to visit as well as vineyards, herb gardens, an orchid centre, a horse sanctuary, craft centres, potteries, a farming museum and a folk museum. You can try your hand at carving decorative decoy ducks and even return to the turn of the century as you wander around a bygone village.

AYLSHAM

BLICKING PARK – NATIONAL TRUST

Park and woodland walk

Blicking, nr Aylsham, Norwich NR11 6NF
☎ Aylsham (0263) 733084

Coarse fishing available in Blickling Lake. Public house and restaurant.

On the B1354, 1 mile north west of Aylsham
Open all year
Free admission. Walks leaflet available
♿ 🚌 🐕

BRUNDALL

STRUMPSHAW FEN

RSPB wildlife reserve

Low Rd, Strumpshaw, Norwich, Norfolk
☎ Norwich (0603) 715191

Fen and grazings featuring 4 hides from which to see marsh harriers, bearded tits, wildfowl and snipe among others. Bean geese in winter, swallowtail butterflies in June, 4 miles of trails with interpretive boards.

Off the A47. From Brundall take a sharp right and right again in Low Road. Entrance across level crossing from car park
Open daily 9.00am–9.00pm or sunset
Admission: adult £2.00, child/OAP £1.00, RSPB members free, guide 50p
♿ 🚌 advance notice required 🐕

CLEY-NEXT THE SEA

MADE IN CLEY

Pottery

High St, Cley-next-the-Sea, Holt, Norfolk NR25 7RF
☎ Cley (0263) 740134

Workshop group of 5 potters and a jeweller. Work is made on the premises and sold in the gallery; a fine Regency shop of great historical interest.

On the A149, in the middle of the village
Open Aug & Sept daily 10.00am–6.00pm, closed Wed rest of year
Free admission
♿ 🚌 no parking available 🐕

CROMER

FELBRIGG WOODS – NATIONAL TRUST

Country park and woodland walks

Felbrigg, nr Cromer, Norwich NR11 8PR
☎ West Runton (026 375) 444

Walks in woodland or lake/park woods. Guide books available. Restaurant and toilets at the hall. Walks leaflets on sale.

2 miles south west of Cromer, off the A148
Open all year
Free admission
♿ 🚌 🐕

DEREHAM

ELMHAM PARK, WINERY AND VINEYARDS

Vineyards and winery

Elmham Wines Limited, Elmham House, North Elmham, Dereham, Norfolk NR20 5JY
☎ Elmham (036281) 363/571 Fax: (036281) 573

The winery, in a fine pan-tiled 18th century building, produces English wine and apple wine from outdoor vineyards and orchards on the estate. Wines may be purchased.

North Elmham is at the junction of the B1110 and the B1145, 5 miles north of East Dereham, drive gates opposite church
Open for parties or interested wine lovers by appointment
Admission: £1.50 per person
♿ 🚌 🐕

DISS

BRESSINGHAM STEAM MUSEUM & GARDENS

Museum, heritage centre and country garden

Bressingham, Diss, Norfolk IP22 2AB
☎ Bressingham (037988) 382/6

Ride through 5 miles of woodland on the narrow gauge engines. Steam museum; Fire Museum; 6 acres of beautiful gardents and the Bressingham Plant Centre. Toilets. Refreshments.

On the A1066, 2½ miles west of Diss
Open Easter–mid Oct daily. Steam days Sundays and Thursdays. Please telephone to confirm
Admission: adult £2.50, child £1.50 (1990 prices)
♿ 🚌 🐕

DAVID GREGSON FURNITURE

Furniture workshop

Bridge Green Farm, Gissing Rd, Burston, nr Diss, Norfolk
IP22 3UD
☎ Diss (0379) 740528

The workshop concentrates on high quality commissioned furniture to original designs on a one-off basis for domestic and corporate clients. A range of smaller items suitable for presentation is also available.

3 miles north east of Diss, village signposted
Open by appointment only
Free admission
&. ⛟ advance notice required 🐾

ROBERT LE BESQUE – WOODWORKER

Woodwork workshop

Oaksedge Workshop, 34 Croft Lane, Diss, Norfolk
IP22 3NA
☎ Diss (0379) 651798 after 6.00pm

A member of the Norfolk Rural Craftsmen's Guild who makes small furniture to commission in English Country, American Shaker and American Colonial styles. Also a range of Noah's Arks for special presents.

At Diss police station on the A1066 Thetford–Diss road, turn north for 200 yards, first house on the left
Open all year, please make an appointment
Free admission
&. 🐾

OLD HALL DECOYS

Decorative duck decoy carving school and supplies centre

Old Hall Farm, Scole, Diss, Norfolk IP21 4ES
☎ Diss (0379) 740911

England's centre for the art of decorative duck carving. Courses are held regularly. Supplies always available. Browse in the gallery or among the live duck and bird collection.

Scole Common, turning off the A140, ½ mile north of Scole
Open most days 11.00am–4.00pm
Free admission
&. ⛟ by prior arrangement
🐾 under strict supervision

PULHAM VINEYARDS LTD

Vineyard

Mill Lane, Pulham Market, Diss, Norfolk IP21 4XL
☎ Pulham Market (037976) 672

Guided tours of 11 acres of vineyards, winery, cellars and bottling plant, plus a free tasting of Magdalen Estate bottled English wines. A leaflet is available from the above address.

From the A140, take the B1134 to Pulham Market, left into Mill Lane, the vineyard is on the left
Open May–Sept daily (except Mondays), strictly by appointment only
Admission: £2.00 per person (1990 prices)
⛟ advance notice required

THELNETHAM WINDMILL

Working windmill

Nr Diss, Norfolk IP22 1JZ

Beautiful tower mill built in 1819 and now fully restored; run by volunteers. Visitors can watch stoneground flour being made by windpower and buy the freshly-made product.

Of the B111, 1 mile east of Hopton, or off the A1066, 2 miles south west of South Lopham
Open Easter–Oct Sundays 11.00am–7.00pm and most Saturdays throughout the year
Admission: adult 50p, child 20p
&. access to ground floor only for those in wheelchairs
⛟ advance notice required 🐾 not inside mill

◄ **EAST DEREHAM** ►

BISHOP BONNERS COTTAGES MUSEUM

Small folk museum

St Withburga Lane, East Dereham, Norfolk
☎ (0362) 693107

3 timber-framed thatched cottages c.1502 with rare coloured frieze. Displays of needlework, Victorian children's clothes and toys, books, local trades and crafts. China, books, pamphlets and postcards for sale.

On the A47, 16 miles from Norwich
Open May–Sept Tues–Sat, 2.30–5.00pm. Parties by appointment only
Free admission but donations welcome
⛟ parking available in the town ✗

► **FAKENHAM** ◄

FOXLEY WOOD

Country walk and nature reserve

c/o Norfolk Naturalists Trust, 72 Cathedral Close,
Norwich, Norfolk NR1 4DF
☎ Norwich (0603) 625540

This woodland nature reserve dates back to before Domesday and is the largest remaining block of ancient woodland in Norfolk. At its most attractive in spring and summer.

9 miles south east of Fakenham, off the A1067
near Bewdeswell, through Foxley village
Open daily except Thursdays 10.00am–5.00pm
Free admission
&. ⊞ advance notice required 🏋

PENSTHORPE WATERFOWL PARK

Waterfowl park and nature reserve

Fakenham, Norfolk NR21 0LN
☎ (0328) 851465

200 acres of lakes, woodland and meadows featuring wild and exotic waterbirds. Visitor centre, conservation shop, courtyard restaurant, wildlife exhibitions, adventure playground.

Signposted on the A1067 Norwich road, 1 mile
south east of Fakenham
Open Jan–March: weekends; 1 April–New Year daily,
11.00am–5.00pm
Admission: adult £2.80, child £1.10, OAP £2.50
&. excellent facilities for access 🏋

► **GREAT YARMOUTH** ◄

THE BYGONE VILLAGE

Recreated turn of the century village, glass blowing, railway exhibits

Fleggburgh, Great Yarmouth, Norfolk NR29 3AF
☎ Great Yarmouth (0493) 369770/508

Recreated turn of the century village set in 40 acres of park and woodland with hobby crafts, glass blowing, narrow gauge railway, working steam, trout lake, animals and music.

Norwich–Acle, then A1064 Acle to Caister Old
Road, to Burgh St Margaret/Fleggburgh
Open all year. Whitsun until September 10.00am–6.00pm.
Please enquire for off season opening times/facilities
Admission: adult £3.50, child £3.00, party rates
negotiable
&. ⊞ 🏋

► **GRESSENHALL** ◄

NORFOLK RURAL LIFE MUSEUM AND UNION FARM

Farming museum

Beech House, Gressenhall, Dereham, Norfolk NR20 4DR
☎ Dereham (0362) 860563

Museum with exhibits displayed in authentic settings; Edwardian cottage and garden; working 1920s farm with heavy horses, cars, sheep etc. Picnic area, tea room, gift shop and childrens activities.

On the B1146, 3 miles north of Dereham
Open Easter–end Oct, Tues–Sat 10.00am–5.00pm, Sun
2.00–5.30pm, closed Mondays except Bank Holidays
(10.00am–5.00pm)
Admission: adult £2.00, child 60p, OAP £1.75, party rates
available (1990 prices)
&. &. ⊞ 🏋 in the museum grounds only

► **HARLESTON** ◄

MILLHOUSE POTTERY

Craft centre – pottery, shop and garden area

1 Station Road, Harleston, Norfolk IP20 9ES
☎ Harleston (0379) 852556

Domestic slipware, decorated jugs, mugs, pie dishes, blue & white tin glazed pottery. A large selection of unglazed and glazed decorative garden pots, bird baths, fountains and large shrub pots.

Situated on the A134, 9 miles from Diss and 7
miles from Bungay.
Open daily 10.00am–5.30pm except Mondays
Free admission
&. ⊞ advance notice required 🏋

▶ **HICKLING** ◀

HICKLING BROAD

Nature reserve

c/o Norfolk Naturalists Trust, 72 Cathedral Close,
Norwich, Norfolk NR1 4DF
☎ Norwich (0603) 625540

*The largest stretch of open water in
broadland is surrounded by extensive reed
and sedge beds. Home of the bittern, marsh
harrier and bearded tit. Stronghold of the
rare swallowtail butterfly.*

Approach via the A149, turning off to Hickling
Green between Potter Heigham and Stalham
Open daily (except Tues) for the trails April–Oct
9.00am–5.00pm. Winter opening 9.00am–4.00pm
Admission by permit from the Warden's Office
& 🚐 advance notice required 🍴

▶ **HOLT** ◀

LETHERINGSETT WATERMILL

Working water mill

Riverside Road, Letheringsett, nr Holt, Norfolk NR25 7YD
☎ Holt (0263) 713153

*This unique watermill built in 1802 is set in
a picturesque setting is being restored to its
full working potential, producing 100%
wholewheat stoneground flour from local
wheat, which can be purchased in mill shop.*

1 mile west of Holt off the A148, 100 yards past
Letheringsett Village sign turn left
Open Tues–Fri 9.00am–1.00pm, 2.00–5.00pm, Sat
9.00am–1.00pm, Sun 2.00–5.00pm, closed Mondays
Admission when operating: adult £1.00, child 50p, OAP
75p. At other times adult 50p, child 25p
& 🚐 advance notice required 🍴

▶ **HUNSTANTON** ◀

COURTYARD FARM

Country walks and bunkhouse accommodation

Ringstead, Hunstanton, Norfolk PE36 5LQ
☎ Holme (048 525) 369

*Working farm, with extensive walking on
public footpaths in beautiful countryside.*

*Cheap but comfortable accommodation
available in the bunkhouse barn, visitors
with horses are always welcome.*

North east of Hunstanton off the Ringstead–
Docking road
Open all year
Free admission; bunkhouse £3.00 per night
& 🐎

▶ **KING'S LYNN** ◀

CONGHAM HALL HERB GARDEN

Herb garden

Lynn Rd, Grimston, King's Lynn, Norfolk PE32 1AH
☎ Hillington (0485) 600250

*A garden for herb enthusiasts with over 250
varieties of herbs, some grown in traditional
Fortial beds. Potager Garden; over 200
varieties of herbs for sale in pots.*

Turn off the A148 King's Lynn–Fakenham Road to
Grimston – do not go to Congham village
Open 1 April–30 Sept daily, except Saturdays,
2.00–4.00pm
Free admission
& no toilet facilities 🍴

W R B FOSTER AND PARTNERS

Vineyard

Lexham Hall, King's Lynn, Norfolk PE32 2QJ
☎ Fakenham (0328) 701288

*An 8 acre vineyard situated in the Nar
Valley producing an Estate bottled dry
fragrant and fruity wine reminiscent of the
Upper Moselle and Alsace.*

From Swaffham take the A1065 to Fakenham, after
5 miles turn right to East & West Lexham,
immediately fork left to West Lexham, proceed
through West Lexham village and after approx 1
mile turn right into Church Farm
Open by appointment only, please telephone
Admission: £28.00 for party of 20, an additional charge
of 60p per head for numbers in excess of 20, the
charge includes a glass of wine
& 🚐 advance notice required 🍴

PARK FARM

Farm shop, open farm, safari rides and country walks

Snettisham, King's Lynn, Norfolk PE31 7NQ
☎ Dersingham (0485) 542425

Entertainment and educational facilities on a farm with chickens, ducks, pigs, cows and a superb herd of red deer. Sheep centre and a new daily sheep show; superb adventure play area; refreshments; farm trails and more.

On the A149 King's Lynn–Hunstanton road, follow brown tourist signs to Farm Park
Open April–Oct daily 10.30am–5.00pm
Admission to farm & safari ride: adult £4.50, child £2.50, OAP £4.00; safari or farm only: adult £2.50, child £1.50, OAP £2.00
& ♿ ✝

SANDRINGHAM

Historic house, grounds, museum, country park and pick your own

Estate Office, Sandringham, King's Lynn, Norfolk, PE35 6EN
☎ King's Lynn (0553) 772675

Sandringham – the private country home of Her Majesty The Queen. House, Grounds, Museum and Country Park open to the public (except when Members of The Royal Family are in residence).

Off the A149, 7 miles north of King's Lynn
Open May–Sept Sun–Thur. Grounds 10.30am–5.00pm, House 11.00am–4.45pm (Sundays Grounds 11.30am–5.00pm, House 12.00 noon–4.45pm)
Please telephone first before visit to confirm opening times
Admission: Grounds: adult £1.70, child £1.00, OAP £1.30, House & Grounds: adult £2.20, child £1.40, OAP £1.70 (1990 Prices)
& ♿ ✝

WELLBANK'S ORCHID WORLD LTD

Orchid display centre

Lynn Rd, Terrington St Clement, King's Lynn, Norfolk PE34 4JX
☎ King's Lynn (0553) 827155

Orchid World has been developed to permanently display a wide selection of orchids, along with other interesting plant types.

Off the A17, 6 miles west of King's Lynn
Open daily except Christmas Day 11.00am–5.00pm
Admission: adult £1.50, child (to 14) 50p, OAPs £1.00, parties, per person £1.00 (1990 prices)
& ♿ ✝

◄ LODDON

HALES HALL

Country gardens

Loddon, Norfolk NR14 6QW
☎ Raveningham (050846) 395

Specialists in rare and exotic fruits, conservatory plants.

A146 turn right at sign for Hales Hall, and follow signs
Open July & Aug, Wed 2.00pm–5.00pm. Nurseries and conservatories Tues–Sat 10.00am–5.00pm, weekends by appointment
Admission to gardens 50p, rest is free
& no facilities/however previous wheelchair disabled visitors managed very well
♿ advance notice required ✝

► NORWICH ◄

THE AROUND NORFOLK WALK

Country walks

c/o Department of Planning and Property, Norfolk County Council, County Hall, Norwich, Norfolk NP1 2DH
☎ Norwich (0603) 222718

A fine 220 mile walk around Norfolk including the Broads, Brecks and Coast comprising Peddars, Angles, Weavers' Way and Coastal Path. Short circular walks based on main walk. Send SAE to above address for leaflets.

Various starting points
Open all year
Free admission
& ✝

BEESTON HALL

Historic house and grounds with woodland walks

Beeston St Lawrence, Norwich, Norfolk NR12 8YS
☎ Horning (0692) 630771

Beeston Hall is a smaller historic house built in 1786 in Gothic style by the Preston family who still live there. Walk to the lake and old ice house, tea room, shop, wine cellars.

Norwich to Wroxham 9 miles, then 2¼ miles beyong Wroxham, off the road to Stalham (A1151), also accessible from the Broads to Neatishead

Open Easter–Sept, Fri, Sun and Bank Holidays 2.00–5.30pm, open Wednesdays during August

Admission: adult £2.00, child 60p, OAP £1.50; grounds only 50p

& ⊞ advance notice required ✕

THE FAIRHAVEN GARDEN TRUST

Country gardens and country walks

2 The Woodlands, Wymers Lane, South Walsham, Norwich NR13 6EA

☎ South Walsham (060549) 449

Views of the broads from this peaceful garden. Trees, including a 900 year old oak, many rare shrubs and plants, candelabra primulas and rhododendrons.

Off the B1140, 9 miles north east of Norwich

Open Easter–May Sundays and Bank Holidays; May–Sept Wed–Sun 2.00–6.00pm

Admission: adult £1.50, child 70p, OAP £1.00

& the garden may be difficult to get around in a wheelchair in wet weather

⊞ advance notice required ✝

MACFARLANE'S GARDEN CENTRE

Garden centre

Blue Boar Lane, Norwich, Norfolk NR7 8RJ

☎ Norwich (0603) 412239

Garden centre and Gardeners Pantry restaurant.

From A47 Norwich ring road, take the A1151 Wroxham road, turning right after 1 mile into Blue Boar Lane

Open all year daily, Mon–Sat 9.00am–5.30pm, Sun and Bank Holidays 10.00am–5.30pm

Free admission

& ⊞ advance notice required ✕

MARRIOTTS WAY

Country walk

c/o Broadland District Council, Thorpe Lodge, Yarmouth Rd, Norwich NR7 0DU

☎ Norwich (0603) 31133

A 7 mile walk along the former M. and G.N. railway with links to the centre of Norwich.

The route passes through farmland, woodland and water meadows alongside the river Wensum.

Between Hellesdon and Attlebridge on the north west outskirts of Norwich

Open all year

Free admission and car parking

& ✝

REDWINGS HORSE SANCTUARY

Horse sanctuary

Hill Top Farm, Hall Lane, Frettenham, Norwich, Norfolk NR12 7LT

☎ (0603) 737432

Redwings provides a caring permanent home for over 700 horses, ponies and donkeys which have been rescued from neglect and slaughter. Please contact us for further details. Gift shop and restaurant.

Take the B1150 from Norwich turning left at the White Horse public house, there are some signs at this turn and also on Hall Lane

Open Easter–Christmas, 2.00–5.00pm every Sunday

Admission: adult £1.00, child/OAP 50p

& need assistance on shingle areas ⊞ ✝

SUTTON WINDMILL POTTERY

Pottery

Church Road, Sutton, Norwich, Norfolk NR12 9SG

☎ Stalham (0692) 80595

Malcolm Flatman designs and makes by hand a large range of domestic stoneware pottery in a variety of glazes. Visitors are welcome to view and buy in the workshop.

Off the A149, 15 miles north east of Norwich, 1½ miles south of Stalham

Open during conventional office hours, and by arrangement at weekends

Free admission

& ✕

TAVERHAM CRAFT CENTRE

Craft centre, garden centre

Fir Covert Rd, Taverham, Norwich NR8 6HT

☎ Norwich (0603) 860522

10 purpose-built workshops grouped round a paved quadrangle in a rural setting, featuring craftspeople at work. Alongside is a garden centre with over 15 acres of plants, trees and accessories. Pet shop; tea room.

7 miles from Norwich on the A1067 Norwich–
Fakenham road
Open all year Mon–Sun 10.00am–5.00pm
Free admission and parking
  🚻

WILLOW FARM DRIED FLOWERS

Dried flower centre

Cangate, Neatishead, Norwich, Norfolk NR12 8YH
☎ Wroxham (0603) 783588

*A small farm specialising in growing and
supplying quality dried flowers. Flower
arranging workshop open throughout the
year. Field growing up to 50 varieties on
show during summer.*

Off the A1151, 2 miles east of Wroxham. Follow
brown tourist signs
Open Mon–Sat 10.00am–12.00 noon and 2.00–4.00pm;
Sundays 2.00–4.00pm; all day Bank Holidays and peak
holiday periods. Closed between Christmas and New
Year
Free admission
  advance notice required ✗

WOLTERTON PARK

Country house and gardens

Erpingham, Norwich, Norfolk NR11 7LY
☎ Saxthorpe (026 387) 4175

*Extensive grounds, gardens, 18th century
Mansion house.*

On the A140, Aylsham 5 miles, Cromer 8 miles
Please telephone for opening hours
  advance notice required ✗

►   *SHERINGHAM*   ◄

SHERINGHAM PARK – NATIONAL TRUST

Country walk

Upper Sheringham, Norfolk
☎ Sheringham (0263) 823778

Off the A148 Holt to Cromer Road
Open all year
Free admission, small car park charge
  boardwalk 🚻

SHERINGHAM POTTERY

Craft centre and pottery

Church St, Sheringham, Norfolk
☎ Sheringham (0263) 823552

*Family pottery where everything is made
entirely by hand on the premises; anything
from ashtrays to coffee sets. House plaques
and lamps are our specialities.*

Please telephone for directions
Open daily 9.00am–5.00pm
Free admission
  🚻

►   *SWAFFHAM*   ◄

COCKLEY CLEY ICENI VILLAGE & MUSEUMS

Historical site, museum and nature walk

Estate Office, Cockley Cley, Swaffham, Norfolk PE37 8AG

*A unique insight into how Britons lived in
the 1st century AD in this Iceni village.
Mediaeval cottage housing a museum; Saxon
church; carriage collection; lake, nature trail
and picnic area.*

3 miles south west of Swaffham off the A1065
towards Oxborough
Open daily Good Friday–Oct 12.00–5.30pm; July–Sept
11.00am–5.30pm
Admission: adult £2.10, child 90p, OAP £1.20, party rates
available
  advance notice required 🚻

WATER GARDENS

Country garden

Gooderstone, King's Lynn, Norfolk
☎ Gooderstone (036621) 645

*River and lake sided by water and
herbaceous plants, shrubs and roses. Aviary
and nature walk being developed for 1991.
Refreshments available.*

Off the A44, 6 miles from Swaffham. Left turning to
Gooderstone at sign
Open 1 April–30 Sept (Oct if fine) daily 10.00am–5.00pm
Admission: adult £1.00, child 30p
  advance notice required ✗

▶ THETFORD ◀

EAST WRETHAM HEATH

Nature reserve

c/o Norfolk Naturalists Trust, 72 Cathedral Close,
   Norwich, Norfolk NR1 4DF
☎ Norwich (0603) 625540

*This nature reserve is an excellent example
of Breckland Heath with meres, pines and
deciduous woodland with much to offer the
visitor. Bird hides, roe deer and some 250
wild flower varieties.*

3 miles north east of Thetford on the A1075
Open all year daily (except Tuesdays) 10.00am–5.00pm
Admission free, car park at the Warden's house
♿ there is a nature trail for the blind
🚌 advance notice required ✖

THE OLD NAG'S HEAD

Farm shop and speciality organic food producer

Holmehale, nr Thetford, Norfolk
☎ (0760) 440592

*Organic vegetables, meat, eggs and butter
for sale.*

Off the A47 through Necton into Holmehale,
4 miles from Swaffham
Always open, but by appointment; ring after 7.00pm
Admission: 50p
♿ ✖

▶ WALSINGHAM ◀

THE TEXTILE CENTRE

Craft centre

Hindringham Rd, Great Walsingham, Norfolk NR22 6DR
☎ Walsingham (0328) 820009

*Textile printing in traditional Norfolk barns
on view to the public. Mostly farm and
animal designs, with books, cards and
textiles for sale. Coffee shop; large car park.*

From the A148 at Fakenham take the B1105 north
   to Little Walsingham, then the B1388 to Great
   Walsingham; approx 6 miles in all. See brown
   tourist signs
Open Easter–31 Oct Mon–Fri 9.30am–5.30pm; weekends
   and Bank Holidays 10.00am–5.00pm
Free admission
♿ 🚌 ✖

▶ WELLS-NEXT-THE-SEA ◀

CARTWRIGHT & BUTLER LTD FACTORY SHOP

High quality preserves shop

Maryland, Wells-next-the-Sea, Norfolk NR23 1DB
☎ Fakenham (0328) 711313

*Finest quality foods at factory prices as
supplied to the premier London hotels and
stores. A wide selection of gifts available –
choose the products for your own
presentation pack.*

Take the B1105 from Fakenham to Wells-
   next-the-Sea, on reaching Wells turn right
   (signposted Cromer), past church, next left at
   Polka Road to bottom of hill on right hand side
Open all year Mon–Fri 9.00am–4.00pm Sat & Sun
   10.00am–4.00pm
Free admission
♿ 🚌 ✖

▶ WROXHAM ◀

WROXHAM BARNS

Craft centre

Wroxham Barns Craft Centre, Tunstead Road, Hoveton,
   Norwich NR12 8QU
☎ (0603) 783762

*18th century restored farm buildings houses
11 craft workshops, the Gallery craft shop
and the Old Barn tea room. In the
surrounding 10 acres of parkland is a picnic
area, playground, and car park.*

1½ miles off the B1354 north of Wroxham, on the
   Tunstead road
Open Jan–Easter Mon–Fri 10.00am–5.00pm, Sat & Sun
   10.00am–6.00pm; Easter–Christmas 10.00am–6.00pm
Free admission
♿ 🚌 advance notice required ✖

NORTHAMPTONSHIRE

Northamptonshire remains mainly agricultural, a landscape of graceful spires, trees and rich pastureland. Woodland remnants survive of the once great Rockingham Forest where the Kings of England hunted the fallow deer.

A wide selection of country walks offers the visitor every opportunity to see and enjoy the Northamptonshire countryside. A forest recreation centre, a country estate interpretation centre, a farming museum and an agricultural museum with vintage tractors are all featured and will give the visitor an appreciation of the countryside past and present.

▶ DAVENTRY ◀

DAVENTRY COUNTRY PARK

Country park and country walks

Welton Road, Daventry, Northamptonshire
☎ Daventry (0327) 77193

*Picnic areas, adventure playground,
woodland walks, bird hides, nature reserve.
Fishing on day or permit basis.*

Daventry
Open all year
Free admission
& ⋔

▶ DESBOROUGH ◀

THE COPPER GALLERY

Craft centre – ornamental iron work

Lower St, Desborough, Kettering, Northamptonshire
NN14 2NP
☎ Kettering (0536) 762333

*Visitors will find copper repoussé pictures
and ornamental ironwork made in the centre,
also a fine selection of British crafts –
watercolours, ceramics, glass, porcelain,
figurines and floral decorations.*

Just off the A6, situated beside the church
Open all year Tues–Sat 10.00am–5.30pm
Free admission
& ⬛ advance notice required ⋔

▶ HARRINGWORTH ◀

STENCIL INTERIORS

Craft workshop

Tal Cottage, Harringworth, Northamptonshire NN17 3AD
☎ Morcott (057 287) 312

*Specialist in stencilling on walls, floors,
fabrics and furniture for period properties,
hotels etc. One day teaching workshops.
Commissioned stencilling.*

Harringworth is 3 miles south east of Uppingham
(Leics) on the north Northamptonshire border.
Uppingham lies on the A47 between Leicester
and Peterborough
Open by appointment only
Free admission
& ⋔

▶ KETTERING ◀

THE LIVING LANDSCAPE TRUST

**Country estate interpretation centre, estate and
nature trails**

Boughton House, Kettering, Northamptonshire NN14 1BJ
☎ Kettering (0536) 515731

*The Trust administers the opening of
Boughton House and Park, where it aims to
provide an opportunity to learn about the
countryside, the necessary work that goes on
there, and its conservation.*

3 miles north of Kettering on the A43 at
Geddington
Open for house and gardens: July–Aug daily 2.00–
5.00pm; grounds: daily April–Oct, 12.00–5.00pm
Admission: adult £1.00, child/OAP 50p, visitors in
wheelchairs free
& ⬛ advance notice required ⋔

▶ NORTHAMPTON ◀

COTON MANOR GARDENS

Country gardens

Nr Ravensthorpe, Northamptonshire NN6 8RQ
☎ Northampton (0604) 740219

*Herbaceous borders, lakes, water gardens, old
hedges and lawns; flamingoes, cranes and
waterfowl roaming at large. Its charm has a
wide appeal to garden and nature lovers.*

11 miles north of Northampton, follow tourist signs
on the A428, or the A50
Open Easter–Sept, Sundays and Bank Holiday Mondays,
also Wednesdays in June, July and August,
2.00–6.00pm
Admission: adult £2.00, child 50p, OAP £1.80
⬛ advanced notice required ⋔

GRAFTON WAY

Country walk

c/o Northampton Countryside Services, Planning &
Transporation Dept, Northampton House, Northampton
NN1 2HZ
☎ Northampton (0604) 20184

*12 mile walk. Starts/ends at Greens Norton,
near Towcester, or starts/ends at Cosgrove,
near Milton Keynes. A leaflet is available
from the above address for 35p.*

Directions as above

Open all year
Free admission
  not suitable for disabled except canal towpath at
Cosgrove ⚓

HANNINGTON VINTAGE TRACTOR CLUB AGRICULTURAL MUSEUM

Farming museum

Out Buildings at Lamport Hall, Lamport Village,
  Northamptonshire
☎ Northampton (0604) 810623

*Collection of old tractors, stationary engines,
dairy, handtools, agricultural machinery,
horse drawn implements and other bygones.*

On the A508, approx 8 miles from Northampton
  and 8 miles from Market Harborough
Open Easter–Sept, Sun and Bank Holidays 2.00–5.30pm
Free admission
& 🚗 ⚓

HOLDENBY HOUSE GARDENS

Historic gardens and rare breeds farm

Holdenby, Northamptonshire NN6 8DJ
☎ Northampton (0604) 770786

*Built in 1583 by Sir Christopher Hatton.
Holdenby House – now based round one
wing of Hatton's palace – provides a
backdrop to a beautiful garden. Rare breeds
of farm animals, pets corner, falconry centre.*

Between the villages of East Haddon and Church
  Brampton, from the A50, and the A428
Open Easter–Sept, Sun and Bank Holiday Mondays
  2.00–6.00pm, also Thursdays in July & Aug
  2.00–6.00pm. House also open by appointment to
  groups of 20 or more
Admission to gardens: adult £1.80, child 80p, OAP
  £1.40. House & gardens: adult £2.75, child £1.00.
& 🚗 ⚓

KNIGHTLEY WAY

Country walk

c/o Northamptonshire Countryside Services, Planning and
  Transportation Dept, Northampton House, Northampton
  NN1 2HZ
☎ Northampton (0604) 20184

*11 mile walk. Starts/ends at Badby, 2½
miles south of Daventry, or starts/ends at
Greens Norton, near Towcester. Youth hostel*

*in Badby. A leaflet is available from the
above address for 35p.*

Directions as above
Open all year
Free admission
⚓

LAMPORT

Gardens and historic house

Lamport, Northamptonshire NN6 9HB
☎ Maidwell (060 128) 272

*Outstanding collections of furniture, books
and paintings; spacious gardens include a
remarkable rockery, first English home of the
gnome. Beautiful stableyard.*

Midway between Northampton and Market
  Harborough on the A508
Open Easter–Sept, Sundays 2.15–5.15pm; July & August
  Thursday afternoons
Admission: adult £2.20, child £1.00, OAP £1.70
🚗 advance notice required ⚓

NASEBY BATTLE AND FARM MUSEUM

Farming museum

Purlieu Farm, Naseby, Northamptonshire NN6 7DD
☎ Northampton (0604) 740241

*Miniature layout of battlefield, 850 model
soldiers set our in battle order, 10 min
commentary. Relics from Naseby battle field;
farm hand tools and machinery; vintage
tractors and village history. 1½ acre picnic
area.*

Off the B4036, between Daventry and Market
  Harborough
Open Easter–Sept, Sun and Bank Holidays 2.00–6.00pm,
  and at other times for parties by appointment
Admission: adult 80p, child 40p
& 🚗 ⚓

NORTHAMPTONSHIRE NENE WAY

Country walk

c/o Northamptonshire Countryside Services, Planning and
  Transporation Dept, Northampton House, Northampton
  NN1 2HZ
☎ Northampton (0604) 20184

*70 mile walk. Starts/ends at Badby, 2½
miles south of Daventry, or starts/ends at*

Wansford, near Peterborough. A leaflet is available from the above address, 35p for 1, or £1.75 for a full set of 5.

Directions as above
Open all year
Free admission
& not suitable except at Irchester Country Park 🐕

SALCEY FOREST

Forest recreation, picnic, play area, forest walks

c/o Foresty Commission, Northants Forest District Office,
Top Lodge, Fineshade, Corby, Northamptonshire
NN17 3BB
☎ Duddington (078 083) 394

Walks, play area, conservation trail, orienteering.

Approx 7 miles south east Northampton, turn right
off the B526 between Horton and Stoke
Goldington. 1½ miles turn right for further ½
mile to Forestry Commission car park
Open all year
Free admission
& one trail specially surfaced 🚐 🐕

► OUNDLE ◄

BARNWELL COUNTRY PARK

Country park

Barnwell Road, Oundle, Northamptonshire PE8 5PB
☎ Oundle (0832) 273435

An attractive mixture of lakes, woodland and riverside meadows, with a network of waterside paths and picnic areas. Visitor centre and ranger service to help you to enjoy the countryside.

Off the A605, just south of Oundle
Open all year
Free admission
& 🚐 advance notice required 🐕

► TOWCESTER ◄

BLAKESLEY GALLERY

Craft centre – art gallery

The Green, Blakesley, Towcester, Northamptonshire
NN12 8RD
☎ Blakesley (0327) 860274

Gallery situated on village green. Converted ancient barn gives plenty of space for varied display of high standard of paintings, ceramics, glass and jewellery. Warm welcome guaranteed.

Off the A5, 3 miles north of Towcester
Open March–Dec, Wed–Sun 10.00am–5.00pm
Free admission
& There is a 'mezzanine' floor which is not accessible to
people in wheelchairs, but items can be carried down for
them to see, this floor is a small part of a large
gallery 🐕

► WELLINGBOROUGH ◄

CHURCH FARM SHOP

Farm shop

Church Farm, Strixton, Wellingborough, Northamptonshire
NN9 7PA
☎ Wellingborough (0933) 664378

See farm animals in a traditional setting. Freshly laid eggs and organically produced vegetables and meats together with farmhouse cooking.

5 miles from Wellingborough on the A509 towards
Newport Pagnell, 12 miles from jct 14 on the M1
Open Tues–Fri 9.00am–5.30pm, Sat 9.00am–5.00pm
Free admission
& 🚐 advance notice required ✕

NORTHUMBERLAND

Northumberland – beautiful, remote and unspoilt countryside with an appealing coastline of cliffs, dunes, fisherman's villages and harbour towns.

Hand feed the animals at one of the farm parks, try out one of the narrow gauge or steam railways, step into history when you cross Hadrian's Wall, see a working corn mill, find out more about the National Park or the Border Forest Park from the visitor centres, walk around a herb nursery, watch a smithy or a potter in action and enjoy what the Northumberland countryside has to offer.

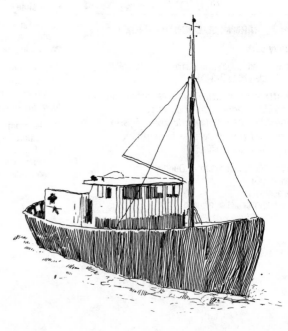

► **ALNWICK** ◄

BREAMISH VALLEY POTTERY

Pottery

Branton, Powburn, Alnwick, Northumberland NE66 4LW
☎ Powburn (066 578) 263

The pottery is situated in an old stable block in a hamlet in the Cheviot foothills. Alistair and Catherine Hardie produce a wide range of hand thrown kitchen and domestic ware.

1 mile west of Powburn, off the A697
Open May–Sept Tues–Sat 10.00am–5.30pm, telephone first for Oct–April
Free admission
க் ★

► **AMBLE** ◄

HAUXLEY NATURE RESERVE

Nature reserve and interpretation centre

Low Hauxley, Amble, Northumberland
☎ Alnwick (0665) 711578

An ex-open-cast mine, restored in the early 1980s. An excellent point for birdwatching on Druridge Bay. Wardens; information available on birds present.

1 mile south of Amble, entrance is between Low and High Hauxley
Open all year daily 9.00am–5.00pm
Admission by day permit which covers all Druridge Bay nature reserves £1.00, child/OAP/unemployed 50p
க் wheelchair access to hides, but no toilets
🚌 advance notice required ★

► **BARDON MILL** ◄

NORTHUMBERLAND NATIONAL PARK VISITOR CENTRE

National park

Once Brewed Visitor Centre, Military Rd, Bardon Mill, Hexham, Northumberland
☎ Hexham (0434) 344396

Visitor centre with exhibitions, audio-visual theatre, information area and shop. Light refreshments (not cafe), picnic area and toilets. Good access to Hadrian's Wall.

On the B6318 Military Road, between Greenhead and Chollerford
Open 16 March–3 Nov daily. March–end Sept 10.00am–6.00pm; Oct and Nov 5.00pm
Free admission
க் 🚌 ★

► **BELFORD** ◄

THE BRENT GALLERY, DAVID BINNS FINE ART

Craft centre and gallery

Fenham-le-Moor, Belford, Norhtumberland NE70 7PN
☎ Belford (0668) 213533

A gallery specializing in wildlife, farmlife and the countryside. Exhibiting work by leading artists, including original paintings, etchings, prints, ceramics and our Fox design and Lindisfarne design pottery.

1 mile east of the A1, signed Fenham-le-Moor, 3 miles north of Belford
Open Easter–Oct daily 10.00am–7.00pm
Free admission
க் 🚌 ✖

► **BERWICK-UPON-TWEED** ◄

ERROL HUT SMITHY AND WOODWORK SHOP

Craft centre

Letham Hill, Etal, Cornhill-on-Tweed, Northumberland TD12 4TP
☎ Crookham (089 082) 317

A small family based business: the smithy specializing in ornamental wrought ironwork, and the woodwork shop in hardwood furniture and spinning wheels.

Off the B6354, 10 miles south of Berwick
Open all year daily 10.00am–5.00pm
Free admission
க் ★

FORD AND ETAL ESTATES

Craft centres, art gallery, corn mill, country walks

c/o Mr F Waters, The Estate Office, Ford, Berwick-upon-Tweed, Northumberland TD15 2QA
☎ Crookham (089 082) 338/224

Ford and Etal are beautiful villages set in spectacular countryside. The many attractions include a working watermill, steam railway, thatched cottages, Flodden Battlefield, Lady Waterford Hall, riding, fishing and much more.

Between Wooler and Coldstream on the A697, 9 miles south west of Berwick-on-Tweed
Open Easter–end Oct
Admission: varies from free to £2.50 depending on attraction
    ☐ 🚻 🐾

HEATHERSLAW CORN MILL

Working corn mill, farming museum, craft centre

Ford and Etal Estates, Berwick-upon-Tweed, Northumberland TD12 4TJ
☎ Crookham (089 082) 338

Restored and working 19th century water powered corn mill. All equipment and processes are visible. Exhibitions, shop, cafe. A leaflet is available from the above address.

15 minutes from Berwick-upon-Tweed on the B6354 and signposted from the A697 between Wooler and Coldstream
Open Easter–end Oct 10.00am–6.00pm daily, winter by appointment, telephone J Bradley (089 082) 297/338
Admission: adult £1.00, child/OAP/unemployed 50p (1990 prices)
    ☐ 🚻 advance notice required 🍴

HEATHERSLAW LIGHT RAILWAY CO LTD

Light railway and railway museum

Ford Forge, Heatherslaw, Cornhill-on-Tweed, Northumberland TD12 4QA
☎ Crookham (089 082) 244/317

15 inch gauge light railway with steam and diesel engines which runs alongside the River Till, from a working water mill to Etal village, a distance of 1½ miles. Leaflets available from the above address.

10 miles from Berwick, on the B6354
Open Easter–end Oct daily, Nov–Christmas weekends only
Admission: adult £2.50, child under 14/OAP £1.50 (child under 4 free)
    ☐ 🚻 advance notice requried

▶ **BLYTH** ◀

NORTH FARM SHOP

Farm shop

South Newsham, Blyth, Northumberland NE24 3PW
☎ Blyth (0670) 353517

Angora goats and pedigree Aberdeen Angus, fresh fruit and vegetables, wholefoods and free range eggs, speciality ice cream and yoghurt, meat and organic goat produce, country clothing, animal feedstuffs.

West of the A193 on South Newsham road, just south of Blyth
Open Wed–Sun 9.00am–5.30pm
Free admission
    ☐ 🚻 🐾

▶ **CAMBO** ◀

WALLINGTON HOUSE, WALLED GARDEN AND GROUNDS

Country park, country walk and country garden

Cambo, Morpeth, Northumberland NE61 4AR
☎ Scots Gap (067 074) 283

12 miles west of Morpeth (B6343), 6 miles north west of Belsay (A696), take the B6342 to Cambo
Open for the grounds: all year; walled garden: March–Sept daily 10.00am–7.00pm, Oct daily 10.00am–6.00pm, Nov–Easter daily 10.00am–.400pm; house Easter–end Oct 1.00–5.30pm except Tues
Admission to house and grounds: £3.00; grounds £1.50
 ☐ special parking bays, conservatory and walled garden terrace accessible, wheelchair access to walled garden 🚻 🐾 in park and garden

---

▶ **CORBRIDGE** ◀

CORBRIDGE SOFT FRUIT

Farm shop, pick your own and country garden

Brocksbushes Farm, Stocksfield, Northumberland NE43 7UB
☎ Hexham (0434) 633400

Attractive setting. Comprehensive selection of fruit, vegetables and flowers.

2 miles east of Corbridge, 15 miles west of Newcastle, entrance on the A69 on north side of Styford roundabout where the A68 and the A69 join

Open June–Aug daily 9.30am–5.30pm, late night closing
  Fridays 8.00pm
Free admission
&. ∞ ⋔

► HEXHAM ◄

HAINING FARM PARK

Farm park and country walk

Nr Stonehaugh, Wark, Hexham, Northumberland
NE48 3ED
☎ Bellingham (0434) 230680

*Traditional Northumbrian hill farm with
Red deer, cows, sheep, rare breed animals
and goats. Guided tours. Visitors can hand
feed the animals.*

18 miles north of Hexham, on the B6320
Open Easter–30 Sept daily 1.30–5.00pm
Admission: adult £1.50, child/OAP 75p (1990 prices)
&. ∞ advance notice required ⋔

HEXHAM HERBS

Country garden and herb nursery

The Chesters Walled Garden, Chollerford, Hexham,
Northumberland
☎ Humshaugh (043 481) 483

*Beautiful walled garden seen on BBC2's
'Gardener's World', with mature herbaceous
borders, box hedging, and many unusual
plants for the keen plantsperson. Extensive
herb display, National Thyme Collection and
Roman Garden.*

½ mile west of Chollerford roundabout, off the
  B6318, 6 miles north of Hexham
Open April–Sept daily 10.00am–5.00pm; by appointment
  in winter
Admission to nursery free, 50p entrance charge to 2 acre
  walled garden
&. ✕

► KIELDER ◄

KIELDER CASTLE VISITOR CENTRE

Visitor centre

Forestry Commission, Kielder Castle, Kielder, Hexham,
Northumberland
☎ Bellingham (0434) 250209

*Showpiece of the Border Forest Park, Kielder
Castle shows the visitor some of the many
facilities, activities and events within the
area. Exhibition room, craft shop and cafe.*

18 miles west of Bellingham on the C200. Centre is
  signposted from village
Open Easter–Oct daily 10.00am–5.00pm, Bank Holidays
  and Aug 10.00am–6.00pm
Free admission
&. ∞ ⋔

► MORPETH ◄

BLAKEMORE FARM VISITOR CENTRE

**Farm interpretation centre, farm trail, nature
reserve and bird hides**

Cresswell, Morpeth, Northumberland
☎ Morpeth (0670) 861855

*Ideal centre for bird watching at the south
end of Druridge Bay. Wardened daily,
information boards on birds present.*

Please telephone for directions
Open times to be decided
Free admission to farm trail and visitor centre. Day permit
  for all Druridge Bay reserves: adult £1.00, child/
  OAP/unemployed 50p, family £1.50
&. ∞ advance notice required ✕

DRURIDGE POOLS NATURE RESERVE

Nature reserve with bird hides

Druridge, Widdrington, Morpeth, Northumberland
☎ Morpeth (0670) 861855

*3 bird hides overlooking wetlands. Good for
wildfowl in winter, and breeding waders in
summer.*

2 miles north of Cresswell
Open all year daily 10.00am–5.00pm
Admission: permit from Hauxley Nature Reserve, allows
  entry to all Druridge Bay Nauture Reserves – adult
  £1.00, child/OAP/unemployed 50p, family £1.50
&. ∞ advance notice required ✕

HERTERTON HOUSE, GARDEN AND NURSERY

Country garden

Hartington, Cambo, Morpeth, Northumberland NE16 4BN
☎ Scots Gap (067 074) 278

1 acre of formal gardens designed around a small 16th century farmhouse. Features separate topiary, physic and flower gardens and good herbaceous plants.

Off the B6342, 9 miles south of Rothbury
Open May–Sept 1.30–5.30pm, closed all day Tues and Thur
Free admission to nursery, gardens £1.00
🚾 advance notice required (mornings and evenings preferred)
🗙

MELDON PARK

Pick your own and country gardens

Morpeth, Northumberland NE61 3SW
☎ Hartburn (067072) 661

Meldon Park is famous for its John Dobson architecture and fine views.

7 miles west of Morpeth, on the B6343
Open for house and gardens daily 25 May–23 June, 24, 25, 26 Aug 2.00–5.00pm; PYO July
Admission: adult £2.00, child 50p, OAP £1.00
♿ 🚾 🗙

► OTTERBURN ◄

THE REDESDALE CHEESE FARM & RIDING CENTRE

Farm shop, riding & trekking

Soppitt Farm, Otterburn, Northumberland NE19 1AF
☎ Farm/dairy (0830) 20506
☎ Riding centre (0830) 20276/(0670) 72293

Speciality farmhouse cheesemaker with farm shop, farm visit and cheesemaking video Easter–October. Riding for all abilities, groups catered for. Leaflet available.

2 miles east of Otterburn, on the B6341
Open all year for farm shop and riding – please telephone as times may vary
Free admission
♿ for riding

► POWBURN ◄

NORTHUMBERLAND NATIONAL PARK VISITOR CENTRE, INGRAM

National Park

Ingram, Powburn, Alnwick, Northumberland
☎ Powburn (066 578) 248

Exhibitions, information area, sales and ice creams.

Travel north through Powburn village on the A697, turn left on to minor road signposted Ingram. Visitor centre is signposted 2 miles up the Breamish Valley
Open 16 March–29 Sept daily 10.00am–6.00pm (5.30pm Sept)
Free admission
♿ 🐕

► ROTHBURY ◄

CRAGSIDE HOUSE AND COUNTRY PARK

Country walks, country park, country house & garden, fishing lake and visitor centre

Rothbury, Morpeth, Northumberland NE65 7PX
☎ Rothbury (0669) 20333

A great Victorian house, the first in the world to be lit by hydroelectricity. 900 acre country park with manmade lakes; hydraulic and hydroelectric machinery; 40 miles of walks; drives; fishing; playground.

Gate 1 mile north of Rothbury, 15 miles north west of Morpeth off the A697 and the B6341
Open for the house 1 April–31 Oct daily (closed Mondays except Bank Holidays) 1.00–5.30pm (last admission 5.00pm); country park 1 April–31 Oct daily 10.30am–7.00pm (dusk if earlier); Nov–March Sat & Sun 10.30am–4.00pm
Admission to house & country park (incl. visitor centre) £3.50, parties £3.00; country park only (incl. visitor centre) £2.00, parties £1.50
♿ parking and toilets at visitor centre. Wheelchairs available. Lift to 1st floor in house. Fishing pier, pathway to Nelly's Moss Lake
🚾 🐕

NORTHUMBERLAND NATIONAL PARK VISITOR CENTRE, ROTHBURY

National Park

Church House, Church St, Rothbury, Northumberland
☎ Rothbury (0669) 20887

Exhibitions, audio-visual displays, information area and shop.

Town centre, clearly signed
Open 23 March–29 Sept daily 10.00am–6.00pm (5.30pm Sept)
Free admission
♿ 🚾 parking in town 🐕

▶ *STOCKSFIELD-ON-TYNE* ◀

WHEELBIRKS JERSEY FARM

Farm visit

Stocksfield-on-Tyne, Northumberland NE43 7HY
☎ Stocksfield (0661) 843378

*Well established estate with pedigree Jersey
herd, combining modern farming and
forestry with traditional conservation. Cream
teas and guided farm walks provided by
arrangement.*

Take the A69 from Carlisle or Newcastle, at the A68
 roundabout cross River Tyne, head south to
 Darlington, left at Broomley for 2 miles
Open all year, please telephone for appointment
Admission charges made by arrangement
♿ 🚌 only minibuses ✗

NORTH HUMBERSIDE

North Humberside has a continuously moving coastline made up of fertile farmland reclaimed from the sea and disappearing coastline slowly being eroded by the sea.

A working family farm with rare breeds, a farm shop with corn dollies made to traditional designs, the only complete and working East Riding windmill, a stately home and its treasures, a potter and her pots and a wildlife conservation area provide the ingredients for an interesting journey around the countryside of North Humberside.

► BEVERLEY ◄

SKIDBY WINDMILL AND MUSEUM

Country walk, museum and windmill

The Hall, Lairgate, Beverley, North Humberside HU17 8HL
☎ Hull (0482) 882255

Skidby Mill is the only complete working example of an East Riding windmill. Erected in 1821 by Robert Garten, millwright of Beverley. Overhauled in 1974, it is now in full working order.

The mill stands off the A164 Beverley–Hessle road, 4 miles south of Beverley
Open May–Sept, Tues–Sat 10.00am–4.00pm, Sunday 1.30–4.30pm
Admission: adult 70p, child/OAP 35p
&. ᗏ ⚑

► BRIDLINGTON ◄

BURTON AGNES HALL

Stately house and grounds

Burton Agnes Hall, Preservation Trust Ltd, Estate Office, Burton Agnes, Driffield, North Humberside YO25 0ND
☎ Burton Agnes (0262 89) 324

Outstanding 16th century architecture. Filled with treasures collected during four centuries. Unique, world famous, carved ceilings and overmantels. Modern French and impressionist paintings. Licensed cafe. Gift shop. Picnic area. Childrens corner.

On the A166, midway between Bridlington and Driffield
Open daily 29 Mar–31 Oct, 11.00am–5.00pm, other times by appointment
Admission: house and grounds adult £2.00, child/OAP £1.50; grounds only 50p (1990 prices)
&. ᗏ advance notice required
⚑ but not in hall

► DRIFFIELD ◄

CRUCKLEY ANIMAL FARM

Farm visit

Cruckley Farm, Foston on the Wolds, Driffield, North Humberside YO25 8BS
☎ Beeford (026288) 337

A working family farm with rare breeds of cattle, sheep, pigs and poultry, hatchery and daily milking demonstration. Pets paddocks, 1½ mile trail to pond and lake. Picnic area, gifts and light refreshments.

At Foston on the Wolds, off the B1249, 6 miles south east of Driffield
Open May–Sept 10.30am–6.00pm, for party bookings and enquiries please telephone
Admission: adult £1.50, child/OAP £1.00 (1990 prices)
&. ᗏ ⚑

► EASINGTON ◄

EASINGTON POTTERY

Showroom and studio

7 South Churchside, Easington, Hull, North Humberside HU12 0TR
☎ Withernsea (0964) 650578

The potter, Gerd Fehrling, specialises in handthrown stoneware, tableware and planters, but also makes various other pieces. Weekly pottery classes for adults and children in the workshop.

From Hull, take the A1033 to Partington, then B1445 to Easington, 21 miles east of Hull
Open most days, 10.00am–5.00pm, but best to telephone first
Free admission
&. ᗏ advance notice required ⚑

► GOOLE ◄

SOUTH FARM CRAFT GALLERY

Craft studio

Blacktoft, nr Gilberdyke, Goole, North Humberside DN14 7XT
☎ (0430) 441889

Craft studios, gallery, shop and licensed restaurant in converted and restored farm buildings.

Open Wed–Sun and Bank holiday Mondays, Jan–Feb 10.00am–4.00pm, Mar–Dec 10.00am–5.00pm. Restaurant open gallery hours and 7.00–11.00pm Wed–Sun
&. ᗏ

▶ *HOWDEN* ◀

HOWDEN MARSH AMENITY AREA

Country walks and wildlife conservation area

Off St Johns St, Howden, North Humberside
☎ Howden (0430) 430904

Maintained by Howden Parish Council. 13 acres with ponds, islands, raised walkways, trees, aquatic and land plants, amphibians, fishing and a picnic area.

Exit 37 from the M62 and aim for Howden Minster, west entrance, St John's Street is immediately opposite the Minster, follow the street until you come to the marsh on your left
Open dawn until dusk, all year
Free admission
& ▥ free parking in town ⋔

▶ *SKIPSEA* ◀

MILL FARM

Farm shop

Mill Lane, Skipsea, North Humberside YO25 8SS
☎ Skipsea (026 286) 211

Dried flowers grown here are available fresh/dried or arranged. Corn dollies made to traditional designs using our own old varieties of wheat.

Take the B1242 into Skipsea village, look for Cross Street which leads onto Mill Lane, farm shop on the right, half way to sea front
Open all year round 9.00am–6.00pm
Free admission
& ⋔

Guide to Symbols

☎ telephone
& disabled welcome
▥ coaches welcome

⋔ dogs welcome (on a leash)
✗ dogs not welcome

NOTTINGHAMSHIRE

Nottinghamshire has the famous Sherwood Forest within its boundaries, home of the legendary Robin Hood and once a royal hunting ground, tracts of the forest still remain. Here agriculture and industry co-exist, the renowned Nottingham lace is one of the products.

Working farms provide the opportunity to stroke and feed tame farm animals, see many rare breeds and the farm shops offer a wide selection of fresh produce and preserves. There are country parks and walks in woodland and around lakes. A country house museum and a working tower windmill and museum provide indoor pursuits, an interesting treat for the odd rainy day, perhaps?

▶ **FARNSFIELD** ◀

THE WHITE POST MODERN FARM CENTRE

Modern farm interpretation centre, gift shop, tea gardens, trail and indoor exhibitions

White Post Farm, Farnsfield, nr Newark, Nottinghamshire NG22 8HL

☎ Mansfield (0623) 882977

A modern working farm where you can stroke and feed lots of tame farm animals who are guaranteed to come up to you!! 'Best of Tourism Award Winner' 1989.

1 mile west of Farnsfield, on the A614 at the White Post island, from jct 27 of the M1
Open all year Mon–Fri 10.00am–5.00pm, Sat, Sun and Bank Holidays 10.00am–6.00pm
Admission: adult £1.65, child 85p, OAP/disabled £1.00, under 5 years free, reduced rates for parties (1990 prices)
& ⚑ ⚐ only in the car park

▶ **KIRKBY IN ASHFIELD** ◀

PORTLAND PARK

Country walk

c/o Ashfield District Council, Urban Road, Kirkby in Ashfield, Nottinghamshire NG17 8DA

☎ Mansfield (0623) 755755

The park is in the form of an established woodland with mixed fauna and flora with some rare species and is located in a former limestone quarry with walks at various levels.

1 mile from Kirkby in Ashfield town centre
Open all year
Free admission
& ⚐

▶ **LINBY** ◀

NEWSTEAD ABBEY

Country walk, country garden and country house museum

Linby, Nottinghamshire NG15 8GE

☎ (0623) 793557

Formerly the home of poet Lord Byron, visitors see his own apartments and many other splendid 19th century rooms. Rose, iris, fern, rock and Japanese water gardens to explore.

Entrance on the A60, 11½ miles north of Nottingham
Open all year for the grounds (except last Friday in November) dawn–dusk. House: Good Friday–30 Sept 1991 daily 11.30am–6.00pm (last admission 5.00pm)
Admission: grounds: adult £1.00, child 50p, OAP 50p; house: adult £1.50, child 50p OAP/UB40 £1.00 (1990 prices)
& wheelchair access to gardens and toilets for disabled visitors
⚑ ⚐ in gardens only

▶ **MANSFIELD** ◀

D D & E BATES AND SONS

Farm shop

Penniment House Farm, Penniment Lane, Mansfield, Nottinghamshire NG19 6PH

☎ Mansfield (0623) 34195

We are a small family run business selling home, local and British grown produce. Cauliflowers and sprouts for the freezer when in season our speciality.

Off the A6075, which is the link road between the main Mansfield–Chesterfield road A617, and main Mansfield–Derby road A38
Open all year Tues–Fri 8.30am–5.30pm, Sat 8.30am–5.00pm, Sun 9.00am–1.00pm, closed all day Mondays
Free admission
& ⚑ ⚐

SHERWOOD FOREST FARM PARK

Rare breeds farm park

Lamb Pens Farm, Edwinstowe, Mansfield, Nottinghamshire NG21 9HL

☎ Mansfield (0623) 822255/823558

Comprehensive display of many rare breeds of farm animals. Over an acre of water gardens overlooking water fowl collection in beautiful lakeside setting. Newly enlarged undercover aviary of exotic birds. Tea room specialises in home-made cakes.

Follow the A6075, west of Edwinstowe towards Mansfield. On the unclassified road between Warsop and Old Clipstone

Open Easter–mid Oct daily 10.30am–5.30pm
Admission: adult £1.75, child £1.25, OAP £1.50, party
rates available on request
& 🚲 advance notice required
🐾 kennels available free of charge

► NEWARK ◄

CHURCH FARM

Farm shop

South Scarle, nr Newark, Nottinghamshire NG23 7JH
☎ Newark (0636) 892003

*Small friendly shop on working farm selling
home produced beef and pork, homemade
cakes, jams and preserves, real dairy ice
cream, locally grown vegetables, fruit and
salads, and animal feeds.*

Off the A1133, 7 miles north of Newark. Also off
the A46, 10 miles south of Lincoln
Open Easter–Oct Tues–Sun 8.30am–6.30pm closed
Monday. Open Oct–Easter Tues–Sat 9.30am–5.30pm
closed Sunday and Monday
Free admission
& 🚲 🐾

► NOTTINGHAM ◄

GREEN'S WINDMILL AND CENTRE

Working windmill, museum and shop

Windmill Lane, Sneinton, Nottingham NG2 4QB
☎ Nottingham (0602) 503635

*A restored, working tower windmill with
adjacent museum telling the story of milling
and of George Green, mathematical physicist
and miller interactive 'hands-on' exhibits
illustrate his work.*

Off the A612, Nottingham–Southwell road, 1 mile
east of city centre
Open Wed–Sun and Bank Holidays 10.00am–5.00pm,
closed Mondays and Tuesdays
Free admission
& the windmill is not accessible to wheelchairs but the
museum is. Disabled visitors may drive into the mill
courtyard, but please telephone first
& 🚲 🐾

Journey Through Britain

Have Fun Getting To Know Britain

An exciting race through the
towns and cities of Britain by
Ravensburger games.

Be first to reach each of the twelve
destinations and answer one of the
many fascinating questions.

A beautifully illustrated and
presented game, price **£12.99**.
Endorsed by the National Tourist
Boards.

English Tourist Board

► RAVENSHEAD ◄

RAVENSHEAD POTTERY

Pottery

23 Milton Drive, Ravenshead, Nottingham NG15 9BE
☎ Mansfield (0623) 793178

The pottery specializes in domestic and decorative stoneware pottery producing punch sets, coffee sets, wine kegs etc., which rely on shape and glaze effects for decoration. Price range £2–£40.

Off the A60 at Newstead Abbey Gates in centre of
    village near shopping precinct
Open any time but it is best to telephone first
Free admission
&. ⊤

► SUTTON IN ASHFIELD ◄

KING'S MILL RESERVOIR

Country walk and country park

c/o Ashfield District Council, Urban Road, Kirby in
    Ashfield, Nottinghamshire NG17 8DA
☎ Mansfield (0623) 755755

Consisting of a large lake, water not used for drinking water. Circular walk around the banks of the lake established animal and bird wild life. Private sailing club and schools operate sailing.

Lying between Sutton in Ashfield and Mansfield,
    adjacent to the A38
Open all year
Free admission
&. ⊨ ⊤

► WORKSOP ◄

CLUMBER PARK

Country park with gardens and walks

The National Trust Estate Office, Clumber Park, Worksop,
    Nottinghamshire S80 3AZ
☎ Worksop (0909) 476592

3,800 acres of park. Bicycle hire, fishing, National Trust shop, cafe, restaurant, many events all year, caravan and camp site.

4½ miles south east of Worksop signposted off the
    A1 and the A57; 11 miles off jct 30 of the M1

Open all year at all times
Admission free. Vehicle charges: midweek, cars £2.00,
    coaches £5.00, mini-coaches, cars and caravans £3.00;
    weekends & Bank Holidays, coaches £10.00
&. ⊨ ⊤

OXFORDSHIRE

Oxfordshire's beautiful countryside lies in the heart of England, it stretches eastwards from Cotswold country to Oxford itself, a city of dreaming spires, willow-bordered rivers and marvellous punting.

There are historic houses with outstanding features, collections and gardens to visit. The farm museum and farm shops will reveal the working life of the Oxfordshire countryside and there are nature reserves, country walks and deer parks to enjoy on foot or perhaps by Shire horse and cart. Vineyards and a real ale brewery offer refreshment before a wander around the arts and crafts of the region which include potteries and a frame maker and picture restorer.

► *ABINGDON* ◄

BOTHY VINEYARD

Farm shop and vineyard

Frilford Heath, Abingdon, Oxfordshire OX13 6QW
☎ Checkendon (0491) 681484

The proprietors are always pleased to welcome interested customers. Free tastings are given and the vineyard may be inspected. Asparagus, red and white currants and honey in farm shop.

1½ miles north of Marcham village, on unclassified road off the A415, 3 miles west of Abingdon, 400 yards east of the A338
Open throughout the year daily (except Tuesdays and Fridays) 10.00am–6.00pm
Free admission
♿ ᕮᓴ minibuses only, by appointment ✝

KINGSTON BAGPUIZE HOUSE AND GARDEN

Historic house and ocuntry gardens

Kingston House, Kingston Bagpuize, nr Abingdon, Oxfordshire OX13 5AX
☎ Longworth (0865) 820259

A charming house of great architectural interest, with panelled rooms and a magnificent staircase. Fine furniture and attractive pictures. Large garden with beautiful trees, flowering shrubs and lawns.

Near Abingdon
Open May, June & Sept, Wed & Sun 2.30–5.30pm and May and Aug Bank Holidays. Groups by written appointment to the above address
Admission: gardens 50p, child under 5 years free; house and garden: adult £2.00, child £1.00, OAP £1.50 (1990 prices)
♿ welcome to garden, house unsuitable
ᕮᓴ by written appointment only ✘

► *BANBURY* ◄

BANBURY SELF PICK

Farm shop and pick your own

Broughton Rd, Banbury, Oxfordshire OX16 9UL
☎ Banbury (0295) 261406

30 acres of a wide variety of soft fruit together with some vegetables. Freshly picked produce usually available.

On the B4035, approx 1 mile from Banbury Cross
Open daily during picking season (approx mid June–30 Sept) 9.00am–8.00pm
Free admission
♿ ᕮᓴ ✝

GRANARY MUSEUM AND GIFT SHOP

Farm shop and museum

Butlin Farm, Claydon, nr Banbury, Oxfordshire OX17 1EP
☎ Farnborough (029589) 258

Housed in the granary, cowshed and covered yard and inlcudes domestic items, World War I and II craft tools, steam roller, 1912 tractors, stationary engines and old Banbury shops. Picnic area, morning coffee and cream teas.

5 miles north of Banbury on the Southam–Coventry road (A423) right hand turn signposted Claydon 1½ miles
Open April–Sept daily, 10.00am–dusk, except Sundays 10.30am–dusk
Admission: adult £1.00, child/OAP 50p
♿ there are no toilet facilities
ᕮᓴ advance notice required ✝

HOOK NORTON POTTERY

Craft centre and pottery

East End Farmhouse, Hook Norton, Banbury, Oxfordshire OX15 5LG
☎ Hook Norton (0608) 737414

Hand made studio pottery. Domestic and individual pieces, large variety of shapes and colours, hand painted. Individual commissions undertaken.

Off the A361 Banbury–Chipping Norton road, follow signs to Hook Norton
Open Jan–Dec daily except Sundays, 9.30am–5.30pm
Free admission
♿ ✘

UPTON HOUSE – NATIONAL TRUST

Country garden

Banbury, Oxfordshire OX15 6HT
☎ (029587) 266

House contains outstanding collection of paintings, tapestries, Sevres porcelain and Chelsea figures. Large garden including wide lawns, terraced borders descending to lakes and a bog garden in a deep valley.

10 miles south east of Stratford-upon-Avon, or 7 miles from Banbury on the A422

Open Easter Sat, Sun and Mon and April weekends 2.00–6.00pm; May–Sept Sat–Wed 2.00–6.00pm; Oct weekends 2.00–6.00pm

Admission: £2.80, parties £1.90; garden only £1.80 child half price

  access to ground floor only, wheelchair available, toilet facilities

advance notice required

► *ELSFIELD* ◄

OXFORD PICK YOUR OWN FARM

Pick your own

Elsfield, nr Oxford OX3 9SW
☎ Stanton St John (086735) 8873

Extensive views over Otmoor. Over 60 crops grown including strawberries, currants, gooseberries, apples, plums, flowers, salads and a huge range of vegetables including unusual items.

Off the B4027 between Islip and Stanton St John, approx 3 miles north of Oxford
Open June–Nov, please telephone before visiting
Free admission and car parking

► *HENLEY-ON-THAMES* ◄

CHILTERN VALLEY WINES

Vineyard and winery

Old Luxters Vineyard and Winery, Hambledon, Henley-on-Thames, Oxfordshire RG9 6JW
☎ Turville Heath (049163) 330

Producers of Single Vintage Estate Bottled English Wines and winner of Best English Wine of the Year 1986 and 1987 vintage at the International Wine and Spirit competition and National Competition.

Take the Hambledon turning on the Henley–Marlow road, left turn 1½ miles after passing village of Hambledon
Open by appointment only
Free admisssion
   advance notice required

COUNTRY WAYS

Horse and cart excursions

Merafield, Crocker End, Common, Henley, Oxfordshire RG9 5BJ
☎ (0491) 641364

Wagon pulled through the Chiltern countryside by Jake and Duchess the heavy horses, a brother and sister team, always accompanied by their friends Barney, the collie, and Pippa, a comical Jack Russell.

Rides start from the old brick kiln, Nettlebed (A423)
Open daily, rides at 11.00am, 3.00pm and 7.00pm
Admission: please telephone for details. Parties up to 20, bookings only

---

THE HAMBLEDEN BREWERY

Brewery

Old Luxters Farm Brewhouse, Hambledon, nr Henley-on-Thames, Oxfordshire RG9 6JW
☎ Turville Heath (049163) 330

Producers of traditional farmhouse real cask conditioned ales.

Take the Hambledon turning on the Henley–Marlow road, left turn 1½ miles after passing village of Hambledon
Open by appointment only
Free admission
   advance notice required

STONOR PARK

Country gardens and walks, historic house and deer park

Stonor, Henley-on-Thames, Oxfordshire RG9 6HF
☎ Turville Heath (049163) 587

Historic family home set in a deer park in the wooded Chiltern Hills. Contains many items of rare furniture, drawings, tapestries and sculptures from Britain, Europe and America.

On the B480, 5 miles north of Henley-on-Thames
Open: Sun 2.00–5.30pm (April–Sept), Wed 2.00–5.30pm (May–Sept), Thur 2.00–5.30pm (July & Aug), Sat 2.00–5.30pm (Aug only), Bank Holiday Mondays 11.00am–5.30pm. Parties by arrangement
Admission: adult £2.50, child/OAP £2.00, group rates available (1990 prices)

▶ **OXFORD** ◀

BERKSHIRE, BUCKINGHAMSHIRE & OXFORDSHIRE NATURALISTS' TRUST (BBONT)

Nature reserves and walks, talks, open days

3 Church Cowley Rd, Rose Hill, Oxford OX4 3JR
☎ Oxford (0865) 775476

BBONT is associated with the Royal Society for Nature Conservation and is one of the largest of the 48 County Wildlife Trusts. It owns and leases over 100 nature reserves, promoting nature conservation and education. Free book 'Where to Go for Wildlife' with membership.

Please telephone for further details
Reserves open daily all year, dawn until dusk
Free admission but donations welcome
&. ⇔ advance notice required
⋔ in some reserves

JOHN MATTOCK LTD

Country garden

The Rose Nurseries, Nuneham Courteney, Oxfordshire OX9 9PY
☎ Nuneham Courteney (086 738) 265

Acres of roses, most recent introductions, old garden roses, landscaping roses and repeat flowering ground cover roses. Large and comprehensive garden centre; 50 seat restaurant (hot lunches and light refreshments).

Off the A423, 7 miles from Oxford
Open Mon–Sat 8.30am–5.30pm , Sun 10.30am–5.30pm.
Closes 5.00pm Nov–Feb
Free admission
&. ⇔ ⋔ not in shop

▶ **STEEPLE ASTON** ◀

ROUSHAM HOUSE AND GARDENS

Country gardens and historic house

Rousham, Steeple Aston, Oxfordshire
☎ Steeple Aston (0869) 47110

William Kent's only surviving 18th century landscape garden, also walled gardens with fine herbaceous borders, small parterre, pigeon house, espalier trees, roses and vegetables. Lovely church. Long Horn cattle in the park.

East of the A423, south of the B4030, 12 miles
north of Oxford, 10 miles south of Banbury
Open all year daily for the gardens, 10.00am–4.30pm;
House: April–Sept, Wed, Sun and Bank Holidays
2.00–4.30pm
Admission to garden: £2.00, no children under 15 years
&. ⇔ ✖

WANTAGE

ARDINGTON GALLERY

Art gallery and frame makers

Unit 4 Home Farm, Ardington, nr Wantage, Oxfordshire
OX12 8PN
☎ Abingdon (0235) 833677

Restoration work on oils, watercolours and fabrics is our main activity. We design and make our own frames as well as restoring period frames for clients.

Right off the A417 going east from Wantage,
clearly signed 'Home Farm Craft Workshops'
Open all year Mon–Sat 9.00am–5.30pm; Easter–Sept
Sundays 2.00–4.30pm
Free admission
&. ⇔ advance notice required ✖

ARDINGTON POTTERY

Craft centre – pottery

The Old Dairy, 15 Home Farm, Ardington, nr Wantage,
Oxfordshire OX12 8PN
☎ Abingdon (0235) 833302

A wide range of highly fired stoneware is displayed in the attractive 19th century picture tiled old dairy. Commissions and commemorative items made to order. Demonstrations for groups by arrangement.

2 miles east of Wantage, off the A417. 15 miles
south of Oxford, 15 miles north of Newbury
Open all year daily except Christmas, Mon–Sat
10.00am–5.00pm, Sun 2.00–5.00pm
Free admission
&. ⇔ no notice needed unless demonstration
required ⋔

CLEARWATER FISH FARM

Farm shop, catch your own and picnic area

Luxbridge Mill, East Hendred, Wantage, Oxford OX12 8LN
☎ Abingdon (0235) 833732

Visitors to the trout farm may feed the fish or catch their own trout (rod provided). Farm shop open all year for fish and smoked trout, seafood, smoked salmon etc.

3 miles east of Wantage, on the A417
Open daily (except Mon) April–Oct 10.00am–6.00pm;
Nov–March 10.00am–5.00pm
Admission: adult 50p, child 35p. Catch your own £1.00 per rod. Farm shop free (1990 prices)
& 🚐 advance notice required 🐴

▶ **WHEATLEY** ◀

WATERPERRY GARDENS

Country walk, country garden, garden shop, tea shop and Saxon church

Wheatley, nr Oxford, Oxfordshire OX9 1JZ
☎ Wheatley (084 47) 254

A high quality plant centre and a delightful garden with river walk, delicious home made food available in the tea shop which has a wine licence.

On the A40, 6 miles east of Oxford follow signpost for Wheatley, follow Garden signs
Open all year (except Christmas and New Year Holidays), summer: 10.00am–6.00pm; winter: 10.00am–4.30pm
Free admission to the gardens Nov–Feb. March–Oct adult £1.50, child (10–16) 75p (under 10 years free), OAP £1.10, party rates £1.00 (min 15 people)
🚐 & 🐴

▶ **WITNEY** ◀

COGGES MANOR FARM MUSEUM

Farm museum and farm interpretation centre with walks

Church Lane, Cogges, Witney, Oxfordshire OX8 6LA
☎ Witney (0993) 772602

A museum of the Oxfordshire countryside, set in the hamlet of Cogges. A working museum providing a window on the landscape, buildings and people of Oxfordshire.

Off the A40 Oxford–Cheltenham road
Open Easter–Nov Tues–Fri and Bank Holiday Mondays 10.30am–5.30pm; Sat and Sun: 12.00–5.30pm; Mondays are special education days for pre-booked parties only
& & 🚐 🐴

WITNEY PARK & PICK YOUR OWN

Farm shop and pick your own

Woodstock Rd, Witney, Oxfordshire
☎ Witney (0993) 776650

Farm shop, nursery and pick your own site.

From Witney to Woodstock on the A4095, entrance to farm shop on the right
Open for farm shop: Mon–Sat 9.00am–5.00pm; pick your own: daily 9.00am–7.00pm in picking season
Free admission
& 🚐 advance notice required 🐴

SHROPSHIRE

Shropshire, delightful hill and valley countryside, is rich and green, unspoilt and studded with country houses and market towns of distinctive black-and-white timbered houses. The countryside around the Clun Forest is excellent for sheep breeding and has produced a breed known as Clun Forest sheep that are very popular for their fine dense fleeces.

Farm visits and museums including a living museum of rare poultry offer a wide range of animals and birds, both rare and not so rare, to meet. If you prefer to watch then there is an RSPB wildlife centre to explore. There are craft centres and working studios to tour, a stately home to enjoy and even a parachute centre for the more adventurous to drop in on!

► BRIDGNORTH ◄

RAYS FARM

Farm visit

Billingsley, Bridgnorth, Shropshire WV16 6PF
☎ Kinlet (029 924) 255

*Red deer, fallow deer, Dexter cattle,
Highland cattle, owls, pigmy goats, turkeys,
donkey, ponies, ducks, hens – all free range.
Farm walk, craft shop, refreshments.*

Off the B4363, 7 miles south of Bridgnorth
Open all year 10.00am–5.00pm, appointment by
   telephone
Admission: adult £1.00, child free
& ➡ advance notice required ✖

► CHURCH STRETTON ◄

ACTON SCOTT WORKING FARM MUSEUM

Farm museum, shop and country walks

Wenlock Lodge, Acton Scott, nr Church Stretton,
   Shropshire SY6 6QN
☎ Marshbrook (069 46) 306/307

*Working farm museum over 23 acres. Step
back into the Victorian countryside and
watch traditional farming activities in the
South Shropshire Hills, together with daily
craft and buttermaking demonstrations.*

Off the A49, 4 miles south of Church Stretton
Open April–Oct, Mon–Sat 10.00am–5.00pm. Sundays and
   Bank Holidays 10.00am–6.00pm
Admission: please contact museum
& ➡ advance notice required ✖

► CRAVEN ARMS ◄

GUY & JEAN SMITH

Farm visit

The Wain House, Black Hill, Clunton, Craven Arms,
   Shropshire SY7 0JD
☎ Clun (058 84) 551

*The owners have diversified into commercial
organic market gardening, but are happy to
show people round. Guy N. Smith is the
author of 'Practical Country Living'
published by Boydell Press.*

From Craven Arms to Clun 8 miles, B4368 over
   Clun bridge, first left before the church. Follow
   the signs for Woodside, stay on this road for
   approx 1½ miles, first on right past white
   cottage
Open by appointment
Admission: adult £1.00, child 50p
& ✖

► LLANFYLLIN ◄

LAKE VYRNWY

RSPB wildlife reserve and visitor centre

Bryn Awel, Llanwddyn, Oswestry, Shropshire SY10 0LZ

*The reserve supports an interesting and
important variety of birds, mammals and
plant life. Nature trails, hides, RSPB shop,
nestwatch scheme, videos and slide shows
available.*

Take the B4393 to Llanwddyn from Llanfyllin and
   proceed to reservoir
Open: weekends 12.00 noon–6.00pm all year. Daily
   Spring Bank Holiday–end Sept
Free admission, guide £1.00
& some provision made for disabled visitors, please
enquire for further details ➡ ✖

► LUDLOW ◄

DINHAM HOUSE

Exhibition and craft centre

Dinham House, Ludlow, Shropshire SY18 1EH
☎ Ludlow (0584) 4240

*18th century, 22 roomed house, home of the
Knights and Johnes family and Lucien
Bonaparte. Exhibition centre: local history,
art/craft exhibitions and working studios.
Tea room, toilets, parking.*

Outskirts of town centre, immediate left of Ludlow
   Castle, taking Wigmore Road
Open daily 10.00am, please contact first to confirm times
Admission: adult £1.00, child 5–14yrs 50p
& ➡ no parking facilities available ✖

THE WERNLAS COLLECTION

Living museum of rare poultry and other farm animals

Green Lane, Onibury, nr Ludlow, Shropshire SY7 9BL
☎ Bromfield (058477) 318

The most extensive collection of large fowl in the UK displayed in spectacular countryside. Other farm animals also. Gift shop.

Off the A49, 5 miles north of Ludlow
Open 1 April–end Oct daily. Closed Mondays except Bank Holidays. Variable winter opening, phone before visiting
Admission: adult £2.00, child £1.00 (under 3s free), OAP £1.75
&. ᴁ advance notice required
ᛉ at our discretion

HODNET HALL GARDENS

Country garden

Hodnet, nr Market Drayton, Shropshire TF9 1NN
☎ Hodnet (061084) 202

Superb landscaped gardens in a natural setting extending over 60 acres. Sweeping lawns and ornamental lakes provide a perfect background for the masses of colour from spring to autumn.

Take the A49 Whitchurch road out of Shrewsbury, turning on to the A53 Market Drayton road, 12 miles north of Shrewsbury
Open April–Sept weekdays 2.00–5.00pm, Sundays and Bank Holidays 12.00 noon–5.30pm
Admission: adult £1.90, child £1.00, OAP £1.50, reduced rates for parties
&. ᴁ ᛉ

► *MARKET DRAYTON* ◄

THE DOROTHY CLIVE GARDEN

Country garden

Willoughbridge, nr Market Drayton, Shropshire TF9 4EU
☎ Pipegate (063081) 237

A hillside garden with many interesting features and unusual plants including a magnificent display of rhododendrons. Interest and colour at all seasons and beautiful views of surrounding countryside.

On the A51, midway between Nantwich and Stone, 3 miles south of Bridgemere Garden World
Open April–Oct daily 10.00am–5.30pm
Admission: adult £1.50, child 50p
&. ᴁ ᛉ

FORDHALL ORGANIC FARM

Country walk and farm trail

Market Drayton, Shropshire TF9 3PS
☎ Tern Hill (063083) 255

Mediaeval site on farm and an old world garden for afternoon tea. Free range cows, sheep, pigs and poultry.

On the A53, 1 mile north from the A41 crossroad at Ternhill
Open all times, please telephone before making a visit
Admission: 75p per person, school parties welcome
&. ᴁ advance notice required ᛉ

► *NEWCASTLE-UNDER-LYME* ◄

HUNGERSHEATH FARM

Pick your own

Ashley, Market Drayton, Shropshire TF9 4EJ
☎ Ashley (063 087) 2231

6 miles from Newcastle-under-Lyme, on the A53 Newcastle–Market Drayton road
Open June–Aug daily 10.00am–8.00pm (asparagus May–June)
Free admission
&. ᴁ ᛉ

► *SHREWSBURY* ◄

BROW FARM TEA ROOM

Farm shop and country walk

Brow Farm, Ratlinghope, Shrewsbury, Shropshire SY5 0SR
☎ Linley (058 861) 641

Campsite adjoining tea room 25p per person per night. Open all year round; wildlife in abundance.

Take the A49 from Shrewsbury, turn right at Leebotwood, follow this road over the Longmynd to farm
Open all year daily 10.00am–7.00pm
Free admission
&. ᴁ advance notice required ᛉ

HOME FARM

Farm trail and visit, rare breed collection, farm museum, country walk

Attingham Atcham, nr Shrewsbury, Shropshire SY4 4TN
☎ Upton Magna (0743 77) 243

A traditional Shropshire dairy and arable farm. Watch the milking of the Jersey herd, see rare breeds and old machinery and enjoy a farmhouse tea.

Situated off the A5 at Atcham, 4 miles east of Shrewsbury
Open April–Oct Sat, Sun & Bank Holiday Mondays 12.00 noon–5.30pm, Mon, Tues & Wed 2.00–5.30pm
Admission: adult £1.20, child/OAP 60p
&. 🚌 🐕

PICK YOUR OWN ASPARAGUS

Pick your own, country garden

Golding, Pitchford, Shrewsbury, Shropshire SY5 7HJ
☎ Acton Burnell (06944) 204

Many rare and tender plants in a terraced garden with sheltered borders. An amphitheatre effect looking down; a 16th century version of the Hanging Gardens of Babylon looking up. A gardener's dream!

Take the A458 out of Shrewsbury, signposted to Bridgnorth. Turn right after Cross House by gipsy encampment. Then follow signs
Open mid April–mid June 10.00am–6.00pm
Admission to gardens: adults £1.00, child 75p
&. 🚌 🐕

PIMHILL ORGANIC FARM CENTRE

Farm shop and picnic area

Lea Hall, Harmer Hill, Shrewsbury, Shropshire SY4 3DY
☎ Bomere Heath (0939) 290342/291147

The farm centre includes a farm shop and country furniture store. Rare breeds of pigs, cows and goats, Jenny the donkey; picnic site, pond and barbecue. All in a natural farm environment.

On the A528, 5 miles north of Shrewsbury, just outside the village of Harmer Hill
Open all year, currently Mon–Sat 9.00am–5.00pm
Free admission
&. 🚌 advance notice required 🐕

Stay on a Farm

Official guide of Farm Holiday Bureau UK

Enjoy the unique hospitality of a working farm. Over 950 properties, between them offering bed and breakfast, half-board, self-catering and camping and caravanning.

All inspected and approved by the National Tourist Boards. Published by William Curtis.

£4.95. Available from all good bookshops.

ST JULIAN'S CRAFT CENTRE FOR SHROPSHIRE

Craft centre

St Alkmand's Square, Shrewsbury, Shropshire SY1 1UH
☎ Shrewsbury (0743) 53516

A well established craft centre offering goods of exceptional quality at modest prices. Many working studios, a changing exhibition area, a weekly craft fair and a vegetarian restaurant.

At the top of Wyle Cop on the right, as one enters the High Street
Open all year, Mon–Sat 10.00am–5.00pm (closed most Thursdays)
Free admission
&. ⊞ ♔

provided. For more information and brochure pack please contact the manager.

3 miles south of Whitchurch, off the A49
Open all year at weekends, occasionally midweek by arrangement
Admission: participants must be members
&. ⊞ ♔

► *TELFORD* ◄

WESTON PARK

Stately home and grounds

Weston under Lizard, nr Shifnal, Shropshire TF11 8LE
☎ Weston under Lizard (095 276) 207

The house, built in 1671, contains a wealth of treasures in elegant surroundings. Woodland adventure playground, museum of country bygones, miniature railway, pets corner and countryside pottery.

On the A5, 7 miles west of jct 12 on the M6, 3 miles north of jct 3 on the M54
Open 13 April–3 June: weekends and Bank Holidays; 4 June–22 July: daily except Mondays and Fridays; 23 July–2 Sept: daily; 3 Sept–30 Sept: weekends only. Park 11.00am–7.00pm, house 1.00–5.00pm
Admission: adult £2.50, child/OAP £1.50; house additional £1.00 for adult, 60p child/OAP
&. ⊞ advance notice required ♔

► *WHITCHURCH* ◄

R L MATSON & SON

Parachute centre

Twemlows Hall, Whitchurch, Shropshire SY13 2EZ
☎ Lyn George, Manager, Whitchurch (0948) 841111 (Club House) (0948) 840541 (Home)

Parachute training courses for beginners at our modern training school. All equipment

SOMERSET

Somerset encompasses the rugged
heathland of Exmoor, the rolling and
wooded Quantock Hills, the spectacular
limestone caves and gorges of the Mendips
and the rich pastures of central Somerset
noted for its dairy produce and its cider.

The rich and varied produce of the region
can be sampled in many farm shops.
Several cider mills offer tours and tastings
as do the vineyards of the area and, as a
refreshing alternative, there is a natural
spring water to taste too. There are historic
houses and country parks, even one where
folk scenes are recreated, there are wildlife
parks and heavy horse centres, country
gardens and tropical bird gardens, farm
museums and bygones museums, craft
workshops and centres where spinning,
weaving, willow basket making, pottery
and ceramics all feature.

▶ **BRIDGWATER** ◀

CRICKET MALHERBIE FARMS LTD

Farm shop

Stowey Court Farm, Nether Stowey, Bridgwater, Somerset
TA5 1LL
☎ (0278) 732207

*Farm shop offering everything from milk to
fresh trout, ciders, and wines and Cricketer
cheeses, cream and butter. Tea rooms. Tour
of farm available – contact the farm shop.*

Off the A39, 8 miles from Bridgwater
Open 1 April–30 Sept 8.30am–5.30pm (10.00am–
4.00pm Sun and Bank Holidays); 1 Oct–31 March
Mon–Sat 8.30am–5.00pm
Free admission
♿ ♨ ✕

FYNE COURT

**Nature reserve, nature trails, woodlands and
ponds**

Somerset Trust for Nature Conservation, Fyne Court,
Broomfield, Bridgwater, Somerset TA5 2EQ
☎ Kingston St Mary (0823 45) 587

*Headquarters of the Somerset Trust for
Nature Conservation and Quantock visitor
centre, 24 acres of nature reserve. Woodland
walks, ponds; varied programme of
exhibitions and events. Trust shop (open
2–5pm), afternoon teas on summer Sundays
and Bank Holidays.*

From Bridgwater take the Durleigh Road
signposted off the A39, then after approx ⅔ mile
turn left onto the Enmore road, stay on this road
for about 5 miles to the Pines Cafe, Fyne Court
and Broomfield are signposted to the left, about
1 mile
Open daily 9.30am–5.30pm
Free admission, car park charge 40p
♿ ♨ ✕

MOORLYNCH VINEYARD

Winery and vineyard with farm shop

Moorlynch, Bridgwater, Somerset TA7 9BU
☎ Ashcott (0458) 210393

*Fine old stone barns house both the
wine-making and the sampling facilities at
this award-winning vineyard. Pleasant
walks among the vines and good local*

*products in the shop. Courtyard wine bar
serves light lunches.*

Off the A39, Bridgwater–Glastonbury or off the
A361 Taunton–Glastonbury, sign at Greinton
Vineyard and wine bar open May–Sept 10.00am–
6.00pm, shop open all year
Free admission
♿ ♨ strictly by appointment ✕

QUANTOCK SHEEP MILKING CENTRE

**Farm visit, interpretation centre, shop and
speciality food producer**

New Stowey Farm, Nether Stowey, Bridgwater, Somerset
TA5 1JR
☎ Bridgwater (0278) 732385

*Working sheep farm with 200 dairy ewes.
'Hands on' experience for visitors; ideal for
schools. Woodland, ponds and panoramic
views.*

7 miles west of Bridgwater off the A39
Open March–Sept Sundays 2.00–5.00pm, school holidays
2.00–5.00pm. Group visits by appointment, please
telephone
Admission: adult £1.50, child 80p (1990 prices)
♿ ♨ advance notice required ✕

STAWELL FRUIT FARM

Farm shop and pick your own

Stawell, Bridgwater, Somerset TA7 9AE
☎ Chilton Polden (0278) 722732

*Situated in a fold of the Polden Hills this
family farm has grown apples on the
outskirts of the quiet rural village since
1916. 23 varieties available as they ripen.*

1 mile off the A39, 5 miles east of Bridgwater
Open Aug–Christmas daily (except Mon and Tues)
11.00am–5.00pm; Jan–May: Sat and Sun only
11.00am–4.00pm
Free Admission
♿ staff on hand to give assistance ♨ ✝

▶ **BURNHAM-ON-SEA** ◀

ANIMAL FARM COUNTRY PARK AND THE
LAND OF LEGENDS

**Country park with souvenir shop, museum and
country walks**

Red Rd, Berrow, nr Burnham-on-Sea, Somerset TA8 2RW
☎ Brean Down (0278) 751628

Folk stories of the West Country recreated in scenes which almost bring the characters to life. Rare breeds and domestic farm animals. Vintage farm machinery, pets corner, childrens play area, tea room.

From the M5 t jct 22, turn towards Burnham-on-Sea and throughout towards Berrow and Brean. Red Road is on your right, animal farm is on right approx 2 miles down
Open Easter–Oct daily 10.00am–5.00pm
Admission adult £2.50, child/OAP £1.50, party rates on request
 & 🚌 advance notice required ✖

BREAN DOWN TROPICAL BIRD GARDENS
Bird gardens

Brean Down, nr Burnham–on–Sea, Somerset TA8 2RJ
☎ Brean Down (027875) 1 209

Family owned and run bird garden featuring many different varieties, set close to the beach. Cafe and gift shop.

7 miles from Burnham or Weston-super-Mare, on the coast road to Berrow
Open daily April–Oct 10.00am–6.00pm
Admission: adult £1.45, child 75p, 20% reduction for parties
& 🚌 advance notice required 🐾

► CASTLE CARY ◄

CASTLE CARY VINEYARD
Vineyard and farm shop

Honeywick House, Castle Cary, Somerset BA7 7LP
☎ Castle Cary (0963) 50323

Vines of different varieties, ages and training methods can be seen whilst walking through this pleasant south facing vineyard. Conducted tours which include a wine tasting are available.

Turn east off the A371, opposite turn to Castle Cary town centre on road to Cole, vineyard is ½ mile on left at bottom of hill
Open all year for the shop 10.00am–5.30pm; vineyards May–Oct
Admission to vineyard free. Conducted tours £1.50 per person (under 16 free)
& in shop but not in vineyard
🚌 advance notice required ✖

HADSPEN GARDEN AND NURSERY
Country garden

Laundry Cottage, Hadspen House, Castle Cary, Somerset BA7 7NG
☎ Castle Cary (0963) 50939

8 acre Edwardian garden in a sheltered situation featuring a walled garden, ponds, woodland area and an ancient meadow. Many unusual plants available in nursery.

2 miles east of Castle Cary on the A371, or 3 miles west on the A371 off the A303 Wincanton turnoff
Open 1 March–1 Oct Thur, Fri, Sat, Sun and Bank Holiday Mondays
Admission: adult £2.00, child £1.00 (under 15s free)
& 🚌 advance notice required ✖

► CHARD ◄

CRICKET ST THOMAS WILDLIFE PARK
Wildlife park, children's farm, heavy horse centre, country garden, walks, farm shop

Cricket House, Cricket St Thomas, Chard, Somerset TA20 4DB
☎ Winsham (0460) 30755

Cricket House, as featured in 'To the Manor Born', is a working estate as well as a leisure park with many attractions including wildlife, adventure playground, children's farm, restaurant and shops.

On the A30, between Chard and Crewkerne
Open daily 10.00am–6.00pm
Admission: adult £4.00, child £3.00, OAP £3.50, reduced rates for parties (1990 prices)
& 🚌 🐾

FORDE ABBEY & GARDENS
Historic house, country garden and pick your own

Chard, Somerset TA20 4LU
☎ Chard (0460) 20231

Forde Abbey is one of the most complete surviving Cistercian monasteries. It contains good furniture and outstanding tapestries, and stands among 30 acres of splendid gardens.

4 miles south via Tatworth, right off the A358

Open for the gardens: daily 10.30am–4.30pm; house:
   April–Oct Sun–Wed and Bank Holidays 1.00–4.30pm
Admission to gardens: £2.30, house £1.20 extra,
   accompanied children (under 15) free, reductions for
   OAPs
 ♿ the gardens are easily accessible 🚌 🐂

HORNSBURY MILL

Water mill, bygones museum and craft centre

Chard, Somerset TA20 3AQ
☎ Chard (04606) 3317

*Complete historic watermill in 5 acre
lakeside beauty spot. Trout; superb working
waterwheel; yesteryear museum; craft shops.
Cream teas a speciality in the restaurant.*

2 miles north of Chard on the A358 Taunton road
Open March–Oct daily 10.30am–6.00pm, Sundays
   12.00–6.00pm
Admission for the combined tour of mill and 'Yesteryear'
   museum: adult £1.20, child 60p
♿ 🚌 advance notice required 🐂

PUDLEIGH MILL FISH FARM

Fish farm, farm visit and farm shop

Combe St Nicholas, Chard, Somerset TA20 3BL
☎ Chard (04606) 3663

*Small working fish farm started in 1970,
run as a family business. Also live fish
transport throughout UK and Europe. Top
quality trout available for purchase.*

1 mile from Chard in the tiny hamlet of Pudleigh,
   take Combe St Nicholas road from Chard and in
   village of Wadeford turn first right
Open April–Sept daily
Free admission
♿ some parts not suitable for wheelchairs 🐂

► CHEWTON MENDIP ◄

CHEWTON CHEESE DAIRY

**Speciality food producer – cheese, farm shop,
restaurant and country garden**

Priory Farm, Chewton Mendip, Bath, Somerset BA3 4NT
☎ Chewton Mendip (076121) 666

*Morning coffee, farmhouse lunches and
cream teas. Guided tours by appointment.*

Off the A39, 6 miles north east of Wells
Open for farm shop: 6 days 9.00am–5.00pm, closes
   4.00pm Jan–March. Open for restaurant: 7 days
   10.30am–4.30pm, closes mid Jan–mid Feb
🚌 by appointment 🐂

THE DECOY GALLERY

Decoy duck gallery

Kingshill, Chewton Mendip, nr Bath, Somerset BA3 4PD
☎ Chewton Mendip (076121) 357

*A wide range of decorative and stylized
wildfowl carvings for sale, plus wildfowl
paintings, prints and books. Courses in
duck carving are also offered.*

200 yards from the A39, between Bath and Wells
   near Chewton Mendip village centre
Open March–Dec daily (except Sun and Mon)
   10.00am–5.00pm
Free admission
♿ ✖

► CHURCHSTANTON ◄

SOMERSET SPRING WATER

Producers of natural spring water, country walk

The Firs, Biscombe, Churchstanton, Taunton, Somerset
   TA3 7PZ
☎ Churchstanton (082360) 385

*World famous spring, one of the finest
natural spring waters for clarity, quality
and taste.*

Through the hamlet of Stapley, coming from the
   Trull road, Culmhead radio station, turn first right
   past Culmhead, right again to Stapley, 1 mile
   from Stapley on the left hand side
Open daily 10.00am–4.00pm
Free admission
♿ wheelchairs are not advisable as we are on a
gradient 🐂

► CREWKERNE ◄

LOWER SEVERALLS HERB NURSERY

Herb nursery and country garden

Lower Severalls, Crewkerne, Somerset TA18 7NX
☎ Crewkerne (0460) 73234

Plantsman's garden beside early Ham stone farm house. Herbaceous borders crammed full of interest; herb garden. Nursery specializes in herbs, unusual herbaceous plants and half-hardy conservatory plants.

1½ miles north east of Crewkerne, turning for Merriott off the A30 or Haselbury road from the B3165
Open 1 Mar–31 Oct daily (except Thur) 10.00am–5.00pm, Sundays 2.00–5.00pm
Free admission
& the garden is easily accessible to disabled visitors with wheelchairs, however the nursery paths are rather narrow and may prove difficult, but assistance is always available
advance notice required ✗

► **DUNSTER** ◄

DUNSTER CASTLE

Historic house, country garden

Dunster, nr Minehead, Somerset TA24 6SL
☎ Dunster (0643) 821314

13th century house, fortified home of the Luttrell family for 600 years, set between the wooded hills of Exmoor and the sea. Terrace garden of rare shrubs within 28 acre park.

In Dunster, 3 miles south east of Minehead on the A369, just off the A39
Open for castle & garden: 1 April– end Sept daily except Fri & Sat, 11.00am–5.00pm; garden & grounds: as above; in June, July and Aug garden & grounds only open when castle is closed. Last admission in all cases ½ hour before closing
Admission to castle & garden: adult £3.50, child under 16 £1.50, parties £3.00, by written arrangement with administrator. Garden & grounds: adult £1.70, child under 16 70p
& advance notice required ✗

MILL POTTERY

Craft centre – pottery

Wootton Courtenay, Minehead, Somerset TA24 8RB
☎ Timberscombe (064384) 297

A fully working individual pottery of quality including a working waterwheel, machinery, informative display about making pots and materials used. Many very durable pots for sale.

Signposted on the A396, 3 miles south of Dunster and the A39, 2 miles west of Minehead
Open all year daily 9.00am–1.00pm and 2.00–6.00pm, Sundays by appointment
Admission: adult 50p, child 25p
& ✗

► **FROME** ◄

WHATLEY VINEYARD & HERB GARDEN

Vineyard, country garden and farm shop

Whatley Vineyard, Whatley, Frome, Somerset BA11 3LA
☎ Nunney (037384) 467

Visitors are welcome to wander around the vineyard and herb garden. The walled herb garden is divided into medicinal, aromatic, culinary and cosmetic plants, most of which can be purchased from the farm shop.

Take the A361 from Frome to Shepton Mallet for 3 miles, turn right following brown signs to vineyard
Open Easter–30 Sept, Wed–Sun 10.00am–6.00pm
Free admission
& the paths are all wide enough for wheelchairs but the toilet facilities do not meet the requirements
advance notice required ✗

► **GLASTONBURY** ◄

SOMERSET RURAL LIFE MUSEUM

Farming museum

Abbey Farm, Chilkwell St, Glastonbury, Somerset BA6 8DB
☎ Glastonbury (0458) 31197

Mediaeval Abbey Barn and Victorian farmhouse housing displays of farming, local crafts and industries. Illustrated life story of a 19th century farm labourer in Somerset. Special exhibitions and events throughout the season.

In Glastonbury approx ½ mile from town centre, just off the A361 to Shepton Mallet
Open Easter–Oct: weekdays 10.00am– 5.00pm, Sat & Sun 2.00–6.00pm. Nov–Easter: weekdays 10.00am–5.00pm, Sat & Sun 2.00–4.00pm
Admission: adult £1.00, child/OAP 25p
& advance notice required ✗

▶ **HIGHBRIDGE** ◀

THE GOAT HOUSE

Speciality food producer – goat dairy products and garment shop

Bristol Rd, Brent Knoll, nr Highbridge, Somerset
TA9 4HJ
☎ Brent Knoll (0278) 760995

At the foot of Brent Knoll in Somerset. The produce from the goat farm opposite the cafe forms part of an extensive menu of delicious meals cooked on the premises.

Adjacent to the A38, opposite Brent Knoll, 1 mile from jct 22 (M5)
Open Mon–Sat 9.00am–5.30pm all year, also various evenings. Closed Tuesday until midday
Free admission
&. ⌷ advance notice required ⍓

▶ **HOLFORD** ◀

RAMBLER STUDIO

Craft centre

Holford, nr Bridgwater, Somerset TA5 1RY
☎ Holford (0278) 74315

Specializes in embroidery, batik and hand weaving. Also silk lampshades, complete lamps, watercolours, miniatures and engraved glass by Sylvia Cave.

Turn off the A39 Bridgwater–Williton road to Holford village, between Plough Inn and garage. Keep left for ½ mile signposted to Holford Combe, studio 100 yards on left
Open May–Oct, any time by appointment
Free admission
&. ⌷ ⍓

▶ **ILMINSTER** ◀

PERRY'S CIDER MILLS

Cider makers – mill and shop

Cider Mills, Dowlish Wake, Ilminster, Somerset
TA19 0NY
☎ Ilminster (0460) 52681

High quality farmhouse cider made from Somerset cider apples. Country style shop, with unusual and useful British gifts.

Museum of farm tools, wagons and photographic displays. Barrel race featured on TV's 'Treasure Hunt'.

Approx 2 miles off the A303 or the A30, 2 miles Ilminster, 5 miles Chard
Open all year, Sun 10.00am–1.00pm, weekdays 9.00am–1.00pm, 1.30–5.30pm, Sat 10.00am–1.00pm, 2.00–4.30pm
Free admission and car parking
&. access to museum and suitable toilets
⌷ advance notice required ⍓

▶ **LANGPORT** ◀

AVR CRACKNELL & SON

Farm shop

Free Range Poultry Farm, Huish Episcopi, Langport, Somerset TA10 9EY
☎ Langport (0458) 250731

This is a small family farm specializing in free-range poultry. Chicks are bought in day-old and reared as naturally as possible, then processed on the farm and marketed locally.

Situated between Yeovil, Bridgwater and Taunton on the B3153, 1½ miles east of Langport
Open daily, closed on Sunday, please telephone to confirm times before visiting
Free admission, donations to charity
&. ⌷ advance notice required ⍓

STEMBRIDGE TOWER MILL

Windmill

High Ham, Langport, Somerset TA10 9DJ
☎ Langport (4058) 250818

The last thatched windmill in England dating from 1822 and in use until 1910.

2 miles north of Langport
Open April–30 Sept Sun, Mon, Wed 2.00–5.00pm
Admission: adult £1.20, child 60p (1990 prices)
&. ⌷ must disembark at end of road and walk ¼ mile ⍓

WEST SOMERSET RURAL LIFE MUSEUM

Bygones museum

The Old School, Allerford, Minehead, Somerset
TA24 8HN
☎ Porlock (0643) 862529

The main hall contains farm and craft implements and a kitchen with a spit and bread oven. The Victorian school room has desks and seats, school books, and a collection of old toys.

5 miles west of Minehead on the A39 road to Porlock, the turning to Allerford village
Open 25 March–14 Oct daily (except Sun) 10.30am–12.30pm and 2.00–4.30pm
Admission: adult 50p, child 10p
& 🐕

▶ MONTACUTE ◀

MONTACUTE HOUSE

Historic house, country garden

Montacute, Somerset TA15 6XP
☎ Martock (0935) 823289

Late 16th century house, fine 17th and 18th century furniture. Elizabethan and Jacobean portraits from National Portrait Gallery. Formal garden and park.

In Montacute village, 4 miles west of Yeovil, south of the A3088
Open (1990) for house: 1 April–4 Nov daily except Tues, 12.00–5.30pm, closed Good Friday, other times by written appointment with Administrator. Garden & Park: throughout the year daily except Tues, 11.30am–5.30pm or dusk if earlier
Admission: house, garden & park: adult £3.50, child £2.00, parties £3.00, garden & park only: adult £1.50, child 80p
& 🐕 in park only

▶ NETHER STOWEY ◀

QUANTOCK WEAVERS

Craft centre

'The Old Forge', Plainsfield, Over Stowey, nr Bridgwater, Somerset TA5 1HH
☎ Bridgwater (0278) 67687

Craft workshop and shop specializing in hand knitted and hand woven garments and rugs in hand spun wool. Other local crafts/spinning equipment and British wool goods for sale.

Follow Tourist Board signs from Nether Stowey bypass on the A39 Bridgwater–Minehead road
Open Mon, Tues, Thurs, Fri 11.00am–5.00pm; Wed, Sat, Sun and Bank Holidays 2.00–5.00pm
Free admission
& 🚐 🐕

▶ RODE ◀

THE TROPICAL BIRD GARDENS

Tropical bird gardens

Rode, nr Bath, Somerset BA3 6QW
☎ Frome (0373) 830326

17 acres, hundreds of exotic birds in natural surroundings – woodlands, flower garden, lake, clematis collection, childrens play area, information centre. Woodland Steam Railway daily Easter–September, weather permitting.

Turn off the A36 at the Red Lion, Woolverton or follow brown and white tourist signs
Open every day (except Christmas Day), 10.30am–7.00pm in summer, 10.30am–sunset in winter (last admittance 1 hour before closing time)
Admission: adult £2.80, child (under 14) £1.40, OAP £2.30 (1990 prices)
& 🚐 🗶

▶ SHEPTON MALLET ◀

AVALON VINEYARD

Vineyard with pick your own

East Pennard, Shepton Mallet, Somerset BA4 6UA
☎ Ditcheat (074 986) 393

Delicious strawberries, guaranteed free of chemicals and sprays. Sample our pure, natural wine and cider made in time-honoured, traditional manner and matured in the cool of our underground cellar.

1½ miles west of the A37, 5 miles south of Shepton Mallet
Open May–Sept, otherwise by appointment
Free admission
& 🐕

PILTON MANOR VINEYARD

Vineyard

Pilton, Shepton Mallet, Somerset BA4 4BE
☎ Pilton (074 989) 325

Vines were first planted at Pilton in 1189 by the monks of Glastonbury. Coffee, teas and lunches are served in the wine bar, set amongst the vines. Conducted tours for pre–booked groups.

Off the A361 west of Pilton village and 2½ miles south of Shepton Mallet
Open June–Sept (except Mondays and Tuesdays) 11.00am–5.00pm
Free admission
♿ 🚌 🐕

WOOTTON VINEYARD

Farm shop and vineyard

North Wootton, Shepton Mallet, Somerset BA4 4AG
☎ Pilton (074 989) 359

The 300 year old farm retains a rural peace despite some modern winemaking equipment. Visitors may walk in the vineyard, wine may be bought from the cellar. Harvest and bottling months offer peak activity.

3 miles south east of Wells, signposted off the A39 to Glastonbury
Open daily 10.00am–1.00pm and 2.00–5.00pm, closed Sundays
Free admission
♿ 🚌 advance notice required 🐕

▶ *SHIPHAM* ◀

GEOPEG GEMS

Craft workshop

Hawthorn Cottage, Hollow Rd, Shipham, Somerset BS25 1TG
☎ Winscombe (0934) 842609

Hand–crafted gemstone trees. Bookends, clocks, pen sets made from African, North and South American agates which are cut and polished to provide permanent, practical and beautiful gifts. Agate jewellery and gemmological specimens.

Off the A38, 2 miles north of Axbridge
Open daily 10.00am–5.30pm
Free admission
♿ 🐕

▶ *SOUTH PETHERTON* ◀

EAST LAMBROOK MANOR GARDEN

Country garden

Nr South Petherton, Somerset TA13 5HL
☎ South Petherton (0460) 40328
Fax (0460) 43244

Grade I listed gardens created by the late Margery Fish. 2 acre cottage style plantsman's garden for all the year enjoyment. Plant nursery offers plants from garden; national geranium collection.

Signposted off the A303, 2 miles north of South Petherton
Open all year except Christmas–New Year, Mon–Sat and Bank Holiday weekends 9.00am–5.00pm. Parties by appointment only, telephone or fax
Admission: adult £1.50, child 50p, party rate £1.20

EELES FAMILY POTTERY

Ceramic showroom

The Pot Shop, A303 (Old Road), Watergore, South Petherton, Somerset
☎ (0460) 41724

Hand thrown, finished and decorated, woodfired earthenware, stoneware and porcelain, in a wide variety of glazes and finishing techniques. Large and small individual pieces.

On the A303 (Old Road) between Ilchester and Ilminster
Open Mon–Sat 9.00am–6.00pm
Free admission
♿ 🚌 good parking 🐕

▶ *STOKE ST GREGORY* ◀

WILLOW AND WETLANDS VISITOR CENTRE

Willow and basket making industry exhibition, craft centre and shop

Meare Green Court, Stoke St Gregory, nr Taunton, Somerset TA3 6HY
☎ North Curry (0823) 490249

A unique opportunity to view all aspects of the willow industry from preparation of the willow to the finished basket. Large range of genuine Somerset baskets on sale. Extensive wetlands exhibition and museum.

Signposted Stoke St Gregory from the A361 at West Lyng and from the A378 'Willow Craft Industry' 1½ miles on left after passing through North Curry

Open all year Mon–Fri 9.00am–1.00pm, and 2.00–5.00pm, guided tours every ½ hour. Shop and showroom: Sat 10.00am–1.00pm and 2.00–5.00pm, parties by appointment

Admission: adult £1.00, child 50p for willow trail; exhibition and showrooms free of charge

& ᴄᴀʀ advance notice preferred ℩

▶ **TAUNTON** ◀

COMBE SYDENHAM COUNTRY PARK

Elizabethan hall, country park, walks, fishponds and deer park

Monksilver, Taunton, Somerset
☎ Stogumber (0984) 56284

Country park set on the edge of Exmoor, featuring 'Magic Story' trails and attractions for all the family. Fly fishing for beginners. Parts of hall and estate under restoration.

Take the A361 Taunton–Bampton road, on to the B3188, entrance 5 miles further on

Open Easter–end Oct daily (except Sun & Fri), 10.00am–5.00pm

Admission: adult £2.50 (1990 prices)

& hall accessible but country walks difficult
ᴄᴀʀ by appointment ℩

FITZHEAD STUDIO POTTERY

Craft centre – pottery, batik and hand–painted silk

Fitzhead, Taunton, Somerset TA4 3JW
☎ Milverton (0823) 400359

A studio using traditional potters skills and tools in a creative and individual fashion, also batik painting of contemporary designs on cotton or silk scarves and pictures.

8 miles west of Taunton on the B3227, signposted from Milverton roundabout

Open any time
Free admission
& ℩

HESTERCOMBE HOUSE

Country garden

Hestercombe House, Cheddon Fitzpaine, Taunton, Somerset TA2 8LQ
☎ Taunton (0823) 337222

A recently restored Edwardian garden designed by Sir Edwin Lutyens and Gertrude Jeckyll, featuring a series of terraces and vistas, orangery, rose garden and pergola.

4 miles from Taunton, follow brown tourist signs from the A358

Open Mon–Fri 9.00am–5.00pm all year; Sat & Sun 2.00–5.00pm 1 May–30 Sept

Admission: a donation is requested, £1.00 towards the garden restoration fund

& ᴄᴀʀ advance notice required ℩

JACOB SPINNERS

Craft centre – spinning

Orchard Cottage, Barrington Hill, Hatch Beauchamp, Taunton, Somerset TA3 6TH
☎ Hatch Beauchamp (0823) 480663

Cottage industry of hand spinning and manufacture of hard wearing, warm garments using no dyes, bleaches or chemicals. Traditional crewnecks and fashion garments spun straight from the fleece.

From the A303 2 miles west of Ilminster. Take turning north signposted Horton Broadway, follow for ½ mile, take first turning on left signposted 'Bickenhall Windmill Hill', Orchard Cottage is 2 miles on left

Open all year, advisable to telephone before visiting
Free admission
& ᴄᴀʀ advance notice required ✗

SHEPPY'S CIDER (R J SHEPPY & SON)

Cider makers with farmshop and cider museum

Three Bridges, Bradford-on-Tone, Taunton, Somerset TA4 1ER
☎ Bradford-on-Tone (0823) 461233

Walk around our excellent farm/cider museum, press room, orchards and visit our farm shop for cider and other goods. Situated in the beautiful Vale of Taunton Deane. Free parking

On the A38, midway between Taunton and Wellington

Open Mon–Sat: 1 May–30 Sept 8.30am–7.30pm; 1 Oct–30 April 8.30am–6.00pm. Sundays Easter–Christmas 12.00–2.00pm

Free admission; £2.25 per head for guided tours (20 minimum, pre-booked)

& ᴄᴀʀ ℩

THE TAUNTON CIDER MILL AND MORSES PLACE

Cider mill, visitor centre and shop

Station Rd, Norton Fitzwarren, Taunton, Somerset TA2 6RD
☎ Taunton (0823) 332211

Working cider mill, guided tour, cinema, exhibition on history of cider, old farming artifacts, mini cider apple orchard, mug collection, sampling of ciders, cider bar, pub food and souvenir shop.

On the B3227, 3 miles west of Taunton
Open daily except Christmas & Boxing Days, booked parties only, casual visitors please ring
Small admission charge
♿ please telephone in advance so arrangements can be made
🚌 advance notice required

▶ WEST BAGBOROUGH ◀

QUANTOCK POTTERY

Craft centre – pottery

Chapel Cottage, West Bagborough, nr Taunton, Somerset
☎ Taunton (0823) 433057

From Taunton follow signs to Minehead, after approx 8 miles turn right to West Bagborough village
Open all year Mon–Fri 9.30am–5.30pm, Sat & Sun 11.00am–5.00pm
Free admission
♿ stairs to showroom and workshop are not suitable for disabled

▶ WILLITON ◀

ORCHARD MILL MUSEUM

Farm museum with working corn mill and waterwheel

Off Bridge St, Williton, Taunton, Somerset TA4 4NS
☎ Williton (0984) 32133

Museum housed in old mill, waterwheel, orchard garden with stream and play area, craft and gift shop, restaurant.

Off the A39, ½ mile west of Williton
Open March–Dec 10.00am–6.00pm, closed Mondays, also closed Tuesdays during March, April, Oct– Dec
Admission: adult 90p, child 45p, charge only for admission to museum
♿ 🚌 advance notice required

▶ WINCANTON ◀

ROSIE'S CIDER

Speciality drink producer – cider, and farm shop

Rose Farm, Lattiford, Wincanton, Somerset BA9 8AF
☎ Wincanton (0963) 33680

Royal Bath and West Cider Champions 1987/88. Victorian cider press, unique collection of over 100 mugs and loving cups. Photogenic thatched 15th century farmhouse. Tourist Information Centre.

From Wincanton follow the A371 westwards, after ½ mile turn left on to the A357 towards Templecombe, on left just past petrol station after passing under the A303
Open 6 days a week except Christmas and New Year holidays 8.30am–6.30pm; Sun 12.00–3.00pm
Free admission
♿ 🚌 advance notice required

▶ YEOVIL ◀

ALPHA GALLERY OF ARTS AND CRAFTS

Craft shop

Burton Cottage Farm, East Coker, Yeovil, Somerset BA22 9LS
☎ West Coker (093 586) 2731

Off the A30, 2 miles west of Yeovil, follow lane to mini 'tree roundabout', turn right, gallery on right after Post Office
Open Easter, then May–Sept, Wed–Sat 10.00am–4.00pm or by appointment
Free admission
♿

BRYMPTON D'EVERCY

Historic house and grounds, museum, 14th century parish church, distillery, vineyard, pick your own and farm shop

Brympton Estate Office, Yeovil, Somerset BA22 8TD
☎ Yeovil (0935) 862528

Large family home with many interesting features, including Britain's smallest legal distillery. Winner of the Christies 'Garden of the Year Award'.

Just west of Yeovil, follow signs from the A30 or
   the A3088
Open May–Sept daily (except Thur & Fri) 2.00–6.00pm
Admission: adult £3.00, child £1.50, discount for OAPs
   and National Trust members (1990 prices)
✗ all exhibits on ground floor
🚌 ✖ in gardens

VALE OF CAMELOT GROWERS

Farm shop and pick your own

Woolston, North Cadbury, Yeovil, Somerset BA22 7BJ
☎ North Cadbury (0963) 40280

Pick your own strawberries, raspberries, gooseberries, loganberries, blackcurrants, etc. Farm shop open in soft fruit season for home grown tomatoes, fresh-dug new potatoes and delicious fresh farm cream.

4 miles west of Wincanton, off the A303
Open approx mid June–late July
Free admission
✗ 🚌 advance notice required 🐹

STAFFORDSHIRE

Staffordshire is a region of rich farmland with tracts of heath and woodland, where the bottle-shaped brick ovens of the Potteries provide a vivid reminder of industrial England.

The country parks and walks of Staffordshire offer a wide selection of countryside, including grassland, wet meadows, reclaimed coal mines, ancestral estates and woodland reserves, to enjoy. There are nature trails and information centres, an activity based museum, working Shire horses, rare breeds centres, even a theme park and a childrens farm. There are farm shops, pick-your-own farms, two working breweries and several speciality food producers to visit.

▶ ALTON ◀

ALTON TOWERS

Leisure park

Alton, Staffordshire ST10 4DB
☎ (0538) 702200

Former home of the Earls of Shrewsbury set in 500 acres; 19th century gardens, splendid fountains; lakes and pools. Over 125 rides, shows and attractions for everyone.

Off the B5417 or the B5032, extensively signposted
Gardens and grounds open all year
Admission prices – to be decided
&. ⌷ 🐴

▶ BURTON-ON-TRENT ◀

BASS MUSEUM VISITOR CENTRE & SHIRE HORSE STABLES

Brewing museum and shire horse stables

Horninglow St, Burton-on-Trent, Staffordshire
☎ Burton (0283) 45301

Presents the story of Britain's premier brewer on a 6 acre site (much under cover). Numerous exhibitions, steam engines, vintage vehicles, the Bass Shire stables, bars, restaurants and function rooms.

On the main A50 in Burton
Open daily except Christmas, Boxing and New Years Days. Last admissions 4.00pm
Admission: adult £2.75, child £1.25, OAP £1.75, family ticket £7.50 (2 adults and up to 3 children). Visitors over 18 receive a free drink (1990 prices)

BRANSTON WATER PARK

Country park and walks

Branston, Burton-on-Trent, Staffordshire
☎ (0283) 45454

Off the A38 (from Birmingham) to Branston industrial estate, follow road down and round depot to track at end
Open all year daily
Free admission
&. 🐴

BYRKLEY PARK CENTRE

Garden centre, farm animals, aquatics

Rangemore, Burton-on-Trent, Staffordshire DE13 9RN
☎ (0283) 716467

Garden centre, farm animals and aquatics. Cafe offering home-made fayre.

Leave the A38 at Branston roundabout, follow signs to Tatenhill, straight over 2 crossroads into Byrkley Park
Open Sept–March 9.00am–5.00pm, April–Aug 9.00am–6.00pm (late nights until 9.00pm Thur, Fri & Sat)
Free admission
&. ⌷ advance notice required
🐕 in car park

HERITAGE BREWERY MUSEUM

Speciality drink producer

Anglesey Rd, Burton-on-Trent, Staffordshire DE14 3PF
☎ Burton (0283) 69226

England's first independent working brewery museum comprises a unique Victorian brewery complex including coopers shop, stables and waggon sheds, large collection of bottled beers and other items of breweriana.

Southwest of the town, follow signs
Open 1 April–30 Sept Mon–Sat 10.00am–4.00pm; 1 Oct–31 March Tues–Sat 10.00am–2.00pm
Admission: adult £2.50, child £1.00, OAP £2.00 (1990 prices)
&. ⌷ advance notice required 🗡

▶ LEEK ◀

DEEP HAYES COUNTRY PARK

Country park, information centre, nature trail

Longsdon, nr Leek, Staffordshire
☎ Leek (0538) 387655

Off the A53, 3 miles south west of Leek
Open all year daily 8.00am–dusk
Free admission

▶ LICHFIELD ◀

HEART OF THE COUNTRY

Farm visit and craft centre

Home Farm, Swinfen, Lichfield, Staffordshire WS14 9QR
☎ Shenstone (0543) 481612/48162

A grouping of 'country shops' in an old farmyard setting, including restaurant/ tea-room facilities. Gift shops, antiques, sportsware and several specialist retailers with the country in mind.

1 mile south of Lichfield on the A38
Open daily 10.00am–5.00pm. Closed Mondays except Bank Holiday Mondays
Free admission
 ♿ ⛶ advance notice required ✂

OLD STABLES FARM SHOP

Farm shop, pick your own and speciality food producer

Packington Moor Farm, Packington, Lichfield, Staffordshire WS14 9QA
☎ Shenstone (0543) 481223/481259

From Lichfield, take the A51 south east towards Tamworth, on reaching Whittington Army Barracks, about 2 miles out, take first right hand turn, into Jerrys Lane, shop about ½ mile on right
Shop open: Tues–Fri 9.30am–6.00pm, Sat 9.30am–5.00pm, Sun 9.30am–12.30pm. Closed Mondays. PYO: late June–mid Aug 9.30am–8.00pm every day
Free admission
♿ ⛶ advance notice required ✂

► NEWCASTLE-UNDER-LYME ◄

STAFFORDSHIRE ORGANIC CHEESE & HOMEMADE DAIRY ICE CREAM

Farm shop

New House Farm, Acton, Newcastle-under-Lyme ST5 4EE
☎ Whitmore (0782) 680366

Organic vegetables, free-range eggs, organic/additive free meat, bakery, organic wines, cider and beers.

4 miles from Newcastle, off the A53, ¾ mile from Whitmore
Open 9.00am–6.00pm daily except Sunday
Free admission
♿ assistance given if required
⛶ advance notice required ✂

► SEDGLEY ◄

BAGGERIDGE COUNTRY PARK

Country park

Gospel End, nr Sedgley, Dudley, South Staffordshire DY3 4AE

An informal and uncommercialised park of 152 acres, formerly one of the largest coal mines in the world. Good paths through varied scenery: hills, woods, meadows and pools. Orienteering, fishing, picnics, youth camp, model boat club, events.

Off the A463, 2 miles east of Wombourne and 1 mile west of Sedgley
Park open daily 9.00am–dusk
Admission: car park 40p
♿ wheelchair trails
⛶ advance notice required ✂

► STAFFORD ◄

BROWN END QUARRY GEOLOGICAL RESERVE, WATERHOUSES

Staffordshire Wildlife Trust, geological reserve, geological interpretive displays

Coutts House, Sandon, Stafford ST18 0DN
☎ Sandon (08897) 534

A small quarry of international geological significance. Beds of Carboniferous Limestone tipped almost vertically help illustrate the geological history of this part of the Peak District. Geological parties must give prior notice.

In the centre of Waterhouses village on the A523 Leek–Ashbourne Road. Parking in National Park car park at old railway station
Open all year
Free admission
♿ parking at reserve entrance, special stile for disabled and hard surface ✂

CANNOCK CHASE COUNTRY PARK

Country park

Nr Hednesford, Cannock, Staffordshire
☎ Hednesford (05438) 71773

Country park with country walks, nature trails and information centres.

Off the A34, 3 miles south of Stafford
Open all year daily 8.00am–dusk
Free admission

CASTERN WOOD, WETTON

Staffordshire Wildlife Trust, nature reserve, nature trail

Coutts House, Sandon, Stafford ST18 0DN
☎ Sandon (08897) 534

Limestone grassland and woodland on steep hillside, rich in wild flowers and butterflies. Spectacular scenery. River Manifold flows underground most of year. Leaflet from above address in return for s.a.e.

At end of unclassified road running south east from Wetton village
Open all year
Free admission
🏇

DOXEY MARSHES WILDLIFE TRUST

Country walk, nature reserve, bird hide and nature trail

Coutts House, Sandon, Stafford ST18 0DN
☎ Sandon (08897) 534

An area of wet meadows and subsidence pools attractive to a wide variety of bird life especially in spring and autumn. Leaflet from above address in return for s.a.e.

Creswell Farm Drive off Eccleshall Road, 1 mile from Stafford town centre
Open all year
Free admission
♿ 🚌 advance notice required 🏇

MIDLAND CRAFTS

Craft centre

Cromwell House, Wolseley Bridge, nr Stafford ST17 0XS
☎ Little Haywood (0889) 882544

Manufacturers of complete range of onyx goods which are offered to the public at trade prices.

On the main A51, 2 miles north of Rugeley
Open all year (except Christmas Day & Boxing Day)
weekdays 10.00am–5.00pm, weekends 1.30–5.30pm
Free admission
♿ assistance given to those in wheelchairs to mount one step 🚌 🏇

SHUGBOROUGH PARK FARM

Country estate, agricultural and county museum, corn mill, rare breeds centre, National Trust shop, farm trail and country garden

Milford, nr Stafford ST17 0XB
☎ Little Haywood (0889) 881388

Ancestral home of Lord Lichfield featuring an activity based museum, with working Shires, Longhorn cattle, rare breeds of sheep and pigs and demonstrations of farm work in Georgian farm buildings.

6 miles east of Stafford, on the A513 Stafford–Lichfield road
Opening times, telephone for details
Admission charges, telephone for details
♿ 🚌 advance notice required 🏇

► **STOKE-ON-TRENT** ◄

CONSALL NATURE PARK

Nature park, information centre

Consall, Wetley Rocks, Stoke-on-Trent, Staffordshire
☎ Wetley Rocks (0782) 550939

Take the A52, then the A522, 8 miles east of Stoke-on-Trent
Open all year daily 8.00am–dusk
Free admission

GREENWAY BANK COUNTRY PARK

Country park, information centre, nature trail

Greenway Bank, nr Biddulph, Stoke-on-Trent, Staffordshire
☎ Stoke-on-Trent (0782) 518200

Take the A500 then the A527, 7 miles north of Stoke-on-Trent
Open all year daily 8.00am–dusk
Free admission

THE MOORLANDS FARM PARK

Farm park, rare breeds centre, farm shop and country walk

Ipstones Edge, Ipstones, Stoke-on-Trent, Staffordshire ST10 2LP
☎ Ipstones (0538) 266479

Rare breeds of cattle, sheep, pigs etc., no longer kept for commercial farming. Pets corner with baby animals, and a childrens play area. Schools welcome anytime.

2 miles from Bottom House crossroads, midway
between Leek and Ashbourne
Open April–Oct, 10.30am–dusk
Admission: adult £1.40, child/OAP 70p (includes bag of
feed)
&. ⇔ ⋔

PARK HALL COUNTRY PARK

Country park, information centre

Weston Coyney, Stoke-on-Trent, Staffordshire
☎ Stoke-on-Trent (0782) 331889

Take the A50, then the A520, 6 miles east of
Stoke-on-Trent
Open all year daily 8.00am–dusk
Free admission

TRENTHAM GARDENS

Country garden and walks

Stone Rd, Trentham, Stoke-on-Trent, Staffordshire
ST4 8AX
☎ Stoke-on-Trent (0782) 657341

*800 acres featuring formal Italian gardens,
wildfowl reserve, nature and heritage trails
with video room, Shire horse centre,
childrens funfair, restaurant and bars, cafe,
garden centre and outdoor sports with
tuition and equipment.*

2 miles from jct 15 (M6), off the A34, 4 miles
south of Stoke
Open April–Sept daily 10.00am–8.00pm
Admission: adult £2.50. child/OAP £1.50. Outdoor sports
extra charge. (1990 prices)
&. ⇔ advance notice required ⋔

▶ *TAMWORTH* ◀

ASH END HOUSE FARM – 'THE CHILDREN'S FARM'

**Farm visit and farm shop with farm activity
courses for children**

Middleton Lane, Middleton, nr Tamworth, Staffordshire
B78 7BL
☎ (021 329) 3240

*A 'Children's Farm' with play areas, picnic
barns – specially arranged with children in
mind – feeding the animals, pony ride and
badge included in admission price – adults
are charged half price!*

Please telephone for directions
Open daily 10.00am–6.00pm
Admission prices still to be decided
&. ⇔ advance notice required ⋔

DRAYTON MANOR PARK & ZOO

Family leisure park, farm visit, zoo

Nr Tamworth, Staffordshire B78 3TN
☎ Tamworth (0827) 287979

*160 acres of parkland, woods and lakes
featuring a 15 acre open plan zoo, a boating
lake, amusement park with over 45 rides and
attractions, and picnic spots.*

8 miles north of Birmingham, on the A4091/A5, jct
9 on the M42
Open Easter–Oct 10.30am–6.00pm
Admission: adult £2.00, child £1.00, car 40p
Discount for organised parties of over 20 people
&. ⇔ free parking ⋔

HODGE LANE LOCAL NATURE RESERVE

Country walk

c/o Tamworth Borough Council, Marmion House,
Lichfield Street, Tamworth, Staffordshire B79 7BZ
☎ Tamworth (0827) 311222

*A small woodland reserve with several
ponds, noted for its diverse range of
woodland/wetland flora and fauna. Nature
walk leaflets available from above offices.*

Approx 2 miles east of town centre – follow
Amington–Shuttington Road and turn right into
Hodge Lane before crossing railway/canal bridge.
Access from cycle/foot path
Open only on Open Days held periodically throughout the
year or by prior arrangement. For details contact the
Countryside Ranger on the above number
Free admission
&. Paths and terrain unsuitable for wheelchair access or
blind persons without a guide ⋔

WARWICKSHIRE MOOR

Country walk

c/o Tamworth Borough Council, Marmion House,
Lichfield Street, Tamworth, Staffordshire B79 7BZ
☎ Tamworth (0827) 311222

*Open grassland and scrubland with
interesting flora and fauna, stout footwear
advised – liable to flooding in winter. Nature
walk leaflets available from above offices.*

Approx 1 mile from Tamworth town centre – follow Amington Road and turn into Moor Lane (Bolehall) approx ¼ mile from Amington Arch
Open at all times with guided walks held periodically. For details contact the Countryside Ranger on above number
Free admission and parking off Moor Lane
& the paths and terrain may be unsuitable for wheelchair access or blind persons without assistance
🚌 advance notice required 🐕

► TUTBURY ◄

JAMES CHAPMAN SHEEPSKIN SHOP & CORNMILL TEA ROOM

Speciality sheepskin and leather shop

The Cornmill, Cornmill Lane, Tutbury, Burton-on-Trent, Staffordshire DE13 9HA
☎ Burton (0283) 813300

Early 18th century corn mill. Speciality shop retailing leather, sheepskin, woollen and fashion clothing (plus accessories) on the site of old tannery established in 1914 but no longer in operation.

½ mile from centre of village, on the road to Rolleston on Dove
Open all year Tues–Sat 9.00am–5.30pm (except Good Friday and Christmas & Boxing Days)
Free admission
& 🚌 advance notice required ✗

► UTTOXETER ◄

CROWTREE ORGANIC FARM

Farm shop, speciality food producer

Loxley, nr Uttoxeter, Staffordshire ST14 8RX
☎ Uttoxeter (0889) 565806

Farm shop – producers and retailers of organically grown fruit and vegetables, eggs and cheese. Home delivery service throughout Staffordshire.

Drive south from Uttoxeter on the A518 Stafford road for 3 miles, look for 'Organic' sign on the right hand side
Open for farm shop Wed–Sat 10.00am–6.00pm
Free admission
& ✗

► WATERHOUSES ◄

STAFFORDSHIRE PEAK ARTS CENTRE

Craft centre and wholefood restaurant

The Old School, Cauldon Lowe, nr Waterhouses, Staffordshire ST10 3EX
☎ Waterhouses (0538) 308431

Delightful setting in old village school. Wide range of exclusive craftwork and paintings; nature trail; delicious wholefood, home cooking, coffees, lunches, afternoon teas.

On the A52, 7 miles from Ashbourne, 13 miles from Stoke-on-Trent
Open April–Oct daily 10.30am–5.30pm; Nov–March weekdays 12.00noon–4.00pm, weekends 10.30am–5.30pm
Free admission
& 🚌 advance notice required
🐕 except in restaurant

► WOLVERHAMPTON ◄

ESSINGTON FRUIT FARM

Pick your own and tearoom

Bognop Rd, Essington, Wolverhampton WV11 2BA
☎ Wolverhampton (0902) 735724

1 mile off the A460 Wolverhampton–Cannock road, at Westcroft
Open daily 9.00am–9.00pm during soft fruit season (approx mid June–end Aug), 9.00am–6.00pm daily except Monday thereafter
Free admission
& disabled may drive right into the field by prior arrangement
🚌 ✗ except guide dogs

► WOMBOURN ◄

HIGHGATE COMMON COUNTRY PARK

Country park, country walk

Wombourne, nr Wolverhampton, Staffordshire
☎ Bobbington (038488) 453

Off the A449(T), 3½ miles south west of Wombourne
Park open all year
Free admission

KINGSWINFORD RAILWAY WALK

Country walk and cycleway

Station Road, Wombourn, South Staffordshire

Important recreational route linking the towns of Wolverhampton and Dudley through rural South Staffordshire, the old railway line now provides safe walking and cycling through attractive and historic surroundings.

Off Station Road, 1 mile from junction of the A449 and the A463

Open May–Aug 9.00am–8.00pm; Sept–April 9.00am–5.00pm (or until dusk). Visitor centre open weekends and Bank Holidays 12.00 noon–5.00pm

Free admission

    well behaved dogs welcome

SUFFOLK

Suffolk's tranquil countryside and arresting skyscapes have provided the inspiration for many landscape artists. Its unspoilt coastline is a haven for naturalists.

There are wildlife reserves, woodland and nature trails, country walks and farm trails. There are many opportunities to observe a 'small country living' being pursued and to sample the produce, organic vegetables and dairy ice cream, wildflowers and dried flowers including traditional corn dollies. There are farm museums and rural life museums, even a reconstructed Anglo-Saxon village to explore. A concert hall, craft workshops, gardens, deer parks, miniature railways and a maze as well as a thoroughbred horse breeding centre feature amongst the attractions to be found in the Suffolk countryside.

▶ *ALDEBURGH* ◀

ALDRINGHAM CRAFT MARKET

Craft centre

Aldringham, nr Leiston, Suffolk IP16 4PY
☎ Leiston (0728) 830397

3 extensive galleries provide relaxed, friendly surroundings, individually made craft products, works of art, ladies clothes, toiletries and other sensibly priced gifts. Coffee shop, car park, childrens play area.

At the B1122/B1353 crossroads, 3 miles north of Aldeburgh
Open daily all year 10.00am–5.30pm, but closed from 12.00–2.00pm on Sundays, also closed Christmas. Please check Sunday hours during autumn and winter months
Free admission
&. ⇌ advance notice required 🐾

▶ *BECCLES* ◀

GRANGE FARM ORCHARDS

Pick your own

Hall Rd, Barsham, Beccles, Suffolk NR34 8JN
☎ Beccles (0502) 715008

A delightful fruit farm on the slopes of the Waveney Valley. 100 acres producing many varieties of fruit from June to October. A day out for all the family

Off the B1062, 3 miles south of Beccles towards Bungay, south of the river Waveney
Open daily June–Oct, 9.00am–5.00pm
Free admission
&. ⇌ 🐾

▶ *BURY ST EDMUNDS* ◀

CRAFT AT THE SUFFOLK BARN

Craft centre, country garden, tea shop, plant shop, wild flower and herb garden

Fornham Road Farm, Great Barton, Bury St Edmunds, Suffolk IP31 2SD
☎ Gt Barton (028487) 317

Traditional Suffolk barn houses crafts from the East of England and a tea shop featuring

home cooking. The gardens show wild flowers, herbs and cottage plants, with plants for sale.

Situated ½ mile from village of Great Barton, 2½ miles centre of Bury St Edmunds. Look for tourist signs 'Wildflower Garden' on the A134 and the A143
Open mid March–Christmas Wed–Sat 10.00am–6.00pm, Sun 12.00–6.00pm, closed Mon (except Bank Holidays) and Tues
Free admission, charity box
&. there is a ramp into barn, wide doors but no special toilet facilities
⇌ advance notice required
🐾 not in tea shop

ELM TREE GALLERY

Gifts and crafts

The Old Bakery, The Street, Woolpit, nr Bury St Edmunds, Suffolk IP30 9QG
☎ Elmswell (0359) 40255

Gallery selling craft and gift items, paintings and light refreshments in Tudor house dating from 1550.

Just off the A45, approx 9 miles east of Bury St Edmunds
Open all year, Tues–Sat 10.00am–5.00pm, Sun 2.30–5.00pm. Closed Mon except Bank Holidays
Free admission
&. 🐾

GIFFORD'S HALL

Country garden, vineyard and farm shop

Hartest, Bury St Edmunds, Suffolk IP29 4EX
☎ Bury St Edmunds (0284) 830464

Smallholding where you may observe the 'small country living' of the Kemp family. Vineyards, wild flowers, vegetables, chickens, farm shop and tea rooms.

Take the B1066 from Bury, 10 miles south to Hartest, turn left at village green, 1 mile
Open 14 April–31 Oct, 10.00am–6.00pm
Admission: adult £1.50, OAP £1.25
&. ⇌ advance notice required 🐾

HARTSHALL NURSERY STOCK

Gardens, woodlands, nurseries and arboretum

Hartshall Farm, Walsham-le-Willows, Bury St Edmunds, Suffolk IP31 3BY
☎ Walsham-le-Willows (0359) 259238

10 acres of trees, shrubs, conifers, roses, herbaceous. Wide choice for sale in pots or bare root, ex stock or to order. (Native to rare, but mainly beautiful).

Walsham-le-Willows is 2 miles from the A143 Bury St Edmunds–Diss road, Hartshall is 2 miles from Walsham church on the Westhorpe road
Open all year except Christmas Day Tues–Sat 10.00am–4.30pm
Free admission
& 🚌 advance notice required 🐎

CAROLINE HOLMES – HERBS

Herb garden, herb courses

Denham End Farm, Denham, Bury St Edmunds, Suffolk IP29 5EE
☎ Bury St Edmunds (0284) 810653

Please send sae for course details.

Take Barrow exit off the A45, 2 miles to Barrow take Denham turn off on right
Open March–Oct Sat 10.00am–6.00pm, or by appointment
Free admission
& 🚌 advance notice required 🐎

ICKWORTH – NATIONAL TRUST

Country walk, garden, deer park

Ickworth, The Rotunda, Horringer, Bury St Edmunds, Suffolk IP29 5QE
☎ Horringer (028488) 270

The creation of one of England's great eccentrics, Ickworth offers the visitor superb paintings, the finest collection of Georgian silver in private hands, extraordinary, dramatic architecture and several miles of waymarked paths.

In Horringer, 3 miles south west of Bury St Edmunds on west side of the A143
Open April & Oct weekends only; May–Sept daily (except Mon & Thur), open Bank Holiday Mondays
Admission to park and garden adult £1.00, child 50p, house, garden and park adult £3.50, child £1.75, party bookings (15 people plus) £2.50. National Trust members free. (1990 prices)
& ground floor accessible, shop and restaurant not. Refreshment may be collected. Lavatory available when house open 🚌 🐎

LARKWOOD FISHERY

Trout farm and fishing lakes

Icklingham Rd, West Stow, Bury St Edmunds, Suffolk IP28 6EZ
☎ Culford (028484) 612

Two 2½ acre lakes and a trout farm attractively sited among trees on the bank of the River Lark at West Stow.

Take the A1101 from Bury St Edmunds towards Mildenhall, at Flempton (4 miles out) turn right to West Stow. Fishery in West Stow village
Open 9.00am–dusk every day, group visits by appointment
Free admission for visits to trout farm; fly fishing: £8.00 per day, or £5.00 per half day & 🐎

LAURELS STABLES

Farm shop with country walk and sheep dairy

Horringer, Bury St Edmunds, Suffolk IP29 5SN
☎ (028488) 281

Smallholding adjoining NT parkland and woodland walks. Large car parking area. Courtesy gate to excellent pub/restaurant next door. B&B (large farmer's breakfast) available in informal cottage with resident dogs.

Please telephone for directions
Open all year daily except Sun
Free admission
& 🚌 advance notice required 🐎

NETHERFIELD COTTAGE

Herb nursery and herb demonstration garden

Nether St, Rougham, nr Bury St Edmunds, Suffolk IP30 9LW
☎ Beyton (0359) 70452

Enclosed 40' x 60' herb garden with more than 200 varieties of herbs, a peaceful aromatic retreat within a domestic setting. 2 small knot gardens and collections of herbs grouped by usage. The setting for Channel 4's 'World of Herbs' series.

1 mile east of Bury St Edmunds on the A45, turn south into Rougham, follow a series of zig-zags to the south east exit from Rougham. We are the last house on the road to Hessett
Open daily 10.30am–6.00pm or dusk
Free admission – 1 hour guided herb lecture tour: £25.00 for up to 20 people by arrangement
& 🚌 advance notice required 🐎

WEST STOW COUNTRY PARK AND ANGLO-SAXON VILLAGE

Anglo-Saxon village, country park, nature trail & woodland

West Stow, Bury St Edmunds
☎ Culford (028484) 718

Reconstructed Anglo-Saxon village, woodland, Breckland heath and lake. The new Visitor Centre helps visitors get the most from a visit to West Stow. Modern displays, information and advice on what to see from the Ranger Service.

Take the A1101 from Bury St Edmunds to
    Mildenhall, West Stow is approx 5 miles
Open all year daily 10.00am–5.00pm
Admission: adult £1.20, OAP/Student/UB40/child 70p,
    reduced rates and guided tours for pre-booked parties
& 🚌 advance notice required 🐎

► **CLARE** ◄

CAVENDISH MANOR VINEYARDS

Vineyards, period house, farm shop, farming museum, farm trail, country garden

Nether Hall, Cavendish, Sudbury, Suffolk CO10 8BX
☎ Glemsford (0787) 280221

Situated on Constable's lovely Stow Valley, period Tudor manor house, surrounded by pioneering vineyard and arboretum, picnic area with free parking. There is a museum, information centre, gallery, vineyard trail, wine and speciality shop, and toilets.

Off the A1092 in centre of Cavendish village
Open daily 10.00am–4.00pm
Admission: adult £2.00, OAP £1.50, child free
& 🚌 advance notice required 🐎

► **HADLEIGH** ◄

CORN CRAFT

Craft centre, shop and tea room

Bridge Farm, Monks Eleigh, Ipswich, Suffolk IP7 7AY
☎ Bildeston (0449) 740456

Corn Craft is a farm and nursery specializing in the growing of dried flowers and the making of corn dollies. Large selection for sale in new Granary Craft and Tea Shop.

On the A1141 between Hadleigh and Lavenham
Open all year 10.00am–5.00pm
Free admission
& 🚌 advance notice required 🐎

► **HALESWORTH** ◄

WESTHALL HERBS

Herb garden and shop

Church Lane, Westhall, nr Halesworth, Suffolk IP19 8NU
☎ Brampton (050 279) 646

Herb farm in a tranquil setting. Sit in the herb garden and enjoy the atmosphere of the English countryside. Talks given to groups by appointment.

4 miles north east of Halesworth, off the B1124,
    close to church
Open April–Oct, Sat, Sun 10.00am–5.00pm, Mon, Wed,
    Thur, Fri 2.00–5.00pm
Free admission
& 🚌 advance notice required 🐎

► **HAVERHILL** ◄

LITTLE BRADLEY FARM

Farm visit

Little Bradley House, Little Bradley, Haverhill, Suffolk
    CB9 7JG
☎ Thurlow (044083) 261

Nature trail passes through mixed farming and one of the best preserved early village sites.

Off the B1061, 5 miles west of Haverhill
Open May–Sept
Free admission
& 🐎

BERNARD ROOKE POTTERY
THE MILL GALLERY
SWILLAND IPSWICH
SUFFOLK IP6 9LW
WITNESHAM (0473-85) 460

Work by Aaron, Felix and Bernard Rooke
Opening Times Monday–Saturday 9.00am–5.30pm.
Sundays & Bank Holidays 11.00am–5.00pm.

▶ *IPSWICH* ◀

BERNARD ROOKE POTTERY

Art gallery and craft centre

The Mill Gallery, Swilland, Ipswich IP6 9LW
☎ Witnesham (0473 85) 460

The pottery produces a wide range of ceramic table and standard lamps, animal sculptures, clocks, plant pots, vases and dishes which are designed and produced by Bernard, Aaron and Felix Rooke.

From Ipswich take the B1077 via Westerfield and Witnesham – fork right to Swilland, entry opposite water tower
Open Mon–Sat 9.00am–6.00pm; Sundays and Bank Holidays 11.00am–5.00pm
Free admission and car parking
& 🚌 advance notice required ✖

HILLSIDE NURSERIES

Farm shop and pick your own

Silver Hill, Hintlesham, Ipswich, Suffolk IP8 3NJ
☎ Hintlesham (047 387) 545

A wide selection of vegetables available in season grown to Soil Association Symbol standards including PYO sweetcorn. We also grow bedding and herbaceous plants, pot plants, trees and shrubs.

On the A1071, 5 miles from centre of Ipswich
Open 10.00am–5.00pm Tues–Sat, closed Sun and Mon
Free admission
& 🚌 advance notice required ✖

▶ *LAVENHAM* ◀

THE PRIORY

Historic house and garden

Lavenham, Suffolk CO10 9RW
☎ Lavenham (0787) 247417

Beautiful timber framed building (Grade I) once lived in by monks, medieaval clothiers, Elizabethan rectors, now a family home with stimulating interior design. Paintings and stained glass by Ervin Bossanyi (1891–1975).

On the A1141 in centre of Lavenham
Open Easter–Oct daily 10.30am–5.30pm. Restaurant
closed Fri
Admission: adult £2.00, child £1.00
& ⛟ advance notice required ✕

► LAXFIELD ◄

LAXFIELD & DISTRICT MUSEUM

Farming museum

The Guildhall, Laxfield, Woodbridge, Suffolk
☎ Ubbeston (098 683) 218

*The museum is housed in an early 16th
century Guildhall. The displays relate to the
domestic and working life of the village in
the late 19th century.*

Take the B1117, 8 miles west of Halesworth,
B1116, 8 miles north of Framlingham, turn right
to Laxfield
Open May Bank Holiday–Sept: Sat & Sun 2.00–5.00pm,
other times by appointment
Free admission but donations accepted
⛟ ✕

► LOWESTOFT ◄

LOWESTOFT FISHING INDUSTRY

Working fishing industry

c/o Amenities Dept, Tourist Information Centre, The
Esplanade, Lowestoft NR33 0QF
☎ Lowestoft (0502) 523000

*Lowestoft is a major UK fishing port and
operates a fleet of deep sea trawlers and
inshore boats. Guided tours include the
harbour, fish market and a look at a trawler.*

From the main A12 road on entering town follow
Tourist Information Centre signs
Open all year (except Christmas and first 2 weeks in
Jan), Mon–Fri mornings only, by appointment
Admission: £1.15 per person, party rates available (1990
prices)
& ⛟ ✕

SOMERLEYTON HALL

**Gardens, maze, miniature railway, tea rooms and
gift shop**

Somerleyton, nr Lowestoft, Suffolk NR32 5QQ
☎ Lowestoft (0502) 730224

*Somerleyton Hall is well worth a visit.
Superb gardens, famous maze, tunnel
garden, deer park, restored Loggia tea room
and gift shop.*

On the B1074, 6 miles from Lowestoft
Open Easter Sun–29 Sept: Thur, Sun & Bank Holidays
2.00–5.30pm, also 2 July–29 Aug: Tues & Wed
2.00–5.30pm
Admission (provisional): adult £3.00, child £1.65, OAP
£2.40; group rates: adult £2.40, child £1.35
& ⛟ ✕

► NEWMARKET ◄

THE NATIONAL STUD

Thoroughbred horse breeding centre

Newmarket, Suffolk CB8 0XE
☎ Newmarket (0638) 663464

*A unique opportunity to see behind the
scenes of a prestigious stud housing and
breeding some of the world's finest
racehorses. Booking essential.*

2 miles south west of Newmarket on jct of the
A1304 (A11) London, and the A1303 (A45)
Cambridge
Open end March–end Sept, 75 minute guided tours at
11.15am and 2.30pm weekdays (ex Bank Holidays),
11.15am Sat when racing at Newmarket, 3.00pm Sun
Admission: adult £2.75, child/OAP £1.50 (1990 prices)
& ⛟ ✕

► SAXMUNDHAM ◄

BRUISYARD VINEYARD & WINERY, HERB & WATER GARDENS

**Farm shop, tea room, vineyard, winery, herb and
water gardens**

Church Rd, Bruisyard, Saxmundham, Suffolk IP17 2EF
☎ Badingham (072 875) 281

Off the A12, 4 miles west of Saxmundham
Open Easter–Nov: Mon–Sat 10.30am–5.00pm, Sun
12.00–5.00pm
Admission to conducted winery tour: adult £2.75, OAP
£2.50, under 14s free (1990 prices)
& ⛟ advance notice required ✝ in vineyard

DUNWICH HEATH

Country walk

Saxmundham, Suffolk IP17 3DJ
☎ Westleton (072873) 505

National Trust tea rooms, shop and information centre. 214 acres heathland, sandy gravel beach.

South of Dunwich village
Open all year
Free admission, car parking charge
♿ 🚌 parking charge 🐕

LAUREL FARM HERBS

Pot grown and fresh cut herbs

Main Rd, Kelsale, Saxmundham, Suffolk IP17 2RG
☎ Yoxford (072877) 223

800 yards north of the end of the Saxmundham bypass beside the A12 on the left hand side of the road
Open April–Oct, closed Tues
Free admission
♿ ✖

MINSMERE

RSPB wildlife reserve

Westleton, Saxmundham IP17 3BY
☎ (072 873) 281

4 nature trails and 8 hides at various vantage points. Beach, reedbeds, woodland and the Scrape: shallow brackish water, mud and islands where a large variety of breeding birds, waders and other wildlife may be seen.

Off the B1125 in Westleton towards Dunwich road or (for cars only) via East Bridge north from Leiston. Car drivers please take special care on narrow lanes within and approaching the reserve
Open every day (except Tues), 9.00am–9.00pm or sunset
Admission: adult £2.50, child 50p, OAP £1.50. Guide 50p
♿ 🚌 advance notice required ✖

SNAPE MALTINGS, RIVERSIDE CENTRE FOR ARTS & ACTIVITIES

Concert hall, shops, galleries

nr Saxmundham, Suffolk IP17 1SR
☎ Snape (072888) 303/5

Delightful old riverside maltings, home of the world famous Maltings Concert Hall. Shops, galleries and restaurants open all

year. River trips and painting and craft weekends Easter to October. Holiday accommodation.

From the A12 turn east onto the A1094, south onto the B1069
Open every day (except 25 & 26 Dec) 10.00am–6.00pm (5.00pm in winter)
Free admission
♿ 🚌 advance notice required 🐕

► **SOUTHWOLD** ◄

RED HOUSE FARM (HINTON) LTD

Farm shop, farm trail and farm visit, pick your own

Red House Farm, Hinton, Saxmundham, Suffolk IP17 3RF
☎ Blythburgh (050 270) 238

Farm shop, delicatessen, bakery, coffee shop/restaurant. Oak barrels and tubs. Pick your own crops in season. Ring above number for details of farm shop and barrels or (050 270) 736 for all other business. Ample free parking.

On the A12, 1½ miles south of Blythburgh
Open April–Sept daily 9.00am–5.30pm, Sun 10.00am–5.00pm; Oct–March daily 9.00am–5.00pm, Sun 10.00am–1.00pm
Free admission
♿ 🚌 🐕

► **STOKE-BY-CLARE** ◄

BOYTON VINEYARD

Vineyard tour and wine tasting

Hill Farm, Boyton End, Stoke-by-Clare, Suffolk CO9 4AN
☎ Haverhill (0440) 61893

From the A604 take the A1092, turn left to Keddington, 1 mile up lane on left
Open May–end Oct most days
Admission £1.50 per person. Ample free car parking
♿ 🚌 advance notice required

► **STOWMARKET** ◄

HAUGHLEY PARK

House, gardens and woods

Nr Stowmarket, Suffolk IP14 3JY
☎ Elmswel (0359) 40205

'Jacobethan' house in warm red brick with five crow-stepped gables on east front. Well kept gardens and woods with a great variety of trees and shrubs.

Signposted 'Haughley Park' on the A45 between
Bury St Edmunds and Ipswich
Open May–Sept Tues 3.00–6.00pm
Admission: adult £1.50, child 50p
   advance notice required

MUSEUM OF EAST ANGLIAN LIFE

Rural life museum

Stowmarket, Suffolk IP14 1DL
☎ Stowmarket (0449) 612229

Open air museum showing aspects of East Anglian life by re-erected buildings, agricultural machinery, industrial and domestic displays. Regular craft demonstrations. Picnic site. Gift shop.

Follow museum signs off the A45
Open April–Oct Mon–Sat 11.00am–5.00pm, Sun 12.00–
5.00pm
Admission charged

STONHAM BARNS

Pick your own, farm shop, restaurant, plant centre

Stonham Aspal, Stowmarket, Suffolk IP14 6AU
☎ Stowmarket (0449) 711755

Stonham Barns – garden and orchid centre, restaurant, farm shop, country wear, PYO fruit and affiliated activities, childrens play area.

On the A1120, 8 miles from Stowmarket, just
through Stonham Aspal village
Open daily (except Mon and over Christmas) summer
10.00am–5.30pm, winter 10.00am–4.30pm
Free admission
   advance notice required
not in shops

► SUDBURY ◄

PARADISE CENTRE

Country garden, paddock with pygmy goats and bantams, picnic/play area

Twinstead Rd, Lamarsh, nr Bures, Suffolk CO8 5EX
☎ Twinstead (078729) 449

We are a nursery growing unusual bulbous and tumerous plants for the amateur and expert. Our stock can be seen in our 5 acre plot. Children can play in the picnic/play area.

11 miles from Colchester, 3½ miles from Sudbury
Open Easter–Nov: Sat, Sun & Bank Holidays, other days
please telephone
Admission: adult £1.00, child 60p, OAP 80p
   advance notice required

► WATTISFIELD ◄

HENRY WATSONS POTTERIES LTD

Craft shop

Wattisfield, Suffolk IP22 1NH
☎ Stanton (0359) 51239

Watsons Pottery is an old established company dating back over 180 years. Visit the Roman kiln and pottery gift shop for a wide range of original ideas for the home.

On the A143 between Bury St Edmunds and Diss
Open all year for the shop: Mon–Sat 9.30am–4.30pm,
closed Sunday & Good Friday, open all other Bank
Holidays. Appointment necessary for factory tours
Admission: 50p per person for factory tours (1990 prices)
   advance notice required, ample parking

► WICKHAM MARKET ◄

AKENFIELD

Country garden

1 Park Lane, Charsfield, Woodbridge, Suffolk IP13 7PT
☎ Charsfield (047337) 402

Plants on sale.

Take the B1078 from Wickham Market
Open end May–Sept
Admission: £1.00 given to charity
   advance notice required

► WOODBRIDGE ◄

EASTON FARM PARK

Farming museum, farm interpretation centre, farm trail and visit

Easton, nr Woodbridge, Suffolk IP13 0EQ
☎ Wickham Market (0728) 746475

Plenty to see and do including farm animals, display dairy, milling every afternoon, pets paddock, unique Victorian dairy, licenced tea room, gift shop.

Signposted off the A12 – take the B1116 to Framlingham, then follow the signs to Easton
Open Easter–Oct 10.30am–6.00pm
Admission: adult £2.75, child £1.60, OAP £2.15 (1990 prices)
& 🚌 advance notice required 🐴

PARLOUR MAID REAL DAIRY ICE CREAMS

Farm shop and speciality food producer

Ilett Farms, Debach House, Debach, Woodbridge, Suffolk IP13 6BZ
☎ Charsfield (047 337) 260

Producers of quality farm fresh dairy ice creams and pure fruit sorbets from our own herd's milk. Natural ingredients without artificial colour or flavour.

Farm and shop situated on the B1078, approx 4 miles west of Wickham Market at Debach
Open March–Oct 11.00am–6.00pm; Nov–Feb 11.00am–dusk
& 🚌 advance notice required 🐴

TANGHAM TRAIL FOR THE DISABLED

Forest nature trail

Forestry Commission, Tangham, Woodbridge, Suffolk IP12 3NF
☎ Orford (0394) 450214

800m trail with 400m short cut option. Toilet facilities in nearby campsite.

Off the B1084 between Woodbridge and Orford, approx 6 miles from Woodbridge
Open daily during daylight hours
Free admission
& 🚌 🐴

SURREY

Surrey has many attractive villages and open spaces despite its proximity to London and its popularity amongst the commuter population. Thousands of acres of commons, wooded valleys and heather-clad hills still remain undeveloped, open to the interested countryside explorer.

The home of the Royal Horticultural Society, there is also a countryside conservation centre and a National Trust information centre to include on your visiting list. Guided visits to working farms can be arranged and there are nature trails, farm walks, country parks and gardens, vineyards, a working windmill, a pottery, an art centre, a weaving workshop and a gold jewellery studio to visit and enjoy. The numerous farm shops and pick-your-own farms give everyone a chance to taste the soft fruits and fresh produce of the area whilst the keen fishermen can 'catch-their-own' at one of the trout fishing lakes.

► *CHERTSEY* ◄

ST ANNS HILL NATURE TRAIL

Nature trail

St Anns Hill Rd, Chertsey, Surrey
☎ Weybridge (0932) 845500 ext 367

Nature trail in wooded park noted for its bluebell display during April and its rhododendron display during May. Unfortunately storm damage has decimated many mature trees. Picnic tables and benches, no barbecues (fire hazard).

St Anns Hill road off the A320, ½ mile from Chertsey
Open all year
Free admission
&. ✝

► *COBHAM* ◄

PAINSHILL PARK

Historic garden

Portsmouth Rd, Cobham, Surrey
☎ Cobham (0932) 68113/64674

Charles Hamilton designed and laid out Painshill between 1738 and 1773. Now, following 30 years of dereliction, the serpentine lake, planting and garden buildings are being restored to 18th century specifications. Light refreshments available.

Entrance off the A245 Portsmouth road in Cobham, adjacent to the River Mole and opposite the Notre Dame convent school. The A245 is off the A3 at the Cobham roundabout
Please telephone for opening times and admission charges. Group tours by arrangement. School groups please telephone (0932) 66743
&. wc ⛙ advance notice required
✘ grazing animals

► *DORKING* ◄

BOX HILL NATIONAL TRUST INFORMATION CENTRE

Country walk, nature trails, shop and information room

Box Hill, Tadworth, Surrey KT20 7LB
☎ Dorking (0306) 885502

Over 800 acres of woods and chalk downland on the top of the North Downs, with magnificent views to the South Downs. Very popular at weekends. Restaurant and snack servery.

On the A24, 1 mile north of Dorking, 2½ miles south of Leatherhead
Open all year for park, walks and trails; shop and information room: April–Oct, Wed–Sun and Bank Holiday Mondays, 11.30am–5.30pm; Nov–mid Dec Wed–Sun 12.00–4.00pm
Admission: car park £1.00, free to NT members
&. ⛙ advance notice required, coaches must approach from the B2032/2033, not the A24 ✝

COOMB FARMHOUSE COUNTRYSIDE TRAINING CENTRE

Countryside conservation training centre, country walks and demonstration areas

Coomb Farmhouse, Balchins Lane, Westcott, Dorking, Surrey RH4 3LE
☎ Dorking (0306) 885080

A Victorian farmhouse (with classroom facilities) at the foot of the North Downs, with an excellent range of wildlife habitats to study.

Off Balchins Lane on the west edge of the village of Westcott, north of the A25 between Guildford and Dorking
Open by appointment for organised groups
Standard charges for school groups from £50–£150 per day per group
&. ⛙ advance notice required ✝

FOLIAGE SCENTED AND HERB PLANTS

Country garden and herb shop

Ranmore Common, Dorking, Surrey RH5 6SY
☎ (04865) 2273/4731

Talks on herbs and conducted tours round the garden, teas can be arranged.

Nursery is close to Ranmore Arms public house, 4 miles from Dorking on Ranmore road, Dunley Hill, or 3 miles from East Horsley
Open April–Sept Wed–Sun and Bank Holidays 10.00am–6.00pm
Admission to main gardens £1.00 per person
&. ⛙ advance notice required ✘

THE HANNAH PESCHAR GALLERY

Art centre and country garden

Black and White Cottage, Standon Lane, Ockley, Surrey
RH5 5QR
☎ Oakwood (030679) 269

*The garden is a controlled wilderness
featuring exotic and sculptural plants in and
around large ponds. The gallery shows new
and adventurous work by mainly young
potters and sculptors.*

Take the A24 towards Horsham, then the A29
through Ockley, on leaving Ockley take Cat Hill
Lane on the right, at T junction look for sign
'Black and White Cottage'
Open Fri & Sat 11.00am–6.00pm, Sun 2.00–5.00pm,
Tues, Wed & Thur by appointment
Admission: adult £2.50, child £1.50, guided tours for
groups (including refreshments) £5.00 per person
& 🚌 advance notice required 🕱

OCKLEY COURT FARM

Farm shop and pick your own

Ockley, nr Dorking, Surrey RH5 5LS
☎ Dorking (0306) 711365

*Soft fruit, salads and vegetables picked fresh
each day at the shop or for you to pick.*

From Dorking go 4 miles south on the A24. At big
roundabout bear right on the A29, after 2 miles
turn left on the B2126. Farm shop is ½ mile on
right, well signed from the A29
Open daily May–Feb 9.00am–8.00pm summer; 9.00am–
5.00pm winter
Free admission
& disabled visitors can go down to the PYO sites where
there is room to picnic 🚌 🕱

POLESDEN LACEY

Historic house, country garden and walks

Nr Dorking, Surrey RH5 6BD
☎ Bookham (0372) 52048/58203

*A Regency house where Queen Elizabeth
spent her honeymoon in 1923. Fine
collections of porcelain, silver, furniture and
paintings. Rose, iris and lavender garden,
over 1000 acres of estate with walks. Shop,
restaurant.*

3 miles west of Dorking, 1½ miles south of Great
Bookham, off the A246 Leatherhead–Guildford
road
Grounds open all year daily, 11.00am to sunset (house
also open, contact National Trust for details)
Admission to garden only: April–Oct £1.50, Nov–March
£1.20 per person
& 🚌 🕱 in garden and on lawns

► **EPSOM** ◄

HORTON PARK FARM

Farm visit, farm shop and craft centre

Horton Lane, Epsom, Surrey KT19 8PT
☎ Epsom (0372) 743984

*30 acre working rare breeds farm with farm
walk. Friendly quality stock on display
representing all classes of farm livestock.
Spinning workshop open daily except
Mondays, 11.00am–4.00pm, tuition by
arrangement. Tea room.*

Off the B280, ½ mile west of Epsom
Open daily 10.00am–6.00pm summer, 10.00am–5.00pm
winter, closed Christmas Day and Boxing Day
Admission £1.10 per person, child under 2 years free,
but 1 adult free with each paying child; OAP £1.00
(1990 prices)
& 🚌 🕱

► **ESHER** ◄

ELMBRIDGE BOROUGH COUNCIL

Country walks

Council Office, High St, Esher, Surrey KT10 9RR
☎ Esher (0372) 62111

*1,250 acres of woodlands, heathland (mostly
commons), ponds and view over River Mole.
800 acres designated a Site of Special
Scientific Interest due to its nature
conservation value.*

Please telephone for directions
Open daily all year
Free admission
& 🕱

▶ FARNHAM ◀

ALICE HOLT FOREST VISITOR CENTRE

Country walk and forestry centre

Alice Holt Forest Visitor and Information Centre, Bucks
Horn Oak, Farnham, Surrey GU10 4LS
☎ Bentley (0420) 23666

*Located in the ancient woodland of Alice
Holt, a pleasant mix of coniferous and
deciduous woodland, the centre incorporates
many walks and other facilities affording the
visitor opportunities to view the wildlife of
the forest.*

Follow the A325 Farnham–Petersfield road, after
about 4 miles turn left at Bucks Horn Oak
crossroads, centre is approx ½ mile on the left
Open April–Sept 10.00am–4.30pm
Free admission
&. ᴙ ⋔

AVALON FARM

Farm shop and pick your own

The Packhouse, Tilford Road, Churt, Farnham, Surrey
GU10 2LL
☎ Hindhead (042873) 5436

Take the Tilford road, by Farnham station, continue
for 6 miles, the farm is on the right hand side,
just past Pride of the Valley Hotel
Open all year, daily 8.00am–5.00pm
Free admission
&. ᴙ ⋔ in car park only

CLARE STREET

Gold jewellery and seal engraving

Little Orchard, 11 Woodcut Rd, Wrecclesham, Farnham,
Surrey GU10 4QF
☎ Farnham (0252) 733232

*Designer and maker of fine gold jewellery,
mainly to commission. Some stock available
for immediate sale, given a weeks notice.
Also seal engraving on gold signet rings,
etc. Workshop in private house.*

Off the A325, south west of Farnham
Open by appointment only, please give at least one day's
notice
Free admission
&. ⋔.

▶ GODALMING ◀

BUSBRIDGE LAKES ORNAMENTAL WATERFOWL

Country park, gardens, farm shop

Busbridge Lakes, Hambledon Rd, Godalming, Surrey
GU8 4AY
☎ Godalming (04868) 21955

*Over 120 species of ornamental waterfowl,
pheasants and exotic birds. 40 acres of
parkland with specimen trees, 3 lakes,
Heritage Garden, follies and grotto. Nature
trails, wide variety of flora and fauna.*

1½ miles from Godalming, on the Hambledon road,
off the B2130
Open Easter, 27 March–7 April incl, 5–6, 26– 27 May,
18–26 Aug incl: 11.00am–5.30pm
Admission: adult £2.70, child/OAP £1.60 approx
&. ᴙ advance notice required ⋔

THURSLEY TEXTILE DESIGNS

Textile gallery and weaving workshop

1 Mousehill Lane, Milford, Godalming, Surrey GU8 5BH
☎ Godalming (04868) 24769

*Shop, gallery and workshop in old English
village, stocking hand woven articles,
tapestries, and designer knitwear made in
our weaving workshop. Also a large selection
of unusual items from all over the world.*

On the A3 at Milford, 2 miles west of Godalming
Open Mon–Sat 10.00am–5.30pm
Admission charge for demonstrating to large groups.
Please telephone for information
ᴙ advance notice required ⋔

▶ GODSTONE ◀

FLOWER FARM

Pick your own

Flower Lane, Godstone, Surrey RH9 8DE
☎ Godstone (0883) 743636

*An attractive pick your own farm set in
scenic Surrey countryside with outstanding
views of the nearby North Downs. Crops are
grown using organic fertilisers and natural
predators.*

½ mile east of Godstone village, on the A25
  towards Oxted
Open June & July 9.00am–7.00pm; Aug & Sept
  10.00am–6.00pm; Oct 10.00am–5.00pm. Closed
  Mondays from Aug onwards
Free admission
   ⅖ ✗

GODSTONE VINEYARDS

Vineyard and shop

Godstone, Surrey RH9 8DE
☎   Godstone (0883) 742367

*Reputedly Surrey's most beautiful
commercial vineyard, nestling at the foot of
the North Downs, with outstanding views.
Due to open for visitors Easter 1991. Wine
sales.*

½ mile north of the M25 (jct 6); Quarry Road (off
  the A22), vineyard entrance 200 yards on right
Please telephone for opening times
Admission charge includes free wine tasting
   ⅖ ✗

► **GUILDFORD** ◄

LOSELEY PARK

**Speciality food producer, farm shop, farm visit,
historic house and garden**

Guildford, Surrey GU3 1HS
☎   Guildford (0483) 571881

*Parkland with Elizabethan historic house;
restaurant in 17th century tithe barn.
Loseley organic produce.*

Leave the A3 at Compton, take the B3000 for 2
  miles; also signposted at Artington off the
  A3100, 3 miles south west of Guildford
Open for farm tours April–Oct, Mon–Sat; please
  telephone to confirm opening times of house,
  restaurant and shop
Admission for farm tours, trailer rides: adult £1.80, child
  £1.50; walks £1.50; house: adult £3.00, child £1.50.
  Party and school rates available
   ⅖ ⛺ advance notice required
🐾 in car park area only

THE ROYAL HORTICULTURAL SOCIETY

Country garden, information and plant centre

The Royal Horticultural Society's Garden, Wisley, Woking,
  Surrey GU23 6QB
☎   Guildford (0483) 224234

On the A3, 20 miles from London, 7 miles from
  Guildford
Open Feb–Oct: Mon–Sat 10.00am–7.00pm or sunset if
  earlier. Jan, Nov & Dec 10.00am–4.30pm or sunset if
  earlier. Open to members only on Sun. Closed 25 Dec
Admission: adult £3.00, child (6–14) £1.20, under 6 free,
  disabled visitors (wheelchair or blind) free, carers for
  same £3.00 (1990 prices)
   ⅖ ⛺ advance notice required
🐾 except for guide dogs

► *HINDHEAD* ◄

GRAYSHOTT POTTERY

Craft shop – pottery

School Rd, Grayshott, Hindhead, Surrey GU26 6LR
☎   Hindhead (042873) 4404

*Spacious showroom attached to the pottery,
stocking a vast range of gifts selected to
appeal to all ages and provide a choice not
available in the high street. Large private car
park and toilets available.*

Taking the B3002 just south of Hindhead traffic
  lights on the A3, turn right at church crossroads,
  pottery is next to village school
Open Mon–Sat 9.00am–5.00pm, please telephone for
  times of demonstrations
Free admission
   ⅖ ✗

► *LIGHTWATER* ◄

LIGHTWATER COUNTRY PARK

Country park

The Avenue, Lightwater, Surrey
☎   Bagshot (0276) 79582

*143 acres of woods, water, wildfowl,
heathland and meadows with nature and
waymarked trails, picnic and play areas
together with a Heathland Visitor Centre
(small entrance fee).*

Signposted off the A322, east of M3 jct 3
Open daily all year
Free admission
⛺ advance notice required 🐾

▶ LINGFIELD ◀

CAREWELL FRUIT FARM

Pick your own and farm shop

St Piers Lane, Lingfield, Surrey
☎ Lingfield (0342) 832091

300 yards east of Lingfield racecourse
Open: farm shop daily except Bank Holidays; PYO
June–end Sept
Free admission
& ⇛ ✗

▶ MERSTHAM ◀

WHITEHALL FARM

Pick your own and trout fishing

Rocky Lane, Reigate, Surrey
☎ Merstham (073 74) 5618

*Pick your own or ready picked soft fruits.
Lovely natural surroundings on North
Downs Way. Easy to find, ample parking,
picnic area. Trout fishing from 2½ acre lake.*

Take the M25, come off jct 8, then first left, site 1
mile on right
Open all year round, fishing 8.00am–9.00pm; PYO
June–Aug 9.00am–8.00pm
No admission charge to PYO
& ⇛ advance notice required
✗ but not in picking area

▶ PIRBRIGHT ◀

SURREY WILDLIFE TRUST

Nature reserves

The Old School, School Lane, Pirbright, Surrey GU24 0JN
☎ Brookwood (0483) 797575

*For details of open days, guided walks, etc.
in nature reserves in Surrey, please contact
Trust Headquarters.*

Over 25 reserves throughout Surrey. Please
telephone Trust Headquarters for details before
visiting as access to some sites is restricted
Open times – please contact the Trust Headquarters
Free admission
& ✗

▶ REDHILL ◀

THE POST MILL

**Working windmill, museum, farm shop and
country walks**

Outwood Common, nr Bletchingley, Surrey RH1 5PW
☎ Smallfield (034284) 3458

*Wholemeal flour from England's oldest
working windmill, built in 1665. Farm
animals and small museum.*

2 miles south of Redhill, turn off at Bletchingley or
turn off the M25 at Godstone onto the A25
Open every Sunday afternoon and Bank Holiday Mondays
2.00–6.00pm, Easter–Oct day and evening parties by
appointment only
Admission: adult £1.00, child 50p, day parties: adult
£1.50, child £1.00, evening conducted tours: £1.50 per
person (1990 prices)
& ⇛ ✗

PRIORY FARM

**Pick your own, farm shop, tea garden and plant
centre**

Nutfield, Redhill, Surrey RH1 4EJ
☎ Nutfield Ridge (0737) 822484/822789
(answerphone), 823304 (office)

*Wide range of English quality fruits, fishing
lakes. Lovely parkland setting – spacious free
car parks, lakes and rolling hills. Play area,
countryside walks, peaceful places to sit, tea
room, shop, fruit picking, plants from the
greenhouse.*

On the A25 between Redhill and Godstone. In
Nutfield look for signs to Priory Farm, also
signposted. Redhill Aerodrome
Open daily including weekends 9.00am–5.30pm (until
7.00pm from 16 June–end July)
& many attractions suitable for disabled visitors, such
as the greenhouse with tea room and the picnic
areas ✗

▶ REIGATE ◀

FANNY'S FARM SHOP

Farm shop and some pick your own

Markedge Lane, off Gatton Bottom, Merstham, Surrey
RH1 3AN
☎ Downland (07375) 54444

Fresh produce, home-made cakes and pies.
Brick-a-brac shop; PYO; horsefeeds. Pet area
and 'Wind in the Willows' walk.

Reigate Hill roundabout, turn left at Merstham sign
into Gatton Bottom, 2 miles first turn left, or
through Merstham village, first left, 2 miles, first
right (under motorway bridge)
Open all year daily 8.30am–7.00pm
Free admission
 ✖ by appointment ✖

► **WALTON-ON-THAMES** ◄

APPS COURT FARM

Farm shop and pick your own

Hurst Rd, Walton-on-Thames, Surrey KT12 2EG
☎ Walton-on-Thames (0932) 244822

Refreshments available.

On the A3050 between Walton (1½ miles) and
Hampton Court (2½ miles)
Open all year Mon–Sat 9.00am–5.00pm, Sun 9.00am–
2.00pm, PYO season (mid June–Aug) 9.00am–7.00pm,
7 days a week
Free admission
& ✖ ✖

► *WOKING* ◄

FARM AND COUNTRY VISITS

Guided visits to working farms

82 Hermitage Woods Crescent, St Johns, Woking, Surrey
GU21 1UF
☎ Brookwood (04867) 5379

Educational, imaginative and enjoyable
walks guided by the farmer plus substantial
free material for teachers/leaders. Pregnant
women should not visit sheep farms at
lambing time due to danger of viral
infection.

Please telephone for directions
Open all year round (by appointment only) for organised
and pre-booked groups and monthly 'open' visits for
pre-booked individuals/families
Admission £1.75 per person for 2 hours guided visit and
½ hour picnic. £2.50 per person 3½ hours guided
visit and ½ hour picnic
& but some farms might be suitable, please telephone
for details ✖ advance notice required
✖ on some farms

SUSSEX

Sussex has many ancient pathways and pretty river valleys crossing the rolling grassy slopes of the South Downs. It is a county rich in history and scenery with several familiar and popular resorts along its attractive coastline.

There are many delightful and enticing walks to follow such as one through an ancient oak and bluebell wood. There are a number of country parks and gardens, farm parks with specialised breeds of sheep or rare breeds, a cacti nursery, working museums, cider mills, a marine life attraction centre, vineyards, speciality food producers including a smoke-house and there are also many craft workshops including one making the traditional Sussex trug baskets from sweet chestnut and willow. A very interesting and varied stretch of countryside for the visitor to explore.

► ALFRISTON ◄

DRUSILLAS PARK

Farm shop, craft centre, country gardens and zoo

Alfriston, East Sussex BN26 5QS
☎ (0323) 870234

The enclosures are specially landscaped to provide a natural environment for the animals and birds; also rose, oriental and award winning cottage gardens. 8 country shops. Restaurants, playland and miniature railway.

On the A27, between Lewes and Eastbourne
Open all year daily 10.30am–5.00pm
Admission: adult £3.75, child £3.50, OAP/groups £2.50
&. ♿ ✝ in grounds only

ENGLISH WINE CENTRE

Speciality drink producer

Drusillas Roundabout, Alfriston, East Sussex BN26 5QS
☎ Alfriston (0323) 870 532/164

Guided tour of cellars, vineyard and museum, wine tasting.

Off the A27, between Lewes and Polegate
Shop open daily 10.00am–5.00pm
Admission: please telephone for details of talks and tours
&. ♿ ✝

► AMBERLEY ◄

AMBERLEY CHALK PITS MUSEUM

Open air museum, trails, craft centre, country walk and working timberyard

Houghton Bridge, Amberley, Arundel, West Sussex
BN18 9LT
☎ Bury (0798) 831370

Working museum. Visit craftsmen, ride on narrow gauge railway, and enjoy many other exhibits and displays. Allow 3 hours for a visit.

Beside the B2139 at Houghton Bridge, immediately adjacent to Amberley railway station
Open beg April–end Oct, Wed–Sun, and daily in school holidays
Admission: adult £3.50, child £1.00, OAP £2.50. Family ticket £8.00. Reductions for booked parties (1990 prices)
&. ♿ ample free parking ✝

► ARUNDEL ◄

THE WILDFOWL AND WETLANDS TRUST

Wildlife trust reserve

Mill Rd, Arundel, West Sussex BN18 9PB
☎ Arundel (0903) 883355

Over 1000 ducks, geese and swans, within 60 acres of beautiful grounds. 7 hides, gift shop and restaurant.

Leave the A27 on Arundel bypass, follow traffic signs, ¾ mile north of Arundel
Open daily April–Oct, 9.30am–6.30pm (5.00pm Nov–March)
Admission: adult £2.70, child £1.40, OAP £1.70 (1990 prices)
&. ♿ ✕

► BEXHILL-ON-SEA ◄

BROAD OAK COUNTRY PARK

Country park and walks

c/o Parks and Recreation Dept, 10 London Rd, Bexhill on Sea, East Sussex TN39 5HY
☎ Bexhill-on-Sea (0424) 220620

Picnic areas, small fitness trail and tree collection.

2 miles from town centre, turn north off the A259 at sign
Open daily
Free admission
&. ✝

► BIGNOR ◄

BIGNOR ROMAN VILLA

Farm trail and country walks

Bignor, nr Pulborough, West Sussex RH20 1PH
☎ Sutton (07987) 259

Situated in unspoilt rural setting. Some of the finest mosaics in the world on display. The 80 foot north corridor is the longest mosaic on view in Great Britain.

Signposted on the A29 and the A285
Open March, April, May and Oct daily 10.00am–5.00pm
(closed Mondays except Bank Holidays); June–Sept
daily 10.00am–6.00pm
Admission: adult £1.65, child 85p, OAP £1.10, special
rates for groups
&. 🚌 🛏 in the grounds only

Admission: adult £2.80, child £1.40 (increased rates
weekends and Bank Holidays), special rates for parties
of over 15 people
&. steep entrance, disabled visitors should ask at ticket
office for alternative entrance. Ground floor only
accessible to wheelchairs. Some uneven paths in garden.
Mill entrance has 2 steps 🚌 🛏

► **BILLINGSHURST** ◄

COSTRONG FARM

**Farm shop, pick your own, herbs and spices
specialist**

Plaistow Rd, Kirdford, Billingshurst, West Sussex
RH14 0LA
☎ Kirdford (040377) 219/391

*18 varieties of apples and pears, full range of
salads grown, large selection of herbs, spices
and health foods, new nursery for plants and
fuschias.*

Take the A272 to Wisborough Green, turn right and
almost immediately first left to Kirdford. In
Kirdford turn right onto Petworth Rd and then
right to Plaistow. Glasshouses and shop situated
1 mile on left
Open daily 9.00am–5.00pm
Free admission
&. 🚌 advance notice required 🛏

► **BURWASH** ◄

BATEMAN'S – NATIONAL TRUST

Country garden, working water mill

Burwash, East Sussex TN19 7DS
☎ Burwash (0435) 882302

*The home of Rudyard Kipling 1902–1936
with furniture, library etc. as in his day. Set
in attractive country garden with a working
water mill, shop and tea room. Events in
summer include open air theatre and
concerts.*

½ mile south of Burwash on the A265, approached
by road leading south from west end of village
Open April–Oct daily (except Thur & Fri) 11.00am–
6.00pm. Open Good Friday

► **CHICHESTER** ◄

CHILSDOWN VINEYARD

Vineyard and winery

The Old Station House, Singleton, Chichester, West
Sussex PO18 0RX
☎ Singleton (024363) 398

*Family run vineyard and winery has been
operating at Singleton's unique old station
since 1972. 'Sip and Shop' free tastings – all
year.*

On the A286, 6 miles north of Chichester on
Midhurst road, fully signposted
Open May–Sept daily 10.00am–6.00pm
Admission: adult £1.50, child 30p, parties (min 20
people) at £2.75 for conducted tour and 1½ glasses of
wine
&. vineyard not accessible to wheelchairs
🚌 advance notice required 🛏

DENNIS HOARE

Farm shop

Adsdean Farm, Funtington, Chichester, West Sussex
PO18 9DN
☎ Chichester (0243) 575212

*Hormone and additive free meats, fresh or
frozen. Frozen foods, vegetables, bread, fish,
ice cream, our own smoked bacon, wholemeal
flour. Visitors welcome to see calves and
pigs.*

½ mile north of the B2146 at Funtington
Open all year, Wed 2.00–5.30pm, Thur 10.00am–4.00pm,
Fri 10.00am–5.30pm, Sat 9.00am–4.00pm
Free admission
&. there are no disabled toilet facilities 🛏

EARNLEY GARDENS

Country gardens, butterfly and bird gardens

133 Almodington Lane, Earnley, Chichester, West Sussex
☎ Birdham (0243) 512637

'Weatherproof' enjoyment for the whole family. 17 theme gardens, butterfly garden, exotic bird garden, childrens play area, small animal farm, refreshments, free parking.

Take the A286 from Chichester towards Witterings then follow signs
Open for the gardens: Easter–Christmas; butterflies: Easter–Oct
Admission: adult £1.50, child (5–16)/OAP £1.00
 ♿ 🚲 ⛪

GERALDINE ST AUBYN HUBBARD

Craft studio – handweaving

Rosebrook, Farm Lane, Nutbourne, Chichester, West Sussex PO18 8SA
☏ Emsworth (0243) 377372

Handwoven cloth made from silk, cashmere and wool yarns, hand dyed in the workshop using natural or synthetic dyes. Available: kimonos, tunics, skirts, shawls and scarves. Block printed ties, cushions.

6 miles west of Chichester, turn off the A27 in Nutbourne, southwards into Farm Lane, at end of lane on right
Open 10.00am–5.00pm daily, preferably by appointment
Free admission
♿ very limited space
🚲 advance notice required ⛪

WEALD AND DOWNLAND OPEN AIR MUSEUM

Farm house and buildings in an open air museum

Singleton, nr Chichester, West Sussex PO18 0EU
☏ Singleton (024363) 348

Rescued historic buildings from south east England including mediaeval farmstead, agricultural buildings, rural craft workshops, working watermill. Special events – heavy horses, rare breeds, sheep dog trials during main season.

Off the A286, 6 miles north of Chichester
Open April–Oct daily 11.00am–5.00pm; Nov–March Wed & Sun, and Public Holidays only 11.00am–4.00pm
Admission: adult £2.80, child/student £1.25, OAP £2.20, party rates available (1990 prices)
♿ 🚲 advance notice required ⛪

▶   *CRAWLEY*   ◀

BUCHAN COUNTRY PARK

Country park, country walks and visitor centre

Horsham Rd, Crawley, West Sussex
☏ Crawley (0293) 542088

Delightful woodland surrounding 2 ponds. A superb teaching environment backed up by a purpose built visitor centre.

Off the A264, 2 miles west of Crawley
Open all year
Free admission
♿ a motorised wheelchair is available free of charge for use in the park 🚲 ⛪

TILGATE PARK NATURE CENTRE

Nature centre

Tilgate Park, Titmus Drive, Crawley, West Sussex RH10 5PQ
☏ Crawley (0293) 21168

Set in 400 acres of parkland, the centre, approved by the Rare Breeds Survival Trust contains many rare breeds and a pets corner. Cafeteria open daily.

Situated 1½ miles due south of Crawley town centre, main access is from Titmus Drive reached from Southgate Avenue via Tilgate Way
Open daily, winter 10.00am–4.00pm, summer 10.00am–6.00pm
Free admission
♿ 🚲 advance notice required ⛪

TULLEYS FARM

Pick your own

Turners Hill, Crawley, Sussex RH10 4PD
☏ Copthorne (0342) 715365/715856

Tulleys Farm is set in beautiful Sussex countryside. Grass parking with scenic views. Childrens play areas. Over 30 crops grown throughout the season with organically based fertilizers.

2 miles east of the M23 leaving at jct 10. ½ mile west of Turners Hill church
Open daily, June–Aug 9.30am–8.00pm; Sept–Nov 9.30am–6.00pm
Free admission
♿ 🚲 ⛪ only in the car park

▶ ## CUCKFIELD ◀

HOLMSTED FARM TOURS

Farm visit and trails

Holmsted Farm, Staplefield Road, Cuckfield, Sussex
RH17 5JF
☎ Haywards Heath (0444) 413571

*Holmsted is a modern, working dairy farm
with attractive natural habitats, woodland,
ponds and hedgerows avaialble for study.
Farmer's wife is a qualified teacher who will
assist with educational requirements.*

Off the B2114, 3 miles north of Cuckfield
Open by appointment
Admission: school parties, child £1.00 per day, 75p per
half day
&. ▦ advance notice required ✖

LAINES ORGANIC FARM

Farm shop

47 Newbury Lane, Cuckfield, West Sussex RH17 5AA
☎ Haywards Heath (0444) 452633

*Very small organic market garden
specializing in a wide variety of vegetables.
Beautiful panoramic views of the South
Downs.*

Just south of the A272 in Cuckfield village
Open daily 10.00am–5.00pm
Free admission
&. ▦ ✖

▶ ## DITCHLING ◀

JILL PRYKE POTTERY AND GALLERY

Craft gallery

8 High St, Ditchling, East Sussex BN6 8TA
☎ Hassocks (07918) 5246

*The gallery offers a range of craftwork of the
finest quality made in Sussex. It also houses
Jill Pryke's workshop and she can often be
seen throwing and decorating her pots.*

4 miles east off the A23 London–Brighton trunk
road, via the B2116 through Hurstpierpoint and
Hassocks
Open Mon–Sat 10.00am–5.00pm, Wed 10.00am–1.00pm,
closed Sun and Bank Holidays
Free admission
&.

▶ ## EASTBOURNE ◀

THE ARLINGTON BLUEBELL WALK

Country walk, farm trail and farm visit

Bates Green Farm, Arlington, nr Polegate, East Sussex
BN26 6SH
☎ Polegate (03212) 5151

*Walk through an ancient oak wood and
enjoy the carpets of bluebells. Descriptive
signs of the flora and fauna. A choice of 5
walks around this conservation farm.*

Follow signs 'Bluebell Walk & Farm Trail' off the
A22 and the A27, approx 9 miles from
Eastbourne and Lewes
Open 21 April–20 May 1990
Admission: adult £1.80, child over 3 75p, OAP £1.50,
party rates available
&. ▦ ✖

BEACHY HEAD COUNTRYSIDE CENTRE

Country walk and visitors centre

Signalman's Cottage, Beachy Head, Eastbourne, East
Sussex BN20 7YA
☎ Brighton (0323) 411145

*Originally the home of the Lloyds of London
signalman who monitored the movement of
merchant shipping, it now houses an
exhibition showing many of the natural
features that make Beachy Head so unique.*

1½ miles west of town off the B2103
Open May–Sept daily 11.00am–4.30pm
Free admission
▦ parking 50 yards west ✖

SEVEN SISTERS SHEEP CENTRE

Working farm, shop and museum

Birling Manor Farm, East Dean, nr Eastbourne, East
Sussex BN20 0DG
☎ East Dean (0323) 423302

*Different aspects of sheep farming, in a
beautiful downland setting, children will
enjoy a chance to touch and feed animals in
the 17th century barn.*

3 miles west of Eastbourne on the A259 turn left
towards Birling Gap, the farm is ½ mile on the
left
Open April–Sept daily 2.00–5.00pm
Admission: adult £1.50, child 80p, OAP £1.00, party rates
available
&. ▦ advance notice required ✖

▶ **EAST GRINSTEAD** ◀

HOATHLY HILL HERBS

Herb display garden

12 Hoathly Hill, West Hoathly, West Sussex RH19 4SJ
☎ Sharpthorne (0342) 810399

Bio-dynamically tended collection of over 260 varieties of culinary, aromatic and medicinal plants from many countries, informally planted, within a housing community. Organically grown pot plants available.

3½ miles west of the A22, 5 miles south of East Grinstead
Open May–Oct, Mon–Sat 2.00–5.00pm
Free admission – donations welcome
& ✝

▶ **ETCHINGHAM** ◀

HAREMERE HALL

Country walk, nature trails and garden

Etchingham, East Sussex TN19 7QJ
☎ Etchingham (0580 81) 245

Early 17th century Manor House. Minstral staircase, panelled Great Hall, carved Flemish fireplace, period furniture. Collection of rugs, ornaments, pottery, plates from Middle and Far East. Terraced gardens.

On the A265 halfway between Hurst Green and Etchingham. Hurst Green is on the A21 London–Hastings road north of Robertsbridge. There is an hourly 70 minute train service from Charing Cross to Etchingham
Open for tours of the garden and hall on the Sunday and Monday of each Bank Holiday weekend, by arrangement for booked parties only
Admission: £2.50
& ⟱ advance notice required ✝

▶ **FERRING** ◀

ROUNDSTONE FARM SHOP

Fruit and vegetable pyo farms

Littlehampton Rd, Ferring, West Sussex BN12 6PW
☎ Rustington (0903) 783817 (shop)
☎ Rustington (0903) 770670 (PYO)

The South's largest pick your own operation offering some 30 crops for picking, adjacent to the Farm Shop which is open throughout the year. Special feature – free tractor train service.

On the A259 between Worthing and Littlehampton
Shop open daily 9.00am–5.00pm; PYO open June–Oct 9.00am–5.00pm
Free car park
& ⟱ ✝

SMUGGLERS ANNEX

Craft outlet

3a Ferring St, Ferring, Worthing, West Sussex BN12 5HL
☎ Worthing (0903) 700191 answerphone available

Craft and gifts including herb sachets and cushions, mob hats, fishermens smocks, hand block printed scarves, aprons, skirts etc.

Ferring lies 4 miles west of Worthing and is reached by the coast road from the centre of Worthing to Sea Lane, Ferring, and by the A259 from Littlehampton and the A27 from Arundel
Open Tues, Fri, Sat (and most Wednesdays) during the year and Tues–Sat from mid June–1 Oct and Nov to end of year 10.00am–1.00pm and 2.30–5.00pm (4.30pm in winter). Other times by appointment. Closed one week in May and early Oct
Free admission
& parking is possible outside the shop and the doors are wide enough for a wheelchair
⟱ advance notice required ✝

▶ **FLIMWELL** ◀

THE WEALD SMOKERY

Farm shop and smoke-house

Mount Farm, The Mount, Flimwell, East Sussex TN5 7QL
☎ Flimwell (058 087) 601

Following careful hand-preparation and curing in specially formulated brines, quality fish and meats are slowly smoked over a mixture of aromatic logs for anything up to 60 hours.

200 yards off the A21 London–Hastings road, on the A268 Hawkhurst–Rye road (at Flimwell major crossroads)
Open all year daily (except Sundays) 10.00am–5.00pm
Free admission
& parking at front door and very easy access to our direct sales area
⟱ advance notice required ✝

► **FONTWELL** ◄

DENMANS GARDEN

Country shop and gardens

Clock House, Denmans Fontwell, nr Arundel, West
Sussex
☎ Eastergate (0243) 542808

*3½ acre garden with an emphasis on colour,
texture and form. Plants are allowed to self
seed and ramble often in gravel. Plant
centre, tea shop, clock house and School of
Garden Design.*

On the A27, midway between Chichester and
Arundel
Open March–Dec daily including Bank Holidays
9.00am–5.00pm
Admission: adult £1.80, child £1.00, OAP £1.50
& ⊶ advance notice required ✶

► **GRINSTEAD** ◄

HEAVEN FARM COUNTRY TOURS

**Museum, nature trail, stable tea rooms, guided
coach tours (Ashdown forest area)**

John W Butler, Heaven Farm, Furners Green, Uckfield,
Sussex TN22 3RG
☎ (0825) 790226

*A farm where time has stood still, offering a
nature trail along bluebell-banked, ancient
woodland paths and 170 year old museum
buildings which recapture the history of the
19th century farm.*

On the A275, 1 mile south of Danehill village
Open: Museum: weekends, April–Sept 2.30–6.00pm.
Guided tours 3.00pm, 4.00pm and 5.00pm; Nature
trail: April–Sept; Tea room: weekends and early
summer season. Party bookings, at other times, for
any of the above, can be willingly arranged. School
groups welcomed.
Admission: adult £1.50, child 75p, OAP £1.00
& ⊶ advance notice required ✶

► **HAILSHAM** ◄

MICHELHAM PRIORY

**Country walk, farming museum, country garden,
working watermill, gardens, moat**

Hailsham, East Sussex BN27 3QS
☎ Hailsham (0323) 844224

*13th–14th century buildings and Tudor
house furnished in period. Exhibitions in
Picture Gallery and Great Barn; Sussex
crafts; blacksmiths, wheelwrights and rope
museum; annual crafts exhibition. Licensed;
luncheons, teas.*

3½ miles west of Hailsham, signposted off the
A22 and A27
Open end March–Oct daily 11.00am–5.30pm
Admission: adult £2.50, child £1.30
& 3 wheelchairs available ⊶ ✶

THE TRUGGERY

Craft workshop

Coopers Croft, Herstmonceux, Hailsham, Sussex
BN27 1QL
☎ Herstmonceux (0323) 832314

*Sussex trug baskets made from sweet
chestnut and willow in the traditional way.
Many sizes available for use in the home or
garden.*

3 miles from Hailsham on the A271 to Bexhill, bus
route no 98
Open Jan–Dec: Mon–Sat 10.00am–5.30pm, also Sundays
and Bank Holidays June–Sept
Free admission
& please telephone before visit ✶

► **HASTINGS** ◄

CARR TAYLOR VINEYARDS

Farm shop, vineyard, trail and winery

Westfield, Hastings, East Sussex TN35 4SG
☎ Hastings (0424) 752501

*Winners of many top awards, Carr Taylor is
one of the foremost vineyards in England.
There is a modern winery, a barn for
wine-tasting and a shop with unusual gifts
and wines. Group tours.*

Off the A28, 6 miles north of Hastings, follow
'Vineyard' signs
Open Easter–Christmas daily 10.00am–5.00pm, also
Jan–Easter weekdays only
Free admission to shop. Vineyard trail: adult £1.00,
OAP 75p & ⊶ advance notice required ✶

SEA LIFE CENTRE

Marine life attraction

Rock-a-Nore Rd, Hastings, Sussex TN34 3DW
☎ (0424) 718776

Multi-level viewing allows visitors to come close to many marine creatures. View sharks from the underwater tunnel, 'touch' pools; sea lab; patio, restaurant and shop.

Follow signs to the Old Town, adjacent to Shipwreck Heritage Centre
Open all year daily from 10.00am
Admission: group discounts available please telephone for details
&. all displays accessible by wheelchair ✗

► HAYWARDS HEATH ◄

BORDE HILL GARDEN

Country garden and woodland walks

Borde Hill, Haywards Heath, West Sussex RH16 1XP
☎ Haywards Heath (0444) 450326

A unique botanical collection with a lake, picnic area and childrens adventure playground plus 2 licensed restaurants. Plants for sale.

1½ miles north of Haywards Heath on the Balcombe road
Open Good Friday–end Oct daily 10.00am–6.00pm
Admission: adult £1.50, child 50p, OAP £1.00, parties of 20 or more £1.00 per person
&. 🚌 🐴

BURSTYE SOAYS

Farm visit

Burstye Farm, Lindfield, Haywards Heath, West Sussex RH16 2QY
☎ Lindfield (04 447) 3376

Farm enterprise devoted entirely to the distinctive small brown sheep, soays – a rare breed virtually unchanged in 6000 years. Conducted tour includes talk and demonstration of spinning and weaving.

On west side of the B2028, midway between villages of Lindfield and Ardingly, look for large clipped hedge at shared entrance
Open by appointment only
Admission: £1.00 per person for groups of over 20, others by arrangement, please telephone
&. 🚌 advance notice required ✗

► HEATHFIELD ◄

HORAM NATURE TRAIL & SUSSEX FARM MUSEUM

Farm museum, interpretation centre, country walks and farm trails

Manor Farm, Horam, Heathfield, East Sussex TN21 0JB
☎ Horam (04353) 2597/3161

The interpretation centre (free) tells the story of the countryside with good explanation of Wealden iron etc. Woods, ponds, streams and open countryside show Sussex at its best throughout the year. Refreshments.

On the A267, midway between Tunbridge Wells and Eastbourne
Open Easter–Oct daily 10.00am–5.00pm
Admission to trail 40p; museum £1.60
&. 🚌 🐴

MERRYDOWN WINE PLC

Cider mill and winery

Horam Manor, Horam, Heathfield, East Sussex TN21 0JA
☎ Horam Road (043 53) 2254

The UK's 4th largest cider maker. The tour consists of an audio visual presentation, followed by a tour of production, and finishes off with a tasting of the products.

On the A267 Tunbridge Wells–Eastbourne road, 12 miles north of Eastbourne, 16 miles south of Tunbridge Wells, situated in Horam
Open Easter–Oct daily except Mondays, booking essential for weekends
Admission: adult £2.00, child £1.00
&. tours not suitable for the disabled
🚌 advance notice required ✗

► HENFIELD ◄

HENFIELD MUSEUM

Local history and farming museum

Village Hall, High St, Henfield, West Sussex
☎ Henfield (0273) 492546

Small local village life and farming museum. Includes many tools and other objects, largely of Victorian and Edwardian times, from local farmsteads, market gardens and small holdings, in the south west Weald.

In Henfield village (8 miles south of Horsham) on east side of High Street, museum in Village Hall
Open Tues, Thur & Sat 10.00am–12.00 noon, Wed 2.30–4.30pm, Fri 10.30am–12.30pm
Free admission, donations welcome
& there is not enough space for wheelchairs ✗

HENFIELD WOODCRAFT AND CAMPSITE

Craft centre

Harwoods Farm, West End Lane, Henfield, West Sussex BN5 9RF
☎ Henfield (0273) 492820

Specialist turner of bowls and platters in English hard woods. Camp site opened 1964, sheltered and peaceful. No youth groups; tents and motor caravans only. Limited fishing. Walking.

In High Street turn opposite White Hart pub into Church Street, continue for 2 miles, farm at end of road and farm lane, dead end
Open all year by appointment for the woodwork
Free admission
& unsuitable for wheelchairs ✗

WOODS MILL COUNTRYSIDE CENTRE

Wildlife reserve with country walks

Sussex Wildlife Trust, Woods Mill, Henfield, West Sussex BN5 9SD
☎ Brighton (0273) 492630

A wildlife and countryside exhibition housed in an 18th century watermill. Nature trail through 15 acres of varied habitat: woods, meadow, marsh, lake. Wide range of events. Refreshments weekends and Bank Holidays.

1½ miles south of Henfield, on the A2037
Opening times, please telephone for details before a visit
Admission on weekdays: adult £1.20, child 60p; weekends: adult £1.60, child 80p
& ✗

▶ *HORAM* ◀

SUSSEX FARM MUSEUM & NATURE TRAILS

Country walk, interpretation centre, farming museum, farm trail & farm visit

Horam Manor Estate, Heathfield, East Sussex TN21 0JB
☎ Horam Road (04353) 2597/3161

An interesting group of barns surrounding a typical 18th century yard. A good display of carts and implements, with farmhouse artefacts. Working blacksmith and other crafts are now established. Refreshments.

Off the A267, midway between Heathfield and Hailsham
Open April–Oct daily 10.00am–5.00pm
Admission for museum: adult £1.60, child 80p; nature trails: adult 40p, child 20p
& ⊞ ✗

▶ *HORSHAM* ◀

HORSHAM MUSEUM

Museum

9 The Causeway, Horsham, West Sussex RH12 1HE

Housed in a 16th century timber-framed building, collections include Japanese bronzes, 18th century mousetraps, a Blacksmith's shop and an unusual flower garden.

Town centre
Open Tues–Sat 10.00am–5.00pm
Free admission
& the nature of the building does not offer good access ✗

LEONARDSLEE GARDENS

Country gardens

Lower Beeding, Horsham, West Sussex RH13 6PP
☎ Lower Beeding (0403) 891212

Grade I listed valley garden with rhododendrons and azaleas along a series of lakes, rock garden. Wallabies and deer park. Restaurant. Plants for sale.

5 miles south east of Horsham at jct of the A279 and the A281, or 3 miles south west of Handcross at bottom of the M23 via the A279
Open 13 April–16 June daily 10.00am–6.00pm, then all weekends 12.00–6.00pm, Oct 10.00am–5.00pm
Admission: May £3.00, May Sun & Bank Holiday Mondays £3.50; April, June & Oct £2.50; July, Aug & Sept £2.00
& ⊞ advance notice required ✗

► **HOVE** ◄

WEST BLATCHINGTON WINDMILL

Windmill and museum

Holmes Avenue, Hove, East Sussex
☎ Brighton (0273) 776017

Smock mill c. 1820. Unusual and attractive 6-sided wooden tower built on earlier square flint/brick base. Much or original machinery and timber survive. Many features of industrial archaeological interest.

Due north of the A27 at top of Holmes Ave or due south of London–Brighton road via Mill Road–King George VI Ave
Open May–Sept Sundays & Bank Holidays, 2.30–5.00pm
Admission: adult 50p, child 25p
& toilet facilities available 🚌 🐴

► **LAMBERHURST** ◄

BARTLEY MILL

Farm shop, farm trail, craft shops, working watermill with children's trout fishing

Bells Yew Green, nr Frant, East Sussex TN3 8BH
☎ Lamberhurst (0892) 890372

Bartley Mill is a 13th century working watermill milling/organic grain in the traditional methods. Additional points of interest include tea rooms with garden and a trout hatchery.

To Lamberhurst on the A21 London–Hastings road. In Lamberhurst turn onto the B2169 road to Frant, after 3 miles turn left, after ¼ mile Bartley Mill is on the right hand side
Open daily 10.00am–6.00pm
Admission: adult £1.50, child/OAP £1.00
& 🚌 advance notice required 🐴

► **LANCING** ◄

COOMBES FARM TOURS

Farm visit and trail

Church Farm, Coombes, Lancing, Sussex BN15 0RS
☎ Shoreham By Sea (0273) 452028

Tractor and trailer rides over 1000 acres in the environmental sensitive area of South

Downs through cattle and sheep, cornfields and conservation areas. See the working dew pond.

Off the A27, 2 miles north of Lancing College at Coombes
Open March–Oct daily, please book by telephone
Admission: adult £2.00, child £1.25, OAP/student £1.75
& 🚌 advance notice required 🍴

► **LEWES** ◄

BENTLEY WILDFOWL AND MOTOR MUSEUM

Country gardens and wildfowl

Halland, nr Lewes, East Sussex BN8 5AF
☎ Halland (0825 84) 573

House and gardens. Art and antique collections; motor museum; wildfowl reserve with rare and beautiful birds; picnic and play area; tearoom. Free parking. Small animal section. Gift shop.

Signposted off the A22 and the A26, 7½ miles north east of Lewes
Open mid March–Oct 10.30am–5.00pm
Admission: adult £2.80, child £1.30, OAP £2.00
& 🚌 🐴

E & I FURNITURE MAKERS

Craft centre, hand made furniture and turnings

Ailies Buildings, Whitesmith Lane, East Hoathly, Lewes, East Sussex BN8 6QP
☎ Chiddingly (0825) 872527

The workshops produce hardwood furniture. A partnership between designer and craftsman – will design and make most things to suit a customer's requirements.

Off the A22 at Whitesmith, 7 miles north east of Lewes
Open all year Mon–Sat 9.00am–5.30pm
Free admission
& 🐴

MARY POTTER STUDIO

Craft centre

Hunters Wood, Laughton, Lewes, East Sussex BN8 6DE
☎ Halland (082584) 438

Studio sells batik, pictures, collages, scarves and cards.

1 mile north of the A273, turn at Roebuck Inn, or
    1½ miles east of the A22, turn at Halland
    crossroads
Open most times
Free admission
& ✗

WENDY BRANDON

Speciality food producer – chutneys

The Old Cowshed, Stonecross Farm, Laughton, nr Lewes,
    East Sussex BN8 6BN
☎ Ripe (032 183) 635 or Brighton (0273) 506863

*A range of handmade preserves – jams,
jellies, chutneys, fruit sauces and sharp
chunky marmalades cooked here. Some of
them are made without salt or added sugar.*

7 miles north east of Lewes on the B2124, at first
    crossroads to east of Laughton village
Open by appointment
Free admission
& ✗

► **MADEHURST** ◄

FAIRMILE BOTTOM PICNIC SITE

Country walk and nature trails

Madehurst, West Sussex
☎ Littlehampton (0903) 715244

*This is an area of woodland and typical open
chalk downland exhibiting a wide variety of
trees, shrubs and wild flowers typical of the
South Downs – especially in early summer.
Refreshments.*

On the A29, 2 miles north east of the village of
    Slindon
Open all year
Free admission
& ⚅ ♞

► **NEWICK** ◄

FLEXERNE VINEYARD

Vineyard

Fletching Common, Newick, East Sussex BN8 4JJ
☎ Newick (082 572) 2548

*Established in 1963 on a south facing
sheltered site of 5 acres. Muller Thurgau*

*vines are grown on the double guyot system.
The wines are produced by High Weald
Winery.*

Midway between Haywards Heath and Uckfield,
    north off the A272 at Newick
Open May–Nov by appointment
Admission: £2.00 per person, children free
& ⚅ by arrangement ♞

► **NUTBOURNE** ◄

NUTBOURNE MANOR VINEYARD

**Farm shop, farm visit, country walks, lakes and
vineyard**

Nutbourne, Pulborough, West Sussex RH20 2HE
☎ West Chiltington (07983) 3554

*Producing some of the finest wines in the
UK. Marvellous views to the South Downs.
See how vines are grown in England today.*

Either via the A29 Billingshurst–Pulborough road,
    signposted Gay St, Nutbourne village, OR via the
    A283 Pulborough signposted West Chiltington–
    Nutbourne, first turning right after garage and
    pub in village of Nutbourne
Open June–Oct Wed–Sun 10.00am–5.00pm
Free admission for private family visits, charge for parties
& ⚅ advance notice required ♞

► **NUTLEY** ◄

WILLOWDOWN DAIRY GOATS

Special foods – dairy goats

Humphreys Farm, Nutley, Uckfield, East Sussex TN22 3LS

*Pedigree British Saaren goats are originally
fed on a free range system. Fresh and frozen
milk, yoghurt, soft cheeses and hard cheeses
are produced on the farm.*

On the A22, 4 miles north of Uckfield just south of
    Nutley village
Open daily
Free admission
& ✗

► PETWORTH ◄

NOAH'S FARMYARD

Childrens farm visit

Grittenham Farm, Tillington, Petworth, West Sussex
GU28 0PG
☎ Lodsworth (07985) 264

The 'hands-on' approach to animals. Get in with, stroke and feed the lambs, calves, guinea pigs, chickens and ducks, sit on the Shetland ponies. Short nature trail to river and picnic area.

Midway between Midhurst and Petworth on the
A272
Open daily April–Oct 10.30am–6.30pm
Admission: adult £1.85, child £1.15, OAP £1.35
&. 🚌 ✗

► PEVENSEY ◄

SHARNFOLD FARM

Pick your own

Hailsham Rd, Stone Cross, Pevensey, East Sussex
BN24 5BU
☎ Eastbourne (0323) 768490

A medium sized pick your own farm. Telephone to check availability of produce.

Situated on the B2104, Stone Cross–Hailsham road,
½ mile from Stone Cross, 3 miles from
Eastbourne town centre
Open June–Sept 9.30am–6.00pm
Free admission
&. 🚌 advance notice required 🐕

► POLEGATE ◄

WILMINGTON PRIORY

Farming museum and country garden

Wilmington, Polegate, East Sussex BN26 5SW
☎ Alfriston (0323) 870537

12th century Benedictine Priory and Tudor Farmhouse, now incorporating an agricultural museum, a restored Tudor kitchen, and a large garden. Overlooking the Priory is the Long Man hill figure.

Wilmington is 2½ miles west of Polegate on the
A27. The priory is south of the main road on the
road to Littlington. The car park is 100 metres
south of the priory with toilets and view of the
Long Man
Open March–Oct weekdays (except Tues) 11.00am–
5.30pm, Sun 2.00–5.30pm
Admission: adult £1.00, child 50p
&. ✗

► RINGMER ◄

RAYSTED CENTRE FOR ANIMAL WELFARE

Animal rescue centre

Ringmer, nr Lewes, East Susex BN8 5AJ
☎ Halland (082584) 252/409

40 acre wildlife sanctuary with lakes where wild fowl live in natural but protected surroundings. Shop.

On the B2192
Open daily 9.00am–4.00pm
Free admission
&. 🚌 🐕

► ROBERTSBRIDGE ◄

SEDLESCOMBE VINEYARD

Wine shop, vineyard trail and wooded walk plus wine tasting

Robertsbridge, East Sussex TN32 5SA
☎ Staplecross (058083) 715

Organic wines, some imported

8 miles north of Hastings on the A229, 1½ miles
north of village of Sedlescombe
Open May–Sept daily 10.00am–6.00pm; Oct–April
weekends only 12.00–5.00pm
Admission: adult £1.75, child free
&. 🚌 advance notice required 🐕

► ROWLAND'S CASTLE ◄

THE POTTERY AT STANSTED PARK

Pottery shop and workshop

Cinnabar Ling, The Pottery, Holme Farm, Stansted Park,
Rowland's Castle PO9 6DT
☎ Compton (0705) 413129

Handthrown stoneware pottery in a rural setting on the edge of Stansted Forest. Visits to the workshop by appointment only.

7 miles north west of Chichester on road past Stansted House and Park, adjacent to Stansted sawmills. Stansted Park lies immediately east of Rowland's Castle village which is off the B2149
Open Mon–Sat 9.30am–5.00pm
Free admission
  advance notice required 🛏

▶   *SEAFORD*   ◀

THE LIVING WORLD

Natural history exhibition

Seven Sisters Country Park, Exceat, nr Seaford, East Sussex BN25 4AD
☎ Alfriston (0323) 870 100

Display of exotic and native creatures, living exhibit include giant silkmoths, tropical butterflies, praying mantids, tarantulas, bees, marine and fresh water aquaria.

On the A259, 5 miles west of Eastbourne, 2 miles east of Seaford
Open Easter–Nov daily 10.00am–5.00pm, weekends in winter and school holidays
Admission: adult £2.00, child uner 16/OAP £1.20, child under 5 free
  🛏

▶   *SELSEY*   ◀

COMPTONS FARM SHOP

Farm shop

Chichester Rd, Selsey, West Sussex PO20 9DX
☎ Selsey (0243) 605455

Fruit, vegetables, free range eggs, Jersey milk and cream, ice cream and sundries. Ample parking.

1 mile north of village on the B2145
Open all year 10.00am–6.00pm, Sat 9.00am–6.00pm
Free admission
  🛏

▶   *SOUTHWATER*   ◀

SOUTHWATER COUNTRY PARK

Country park

Cripplegate Lane, Southwater, West Sussex RH13 7XA
☎ Southwater (0403) 731218

Opened in 1985, this former brickworks site is now a popular area for a variety of recreational activities, and is an increasingly important site for wildlife. Fishing, picnic area, guided walks.

Off the A24, 3 miles south of Horsham
Open all year
Free admission
  by prior booking 🛏

▶   *STEYNING*   ◀

STEYNING VINEYARD

Vineyard

Horsham Rd, Steyning, West Sussex BN4 3AA
☎ Steyning (0903) 814988

Taste Nash English wine at the Country Hotel or on the terrace overlooking the lake on the edge of the South Downs. Learn about growing grapes and making wine. Shop.

On the B2135 west of Steyning and off the A283 bypass
Open daily 10.30am–6.00pm
Free admission
  advance notice required 🍴

▶   *UCKFIELD*   ◀

BEECHES FARM

Country garden

Buckham Hill, nr Uckfield, East Sussex TN22 5XZ
☎ Uckfield 2391

Elizabethan farmhouse, open by appointment only. Teas provided if required.

On the Isfield road from centre of Uckfield, approx 1½ miles with no turnings, entrance on left
Open all year 10.00am–dusk
Admission: adult 50p, child 15p
  advance notice required 🛏

WILDERNESS WOOD

Country walk, forestry centre, woodland trail and picnic place

Hadlow Down, nr Uckfield, East Sussex TN22 4HJ
☎ Hadlow Down (082585) 509

Family-run working wood in the heart of the Sussex Weald. Woodland trail, picnic and play areas, barbecues. Spring bluebell walk. Wooden barn with displays. Wood products on sale. Refreshments available summer weekends.

On the A272, 5 miles east of Uckfield, in Hadlow Down village
Open daily 10.00am–dusk
Admission: adult £1.00, child (3–15yrs) 50p, OAP 80p (1990 prices)
& ⛟ advance notice required ⛥

► **WISBOROUGH GREEN** ◄

CHEESEMANS

Country walk, pottery for sale

Brick Kiln Common, Wisborough Green, West Sussex RH14 0HZ
☎ Wisborough Green (0403) 700481

Pottery for sale and can be seen in the making.

From Petworth take the A272 towards Billingshurst, second turn on right, right at T junction, right again at sign 'Brick Kiln Common' then to end of lane and car park
Open daily
Free admission
& ⛥

► **WORTHING** ◄

HOLLY GATE CACTUS NURSERY

Cactus nursery and garden

Billinghurst Rd, Ashington, West Sussex RH20 3BA
☎ Worthing (0903) 892930

20,000 exotic plants displayed in the cactus garden enclosed in a large glasshouse. Thousands of plants for sale including cactus, succulents, alpines and geraniums plus books, cards and handicrafts.

10 miles north of Worthing, from the A24 bear left onto the B2133 to Adversane, nursery is ½ mile along on the right
Open daily 9.00am–5.00pm
Admission: adult £1.00, child/OAP 75p (charge to garden only)
& ⛟ advance notice required ⛥

TYNE AND WEAR

Tyne & Wear, an industrial heartland and a very densely populated part of the country still retains many wooded valleys to the east, many are being preserved. Hadrian's Wall, a spectacular relic of Roman Britain, ends here, another reminder of the region's rich and colourful past. The coastline has low, rocky cliffs and long, sandy beaches with several popular resorts.

For a taste of the countryside there are farm shops and pick-your-own options with a wide range of produce including organic cheese, homemade dairy ice cream, and a full selection of soft fruits. A taste of history is provided by a castle, manor house and hall with formal gardens.

▶ NEWCASTLE-UPON-TYNE ◀

BELSAY HALL, CASTLE AND GARDENS

Historic hall and castle and country gardens

Belsay, Newcastle-upon-Tyne, NE20 0DX
☎ Belsay (0661 881) 636

14th century castle, 17th century manor house, 19th century hall. 30 acres of landscaped grounds with formal, winter, meadow and quarry gardens. Shop and exhibition. High Sheriff's coach.

Belsay is 14 miles north west of Newcastle, on the A696 to Jedburgh

Open: Good Friday or 1 April (whichever is earlier) to 30 Sept daily 10.00am–6.00pm; 1 October to Maundy Thursday or 31 March (whichever is earlier) Tues to Sat 10.00am–4.00pm (closed Mondays in winter season)

Admission: adult £1.70, child 85p, OAP/UB40 £1.30 special reduction for parties

& (3 wheelchairs for free hire)

🚐 🦮 in grounds only

MILBOURNE FARM FRUIT

Farm shop, pick your own, farm animals and picnic area

East Town Farm, Milbourne, Ponteland, Newcastle-upon-Tyne NE20 0EE
☎ Belsay (0661 881) 278

Strawberries, with a full selection of the best varieties, together with raspberries, gooseberries, black and red currants. Also early plums and apples and a wide range of summer vegetables.

From Newcastle take the A696, past Newcastle airport, straight through Ponteland and follow signs after 2 miles

Open July, Aug, early Sept, daily 10.00am–7.00pm

Free admission

& 🚐 🦮 but not on fruit fields

Stay on a Farm

Official guide of Farm Holiday Bureau UK

Enjoy the unique hospitality of a working farm. Over 950 properties, between them offering bed and breakfast, half-board, self-catering and camping and caravanning.

All inspected and approved by the National Tourist Boards. Published by William Curtis.

£4.95. Available from all good bookshops.

WARWICKSHIRE

Warwickshire's gentle green countryside seems untouched by time. The River Avon flows in a broad peaceful willow-lined valley through pastureland that has changed little since Shakespeare's day. The Forest of Arden, north of Stratford-upon-Avon, was the setting for Shakespeare's 'As You Like It', little of the forest remains today but there are wooded walks along the river bank that take the walker near places associated with Shakespeare's life.

A haven for country lovers, there are many delightful walks, through parks, along canals and across farmland. When you stop you might peruse the work of local artisans at work, potters, sculptors or artists, or perhaps visit the National Centre for Organic Gardening, a folk and farming museum, a speciality food producer, a watermill, a falconry centre, one of the farm parks or even a butterfly farm and safari park – they can all be found in the Warwickshire countryside.

► **ALCESTER** ◄

RAGLEY HALL

Historic house and grounds

Alcester, Warwickshire B49 5NJ

☎ Alcester (0789) 7620900

Set within beautiful gardens and parkland Ragley is filled with important collections of furniture, paintings and china. It possesses England's finest Baroque plasterwork. Woodland walk and adventure playground.

2 miles south west of Alcester on the Birmingham–Alcester–Evesham road (A435), 8 miles from Stratford-upon-Avon
Open April–Sept, please telephone for more details
Admission to house & grounds: adult £3.50, child/OAP £2.50; grounds: adult £2.50, child £1.50, OAP and party rate £2.50
& toilet, gift shop, tea rooms and gardens may be entered via level access with no steps ᙠ ᛏ

► **BEDWORTH** ◄

BEDWORTH SLOUGHS LOCAL NATURE RESERVE

Nature reserve

Leisure and Amenities Division, Nuneaton & Bedworth Borough Council, Coton Rd, Nuneaton, Warwickshire CV11 5AA

☎ Nuneaton (0203) 376376

Former Site of Special Scientific Interest, but now preserved under a Local Nature Reserve status by the Borough Council. Small urban wetland now maintained informally for the benefit of flora and fauna.

Car park off Newtown Road, ½ mile west of Bedworth town centre
Open at all times
Free admission
& ᙠ advance notice required, parking restricted ᛏ

► **COVENTRY** ◄

COOMBE ABBEY COUNTRY PARK

Country park, walk and garden

Brinklow Rd, Binley, nr Coventry CV3 2AB
☎ Coventry (0203) 453720

A haven for lovers of the countryside, featuring walks and a good fishery. Well signposted. Telephone for more information.

Take the A427 Coventry–Brinklow road. Signposted from the M6, the M69, the A45 and the A46 Coventry eastern by pass
Open daily 9.00am–dusk
Admission: car parking charge only
& ᙠ advance notice preferred ᛏ

PAUL GANDY CERAMICS

Craft centre – ceramics

Marton Farm House, Marton, nr Rugby, Warwickshire CV23 9RH

☎ Marton (0926) 632923

Highly individual architectural and landscape studies conditioned by the pottery techniques used. Stoneware fired, matt glazed and double dipped for 'graphic' surface. Comissions: Dept of Environment, Victoria and Albert Museum.

10 miles south of Coventry on the A423 Coventry–Banbury road. Property on village's main road
Open by appointment only
Free admission
& ᙠ advance notice required ᛏ

RYTON GARDENS

Organic gardening centre with country walks

National Centre for Organic Gardening, Ryton-on-Dunsmore, Coventry CV8 3LG

☎ Coventry (0203) 303517

Ryton Gardens is home of the Channel 4 TV series 'All Muck and Magic?' Extensive organic demonstration gardens; award winning cafe and shop; flowers, herbs, vegetables and fruit. Guided tours. Entry tickets valid for a whole year.

On the B4029, signposted off the A45, 5 miles south east of Coventry
Open April–Sept 10.00am–6.00pm; Oct–March 10.00am–4.00pm
Admission: adult £2.00, child/OAP £1.00, reduced rates for parties
& ᙠ advance notice required �

RYTON POOL PICNIC AREA

Picnic area

Ryton-on-Dunsmore, nr Coventry, Warwickshire
☎ Marton (0926) 410410 ext 2342

Picnic area with adventure playground.

Off the A445, 5 miles east of Leamington Spa
Open daily dawn–dusk
Admission: entrance and car parking free
&. 🚌 🐾 under control

► KENILWORTH ◄

FAT HEN FRUIT

Pick your own

Fat Hen Fruit Farm, Rouncil Lane, Kenilworth,
Warwickshire CV8 1NN
☎ Haseley Knob (0926) 484433

2 miles out of Kenilworth on the Beausale road
Open during soft fruit season ususally end June–mid
August, daily 10.00am–8.00pm
Free admission
&. except for toilet facilities 🐾

► LEAMINGTON SPA ◄

CHURCH LEYES FARM

Farm visit – organic farm

Napton on the Hill, nr Rugby, Warwickshire CV23 8NR
☎ Southam (0926 81) 2143

*A 40 acre mixed farm on top of a hill
overlooking south Warwickshire and the
surrounding 7 counties. A photographers'
and artists' paradise. Special interest wild
gardens and conservation areas. School
parties very welcome.*

½ mile off the A425, 10 miles east of Leamington
Spa and 7 miles west of Daventry, situated
between the church and the windmill
Open every Sunday May–Sept (except 19 May 1991)
11.00am–5.00pm. Educational and conservation parties
throughout year by appointment only. Appointments
can be made between 7.00 and 9.00pm Mon–Thur
Admission: adult £1.00, child (4–16 years) 25p, OAP
75p. Party rates on application
&. every assistance offered. We welcome able bodied
mentally handicapped of all ages
🚌 mini coaches only allowed 🐾

► MARKET BOSWORTH ◄

BOSWORTH CRAFTS

Craft centre and leather workshop

23 Main St, Market Bosworth, Nuneaton, Warwickshire
CV13 0JN
☎ Market Bosworth (0455) 292061

*Small country craft shop and workshop,
producing high quality leather goods, many
of which are hand carved. Other crafts
include pottery, jewellery, turned wooden
items etc.*

Midway between Coalville and Hinkley (A447), turn
off onto the B585 to Market Bosworth
Open Jan–April: 9.00am–5.15pm, Sat 10.00am–1.00pm;
May–Dec: 9.00am–5.15pm, Sat 10.00am–5.15pm
Free admission
&. 🐾

► NUNEATON ◄

JOHN LETTS SCULPTURES

Sculptor's studio

The Old School, Church Lane, Astley, Nuneaton,
Warwickshire CV7 8EW
☎ Fillongley (0676) 42073

*Original and limited edition works by John
Letts and Keith Lee on sale at the studio.
John Letts is the creator of the George Eliot
statue in Nuneaton town centre, and
'Neptune' at the Hinkley Island Hotel.*

3 miles south of Nuneaton from the B4112 follow
the B4102 Meriden road to Astley crossroads,
turn right 200 yards on right
Open Mon–Sat 10.00am–6.00pm, Sundays by prior
arrangement
Free admission
&. 🚌 advance notice required 🐾

WALKS AROUND CALDECOTE

Country walk

Leisure and Amenities Dept, Nuneaton & Bedworth
Borough Council, Coton Rd, Nuneaton, Warwickshire
CV11 5AA
☎ Nuneaton (0203) 376376

A 4 mile circular walk comprises farmland, canal towpath, public open space and a disused railway line. Features of interest include Caldecote church, disused windmill, a nature reserve and interesting view over a large granite quarry.

Car park available at Poor's Piece nature reserve, 1 mile north west of Nuneaton town centre off Manchester Road, and at Sandon Park, Shawe Ave, Weddington
Walk open at all times. Nature reserve by permit
Free admission
& ▥ with advance notice but parking restricted 🐾

WALKS AROUND CHILVERS COTON

Country walk/town centre walk

Leisure and Amenities Dept, Nuneaton & Bedworth Borough Council, Coton Rd, Nuneaton, Warwickshire CV11 5AA
☎ Nuneaton (0203) 376376

Circular walk of approximately 3 miles through formal gardens, open space and aloong the Coventry Canal – the old parish boundary where the famous Victorian novelist George Eliot (Mary Anne Evans) spent much of her early life.

Car parking available at short and long stay car parks (pay and display) within the town centre (free on Sundays)
Free admission
& ▥ 🐾

WALKS AROUND GALLEY COMMON

Country walk

Leisure and Amenities Dept, Nuneaton & Bedworth Borough Council, Coton Rd, Nuneaton, Warwickshire CV11 5AA
☎ Nuneaton (0203) 376376

An open country walk through farmland, taking in a small oak woodland, a herb-rich ridge and furrow meadow, and informal public open space with a small lake and meandering stream.

Car parking available at Galley Gap public house, Kingswood Rd, Nuneaton
Open at all times
Free admission
& ▥ 🐾

WALKS AROUND WEDDINGTON

Country walk

Leisure and Amenities Dept, Nuneaton & Bedworth Borough Council, Coton Rd, Nuneaton, Warwickshire CV11 5AA
☎ Nuneaton (0203) 376376

Circular walk of approximately 3 miles or linear walk of approximately 1½ miles. Through farmland, public open space, and along a disused railway encompassing the area around Weddington.

Car parking in layby off the A444, 1 mile north of Nuneaton and at Sandon Park, end of Shawe Ave
Open at all times
Free admission
& ▥ with advance notice but parking restricted 🐾

WALKS AROUND WHITTLEFORD PARK

Country walk

Leisure and Amenities Dept, Nuneaton & Bedworth Borough Council, Coton Rd, Nuneaton, Warwickshire CV11 5AA
☎ Nuneaton (0203) 376376

The park covers approx 74 acres and contains 2½ miles of surfaced footpaths. A former derelict area of brick and tile works, which has been restored to an attractive, natural looking park using recolonized species, creating a variety of habitat types.

Car park off Queen Elizabeth Rd, 1 mile west of Nuneaton town centre
Open at all times
Free admission
& ▥ with advance notice but parking restricted 🐾

► *RUGBY* ◄

DRAYCOTE WATER COUNTRY PARK

Country park

Nr Dunchurch, Warwickshire
☎ Warwick (0926) 412342

21 acre park overlooking reservoir, waterside picnicking, adventure playground.

Off the A426, 4 miles south of Rugby
Open dawn–dusk daily
Free admission, car parking 50p, coaches £2.50
& ✗

MUSEUM OF COUNTRY BYGONES TRUST

Folk and farming museum

Louisa Ward Close, off High St, Marton, nr Rugby,
Warwickshire CV23 9RP
☎ Marton (0926) 633361

Rare display of domestic paraphernalia and farmworkers implements. Large selection of the hand tools of the wheelwright and carpenter, shepherd, thatcher, poacher and saddler with heavy horse harness on display.

Equal distances between Rugby, Coventry and
Leamington Spa on the A423 between
Princethorpe and Long Itchington, 4 miles north
of Southam
Open Easter–Oct daily incl Sundays and Bank Holidays
10.00am–8.00pm. Parties by appointment, either by
letter or telephone please
Admission: adult 50p, child/OAP 25p
⅃ ♿ 🐾

PAILTON STUDIO POTTERY

Pottery studio

12 Lutterworth Rd, Pailton, Rugby, Warwickshire
CV23 0QE
☎ Rugby (0788) 832064

Stoneware pottery made on the premises. Tea, coffee, dinner and wine sets, plant holders, storage jars, ornaments. Some items can be made to order, and some personalised. Also prints and paintings.

In the centre of Pailton village, next to the Post
Office on the A427 Coventry–Market Harborough
road
Open daily, Mon, Tues, Wed and Fri 9.30am–6.00pm;
Thur 12.00–6.00pm; Sat 3.30–6.30pm; Sun 11.30am–
6.30pm
Free admission
⅃ ♿ advance notice required 🐾

▶ *STRATFORD-UPON-AVON* ◀

CHARLECOTE PARK – NATIONAL TRUST

Country house and deer park

Warwick CV35 9ER
☎ Stratford-upon-Avon (0789) 470277

Home of the Lucy family since 1247, altered in the 19th century. Richly decorated and furnished principal rooms, fine carriage collection, Victorian kitchen and brewhouse. Capability Brown gardens and parkland. National Trust shop and restaurant.

5 miles east of Stratford-upon-Avon, off the B4086
Open Easter Sat–30 Oct Tues and Wed, Fri–Sun and
Bank Holiday Mondays 11.00am–6.00pm
Admission: £3.00 per person, family ticket (2 adults & up
to 4 children) £8.30 (1990 prices)
⅃ ♿ advance notice required. Weekday concessions
🐾 except guide dogs

THE DEFINE ART GALLERY

Art gallery, demonstrations by artist

Newbold-on-Stour, Stratford-upon-Avon, Warwickshire
CV37 8TS
☎ Alderminster (078987) 566

The artist/owner of the gallery is in residence to make and demonstrate her very unusual sculptured pictures which are framed by her husband in their workshop on the premises.

On the Stratford–Oxford road, 6 miles south of
Stratford
Open all year round. Please telephone to ensure that the
artist is at the studio/gallery
Free admission
⅃ ♿ advance notice required 🐾

HATHAWAY COTTAGE CRAFTS

Craft centre and craft demonstrations

Anne Hathaway's Cottage, Shottery, Stratford-upon-Avon,
Warwickshire
☎ Stratford (0789) 292100 ext 14

The centre was established 8 years ago to promote and encourage local craftworkers, and provide visitors with a much-appreciated selection of worthwhile gifts, handmade in the Heart of England.

Shottery is 1 mile west of Stratford. The cottage is
well signposted
Open April–Sept Mon–Sat 9.00am–6.00pm; Sun
10.00am–6.00pm
Admission to the craft centre is free, but there is an
admission charge to Anne Hathaway's Cottage
⅃ ♿ 🐾

HEART OF ENGLAND FALCONRY

Falconry centre

Mary Arden's House, Wilmcote

Flying displays of hawks, falcons and owls every day. Half day courses available at short notice. Winter hawking parties. Audience participation welcomed.

3 miles north west of Stratford
Open 25 March–27 Oct 9.00am–6.00pm; 28 Oct–24 March Mon–Sat 9.00am–4.30pm
Admission: adult £2.00, child 80p
& ⛟ ✕

PETER DINGLEY GALLERY

Craft gallery

8 Chapel St, Stratford-upon-Avon, Warwickshire CV37 3EP
☎ Stratford-upon-Avon (0789) 205001

One-man exhibitions in spring and autumn, the work of 10 potters in summer, varied craftwork always on show. Gallery was one of the first in the country to specialize in British work.

Opposite Shakespeare Hotel in the centre of Stratford
Open daily (except Sun and Thur afternoons) 9.30am–1.30pm and 2.30–5.30pm
Free admission
& every assistance offered ✕

STRATFORD-UPON-AVON BUTTERFLY FARM AND JUNGLE SAFARI

Butterfly farm

The Tramway, Swans Nest Lane, Stratford-upon-Avon, Warwickshire CV37 7LS
☎ Stratford-upon-Avon (0789) 299288

Up to 1000 free-flying tropical and European butterflies, birds and other exotic creatures. Insect city features the world's largest spider. Wildlife gift shop, regular video showings, full educational service, teachers telephone for free education pack.

On the south side of the river Avon but within Stratford itself. Nearest major road is the A34 from Oxford
Open March–end Nov daily 10.00am–6.00pm; Dec–Feb 10.00am–dusk, closed Christmas Eve and Christmas Day

Admisssion: adult £2.50, child/OAP £1.75, family ticket £6.50. Group rates available
& except for toilet facilities
⛟ advance notice required ✕

WELLESBOURNE WATERMILL

Watermill, craft centre, speciality food producer

Mill Farm, Kineton Rd, Wellesbourne, Warwickshire CV35 9HG
☎ Stratford-upon-Avon (0789) 470237

Wellesbourne Watermill produces stoneground flour again after a break of 50 years. The public can see the dramatic waterwheel and machinery in action. Picnic watermeadows, farm animals, local crafts.

Off the B4086 Wellesbourne–Kineton road, 6 miles east of Stratford-upon-Avon
Open Easter–30 Sept, Thur–Sun and Bank Holidays 11.00am–4.30pm. Oct–March 1992 Sunday afternoons (this has yet to be confirmed)
Admission: adult £1.50, child/OAP £1.00 (1990 prices)
& access to mill grounds
⛟ advance notice required ✕

► *TYSOE* ◄

MEG RIVERS CAKES

Speciality food producer

Main St, Middle Tysoe, Warwickshire CV35 0SE
☎ Tysoe (0295 88) 8101

Unique cottage-style bakery in a picturesque village typifying an era synonymous with the cake production and presentation. Top quality fruit cakes by mail order, small shop. Small groups by arrangement.

Off the A422 Banbury–Stratford road and on the Warwickshire, Cotswolds Leisure Drive
Open Mon–Sat 10.00am–4.00pm
Free admission
& ✕

► *WARWICK* ◄

HATTON COUNTRY WORLD

Farm park, craft village, cafe, farm shop, garden centre, animal shop, pick your own, farm trails

Georges Farm, Hatton, Warwick CV35 8XA
☎ Claverdon (0926 84) 2436/3411

*A day of rural delight including Craft
Centre of the Year (30 workshops) and farm
park with displays of rare breeds, antique
agricultural machinery, wild flowers and an
adventure playground.*

Signposted from the A4177 Warwick–Birmingham
  road, 3 miles north of Warwick
Open for the farm park spring–autumn; PYO in season;
  others 7 days a week all year
Admission: farm park approx £2.00; others free
&. ⚌ ⋔

WINDMILL FARM SALES

Farm visit and farm shop

Windmill House Farm, Hatton, nr Warwick CV35 7HU
☎ Haseley Knob (0926) 484216

*Sale of farm fresh eggs, Jersey milk and
cream, other dairy products, fresh fruit and
vegetables, honey and preserves, table
poultry, meat for freezing, flowers and
plants.*

4 miles north of Warwick, 1 mile west of the A41
  Warwick–Birmingham road adjacent to the
  Shrewley/Five Ways traffic island road
Open every Sunday except the first Sunday after
  Christmas, 10.00am–1.00pm
Free admission
&. ⚌ ⋔

► WHICHFORD ◄

WHICHFORD POTTERY

Craft centre – pottery

Whichford, Shipston-on-Stour, Warwickshire CV36 5PG
☎ (0608) 84416

*Specializes in making frost-proof handmade
teracotta flowerpots – from plain seedpans to
vast Baroque urns.*

Turn off the A34 at Long Compton, Whichford is
  2½ miles on. Pottery is on the left as you enter
  Whichford
Open all year Mon–Fri 9.00am–5.00pm, Sat & Bank
  Holidays 10.00am–5.00pm
Free admission
&. every assistance offered
⚌ advance notice required ⋔

WEST MIDLANDS

The West Midlands, once thick woodland, is now dominated by the industrial city of Birmingham. As it has grown Birmingham has blended old and new. It is the centre of Britains's canal system and has over 6000 acres of parks and open spaces. The West Midlands offers many opportunities for the country lover to explore and enjoy.

There are water parks to wander and country parks to roam, nature centres, rare breed centres, museums, potteries, stained glass workshops and farms to visit and local wines, ice creams and other fresh local produce to sample.

▶ BIRMINGHAM ◀

A E BECKETT & SONS LTD

Farm shop, bakery and pick your own

Heath Farm, Wythall, Birmingham B47 6AJ
☎ Wythall (0564) 823402 Fax (0564) 826848

Award-winning farm shop, bakery and pick your own.

1 mile north on the A435 from jct 3 on the M42, situated adjacent to Becketts Island
Open Mon–Fri 8.00am–6.00pm, Sat 8.00am–5.00pm, Sun 9.30am–12.30pm
Free admission
& assistance is offered on a personal basis
🚌 advance notice required ⌁

BIRMINGHAM NATURE CENTRE

Zoo, nature trail and natural history museum

Pershore Rd, Birmingham B5 7RL
☎ Birmingham (021) 472 7775

6 acres comprising natural outdoor enclosures, British wildlife, amphibians and reptiles, bees, butterfly aviary and finch aviary plus local species of plants and animals.

2 miles from Birmingham town centre on the A441. Parallel to Bristol Road section of the A38
Open daily 24 March–4 Nov 10.00am–5.00pm and 10.00am–dusk winter weekends
Free admission
& 🚌 ✖

FRANKLEY LODGE FARM

Dairy farm

Frankley Lodge Rd, Northfield, Birmingham B31 5PZ
☎ Birmingham (021) 475 1609

Visit a working dairy farm. See cows being milked; have a trailer ride to see pigs and horses; feed lambs, calves, ducks, chickens and rabbits. Country walk.

On the A38 Northfield–Frankley Beeches Road–Hoggs Lane, Frankley Lodge Road
Open by appointment only
Admission £2.00 per person, groups of 15–30 people preferred (1990 prices)
& ✖

▶ DUDLEY ◀

COTWALL END NATURE CENTRE

Nature centre with country walks and craft centre

Catholic Lane, Sedgley, Dudley, West Midlands DY3 3YE
☎ (0902) 674668

Domestic and wild native animals house in attractive surroundings. Wooded nature trails in Cotwall End valley and working craft units provide interest for all visitors. A leaflet is available from the above address.

Off the A459, 3 miles north of Dudley, 4 miles south of Wolverhampton
Open all year 9.00am–7.00pm or 4.30pm during winter. Group bookings in advance
Free admission
& 🚌 ⌁

HALFPENNY GREEN VINEYARDS

Vineyard, shop, rare breed centre

Halfpenny Green, Bobbington, Stourbridge, West Midlands DY7 5EP
☎ Bobbington (038 488) 387

Vineyard and visitor centre with wine and gift shop. Lunch and afternoon tea. Guided and unguided tours; rare breeds; childrens play area.

6 miles west of Dudley, ¼ mile off the B4176 following Airport signs
Open 1 Feb–23 Dec, daily (except Mondays) 10.00am–6.00pm
Admission free, £1 per person for unguided vineyard tours
& 🚌 ✖

▶ HENLEY-IN-ARDEN ◀

TORQUIL POTTERY

Pottery workshop, exhibition gallery and shop

81 High St, Henley-in-Arden, Solihull, West Midlands B95 5AT
☎ Henley-in-Arden (05642) 2174

Beautiful Tudor half timbered building probably once a coaching inn and now the home of resident potter Reg Moon. The gallery is used for exhibitions of fine art and craft 2 or 3 times a year.

On the A34, Stratford–Birmingham road, 8 miles north of Stratford

Open all year daily (except Sun and Bank Holidays)
10.00am–6.00pm, workshop by request
Free admission
 ♿ ✈

▶ **NUNEATON** ◀

HARTSHILL HAYES COUNTRY PARK

Woodland walks, visitor centre, cafe

Oldbury Rd, Hartshill Hayes, Nuneaton, West Midlands
☎ Hartshill Hayes (0203) 395141

*Over 100 acres of magnificent woodlands
beneath an open hilltop overlooking 4
counties. Walks leaflets available at the
visitor centre. Walks, picnicking, views,
adventure playground.*

Please telephone for directions
Free admission, car park charge 50p
♿ ✈

▶ **SOLIHULL** ◀

FARMER TED'S EARLSWOOD ICES

**Farm shop, dairy ice cream producer and tea
room**

Manor Farm, Wood Lane, Earlswood, Solihull, West
Midlands B94 5JH
☎ Earlswood (05646) 2729

*Craft workshops open to the public including
upholstery, woodwork, ceramics, embroidery
and stained glass. See the cows being milked
between 4.00–5.00pm; walk round the
adjoining lakes and woods.*

Off the B4102, Solihull–Redditch road at Earlswood
Reservoir Hotel, or 2 miles from M42 jct 3
Shop open all year daily except Mondays 9.00am–
6.00pm. Tea room open weekends and Bank Holidays
Free admission
♿ ⛺ advance notice required ✈

UMBERSLADE FARMS

Farm visit, farm gate sales and country walk

The Leasowes, Tanworth-in-Arden, Solihull, West
Midlands B94 5AE
☎ Tanworth-in-Arden (05644) 2251

*Farm encourages visits by schools and
families with young children, providing them
with the opportunity to get close to farm*

*animals in a genuine farm environment.
Light refreshments available, car park,
playground and picnic area.*

In the village of Tanworth-in-Arden, 8 miles south
west of Solihull
Open April–Oct daily 12.00–6.00pm, groups of 10+ by
appointment only
Admission: £1.30 per person, children under 5 75p,
working farm guided visit £1.85 (minimum group size
15)
♿ ⛺ advance notice required ✈

▶ **TAMWORTH** ◀

KINGSBURY WATER PARK

**Country park, country walks and interpretation
centre**

Bodymoor Heath Lane, Bodymoor Heath, Sutton Coldfield,
West Midlands B76 0DY
☎ Tamworth (0827) 872660

*20 beautiful lakes in 600 landscaped acres,
miles of footpaths through woodland and
meadow. Visitor centre, gift and coffee shop,
sailing, windsurfing and fishing.*

Between the A4097 and the A4091, 6 miles south
of Tamworth, 1 mile from jct 9 of the M42
Open daily, dawn–dusk
Free admission, car parking charge winter 50p, summer
£1.00
♿ ⛺ ✈

▶ **WALSALL** ◀

WALSALL LEATHER CENTRE MUSEUM

Museum

Wisemore, Walsall, West Midlands WS2 8EQ
☎ Walsall (0922) 721153

*Museum housed in a former leather factory
dating from 1891, and tells the story of
Walsall's leather crafts through working
demonstrations and displays of leather goods
past and present. Shop and cafe.*

Off the A34, on the north side of Walsall town
centre
Open April–Oct, Tues–Sat 10.00am–5.00pm, Sun
12.00–5.00pm, Nov–March closes at 4.00pm
Free admission
♿ ⛺ advance notice required ✈

WILTSHIRE

Wiltshire encompasses the vast green expanse of the Salisbury Plain with its famous prehistoric sites in the south, the unspoilt water-meadow landscape of the Lower Avon and the upper reaches of the Thames in the north.

A region rooted in history, it has many historic houses and unusual gardens to tour. There are farming museums and agricultural museums, fish farms and trout lakes, speciality pork producers and vineyards with locally produced wine, working dairy farms and organic farms, a small working pottery and a hand marbling studio, in fact everything a country lover might wish for.

▶ ## BRADFORD-ON-AVON ◀

ELMS CROSS VINEYARD

Vineyard

Bradford-on-Avon, Wiltshire BA15 2AL
☎ Bradford-on-Avon (02216) 6917

4 acres of vineyard, wine made and bottled in the winery adjacent to the vineyard. Individual visitors welcome, free wine tasting.

1 mile from Bradford towards Frome – right fork off the B3109
Open April–Oct; Fri, Sat and Mon. Group visits by appointment only
Free admission for wine shop. Group tour and wine tasting £2.50 per person including slide show on wine production
&. ⊞ advance notice required 🐎

IFORD MANOR GARDENS

Country garden

Iford Manor, Bradford-on-Avon, Wiltshire BA15 2BA
☎ Bradford-on-Avon (02216) 3146

An unusual garden in the Italian style, designed by Harold Pelo, round an old manor house. Romantic riverside setting with terraces, colonnade, statues and a unique cloister.

Off the A36, 7 miles south east of Bath
Open April Sundays and Easter Mon (no teas); May–Sept Tues, Wed, Thur, Fri, Sun and Bank Holiday Mon (teas Sun & Bank Holidays only); Oct Sun (no teas) – 2.00–5.00pm, other times by appointment
Admission: adult £1.00, child/OAP 70p
&. ⊞ advance notice required 🐎

▶ ## CALNE ◀

QUEMERFORD GATE FARM SHOP AND TROUT LAKE

Farm shop, trout lake and craft centre

Cherhill, nr Calne, Chippenham, Wiltshire
☎ Calne (0249) 812388

Farm shop selling a range of fresh meat, vegetables, pet food and bedding plants. Trout and coarse fishing lakes, tackle shop. Tea room, barbecue shelter, animal farm for children.

Take the A4 out of Calne heading towards Marlborough, situated about 2 miles out of Calne
Open all year Mon–Fri 8.00am–6.00pm; Sat 9.00am–5.00pm
Free admission
&. ⊞ advance notice required 🐎

▶ ## CHIPPENHAM ◀

DYRHAM PARK

Historic house and garden, country walk

Dyrham, nr Chippenham, Wiltshire SN14 8ER
☎ Abson (027582) 2501

Mansion built for William Blathwayt between 1691 and 1710; rooms little changed since then. 263 acres of ancient parkland with herd of fallow deer.

8 miles north of Bath on the A46, 12 miles east of Bristol, 2 miles south of Tormarton interchange with M4 exit 18
Open for house & garden: 1 April–4 Nov daily except Thur and Fri, 12.00–5.30pm (last admission 5.00pm); park: all year daily 12.00–5.30pm or dusk if earlier (1990 times)
Admission: house, garden & park: £3.50; park only £1.00. Coaches by appointment
&. ⊞ advance notice required 🐎 park only

LACKHAM COLLEGE

Country garden, country walk, farming museum

Lacock, Chippenham, Wiltshire SN15 2NY
☎ Chippenham (0249) 443111

Museum of farm buildings, machinery and rural life. Woodland and river bank walks, animal centre, gardens; light refreshments and picnic area; adventure playgrounds; souvenir and plant sales.

Off the A350, 3 miles south of Chippenham
Open 1 April–6 Oct 1991 (approx) 11.00am–5.00pm. Last entry 4.00pm
Admission: adult £2.20, child £1.00, OAP £1.50 (1990 prices)
&. ⊞ advance notice preferred

D J & E M RANDOLPH

Pick your own

West Foscote Farm, Grittleton, Chippenham, Wiltshire SN14 6AH
☎ Castle Combe (0249) 782413

An extensive programme of hardwood tree planting has begun, the first 2 hectares having been completed winter 1989. Viewing may be possible by prior arrangement.

Leave town on the A420 Bristol road. First turn right – signposted to Chipping Sodbury and Yatton Keynell. In Yatton Keynell fork right towards Grittleton. Take left turn towards Castle Combe just before bridge over the M4. First farm on right
Open during strawberry season 10.00am–7.30pm daily
Admission and car parking free
& ⊞ ✗

SHELDON MANOR

Country garden and mediaeval manor house

Chippenham, Wiltshire
☎ Chippenham (0249) 653120

700 year old manor house; survivor of a deserted mediaeval village. Much to see inside and out; distinguished catering, and a warm welcome.

From Chippenham, take the A420 Bristol road. Follow signs to Sheldon Manor
Open Sun, Thur and Bank Holidays 12.30–6.00pm.
Parties are welcome at any other time by arrangement
Admission to house and gardens: adult £2.25, child 50p, OAP £2.00; gardens only: adult £1.20, OAP £1.00. Coach parties £2.00 per head
& ⊞ ✗

► DEVIZES ◄

BROADLEAS GARDENS LTD

Country garden

Broadleas, Devizes, Wiltshire SN10 5JQ
☎ Devizes (0380) 722035

8 acres on greensand soil, full of rare and unusual plants; magnolias, azaleas, camellias. Interesting features include the 'Deu' with lush plantings on steep sides of old dry river bed.

1 mile from the centre of Devizes on the A360 to Salisbury. Signed from centre of Devizes
Open April–Oct, Wed, Thur and Sun 2.00–6.00pm
Admission: £1.50 per person, child (under 14) 50p (1990 prices)
& ⊞ ✗

SALLY LEWIS

Small working pottery

Braybrooke Pottery, 17 Andover Rd, Upavon, Pewsey, Wiltshire SN9 6AB
☎ Stonehenge (0980) 630466

Domestic, decorative and commemorative earthenware and stoneware pottery; individually thrown and decorated. Special commissions welcome.

8 miles east of Devizes on the A342 to Andover near intersection with the A345 Marlborough/ Salisbury
Open most times, telephone to confirm
Free admission
& ✗

RUSHALL FARMS

Organically grown flour, cornmill

The Manor, Upavon, Pewsey, Wiltshire SN9 6EB
☎ Stonehenge (0980) 630264

Starting in 1970, Rushall Farm was converted to organic farming by 1985 and now produces some 7–800 tonnes of wholemeal flour each year, also bread and garlic croutons. The largest organic farm in the country.

On the A342, 8 miles east of Devizes, 1 mile west of Upavon. 12 miles from Avebury, 9 miles from Stonehenge
Open all year 7.30am–12.30pm and 1.30–4.30pm
Admission: parties £1.00 per head by appointment at above address
& ⊞ advance notice required ✗

► MARLBOROUGH ◄

CHURCH FARM TROUT

Fish farm shop

Church Farm, Mildenhall, Marlborough, Wiltshire SN8 2LU
☎ Marlborough (0672) 513477

Fresh trout from the Kennet or smoked trout using home grown oak, with a delicate, distinctive flavour. Smoked and fresh trout paté to our own recipe. Orders may be placed by telephone for delivery or collection.

At the green in Marlborough take the road signed for Aldbourne and Ramsbury. Mildenhall is 1½ miles out of the town. 1st turn right in village, follow lane to Church farm
Open all year incl weekends 7.00am–5.00pm
Free admission
&. ⛌ advance notice required ⛏

▶ MELKSHAM ◀

SANDRIDGE FARM

Farm shop, producers of speciality pork and bacon products

Bromham, Chippenham, Wiltshire SN15 2JL
☎ Devizes (0380) 850304

Producers of farmhouse-cured bacon and sausages, also Wiltshire 'village hams'. Exhibition on bacon curing and viewing windows to the production areas. Reviving a variety of traditional cures.

3 miles east of Melksham on the A3102, turn right towards Bromham. Farm sign 150 yards on the right
Open all year daily 10.00am–5.00pm
Free admission
&. ⛏

▶ PEWSEY ◀

THE MANOR HOUSE

Country garden

Milton Lilbourne, Pewsey, Wiltshire SN9 5LQ
☎ Marlborough (0672) 63344

The garden is at its best in May and June with azaleas, roses and herbaceous plants. A new feature is a section devoted to shrubs and wild flowers.

Take the B3087 from Pewsey to Burbage. Milton Lilbourne is 2 miles from Pewsey
Open April–Oct inclusive Wed 2.00–6.00pm
Free admission. Voluntary contributions to cancer research &. ⛌ ⛏

▶ SALISBURY ◀

FARMER GILES FARMSTEAD

Farm visit, farming museum, nature walk

Teffont Magna, Salisbury, Wiltshire SP3 5QY
☎ Teffont (072276) 716338

A working dairy farm with 20,000 sq ft under cover without steps, ideal for all. Watch the milking, see the highland and other cattle, shire horses, other animals and birds. Exhibitions, shop, restaurant and beech belt nature walk.

Just off the A303 London–Exeter road, 11 miles from Salisbury, 12 miles from Stonehenge
Open Easter–31 Oct daily 10.30am–6.00pm
Admission: adult £2.00, child £1.00, OAP £1.50
&. ⛌ ⛏

FITZ HOUSE GARDEN

Country garden

Teffont Magna, Salisbury, Wiltshire SP3 5QP
☎ Teffont (0722) 716257

Hillside terraced gardens frame listed group of stone buildings in one of Wiltshire's prettiest villages. Spring bulbs, blossom, azaleas, profusion of roses, clematis, mixed borders, small pools. Scented, very tranquil.

On the B3089, 10 miles west of Salisbury
Open Easter–end Sept 2.00–5.30pm on Sundays, some Sats small parties by arrangement by letter
Admission: adult £1.50, child 75p
✖

HEALE GARDENS AND PLANT CENTRE

Country garden

Heale House, Middle Woodford, Salisbury, Wiltshire SP4 6NT
☎ Middle Woodford (072 273) 207/504

Japanese tea house, garden, gift shop and plant centre featuring a wonderful collection of plants, shrubs, musk and other roses. Lunches, teas and tours of the house for parties of over 20 by arrangement.

4 miles from Salisbury, Wilton and Stonehenge, on the Avon Valley road between the A360 and the A345
Open for garden, plant centre and shop throughout the year 10.00am–5.00pm
Admission: adult £1.75, child under 14 free. Groups of over 20 £1.50 (1990 prices)
&. except for toilet facilities
⛌ advance notice required ⛏

ROLLESTON MANOR FARM

Pick your own at Dan's Barn

London Rd, Shrewton, nr Salisbury, Wiltshire SP3 4DR
☎ Shrewton (0980) 620483

Farm gate sales of raspberries, strawberries, gooseberries and broad beans.

Off the A303, 2 miles north west of Stonehenge on the B3086
Open end June–end July daily 10.00am–8.00pm
Free admission
&. 🚌 🛉

▶ *SHERSTON* ◀

SHERSTON EARL VINEYARDS

Vineyard and farm shop

Sherston, nr Malmesbury, Wiltshire SN16 0PY
☎ Malmesbury (0666) 840716

At the foot of the Cotswolds, in a designated ara of outstanding natural beauty. Various single apple ciders e.g. Kington Black, matured on oak. Play equipment. Apple juice, ice creams for children.

Taking the B4040 Bristol road towards Malmesbury, turn right opposite church, right at bottom of Tanners Hill and right at the top of Thompsons Hill
Open daily 10.00am–5.00pm, Sun telephone for opening times
Free admission
&. 🛉

▶ *SWINDON* ◀

COATE AGRICULTURAL MUSEUM

Agricultural museum

Coate Water, Marlborough Rd, Swindon, Wiltshire SN3 6AA
☎ Swindon (0793) 22837

Temporary displays of the larger items such as waggons, carts, implements etc.

Off the B4006, 2 miles from town centre, 2 miles from motorway jct 16
Open Easter–Sept Sun 2.00–5.00pm. At other times by appointment for organised parties (0793) 493181
Free admission
&. 🚌 🛉

LYDIARD COUNTRY PARK

Country park and mansion

Visitors Centre, Lydiard Tregoze, Swindon, Wiltshire SN5 9PA
☎ Swindon (0793) 771419

Georgian mansion containing a number of state rooms open to the public. Country park steeped in history, walks through 260 acres of park and farmland. Picnic area, play area, visitor centre, refreshments.

5 miles west of Swindon. Follow signs to Lydiard from the A420 intersection of the M4 (jct 16)
Open for the park 8.30am–dusk; please telephone the mansion for details of opening times (0793) 770401
Free admission
&. 🚌 advance notice required 🛉

▶ *TISBURY* ◀

COMPTON MARBLING

Hand-marbling

Lower Lawn Barns, Fonthill Gifford, Tisbury, Wiltshire SP3 6SG
☎ Tisbury (0747) 871147/871155

A beautiful quadrangle of 19th century farm buildings. Showroom with enormous range of handmade products including stationery, lighting and boxes. Demonstrations by arrangement only.

Tisbury–Hindon road, left at Beckford Arms public house, ½ mile, first house on left
Open Mon–Fri 10.00am–5.00pm by appointment only
Free admission
&. 🚌 🛉

FONTHILL VINEYARD

Vineyard

The Old Rectory, Fonthill Gifford, Tisbury, Wiltshire SP3 6QH
☎ Tisbury (0747) 870231/871230

Area of outstanding natural beauty with 2000 acres of picturesque woodland protecting the vineyard's microclimate – at an altitude of 450ft it is planted on rich greensand soil overlying limestone rock.

15 miles west of Salisbury, 1 mile south of the B3089. The vineyard is adjacent to Fonthill Gifford church on the Hindon–Tisbury road

Open June–Sept by prior arrangement, please telephone
Admission: including tasting £2.50 per person, groups
with wine and ploughman's (preferably evenings) £4.50
per head
  🚫 🚭 advance notice required 🐴

▶   *TROWBRIDGE*   ◀

THE COURTS – NATIONAL TRUST

Country garden

Holt, Trowbridge, Wiltshire BA14 6RR
☎ (0225) 782340

*18th century house (not open) with an
ornamental facade, flanked by a 7 acre
garden of mystery containing ponds, fine
lawns, herbaceous borders, topiary and
arboretum.*

3 miles south west of Melksham on the south side
of the B3107, 2½ miles east of Bradford-
on-Avon on the B3107, 3 miles north of
Trowbridge
Open 1 April (or Good Friday if earlier)–31 Oct daily
except Sat 2.00–5.00pm. Open to parties at other
times by prior arrangement with head gardener on
above number
Admission: £1.00 per person, accompanied children free
(1990 prices)
  🚫 🚭 advance notice required 🦋

▶   *WARMINSTER*   ◀

STOURHEAD HOUSE & GARDEN

Historic house, country garden

Stourton, Warminster, Wiltshire BA12 6QH
☎ Bourton (0747) 840348

*House designed in 1721 contains many fine
works of art, notably furniture designed by
Chippendale the Younger. The lakes and
temples of the garden contribute to one of
the most famous examples of early 18th
century English landscape movement.*

At Stourton, off the B3092, 3 miles north west of
Mere
Open for garden: all year daily 8.00am–7.00pm or sunset
if earlier; house: 1 April–4 Nov, Sat–Wed 12.00–
5.30pm or dusk if earlier, last admissions 5.00pm
(1990 times)
Admission to house: £3.00, parties £2.50 (by written
arrangement only); garden: 1 March–30 Oct £3.00,
parties £2.50, Nov–end Feb £2.00, no reduction for
parties
  🚫 🚭 gardens only, Nov–end Feb 🐴

▶   *WESTBURY*   ◀

THE WOODLAND PARK AND HERITAGE MUSEUM

Woodland park and museum

Brokerswood, Westbury, Wiltshire BA13 4EH
☎ Westbury (0373) 822238/823880

*80 acre country park, run as a commercial
forest. Lake with wildfowl, picnic and BBQ
sites, adventure playground, shop and
tearoom. Interpretation Centre available at
no extra charge. Fishing bookable in
advance.*

From Westbury take the A3098 to Westbury Leigh,
follow signs to Woodland Park
Open daily 10.00am–sunset (museum closes 5.00pm)
Admission: adult £1.50 (incl museum admission and car
parking), child (under 14) free
  🚫 on dry days
🚭 advance notice required 🐴

WORCESTERSHIRE

Worcestershire has pretty river valleys, ancient woodlands, pleasant pastureland, hop fields and orchards of cider apples and cherries. Worcester porcelain and bone china is well known, it has been produced at the Worcester Royal Porcelain Company since the mid-eighteenth century.

Discover Worcestershire's rolling countryside by following any of the country walks, get to know its rural traditions by visiting one of its rural or farming museums, see farming in action now at one of the farm parks or poultry centres, feed your enthusiasm for gardening by visiting one of the country gardens, enjoy the excellence of handmade crafts at one of the craft workshops or the taste of the countryside at one of the farm shops.

▶ **BEWDLEY** ◀

BEWDLEY MUSEUM

Industrial and craft museum

The Shambles, Load St, Bewdley, Worcester DY12 2AE
☎ Bewdley (0299) 403573

Hornmaking, basketmaking, charcoal burning, a Victorian waterwheel; regular demonstrations of ropemaking and clay pipemaking. A John Pickles horizontal reciprocating saw operates on first Sunday in month.

3 miles west of Kidderminster on the B4190 in centre of Bewdley
Open March–Nov, Mon–Sat 10.00am–5.30pm, Sun 2.00–5.30pm
Admission: adult 50p, child (5–16 years) 20p, OAP 20p, school parties 10p per child
&. no toilet facilities ▨ ⊁

▶ **BROADWAY** ◀

BROADWAY TOWER COUNTRY PARK

Country park

Broadway, Worcestershire WR12 7LB
☎ Broadway (0386) 852390

Historical tower with exhibitions set in acres of Cotswolds scenery. Animals, picnic, barbecue, ball games area, gift shop, full refreshments available.

Open 1 April–31 Oct daily 10.00am–6.00pm
Admission: adult £1.75, child/OAP £1.00, family ticket £5.00 (1990 prices)
&. ▨ advance notice required ⊁

▶ **BROMSGROVE** ◀

AVONCROFT MUSEUM OF BUILDINGS

Farming museum

Stoke Heath, Bromsgrove, Worcestershire B60 4JR
☎ Bromsgrove (0527) 31886/31363

An open air museum containing over 20 buildings spanning 7 centuries of English history – from a working windmill to a furnished prefab. Free car park and picnic site, also a shop and refreshments available.

2 miles south of Bromsgrove off the A38 Bromsgrove bypass (400 yards north of jct with the B4091), 3 miles north of M5 jct 5 and 3½ miles south of M42 jct 1
Open March–Nov as follows: June, July & Aug daily 11.00am–5.30pm; April, May, Sept & Oct 11.00am–5.30pm, closed Mon, open Bank Holidays. March & Nov 11.00am–4.30pm, closed Mon and Fri
Admission: adult £2.30, child £1.15, OAP £1.50, family ticket £6.00 (2 adults and 2 children) (1990 prices)
&. ▨ advance notice required ⊁

DAUB & WATTLE'S POTTERY

Craft centre – pottery

Windsor St, Bromsgrove, Worcestershire B60 2BG
☎ Bromsgrove (0527) 79979

The brick floored and oak beamed pottery has changed little since 1821 when it housed Benjamin Sanders' button factory

Rear of high street in Bromsgrove town centre
Open all year Tues–Sat
Free admission
&. ▨ advance notice required ⊁

▶ **DROITWICH** ◀

CLACKS FARM

Country garden

Boreley, Ombersley, Droitwich, Worcestershire WR9 0HX
☎ Worcester (0905) 620250

2½ acre garden with ornamental borders, vegetable and fruit plots, water garden and several amateur greenhouses. Advice given on open days by experts. Refreshments available but no food.

Off the A449 Worcester–Kidderminster road, 1 mile from Ombersley turn into Woodfield Lane and follow signs
Open weekends May 11–12, June 8–9, July 13–14, Aug 10–11, Sept 7–8, there will be other weekends, send sae early 1991
Admission: adult 75p, child 25p
&. ▨ advance notice required ⊁

JINNEY RING CRAFT CENTRE

Craft centre

Bromsgrove, Worcestershire B60 9BU
☎ Hanbury (052784) 272

8 quality craft workshops, art and craft gallery, restaurant and coffee area, gift shop.

Off the B4090, east of Droitwich
Open all year, Wed–Sat 10.30am–5.00pm, Sun 2.00–
5.30pm
Free admission
&. 🐂

THE ALMONRY MUSEUM

Rural and local history museum

Abbey Gate, Evesham, Worcestershire WR11 4BG
☎ Evesham (0386) 446944

*The museum has rooms on Evesham Abbey,
the Battle of Evesham 1265, the history of
telephones, Victoriana and Civic Regalia. A
full range of craft displays.*

Opposite Merstow Green coach and car park on the
A4184 immediately to the south of the Town Hall
in the centre of Evesham
Open all year Mon–Sat 10.00am–5.00pm, Sun 2.00–
5.00pm
Admission: adult 60p, accompanied children free,
student/OAP 25p (1990 prices)
&. 🚌 advance notice required 🐂

ANNARD WOOLLEN MILL

**Woollen mill, workshop, craft centre and farm
trail**

Handgate Farm, Church Lench, Evesham, Worcestershire
WR11 4VB
☎ Evesham (0386) 870270

*The mill specializes in designs for hand
knitters in mohair and natural fibres. Many
complete garments on display together with
a large range of colours to choose from for
your own creation. Tea shop.*

From Evesham take the A435 north, at Lenchwick
roundabout follow signs to Church Lench, or
signs to Woollen Mill
Open daily except Christmas Day and Boxing Day,
10.00am–5.00pm
Free admission
&. 🚌 advance notice required 🐂

DOMESTIC FOWL TRUST

Farm interpretation centre, trail, museum, shop

Honeybourne Pastures, Honeybourne, nr Evesham,
Worcestershire WR11 5QJ
☎ Evesham (0386) 833083

Conservation of pure breed poultry.

Off the B4035, 4 miles east of Evesham
Open all year daily (except Fri) 10.30am–5.00pm
Admission: adult £2.00, child 90p (1990 prices)

JOHN HAINES & SONS

Pick your own

Greenhill Farms, Blayneys Lane, Evesham, Worcestershire
WR11 4TR
☎ Evesham (0386) 48277

*Approaching the centenary of our business
our aim is to continue the tradition of
supplying a selection of high quality seasonal
produce and free packaging with friendly
and efficient service.*

On the A435, 1 mile north of Evesham town centre
Open June–Sept 10.00am–6.00pm
Free admission
&. except for toilet facilities
🚌 advance notice required 🐂

TWYFORD COUNTRY CENTRE

Farm shop and garden centre

W D Fisher & Son Ltd, Twyford Country Centre,
Evesham, Worcestershire WR11 4TP
☎ Evesham (0386) 446108/442278 (coaches 45650)

*Centre includes a country cafe, cane
furniture dept, natural health and beauty
shop, conservatory show site, multi crafts
centre, wildlife centre, miniature railway and
countryside walks to river and lake.*

On the A435, 1 mile north of Evesham
Open April–Sept daily 9.00am–6.00pm; Oct–March daily
9.00am–5.00pm
Free admission
&. 🚌 advance notice required 🐂

THE FALCONRY CENTRE

Falconry centre

Hurrans Garden Centre, Kidderminster Rd South, Hagley,
Worcestershire
☎ (0562) 700014

*The Falconry Centre houses some 120 birds
of prey, 75 of which are on view to the
general public. A recent new addition is
Boadicea, the tawny eagle. Bird rehabilitation
centre. Small souvenir shop.*

Off the A456, 4 miles north of Kidderminster
Open all year (except Christmas Day & Boxing Day)
10.30am–5.30pm
Admission: adult £1.95, child/OAP £1.25, 75p disabled.
10% discount for parties of over 25
&. ⛺ advance notice required ✖

▶ KIDDERMINSTER ◀

CHADDESLEY GROWERS

Pick your own

1 Potters Park, Chaddesley Corbett, Kidderminster,
Worcestershire DY10 4QA
☎ Chaddesley Corbett (056283) 461

*Small family run PYO enterprise set in
pleasant surroundings. Our aim is to supply
good fruit at reasonable prices, coupled with
personal service.*

On the main A448 Bromsgrove–Kidderminster road,
farm is 200 yards from turning to Chaddesley
Corbett village centre on Kidderminster side next
to village hall
Open mid June–early Aug daily 10.00am–8.00pm for
PYO soft fruit
Free admission
&. ⛺ advance notice required 🐕

KINGSFORD COUNTRY PARK

Country park

Rangers Depot, Blakeshall, Wolverley, Kidderminster,
Worcestershire DY11 5XR
☎ Kidderminster (0562) 851129

*Wander through peaceful pine and birch
woodland, admire the magnificent views over
3 counties, or discover Worcestershire's
rolling countryside, by following one of the
3 waymarked long distance footpaths.*

About 4 miles north of Kidderminster and adjacent
to Kinver Edge
Open dawn until dusk
Free admission
&. ⛺ 🐕

NORTH WORCESTERSHIRE PATH

Country walk

Hereford and Worcester Countryside Service, County Hall,
Spetchley Rd, Worcester WP5 2NP
☎ (0905) 766475

*A waymarked path along the southern edge
of Birmingham. 23 miles between Forhill
picnic site, near Hollywood, (off the A435)
and Kingsford Country Park near
Kidderminster.*

For directions telephone the NWP Ranger on
(0527) 579201
Open at all times
Free admission
&. 🐕

W G STANLEY & SON

Farm shop, pick your own and plant centre

Fishers Castle Farm, Harvington, nr Kidderminster,
Worcestershire DY10 4NF
☎ Kidderminster (0562) 700188/700648

*Family run farm. New farm shop and plant
shop.*

2 miles south of Hagley on the A450, on the right
hand side
Open all year Tues–Sat 9.00am–6.00pm, Sun 9.00am–
12.30pm; closed Mon
Free admission
&. except for toilet facilities
⛺ advance notice required ✖

STONE HOUSE COTTAGE GARDENS

Country garden and nursery

Stone, nr Kidderminster, Worcestershire DY10 4BG
☎ Kidderminster (0562) 69902

*A very beautiful walled garden with towers
– full of unusual wall shrubs, climbers and
herbaceous plants – visited by gardening
enthusiasts worldwide. Most plants available
for sale in adjacent nursery.*

2 miles south east of Kidderminster (A448)
Open April–Oct Wed–Sat 10.00am–6.00pm (also Sun in
May & June, 2.00–6.00pm)
Free admission, but collection box for National Garden
Scheme and Mother Theresa
&. except toilet facilities
⛺ advance notice required ✖

WORCESTERSHIRE WAY

Country walk

Rangers Depot, Blakeshall, Wolverley, Kidderminster,
Worcestershire DY11 5XR
☎ Kidderminster (0526) 851129

Just follow the waymarkers and the Worcestershire Way will lead you through ancient woodland and orchards, through historic villages and river valleys, to hilltops giving unparalleled views over beautiful English countryside.

Runs approx 35 miles from the Malvern Hills north to Kingsford Country Park near Kidderminster
Open at all times
Free admission
 🚻 🚌 ⛹

► LITTLE WITLEY ◄

EASTGROVE COTTAGE GARDEN NURSERY

Country garden

Sankyns Green, nr Shrawley, Little Witley, Worcestershire WR6 6LQ
☎ Great Witley (0299) 896389

Set in 5 acres of unspoilt meadow and woodland, 1 acre of peaceful garden, of particular interest to plantsmen. Expanding collection of hardy plants in old world country flower garden, full of colour.

8 miles north west of Worcester on the road between Shrawley (B4196) and Great Witley (A443) at Sankyns Green
Open 1 April–1 Nov 2.00–5.00pm. Closed Tues & Wed and throughout Aug (evening group visits by arrangement)
Admission: adult £1.00, child 20p (1990 prices)
 🚻 🚌 advance notice required ⛹

► PERSHORE ◄

JENNIE HILL GALLERY OF LOCAL ARTS

Craft centre and art gallery

86 High St, Pershore, Worcestershire WR10 1DU
☎ Evesham (0386) 553969

Paintings and craft from local artists and craftsmen, with a special emphasis on helping new or young skills to succeed. Commissions carried out for customers.

Between Worcester (8 miles) and Evesham (6 miles) on the A44
Open throughout the year Mon–Sat (½ day Thur) 9.30am–1.00pm and 2.00–5.30pm
Free admission
 🚻 ⛹

► SPETCHLEY ◄

SPETCHLEY FRUIT FARM

Farm shop and pick your own

Spetchley, Worcestershire WR7 4QL
☎ Spetchley (0905) 65639/776098

We are situated in beautiful countryside with large picnic areas and wonderful views over the Malvern and Breden Hills.

5 miles from Worcester, off jct 6 of the M5 on the B4084
Open July–Aug PYO, April–Oct farm shop. In season open 10.00am–8.00pm
Free admission
 🚻 🚌 ⛹

► STOURPORT-ON-SEVERN ◄

ASTLEY VINEYARDS

Vineyard and wine shop

The Crundels, Astley, Stourport-on-Severn, Worcestershire DY13 0RU
☎ Stourport (02993) 2907

Small family-run vineyard with record of awards in national and international tastings in a picturesque section of the Severn Valley, demonstrating traditional and experimental methods of training.

3 miles south of Stourport off the B4196, or 10 miles north of Worcester off the B4196
Shop open normal retail hours, customers welcome to walk round vineyard
Organised parties by appointment – £2.50 per head for a minimum of 20 people to include lecture, vineyard tour and tasting
 🚻 🚌 advance notice required ⛹

► UPTON-UPON-SEVERN ◄

MIDSUMMER WEAVERS

Workshop, craft weaving

London Lane, Upton-upon-Severn, Worcestershire WR8 0HH
☎ Upton-upon-Severn (06846) 3503

Specialists in weaving cloth in purely natural fibre, using all British yarn. In the shop we sell skirts, suits and accessories made from our cloth, all in our own designs.

Exit the M5/M50 interchange. Exit the M50 to
Malvern follow the A38 to Worcester for 3 miles,
turn left to Upton-upon-Severn. Workshop/shop
is in town centre near the Heritage Centre
Open all year Tues–Sat 9.30am–1.00pm, 2.00–5.30pm
Free admission
& 🚐 advance notice required
🐕 except guide dogs

▶ *WORCESTER* ◀

BEVERE VIVIS GALLERY

Art gallery and pottery shop

Bevere Knoll, Bevere, Worcester WR3 7RQ
☎ Worcester (0905) 51291

*A friendly art gallery and pottery shop
which exhibits and sells original paintings,
wildlife prints, pottery and collectors
postcards – all created by local artists.*

Off the A449, 3 miles north of Worcester city
centre, near northern link to the M5
Open every Sat and Bank Holiday throughout the year,
also 22 June–29 Sept and 1–22 Dec Wed, Thur, Fri &
Sat 10.30am–5.00pm
Free admission
& 🚐 minibuses only 🐕

BROUGHTON TROUT

Trout farm and farm shop

Manor Farm, Broughton Hackett, Worcester WR7 4BB
☎ Upton Snodsbury (090560) 839

Fresh trout and smoked products.

Off the A422 Stratford road, 5 miles east of
Worcester
Open all year Tues–Sun incl, April–Oct 10.30am–4.30pm;
Nov–March 10.30am until dusk, closed Mon (except
Bank Holidays)
Free admission
& every assistance given
🚐 advance notice required 🐕

GOODMAN'S GEESE

**Goose producer, pick your own, farm shop and
country walk**

Walsgrove Farm, Great Witley, nr Worcester WR6 6JJ
☎ Great Witley (0299) 896272

*Farm with dairy, soft fruit, geese set in
beautiful countryside in the Abberley Hills
region. Oven-ready geese available to order
mid Sept to Christmas, Bronze turkeys to
order for Christmas. Pick your own
25 June–25 July*

12 miles north west of Worcester. Take the A443
from Worcester to Great Witley via Holt Heath, in
Great Witley take the B4203 to Bromyard, turn
first left 100 yards
Open for farm walks by appointment only
Admission: a small charge is made subject to number in
party
& 🚐 advance notice required 🐕

HOP POCKET CRAFT SHOP

**Craft shop, country garden, farm trail and farming
museum**

New House, Bishops Frome, Worcester WR6 5BT
☎ Bosbury (053186) 323

*Work from over 100 craftsmen on display in
a converted hop kiln. Tea rooms with homely
cooking. Visitors may amble through the
beautiful gardens featuring huge topiary
bowers.*

Just off the A4103 Worcester–Hereford road
Open all year Tues–Sat 10.30am–5.30pm, Sun 2.30–
5.00pm, Jan–Feb Fri, Sat & Sun afternoons. Closed
Mon except Bank Holidays
Admission: no charge for craft shop, hop tours/open
weekends adult £2.00, child/OAP £1.00
& one shallow step into craft shop
🚐 advance notice required

SPETCHLEY PARK GARDEN

Country garden

Spetchley Park, Worcester WR5 1RS
☎ Spetchley (0905 65) 224

*Garden with large collection of trees, shrubs
or plants, has much interest throughout the
spring and summer months. Plants on sale.
House not open.*

3 miles east of Worcester on the A422
Open April–Sept daily (except Sat), weekdays 11.00am–
5.00pm, Sun 2.00–5.00pm, Bank Holiday Mon
11.00am–5.00pm
Admission: adult £1.60, child 80p. Pre-booked parties of
25 or more adult £1.40, child 80p
& except toilet facilities 🚐 🐕

WORCESTER WOODS COUNTRY PARK

Country park

County Hall, Spetchley Rd, Worcester WR5 2NP
☎ Worcester (0905) 350770

Picnic and play areas. Trails, events and activities. Refreshments. Tourist information.

1 mile from jct 7 of the M5, 2 miles east of Worcester city centre on the A422 Worcester–Stratford-upon-Avon road. The Worcester Countryside Centre is adjacent to the County Hall and is the centre for the Country Park

Open dawn until dusk. Countryside Centre open 10.00am–5.00pm

Free admission

& ﹈ ⅂

YORKSHIRE

Yorkshire is a mixture of the Pennines, huge expanses of heather and peat moorland, the beautiful Yorkshire Dales with its waterfalls, the rich historic beauty of the monastic buildings, castles, great houses and the industrial architecture that reflects the importance of this area during the Industrial Revolution.

The rich variety of Yorkshire's landscape can be experienced by visiting one of the farming and folk museums, a farm interpretation centre, a working farm where educational visits can be arranged, a farm with working heavy horses, a countryside centre, a forest park or a historic house and gardens. A wide range of products is also available from locally made ropes, sheepskin products, rocking horses, woollens, and handmade oak furniture to stone-ground flour, trout, and soft fruits.

► BARNOLDSWICK ◄

CRAVEN LAMBSKINS

Farm shop, sheepskin products

Woodend Farm, Salterforth, Barnoldswick, Yorkshire
BB8 5SN
☎ Barnoldswick (0282) 812146

This country shop, although small, carries a unique selection of over 700 sheepskin coats and jackets, in all styles.

On the B6251, 2 miles south of Barnoldswick
Open daily 10.30am–6.00pm
Free admission
& 🐴

► BEDALE ◄

CRAKEHALL WATER MILL

Working water mill, producer of stoneground wholemeal flour

Little Crakehall, nr Bedale, North Yorkshire DL8 1HU
☎ Bedale (0677) 23240

Flour for sale, tea and coffee room at weekends. A water mill was recorded in the Domesday Survey and there has been a mill on the site ever since.

2 miles west of Bedale, on the A684 Bedale–
Leyburn road
Open April–Sept (except Mondays and Friday) 10.00am–
5.00pm
Admission: adult £1.00, child/OAP 50p
& 🚐 advance notice required 🗶

GIBSON'S FARM SHOP

Farm shop

Hopetown House, Burneston, Bedale, North Yorkshire
DL8 2JN
☎ Thirsk (0845) 567252

We specialize in pork and pork products from our own pigs. We also stock beef, lamb, game and poultry supplied by other members of the family and local firms.

At the side of the north bound carriageway of the
A1, 5 miles south of Leeming Bar motel, 4 miles
north of Thirsk/Ripon interchange
Open Mon–Fri 8.00am–6.00pm, Sat 8.00am–5.00pm
Free admission
& 🚐🗶

► BIRSTALL ◄

OAKWELL HALL COUNTRY PARK

Manor house, gardens, country park, craft centre

Nutter Lane, Birstall, Batley, West Yorkshire WF17 9LG
☎ Batley (0924) 474926

16th century manor house and gardens with visitor centre, shop and craft workshops. Country park including bridleway, equestrian arena, wildlife gardens, picnic areas, adventure playground. Events programme throughout the year.

Situated off the A652, Dewsbury–Bradford road, ½
mile from the centre of Birstall
Open dawn until dusk for the country park; house and
visitor centre: Mon–Sat 10.00am–5.00pm, Sun
1.00–5.00pm. Closed Christmas & Boxing Day
Free admission
& 🚐 advance notice required
🐴 in park only

► BRADFORD ◄

BRACKEN HALL COUNTRYSIDE CENTRE

Countryside centre

Glen Rd, Baildon, Shipley, West Yorkshire BD17 5EA
☎ Bradford (0274) 584140

Situated between moors and woodland, houses a combination of traditional displays and interactive games to help you discover the ecology, history and geology of the surrounding area. Wildlife garden.

4½ miles from Bradford, off the B6151
Open April–mid Dec Wed–Sun and Bank Holidays
11.00am–5.00pm; Dec–March Wed and Sun only
11.00am–5.00pm
Free admission
& the centre and toilets are accessible to the disabled
🚐🐴

► BRIDLINGTON ◄

PARK ROSE POTTERY & LEISURE PARK

Craft centre, woodland nature trail, childrens play areas and picnic areas

Carnaby Covert Lane, Bridlington, East Yorkshire
YO15 3QF
☎ Bridlington (0262) 602823

Parking and pottery walkabout, childrens play and picnic areas, bar, cafe, gift shop and seconds warehouse.

Park Rose is 2 miles south of Bridlington near Carnaby just off the A165 and the A166
Open all year daily from 10.00am
Free admission
  ⤫

▶ DONCASTER ◀

CUSWORTH HALL MUSEUM

Folk life museum, country park and country walk

Cusworth, Doncaster, South Yorkshire DN5 7TU
☎ Doncaster (0302) 782342

Cusworth Hall is a lively, family museum in the beautiful former home of the Battie Wrightsons, in 50 acres of parkland. Displays on South Yorkshire life are complemented by a programme of exhibitions and events.

Off junction of the A635 and the A638, 2 miles north of Doncaster
Open Mon–Fri 10.00am–5.00pm, Sat 11.00am–5.00pm, Sun 1.00–5.00pm, early closing in Dec and Jan Jan
Free admission
& wheelchair lift to ground floor ⤫

WELLINGLEY GRANGE (FARM TOURS)

Educational farm visits

Tickhill, Doncaster, South Yorkshire DN11 9LL
☎ Doncaster (0302) 742254

Farm nature trail, pony rides, ducks, chicks, pigs, lambs, calves, tractors, farm machinery, refreshments.

Signposted off the A60 Wadworth–Tickhill road
Open by appointment only, farm open days 2 Sundays in March/April (lambing time), 1 Sunday in June (sheep shearing), 10.00am–5.00pm, please ring for dates
Admission: child 75p, no charge for any leaders/teachers
& access to all areas of farm tour is possible with wheelchairs
⤫ advance notice required ⤫

▶ DRIFFIELD ◀

CHURCH FARM GALLERIES

Contemporary art and craft galleries

Church Farm, Garton-on-the-Wolds, nr Driffield, Yorkshire YO25 0ES
☎ Driffield (0377) 43988

The galleries specialise in glass, ceramics, wood, paintings, limited edition etchings and prints, jewellery, traditional toys and cards. Cream teas and homemade cakes are served during the summer months.

Off the A166 at Garton-on-the-Wolds
Open all year 10.00am–5.00pm (4.00pm in winter), except Mon & Tues, or by appointment
Free admission to galleries
& except for toilet facilities ⤫

THORPE HALL CARAVAN AND CAMPING SITE

Country walk, country garden and educational nature walks

Rudston, Driffield, East Yorkshire YO25 0JE
☎ Kilham (0262 82) 393/394

The caravan and camping park is sheltered in the old kitchen garden walls of Thorpe Hall. Visitors belonging to naturalist trust (e.g. RSPB, RSNC etc.) can be issued with an estate pass and have access to 2,000 acres.

The site is well signed and situated on the B1253, 4½ miles inland from Bridlington
Open afternoons for the garden walk (except Sundays) for campers only. Camp site open March–Oct. School visits by appoointment
Free admission. 1990 caravan/camping price £4.50/6.00 per night depending on season
& ⤫

▶ ELLAND ◀

NORTH DEAN NATURE CENTRE

Country walk and nature centre

Clay House, Greetland, Halifax, West Yorkshire
☎ Elland (0422) 74014

2 miles south of Halifax
Open April–Sept daily (except Mondays) 10.00am–4.00pm, open weekends in winter
Free admission
& ⤫

► GRASSINGTON ◄

KENT TRADITIONAL FURNITURE

Cabinet maker's workshop

Moor Lane, Grassington, North Yorkshire BD23 5BD
☎ Skipton (0756) 753045

Kent Furniture produce a range of hand crafted solid oak furniture which is sent to customers worldwide. Most standard pieces of furniture are on display in the showroom.

10 miles from Skipton on the B6265
Open all year daily 10.00am–6.00pm
Free admission
&. ⋔

► HALIFAX ◄

WEST YORKSHIRE FOLK MUSEUM

Farming and folk museum, craft centre, house of 15th century yeoman farmer

Shibden Hall, Halifax, West Yorkshire HX3 6XG
☎ Halifax (0422) 352246

15th century half-timbered house with period room displays. Fine 17th century barn with carriages and agricultural tools. Craft workshops round an open courtyard: blacksmith, cooper and saddler.

1½ miles east of Halifax off the A58 Leeds road
Open April–Sept daily 10.00am–6.00pm, Sundays 2.00–
5.00pm; March, Oct & Nov daily 10.00am–5.00pm,
Sundays 2.00–5.00pm; Feb Sundays only 2.00–
5.00pm; closed Dec & Jan
Admission: adult 60p, child/OAP 30p
&. ⋙ advance notice required
⋔ except guide dogs

► HARROGATE ◄

RICHARD BRAY GLASS ENGRAVER

Craft centre – glass engraving

Brimham Rocks Farm, Brimham Rocks, Summerbridge,
Harrogate, North Yorkshire HG3 4DW
☎ Harrogate (0423) 780786

10 miles north of Harrogate, off the B6265 Pateley
Bridge–Ripon road signposted Brimham Rocks,
at the side of Rocks
Open daily all year, please telephone for Sunday visits
Free admission
&. ⋔

STRAWBERRY FARM

Farm shop and pick your own

Birstwith, Harrogate, North Yorkshire HG3 3AW
☎ Harrogate (0423) 771360/770200

Award-winning Strawberry Farm, self-pick fruit and vegetables, farm shop, country walks, childrens play area and shady picnic grounds.

Take the A59 out of Harrogate, turn right after
2 miles, follow signs to Hampsthwaite and
Birstwith
Open July–Sept approx, daily 9.00am–8.00pm
Free admission
&. ⋙ ⋔ in limited areas

YORKSHIRE AGRICULTURAL SOCIETY

Agricultural show

Great Yorkshire Showground, Hookstone Oval, Harrogate,
North Yorkshire HG2 8PW
☎ Harrogate (0423) 561536

Horses, cattle, sheep, pigs and goats. Over 600 trade and machinery stands, military bands, top class showjumping, main ring displays, wool pavilion, flower shop, forestry and woodland walk, rare breeds.

On the A661 Harrogate–Wetherby road
Open 9 & 10 July 8.00am–7.30pm and 11 July 8.00am–
6.00pm
Admission: days 1 & 2 adult £7.50, child/OAP £4.00; day
3 adult £6.00, child/OAP £3.00
&. ⋙ free parking ⋔

► HAWES ◄

BLACKBURN TROUT FISHERY

Country walk, trout producer

B H Moore, Blackburn Farm, Gayle, Hawes, North
Yorkshire DL8 3NX
☎ Wensleydale (0969) 667524

In peaceful surroundings catch your own rainbow trout in a one acre well stocked lake, or buy some from the farm house. For a longer stay book our farm flat. Picnic area.

East Gayle Lane
Open April–Nov 7.30am–8.30pm
Free admission, please telephone for angling charges
⋔

DALES COUNTRYSIDE MUSEUM

Museum

Station Yard, Hawes, North Yorkshire
☎ Wensleydale (0969) 667450

The museum contains a fascinating collection of bygones from Dales life, including lead mining relics, farming equipment and domestic items, also Hawes National Park Centre.

Open: April–Oct 10.00am–5.00pm
& the main part of the museum is not suitable for wheelchairs 🚌

W R OUTHWAITE & SON, ROPEMAKERS

Ropemakers

Town Foot, Hawes, North Yorkshire DL8 3NT
☎ Wensleydale (0969) 667487

Watch ropemaking in progress at the workshop. Car parking, toilets, cafe and picnic area nearby.

On the A684 at start of one-way system, adjacent to childrens playground
Open all normal working days all year, Mon–Fri 9.00am–5.30pm, most Saturdays in school holidays and Bank Holiday Mondays 10.00am–4.00pm, closed Sundays
Free admission
& 🚌 🐴

▶ **HEBDEN BRIDGE** ◀

HARDCASTLE CRAGS (NATIONAL TRUST)

Country walks

Midgehole Rd, Hardcastle Crags, Hebden Bridge, West Yorkshire
☎ Hebden Bridge (0422) 844518

Hardcastle Crags comprises two steep sided, wooded valleys with streams and waterfalls. Rock outcrops 'the Crags' are an attractive feature and Gibson Mill, a disused 19th century cotton mill, forms a focal point. Programme of guided walks arranged each season, nature trails.

1½ miles north of Hebden Bridge
Open all year
Admission: April–Oct car 70p, motor cycle 20p, minibus £1.50, coach £4.00
& 🚌 advance notice required 🐴

▶ **KILBURN** ◀

ROBERT THOMPSON'S CRAFTSMEN LTD

Craft centre – furniture

Kilburn, Yorkshire YO6 4AH
☎ Coxwold (03476) 218

Specialists in hand-made domestic, church and boardroom furniture executed from naturally seasoned English oak. Also a range of carvings, gifts and small items. All bearing the world famous mouse trade mark.

Off the A170, 7 miles east of Thirsk
Open Mon–Thur 8.00am–12.00 noon, 12.45–5.00pm; Fri 8.00am–12.00 noon, 12.45–3.45pm; Sat 10.00am–12.00 noon; closed Easter week and 3 weeks at Christmas
Free admission
& 🚌 advance notice required

▶ **LEEDS** ◀

HAREWOOD BRIDGE SOFT FRUIT & VEGETABLE FARM

Farm shop and pick your own

M L & R C Snowden, Wharfedale Grange, Harewood, Leeds, Yorkshire LS17 9LW
☎ Leeds (0532) 886320/886206

Primarily a family run farm shop supplying a wide range of freshly picked seasonal vegetables and fruit produced on the farm. Garnishing vegetables supplied to the trade, pigeon corn to fanciers.

First farm on the left, north of Harewood Bridge on the A61 between Leeds and Harrogate, 1½ miles north of Harewood on the A61, opposite redbrick house
Open July until mid August 9.00am–6.00pm
Free admission
& 🐴 but not in fields

TONG GARDEN CENTRE

Garden centre, pick your own, country walk and craft centre

Tong Lane, Tong Village, Westgate Hill, Bradford, Yorkshire BD4 0RY
☎ Leeds (0532) 853506

Off the A650, 4 miles south east of Bradford
Open daily (except Christmas Holiday) 9.00am–6.00pm,
    until 8.00pm during summer period
Free admission
& ⟨⟩ ✕

7 miles west of Leyburn along the A684, take left
    turn onto the B6160 to West Burton
Open all year (but closed mid Dec–mid Jan) 10.00am–
    5.00pm
Free admission
& ✝

▶   *LEYBURN*   ◀

AYSGARTH POTTERY

Craft centre – pottery

The Old Quaker Meeting House, Carperby, nr Leyburn,
    North Yorkshire DL8 4DJ
☎ Wensleydale (0969) 663719

*Aysgarth Pottery's workshop and plant
nursery opens most afternoons April–Oct.
Well stocked shop, full of quality crafts,
opens daily in Aysgarth village itself (not at
the waterfalls).*

Off the A684 to village of Carperby, 6 miles from
    Leyburn
Open most afternoons April–Oct
Free admission
& ✝

CHANDLER GALLERY

Craft and gift shop, art gallery

8 Commercial Square, Leyburn, North Yorkshire DL8 5BP
☎ Wensleydale (0969) 23676

*Varying programme of exhibitions, plus
permanent stocks of paintings and original
prints.*

On the A684/A6108 top square of town, opposite
    the Bolton Arms public house
Open Mon–Sat 9.30am–5.00pm, Wed (Easter–Christmas)
    9.30am–12.30pm, Sun (July–Aug) 11.00am–4.00pm.
    Closed first 2 weeks in Feb
Free admission
& goods can be taken outside for inspection when
practicable ✝

MOORSIDE DESIGN

Craft centre – ceramic animals

West Burton, Leyburn, North Yorkshire DL8 4JW
☎ Wensleydale (0969) 663273

*Ceramic workshop specialising in cats and
other animals, terracotta garden pots. Small
alpine and herb garden.*

▶   *MIDDLESBROUGH*   ◀

CAMPHILL VILLAGE TRUST (LARCHFIELD COMMUNITY)

Country walk and farm visit

Stokesley Road, Hemlington, Middlesbrough, Cleveland
    TS8 9DY
☎ Middlesbrough (0642) 593688

*Bio-dynamic farm and market garden
working with disabled and voluntary groups
in association with Middlesbrough Borough
Council. Wheelhouse coffee bar – manned by
volunteers from Friends of Larchfield.*

Take the B1365 south of town to Stokesley via
    Acklam, Blue Bell and Hemlington. 500 yards on
    the right after 'Gables' roundabout. 5 miles from
    Middlesbrough town centre, 5 miles from
    Stokesley
Please telephone for details of opening times. Open for
    refreshments Mon–Fri 10.00am–12.00
    noon
Free admission
& ⟨⟩ advance notice required ✝

▶   *NORTHALLERTON*   ◀

J C, G M & A McDONALD

Farm shop and country park

The Chequers, Osmotherley, Northallerton, North
    Yorkshire DL6 3QB
☎ Osmotherley (060983) 291

*Farmshop, tea room with home baking,
holiday cottages, caravans and camping in
National Park. Beautiful area for walking,
bird watching, riding and fishing. Parties
please notify in advance.*

2 miles from Osmotherley on Helmsley road
Open daily, except Christmas and New Year
& ⟨⟩ ✝

▶ **OLD MALTON** ◀

EDEN FARM INSIGHT

Farm interpretation centre, farm trail, museum, cafe, craft shop, picnic area, teaching room for schools

Eden Farm, Old Malton, North Yorkshire YO17 0RT
☎ (0653) 692093

A working farm giving an insight into farming in the Ryedale area past and present. Cattle, calves, ewes, lambs, sows, piglets, horses and poultry. Large farm museum and forge. Indoor displays on wet days.

½ mile west off the A169/A64, 2 miles north of Malton
Open Easter–Oct, daily 10.00am–4.30pm
Admission: adult £2.50, child/OAP £1.50, family ticket £6.50, parties by arrangement
&. except for toilet facilities ⊞

▶ **PICKERING** ◀

BECK ISLE MUSEUM OF RURAL LIFE

Museum of rural life

Bridge St, Pickering, North Yorkshire YO18 8DU
☎ Pickering (0751) 73653

22 rooms packed with collections from the Victorian age, with something of interest for all, includes many typical shops of that era. Farm exhibits in outbuildings.

Direct on the A170, 16 miles west of Scarborough
Open April–Oct daily 10.00am–12.30pm, 2.00–5.00pm, Aug 10.00am–6.00pm
Admission: adult £1.00, child 50p, parties are welcome by appointment
&. ⊞ advance notice required ✖

DALBY FOREST DRIVE AND VISITOR CENTRE

Forest park, country walks, wayfaring course, forest visitor centre and shop

Forestry Commission, 42 Eastgate, Pickering, North Yorkshire YO18 7DU
☎ Pickering (0751) 72771

On Dalby forest drive you can park and picnic, walk one of 17 waymarked walks,

practise orienteering, buy souvenirs at the visitor centre or just study nature.

Off the A170, 3 miles north of Thornton Dale
Open all year for the forest drive. Visitor centre: April–Oct 11.00am–5.00pm
Admission: car £1.50 (toll fee to forest drive), visitor centre free
&. lakeside wheelchair path, toilet facilities
⊞ advance notice required ✖

▶ **POCKLINGTON** ◀

BURNBY HALL GARDENS & MUSEUM

Garden and museum

The Balk, Pocklington, East Yorkshire
☎ Pocklington (0759) 302068

Picturesque tree-lined grass walk with bordering shrubs and plants. Formal rose garden, pergola and herbaceous borders. Interesting pathways linking the two lakes. New Monet-style bridge.

Off the A1079, 12 miles east of York
Open Easter–mid Oct 10.00am–6.00pm, cafe daily from end May
Admission: adult £1.00, child (5–16 yrs) 40p, OAP 75p, special party rates
&. wheelchairs available
⊞ ✖ except guide dogs

▶ **REETH** ◀

BLACKSMITH'S CERAMICS

Workshop and showroom

Blacksmith's Shop, The Green, Reeth, Richmond, North Yorkshire DL11 7LQ
☎ Richmond (0748) 84648 (evenings)

Ray and Jane Davies make a wide range of stoneware pottery including wall plant pockets, garden ornaments, hanging baskets, name plates, bird baths, plaques for dried flowers and inlaid mirrors.

Reeth is 10 miles west of Richmond on the B6270
Open Easter Monday–mid Oct daily (except Sundays) 10.00am–5.30pm
Free admission
&. ✖

▶ RICHMOND ◀

YORKSHIRE HERBS

Herb growers

The Herb Centre, Middleston Tyas, Richmond, North
Yorkshire DL10 6RR
☎ (0325) 377686

*This is a working herb centre and visitors
are welcome to wander around freely and
enjoy the pleasure and aroma that herbs
impart.*

2 miles east of the A1 from Scotch Corner – on the
minor road between the villages of Middleton
Tyas and Croft
Open Easter to end Sept Wed–Sat and Bank Holidays,
10.00am–5.00pm
Free admission
Ġ 🚌 advanced notice required 🗡

▶ RIPLEY ◀

RIPLEY CASTLE

Castle, country garden, deer park and lakes

*Ripley Castle isset in beautiful parkland
with formal walled gardens. Shops, tearooms,
parking and toilets*

Off the A61, 3 miles north of Harrogate
Castle open April, May & Oct, Sat & Sun
11.30am–4.30pm, June–Sept Tues–Sun 11.30am–
4.30pm, also Easter and Bank Holidays (in season)
11.00am–4.30pm. Gardens open daily April–Oct
11.00am–4.30pm
Admission: castle & gardens adult £2.50, child £1.25,
OAP £2.30; gardens only adult £1.00, child 50p, OAP
75p
Ġ 🚌 advanced notice required 🗡

▶ RIPON ◀

DALES FLORA

Dried flower shop and specimen garden

Low Missise Farm, Laverton, Ripon, North Yorkshire
☎ Kirkby Malzeard (076583) 653

*Converted barn selling dried and preserved
flowers, herbs, baskets and gifts. Specimen
gardens. One day instruction courses are
available.*

Take the Kirkby Malzeard road out of Ripon
(opposite Co–operative). Laverton is ½ mile from
Kirkby Malzeard
Open Wed–Sat 11.30–4.00pm, advisable to telephone if
coming on Sunday or Tuesday
Free admission
Ġ 🚌 advanced notice required 🗡

LIGHTWATER VALLEY

Theme park and working farm centre

North Stanley, Ripon, North Yorkshire HG4 3HT
☎ Ripon (0765) 85321, hotline (0765) 85368

*Set in 125 acres of country park and
lakeland, over 80 rides and attractions, 3
boating lakes, fishing, golf course, adventure
playground, nature trail, shopping arcade
and restaurant.*

3 miles north of Ripon on the A6108
Open (1990) 7–29 April, weekends and Bank Holidays in
May, and 29–31 May, June excluding 4–5, 11–12,
18–19, all July, Aug, Sept and Sundays in October
Admission: adult/child £6.95, under 4s free, groups (12+)
£5.95 with 1 in 20 free, school/birthday party rates,
OAP £4.95
Ġ 🚌 🗡

NEWBY HALL & GARDENS

Historic house and country garden

The Estate Office, Newby Hall, Ripon, North Yorkshire
HG4 5AE
☎ Boroughbridge (0423) 322583

*Set in 25 acres of award-winning gardens,
Newby Hall is a renowned Adam house.
Adventure gardens, miniature railway,
woodland discovery walk, plant stall, shop
and licensed restaurant.*

Situated off the B6265 between Ripon and
Boroughbridge. Ripon 4 miles, Boroughbridge 2
miles
Open April–Sept Tues–Sun and Bank Holiday Mondays
11.00am–5.00pm, house from 12.00 noon
Admission: house and gardens: adult £3.60, child £2.00;
gardens only: adult £2.00, child £1.50, family tickets
and reductions for OAP and disabled (1990 prices)
Ġ disabled have access to gardens and ground floor of
house, toilets for disabled in restaurant, wheelchairs
available on request 🚌 🐕 in picnic area only

PLUMPTON HALL FARM

Educational farm visit, trail and farm interpretation centre

K W & D Slater, Plumpton Hall, Studley Roger, Ripon, North Yorkshire HT4 3AY
☎ Ripon (0765) 3540

Old established mixed dairy farm with pigs, cereals and potatoes. Qualified teaching staff provide in depth studies into all aspects of farming to suit pupils aged 7–18 years. Organised school parties only.

Left off the B6245, 1 mile west of Ripon
Open, please telephone for prospectus
Admission: £1.50 per person
& ⟡ advanced notice required ✘

► **ROTHERHAM** ◄

ULLEY COUNTRY PARK

Country park and country walk

Pleasley Rd, Ulley, Via Sheffield, South Yorkshire S31 0YL
☎ Rotherham (0709) 365332

Formerly Ulley Reservoir, the park offers walks, coarse angling, quiet picnic spots and a wide variety of flora and fauna; further information and assistance may be gained from the Rangers Office.

3 miles south of Rotherham town centre, alongside the A618 Rotherham–Aughton road
Open all year dawn until dusk
Free admission
& ⟡ ✘

► **SCARBOROUGH** ◄

RAVENSCAR – NATIONAL TRUST

Country walks

Information Centre, Ravenscar, Scarborough, North Yorkshire
☎ Scarborough (0723) 870138

Information centre for 9 miles of spectacular coastal scenery, programme of guided walks.

10 miles north of Scarborough off the A171
Open all year for walks; information centre: April, May & Sept at weekends; June–end Aug daily
Free admission
& ✘

STAINTON DALE SHIRE HORSE FARM

Farm interpretation centre, farm visit, museum, shop and park

East Side Farm, Staintondale, nr Scarborough, North Yorkshire YO13 0EY
☎ Scarborough (0723) 870458

Small period farm based on Shire horses situated on North Yorkshire moors National Park coastline. Tea room, play and picnic area.

Just off the A171 Scarborough to Whitby road between Cloughton and Ravenscar, 9 miles north of Scarborough
Open 6 May–30 Sept Sun, Tues, Wed, Fri and Bank Holidays 10.30am–4.30pm
Admission: adult £2.00, child £1.00, OAP £1.50, after 2 children family reduction to 50p each child
& ✘

► **SELBY** ◄

HADDLESEY HERB & HEATHER CENTRE

Pick your own, herb gardens, heather and conifer gardens

West Haddesley, nr Selby, North Yorkshire YO8 8QA
☎ Gateforth (075782) 279

National collection holders of santolina (cotton lavender), plant nursery, terracotta pots and hanging baskets to order. Herb shop, tea room, herb courses. Talk and tour of the nursery.

Jct 34 off the M62, A19 towards Hull, turn off 6 miles south of Selby towards West Haddlesey
Open March–Oct daily except Wed, Nov–Feb weekends 10.00am–6.00pm
Free admission
& ⟡ ✘

► **SHEFFIELD** ◄

ABBEYDALE INDUSTRIAL HAMLET

Industrial hamlet

Abbeydale Rd South, Sheffield, Yorkshire S7 2QW
☎ Sheffield (0742) 367731

An 18th century agricultural edge-tool works, powered by 4 waterwheels, restored to preserve the simple but functional vernacular

*architecture, and the living and working
conditions of a bygone age.*

On the A621, Sheffield–Bakewell road, approx 4
   miles south west of Sheffield city centre
Open all year Wed–Sat 10.00am–5.00pm, Sun 11.00am–
   5.00pm, closed 24–26 Dec, open Bank Holiday
   Mondays
Admission: adult £1.50, child/OAP 75p, family (2 adults
   and 2 children)
  🚻 🚌 🐕

GRAVES PARK APPROVED RARE BREEDS CENTRE

Rare breeds centre and country walk

c/o City of Sheffield Metropolitan District, Head Office,
   PO Box 151, Meersbrook Park, Sheffield, Yorkshire
   S8 9FL
☎ Sheffield (0742) 500500

*A complete service of leisure opportunities in
one of the largest and most beautiful parks
in Sheffield with a waterfowl collection,
fishing, sport, orienteering and nature trail,
adjoining the rare breeds centre.*

Road signs on the A61 Sheffield–Chesterfield road,
   south of city
Open all year
Free admission
 🚻 except for toilet facilities 🚌 🐕

▶ *SKIPTON* ◀

ABBOTS HARBOR

Farm, village shop, cafe and licensed restaurant

Sawley House, East Marton, nr Skipton, North Yorkshire
   BD23 3LP
☎ Earby (0282) 843207

*Situated in a barn built by Cistercian monks
who lived and farmed here from 1134–1500.
Used as a resting place by monks travelling
between abbeys in the area.*

4 miles from Skipton on the A59, turn at
   Crosskeys, East Marton, down lane to where
   Leeds/Liverpool Canal and Pennine Way meet,
   approx 100 yards
Open all year 8.30am–6.00pm
Free admission
🚻 🐕

EMBSAY STEAM RAILWAY

Steam railway

Embsay Station, Embsay, nr Skipton, North Yorkshire
   BD23 6AX
☎ Skipton (0756) 794727, talking timetable (0756)
   795189

*Steam railway running for 2 miles to
Holywell Halt. Shop, cafe, small museum,
collection of 14 steam locomotives, carriages
and rolling stock.*

2 miles east of Skipton, signposted from the A59
   Skipton by-pass
Open Aug daily except Mon and Fri, July Tues and Sat,
   Sun and Bank Holidays all year
Admission: fares adult £2.00, child £1.00 (1990 prices)
🚻 🚌 🐕

PARCEVALL HALL GARDENS

Country garden

Skyreholme, Skipton, North Yorkshire BD23 6DE
☎ Burnsall (0756) 72311

*Bradford Diocesan Retreat House. 16 acres
of gardens offer magnificent views from the
terrace over unspoiled Wharfedale. Orchard,
picnic area, rock garden and pools, home to
many birds, animals and wild flowers.*

From the B6265 follow the signs to Parcevall Hall,
   5 miles from Grassington
Open Easter–31 Oct 10.00am–6.00pm, please telephone
   before visit in winter
Admission: adult £1.00, child 50p (1989 prices)
🚌 advanced notice required 🐕

▶ *SPALDING MOOR* ◀

THE ROCKING HORSE SHOP

Craft workshop – rocking horses

Old Rd, Holme upon Spalding Moor, Yorkshire YO4 4AB
☎ Market Weighton (0430) 860563

*The Rocking Horse Shop displays traditional
wooden horses old and new. Special
commissions undertaken. We supply a
comprehensive range of plans and accessories
for craft enthusiasts and woodworkers.*

Take the A1079 from York–Hull, or leave the M62
   at jct 37
Open Mon–Sat 10.00am–4.00pm, please telephone for
   appointment
Free admission
🚻 🐕

► STOKESLEY ◄

CRATHORNE BERRY FARM

Pick your own

Crathorne, Yarm, North Yorkshire TS15 0BB
☎ Stokesley (0642) 700295

A beautifully cared for field with unrivalled views of the Cleveland hills. Pick strawberries, raspberries, gooseberries, red and blackcurrants, play and picnic area.

Off the A19 at Crathorne
Open daily during picking season (normally end June–early Aug) 9.30am–8.00pm
Free admission
& ✗

► SWALEDALE ◄

SWALEDALE WOOLLENS LIMITED

Woollens centre, cottage shop

Strawbeck, Muker, Richmond, North Yorkshire DL11 6QG
☎ Richmond (0748) 86251/4768

Swaledale Woollens have revived a hand knitting industry originating in the 16th century. Wide selection of local knitwear available at the unique cottage shop in Muker.

20 miles from Richmond and 10 miles from Hawes in Wensleydale
Open daily 10.00am–5.30pm, Sundays from 1.00pm. Closed Sun & Mon during Jan–March
Free admission
& ⇔ advanced notice required ✗

► WAKEFIELD ◄

YORKSHIRE SCULPTURE PARK

Open air sculpture park, landscaped parkland

Bretton Hall, West Bretton, Wakefield, West Yorkshire WF 4LG
☎ Wakefield (0924) 830302

Open air exhibitions, YSP collection, artists residencies and demonstrations, workshops and tours for schools and the public. Information centre, shop and cafe. First phase of Access Sculpture trail with access for people with disabilities opened 1989.

Exit 38 from the M1 is approx 1 mile from the park. Follow the Huddersfield road and turn left in West Bretton village for the park
Open daily 10.00am–6.00pm in summer, 10.00am–4.00pm in winter
Free admission
& electric 3 wheel scooter available for use by disabled visitors
⇔ advanced notice required ✗

► WETHERBY ◄

LILAC FARM PICK YOUR OWN

Pick your own and ready picked

Lilac Farm, Jewitt Lane, Collingham, Wetherby, West Yorkshire LS22 5BA
☎ Collingham Bridge (0937) 73162

Take the A58 Wetherby–Leeds road, farm is directly behind Barleycorn Inn, Collingham
Open daily 10.00am–7.00pm in season
Free admission
& ⇔ ✗

► YORK ◄

ACORN INDUSTRIES

Craft centre

Brandsby, Yorkshire YO6 4RG
☎ Brandsby (03475) 217/382

Acorn Industries is a family run firm, making handmade furniture, mainly in oak, but also other timbers. A large number of small items are always available for sale.

Leaving York take the B1363 north to Helmsley, passing through Sutton–on–Forest and Stillington
Open all year Mon–Fri 8.15am–5.15pm, Sat 8.15am–12.15pm
Free admission
& ⇔ advanced notice required ✗

E E G BULLIVANT & DAUGHTERS

Farm shop, producer of antibiotic and hormone free lamb, pork and beef products (frozen)

Vicarage Farm, Claxton, York YO6 7RY
☎ Flaxton Moor (090486) 222

We mill and mix our own feed and grow our own hay and roots for winter. No bought-in animal protein is fed to our stock.

1 mile off the A64 turning right at Claxton Hall,
6 miles from York, 10 miles from Malton
Open any time, by appointment please
Free admission
&. every assistance offered ✘

HASHOLME HEAVY HORSES

**Farm interpretation centre, farm trail, farm visit,
working horse implements, heavy horses and
other farm animals**

Hasholme Carr Farm, Holme on Spalding Moor, York
YO4 4BD
☎ Market Weighton (0430) 860393

*Family farm worked mainly with horses
which are also used for training courses,
forestry and film work. Mares and foals in
season.*

20 miles south east of York, 10 miles east of jct 37
of the M62, off the A614, signposted
Open Easter–Sept daily (except Fridays) 10.30am–5.00pm
Admission: adult £1.50, child 75p, OAP £1.25, under 5s
free, wheelchairbound 75p
&. animals can be viewed from hard level roads during
summer months
🚌 advanced notice required 🐴

SUTTON PARK

**Country house, country garden, woodland walks
and nature trail**

Sutton-on-the-Forest, York YO6 1DP
☎ Easingwold (0347) 810249

*Charming house, built in 1730 by Thomas
Atkinson, containing 18th century furniture
and paintings mostly from Buckingham
House, now Buckingham Palace, also an
important collection of porcelain. Tea room
and shop.*

On the B1363, 8 miles north of York
Open every Wed 2 May–12 Sept, Easter weekend and
Bank Holiday Mondays 1.30–5.30pm (last admission
5.00pm)
Admission: adult £2.20, child £1.10, OAP £1.45, coach
parties £1.80 (OAP £1.45); garden only adult £1.00,
child 50p, OAP 75p, coach parties 75p (1990 prices)
&. 🚌 ✘

CHANNEL ISLANDS

The Channel Islands, famous for their spring flowers, tomatoes and rich creamy milk, benefit from their more southerly location and the warming effects of the Gulf Stream. Sunshine, beaches of sand and exotic shells, fishing harbours and colourful villages give them great appeal. Their position between England and France has led to a mixture of cultures and has even led to their occupation at different periods of history.

There is a museum on Jersey which will introduce the visitor to the agriculture, archaeology and geology of the area – it is close to one of the finest Neolithic tombs in Western Europe.

▶ JERSEY ◀

LA HOUGUE BIE MUSEUM

Museum

La Hougue Bie, Grouville, Jersey, Channel Islands
☎ Jersey (0534) 53823

*Small museum of Agriculture, Archaeology
and Geology with a German bunker and a
Mediaeval chapel set in a quiet park
surrounding one of the finest Neolithic
tombs in western Europe.*

On the B28, 3 miles north east of St Helier
Open Feb–Nov, daily 10.00am–5.00pm
Admission: adult £1.20, child under 10 free, student/OAP
  60p

ISLE OF WIGHT

The Isle of Wight offers a well-preserved rural setting with pretty seaside towns and famous sailing centres around its shores.

There are historic houses and gardens to stroll around, farms to visit, farm trails to follow, a farm studies centre, a farm interpretation centre, a farming museum and a watermill to explore. There are vineyards and wineries, a glass workshop, a butterfly world and water gardens to enjoy. There is even a craft village where you can have goods made to order.

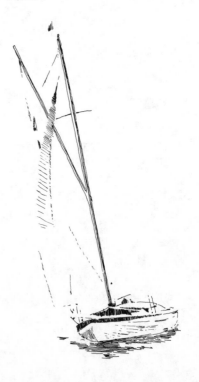

► **ALUM BAY** ◄

ALUM BAY GLASS

Glassworks

Alum Bay, Isle of Wight PO39 0JD
☎ (0938) 753473

Alum Bay Glass Workshop makes by hand beautiful glass and costume jewellery in a myriad of colours. Glassmaking may be watched when in progress. Shop open all year.

Take the B3322 from Freshwater West, at the end is Alum Bay
Open Easter–Oct daily 9.30am–5.00pm (no glass making on Saturdays), rest of year Mon–Fri 9.30am–12.30pm and 1.30–5.00pm, open for sales most Sat & Sun in winter
Admission to view the glass making: adult 40p, child 20p, OAP 30p. Free in winter
点 ᗡ 🍴

► **EAST COWES** ◄

BARTON MANOR VINEYARD & GARDENS

Vineyard

Whippingham, East Cowes, Isle of Wight PO32 6LB
☎ Isle of Wight (0983) 292835

10½ acre vineyard set in 20 acre gardens originally laid out by Queen Victoria and Prince Albert, and later extended by King Edward VII. Winery, 2 videos, wine bar and cafe, collections, shop.

Next to Osborne House on the A3021 East Cowes–Newport and Ryde road
Open daily May–2nd Sunday in October, plus weekends in April and Easter 10.30am–5.30pm
Admission: adult £2.50, child (15 & under, one per adult) free. Includes souvenir tasting glass, 2 tastings & colour guide (1989 prices)
点
ᗡ advance notice required. Not in July and Aug 🍴

► **NEWPORT** ◄

ARRETON COUNTRY CRAFT VILLAGE

Craft centre and restaurant

Arreton, nr Newport, Isle of Wight PO30 5AA
☎ Isle of Wight (0983) 528353

Fully working craft village. Have goods made to order – buy direct from the maker. Home baking in licensed restaurant, all under cover.

Arreton is on the main Newport–Sandown road (A3056) approx 5 miles south of Newport
Open April–Oct Mon–Fri 9.30am–5.00pm, Sun 12.00–5.00pm and Bank Holiday weekends
Admission: adult £1.60, child £1.00, OAP £1.40, special party rates. Entrance tickets last 1 week to allow for return visits.
点 ᗡ 🍴

CALBOURNE WATER MILL & RURAL MUSEUM

Farming museum

Newport, Isle of Wight PO30 4JN
☎ Calbourne (0983) 227

Early 17th century mill containing an 1890 roller plant. Stone ground flour, milled on the premises is available in the gift shop/cafe, which serves freshly baked bread and cakes.

Midway on the B3401 Newport–Freshwater road
Open Easter–Oct daily 10.00am–6.00pm
Admission: adult £1.40, child 70p, OAP £1.20 (1990 prices)
点 ᗡ 🍴

CLAMERKIN FARM PARK

Farm visit, country walk and farm interpretation centre

Newtown, Newport, Isle of Wight PO30 4PD
☎ (0983) 78396

Meet and feed rare breed pigs (8 different breeds) and other farm animals in a unique setting on the shores of the Newtown River. Refreshments available.

Newtown on the Cowes–Yarmouth road
Open Easter–Oct 10.30am–6.00pm
Admission: adult £1.20 child (4–16 years) 60p, OAP £1.00 (1990 prices)
点 the park is level and suitable for wheelchairs but there are no toilets for the disabled ᗡ 🍴

▶ *RYDE* ◀

LITTLE UPTON DAIRY FARM VISITS

Farm shop, country walk, farm trail and farm visit

Little Upton Farm, Gatehouse Road, Ashey, nr Ryde, Isle
of Wight PO33 4BS
☎ Ryde (0983) 63236

*An educational visit for children of all ages;
over 12 years experience with school parties.
Prior booking essential – 3 visits per day
10.00am, 12.00 noon and 2.00pm. Acclaimed
by Times Education Officer – David Tyrler.*

2 miles south of Ryde, on the Havenstreet road at
Upton Cross
Open by appointment only
Admission: £1.45 per person. School parties a speciality
& ♿ advance notice required 🐕

NUNWELL HOUSE AND GARDENS

**Historic house and garden, nature trail and
country walk**

Coach Lane, Brading, Isle of Wight PO36 0JQ
☎ Isle of Wight (0983) 407240

*King Charles spent his last night of freedom
in 1647 at this house. Garden developed in
17th century. Finely furnished rooms; family
and Home Guard museums; in 1990 the
National Exhibition 'They Stood Alone'.*

Take the A3055 Sandown road to outskirts of
Brading. Turn right into Coach Lane, first large
gates on left, signposted off the A3055
Open Sun 6 July–Thur 27 Sept. Closed Fri and Sat
Admission: adult £1.80, child 60p, OAP £1.50
& there are many steps, but help is available
♿ advance notice required 🐕

From Sandown take the A3055 to Ryde. Left at
traffic lights in Brading. Follow Downs Road to
Newport. Take signposted left turn on hill
Open all year Mon–Fri 9.00am–4.30pm, Sat 10.00am–
12.30pm
Free admission
& 🐕

BRANSTONE FARM STUDIES CENTRE

Farm trail and farm visit

Branstone, Sandown, Isle of Wight PO30 0LT
☎ Sandown (0983) 865540 (warden)

*Centre run by the I.O.W.C.C. Education
Dept. allowing children to experience life on
a working farm. Milking routine from
3.30pm. Guided tour of 2 hours; follow-up
work afterwards in the teaching block.*

Open: tours at 10.00am and 2.00pm
Admission: approx £1.50 for school children (adults free)
& ♿ 🐕

MORTON MANOR

**Farm shop, English vineyard, historic house and
gardens**

Brading, nr Sandown, Isle of Wight PO36 0EP
☎ Isle of Wight (0983) 406168

*A beautiful historic house with fine furniture
and fittings. Magnificent gardens
complement its setting, as does the vineyard
incorporating the winery and museum.
Quality gifts and catering available.*

Off the main A3055 Sandown–Ryde road, well
signposted at Yarbridge Cross south of Brading
Open April–Oct daily (except Saturdays) 10.00am–5.30pm
Admission: adult £2.20, child £1.00, OAP £1.75, party
rate £1.50 (subject to alteration)
& ♿ 🐕

▶ *SANDOWN* ◀

ADGESTONE VINEYARDS LTD

Farm shop and speciality drink producer

Upper Rd, Adgestone, Sandown, Isle of Wight PO36 0ES
☎ Isle of Wight (0983) 402503

*Visitors are welcome to stroll through the
vineyard, view the working winery and talk
with our friendly staff. The wine is available
from the vineyard shop.*

▶ *VENTNOR* ◀

BLACKGANG CHINE THEME PARK

Country park

Nr Ventnor, Isle of Wight PO38 2HN
☎ Isle of Wight (0983) 730330

*Gardens and themed tableaux continually
being added to, set in 30 acres of heritage*

coastline including Adventure Land, Fantasy Land and Frontier Land. Also 2 exhibitions about woodland crafts and maritime history.

Off the A3055, 6 miles south of Ventnor
Open Easter–late Oct daily 10.00am–5.00pm; floodlit
    evenings: June–late Sept daily, open to 10.00pm
Admission: adult £2.99, child (3–13) £1.99 (1990 prices)
 ♿ ♲ 🏬

►   *WOOTTON*   ◄

BUTTERFLY WORLD AND FOUNTAIN WORLD

Indoor butterfly farm and Japanese and Italian water gardens

Staplers Road, Wootton, Isle of Wight PO33 4RW
☎   Isle of Wight (0983) 883430

Beautiful indoor garden with exotic butterflies on the wing. Also exotic insect display. Fountain World comprises a classical Italian Garden and a Japanese Garden with large and amazing Koi Carp.

Midway between Wootton and Newport on the
    alternative road via Wootton Common and
    Staplers
Open Good Friday–31 Oct 10.00am–5.00pm
Admission: adult £2.00, child/OAP £1.35
 ♿ ♲ ✕

NORTHERN IRELAND

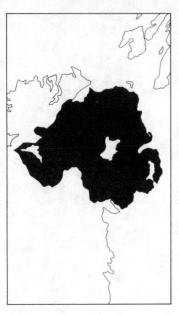

Northern Ireland is a land of lakes,
Celtic mystery, enchanting mountains,
beautiful coastlines, rich farmland and
strongly rural communities.

To experience the delights of the
countryside the visitor is recommended
to take one of the country walks, follow
a nature trail, visit a forestry centre or a
countryside interpretation centre.
There are also farms, bird gardens,
museums and exhibitions to visit. Take
a look at the history of the region's famous
linen industry at one of the old beetling
mills, watch lead crystal being blown and
handcut, or try your hand at a spot of
fishing or boating – both are very popular
pastimes in Northern Ireland.

► BALLYCASTLE ◄

WATERTOP OPEN FARM

Farm visit, trail, interpretation centre, museum and country walk

188 Cushendall Rd, Ballycastle, Co Antrim BT54 6RN
☎ Ballycastle (02657) 62576

Scenic 500 acre hill farm offers pony-trekking, fishing, boating, farm tours as well as camping & caravanning. Daily attractions include sheep-shearing and 'Paddiwagon' trips. Tea room.

6 miles from Ballycastle, off the A2 to Cushendall beside Ballypatrick Castle
Open end June–early Sept 10.00am–5.30pm
Admission: adult 60p, child 40p
& most buildings accessible by wheelchair. Experience with disabled groups
advance notice required ⚞

► BALLYMENA ◄

GLENARIFF FOREST PARK

Forestry centre, exhibition, nature trail, cafe, nature reserve

98 Glenariff Rd, Ballymena BT44 0QX
☎ Martinstown (030 588) 232

A varied selection of walks offer spectacular views of the glen and its waterfalls.

On the A43, Ballymena 10 miles, Waterfoot 5 miles
Open all year 10.00am–sunset
Admission: £1.60 per car, £10.00 per coach
& ⚞ ⚞

► BELFAST ◄

PICKWICKS

Pick your own

28 Carrowreagh Rd, Dundonald, Belfast BT16 0TS
☎ Belfast (0232) 480801

Newtownards–Dundonald dual carriageway, turn left at 'European Components' factory going towards Newtownards, second field on right
Open during soft fruit season
Free admission
& ⚞ ⚞

STREAMVALE OPEN FARM

Farm visit, pick your own and farm trail

38 Ballyhanwood Rd, Belfast BT5 7SN
☎ Dundonald (02318) 3244/89966

Pets corner, feeding hends and ducks, nature trail, deer, bottle feeding lambs and kids. Viewing gallery to watch milking, hatchery, aquarium, pony rides, chicks. Pick your own soft fruit.

½ mile past Dundonald International Ice Bowl on King's Road, East Belfast
Open June–Sept: daily 12.00 noon–6.00pm. Oct–May: Sat, Sun & Wed 2.00–6.00pm. Easter Week & Bank Holidays, daily 12.00 noon–6.00pm
Admission: adult £1.50, child/OAP/disabled £1.20, family ticket £5.50
& ⚞ ⚞

► CASTLEWELLAN ◄

CASTLEWELLAN FOREST PARK

Farm shop, craft centre, country park, forestry centre, national arboretum

Castlewellan, Co Down BT31 9BU
☎ (03967) 78664

Castlewellan offers historic buildings and relics. For the more adventurous, signposted walks, with famous view points of the Mourne mountains. An outstanding arboretum, (world famous) and game fishing on the lake.

30 miles south of Belfast off the A24, 4 miles west of Newcastle
Open daily all year
Admission: car £2.00, minibus £4.00, motor cycle £1.00, coach £10.00 (1990 prices)
& ⚞ ⚞ on a leash in arboretum

► COMBER ◄

CASTLE ESPIE CENTRE, WILDFOWL & WETLANDS TRUST

Waterfowl collection, coffee room, exhibition, walks and art gallery

78 Ballydrain Road, Comber, Co Down BT23 6EA
☎ Comber (0247) 874146

Castle Espie provides a unique mixture of the finest collection of waterfowl in Ireland with beautiful grounds and outstanding views over Strangford Lough.

Off the A22 to Downpatrick for ¼ mile, turn left, 2 miles down Ballydrain Road
Open all year (except Christmas Eve & Christmas Day) Mon–Sat from 10.30am, Sun from 2.00pm
Admission: adult £1.80, child 90p
  📠 advance notice required 🐕

► COOKSTOWN ◄

WELLBROOK BEETLING MILL

Watermill

20 Wellbrook Rd, Corkhill, Cookstown, Co Tyrone BT80 9RY
☎ Tulnacross (06487) 51735

A water mill used for closing up the weave of linen, the action of the wooden beetles gives the cloth its smooth lustrous finish.

½ mile off the A505 Cookstown–Omagh road
Open Good Friday and Easter week, April–June Sat, Sun and Bank Holidays, July–Aug daily except Tues, Sept Sat and Sun 2.00–6.00pm
Admission: adult £1.00, child 50p
  📠

► CRAIGAVON ◄

MONEYPENNY'S LOCKS

Country walk

c/o Visitor Centre, Oxford Island, Craigavon, Co Armagh BT66 6NJ
☎ Lurgan (0762) 322205

Moneypenny's Lock and Lock House date from the beginning of the last century. The original part of the Lock House is being restored to illustrate the way of life of the lock keepers and bargees during the period when the Newry Canal was at its busiest.

Turn off the A50 from Portadown at junction of Tandagree road. Park at Dyne's Bridge and follow Ulster Way signs along canal towpath
Open all year for walk
Free admission
  🐕

OXFORD ISLAND NATURE RESERVE

Nature reserve

Visitor Centre, Oxford Island, Craigavon, Co Armagh BT66 6NJ
☎ (0762) 322205

Nature reserve on the south eastern shore of Lough Neagh with Visitor Centre, birdwatching hides, programme of countryside events and network of paths. The reserve offers visitors the opportunity to view breeding and wintering wildfowl.

1 mile from the Lurgan interchange (roundabout 10) on the M1
Visitor centre open Mon–Fri 9.00am–5.00pm, Sun 10.00am–5.00pm
Unlimited public access to the reserve which is open all year
Free admission
  paths suitable for disabled visitors with wheelchair access to one birdwatching hide
📠 🐕

► CRUMLIN ◄

TALNOTRY COTTAGE BIRD GARDEN

Bird garden

2 Crumlin Road, Crumlin, Co Antrim BT29 4AD
☎ Crumlin (084 94) 22900

A walled garden houses the most varied collection of ornamental pheasants, partridges, pea fowl, jungle fowl and quail to be seen in Ireland. Many world-endangered species are bred.

At T junction where A26 from Antrim joins A52 in Crumlin
Open Easter–end Aug Sun & Bank Holidays 2.00–6.00pm, other times by arrangement
Admission: adult £1.70, child 60p
  manual assistance available
📠 advance notice required
🐕 except guide dogs

► DUNGANNON ◄

PARKANAUR FOREST PARK

Country walk, forestry centre, nature trail, deer park, gardens and exhibitions

c/o Pomeroy Forest Office, 56 Tanderagee Road, Pomeroy, Co Tyrone
☎ Pomeroy (086 87) 58256

This forest park is based on an old estate, the house of which is still in use. Much of the estate woodland still survives giving Parkanaur its unique character.

5 miles south on bypass or old Ballygawley road
Open all year dawn until dusk for park. Main exhibition Easter–Oct
Admission: car £1.00, motorcycle 50p, coach £8.50
&. most footpaths are suitable for wheelchairs, as is the entrance to the main exhibition
🚌 advance notice required 🏴

TYRONE CRYSTAL LTD

Manufacture and decoration of full lead crystal

Killybrackey, Dungannon, Co Tyrone
☎ Dungannon (08687) 25335 Fax (08687) 26260

Each piece of Tyrone Crystal is individually handcrafted as the full lead crystal is mouth blown and hand cut. Visitors can view every aspect of production in their new factory.

Take the A29 at end of the M1, 2 miles through town centre following signposts to Dungannon
Open all year Mon–Thur except industrial holidays
Free admission
&. there are no special toilet facilities 🚌 🏴

▶ *ENNISKILLEN* ◀

ARDESS CRAFT CENTRE

Craft centre and country garden

Ardess House, Kesh, Co Fermanagh BT93 1NX
☎ Kesh (03656) 31267

Off the B82, 14 miles north of Enniskillen
Open all year Mon–Sat 10.00am–5.00pm, Sun 2.00–5.00pm
Admission by voluntary contributions (suggest 50p per adult)
&. access to craft workshop and craft shop, but no special toilet facilities
🚌 advance notice required 🏴

▶ *LIMAVADY* ◀

NESS WOOD COUNTRY PARK

Country park and country walk

c/o Roe Valley Country Park, 41 Leap Road, Limavady, Co Londonderry BT49 9NN
☎ (0504) 762074

Ness Wood is a remnant of extensive natural oak woodland now commemorated by over 1000 place names in Ireland containing the word Derry. The main feature of Ness is a spectacular waterfall from which the area derives its name.

Off the A6 Londonderry–Dungiven road or the A6 Belfast–Londonderry road, well signposted
Open all year
Free admission
&. the terrain is very rough 🚌 🏴

ROE VALLEY COUNTRY PARK

Country park, country walk, countryside interpretation centre, museum, flax scutching mills, linen weaving and beetling mills

41 Leap Road, Limavady, Co Londonderry
☎ Limavady (05047) 62074

Roe Valley Country Park stretches for 3 miles along both sides of the River Roe. Facilities such as caravan and camp site, countryside museum and cafe are all available at Dogleap Centre.

Take the A6 from Belfast to Londonderry, then the B192 at Dungiven towards Limavady, well signposted
Open all year daily
Free admission
&. 🚌 🏴

▶ *LISNASKEA* ◀

TEACH A CEILI

Country walk

Inniscorkish, Lisnaskea, Fermanagh
☎ Lisnaskea (03657) 21360

Private nature trail on island, 80 acres, bounded by indigenous trees, scrub and water. Abounding in wildlife. Guesthouse, restaurant; free boat service for patrons, jetty space for boats; orienteering (maps provided).

Take the B127 Derrylin road 2 miles, turn right for Kilmore Quay 1 mile. From Lisnaskea telephone above number for boat service
Open April–Oct 10.00am–4.00pm
Admission: adult £2.00, child 50p (must be accompanied)
&. 🚌 advance notice required 🏴

▶ **MARKETHILL** ◀

GOSFORD FOREST PARK

Forestry centre, nature trails and poultry collection

54 Gosford Road, Armagh BT60 1UG
☎ Markethill (0861) 551277

Forestry exhibitions, deer park and cafe.

On the A28 Newry–Armagh road adjacent to
   Markethill
Open all year 10.00am–sunset
Admission: adult 50p, child 25p, coach £10.00
&. ▥ ⊁

▶ **NEWTOWNSTEWART** ◀

BARONSCOURT ESTATE

Garden centre

Baronscourt Estate Office, Newtownstewart, Omagh,
Co Tyrone BT78 4EZ
☎ Newtownstewart (06626) 61683

*The garden centre offers a wide range of
unusual plants. Located in the picturesque
setting of Abercorn Estates. Visitors may
browse through the connoisseur section for
special plants.*

3 miles south west of Newtownstewart on the road
   to Drumquin
Open Mon–Sat 10.00am–4.30pm, Sun 2.00–4.30pm,
   closed 25–26 Dec
Free admission
&. there are no special toilet facilities ▥ ⊁

▶ **OMAGH** ◀

ULSTER–AMERICAN FOLK PARK

**Outdoor museum of emigration with craft and
farm demonstrations**

Camphill, Omagh, Co Tyrone
☎ Omagh (0662) 3292/3

*An outdoor museum of emigration with
traditional thatched cottages and farm
buildings. American log houses, craft
demonstrations, Ship and Dockside Gallery.
Gallery exhibitions and audio-visual
presentations.*

Open Easter–early Sept: Mon–Sat 11.00am–6.30pm, Sun
   & Bank Holidays 11.30am–7.00pm, Sept–Easter
   Mon–Fri 10.30am–5.00pm
Admission: adult £2.00, child/OAP/disabled £1.00, family
   ticket £6.00
&. ▥ ⊁

▶ **PORTADOWN** ◀

ARDRESS HOUSE

**Farming museum, farm interpretation centre,
country garden, country house**

Annaghmore, Portadown, Co Armagh DT62 1SQ
☎ Annaghmore (0762) 851236

*17th century farmhouse with 18th century
extensions. Garden and woodland walk,
enclosed cobbled farmyard with display of
early agricultural machinery, some rare farm
animals.*

7 miles from Portadown on Moy Road (B28), 3
   miles from intersection 13 on the M1 from
   Belfast
Open Good Friday and Easter week 2.00–6.00pm; April,
   May, June and Sept weekends and Bank Holidays
   2.00–6.00pm; July and Aug daily (except Tuesdays)
   2.00–6.00pm
Admission to house and farm: adult £1.25, child 60p;
   farm only: adult 50p, child 25p; additional estate
   charge adult 50p, child 25p
&. ▥

▶ **PORTRUSH** ◀

PORTRUSH COUNTRYSIDE CENTRE

Country park, countryside interpretation centre

8 Bath Rd, Portrush, Co Antrim BT56 8AP
☎ Portrush (0265) 823600

Take the M2 from Belfast heading north, following
   signs for Portrush
Open June–Aug daily (except Tues) 1.00–9.00pm; for
   party visits out of season please telephone
Free admission
&. ▥ advance notice required ⊁

► *STRABANE* ◄

THE SPERRIN HERITAGE CENTRE

**Local history and heritage centre, craft shop,
Glenelly kitchen**

274 Glenelly Road, Cranagh, Gortin, Omagh, Co Tyrone,
   BT99 8LS
☎ Gortin (06626) 48142

*The centre is situated in the beautiful and
mystic Sperrin Mountains. The 'Sperrin
Options' and gold panning provide an
interesting and enjoyable day's outing.*

On the B47, 8 miles east of Plumbridge
Open summer: Mon–Fri 11.00am–6.00pm, Sat
   11.30am–6.00pm, Sun 2.00–7.00pm
Admission: adult £1.25, child 50p, family group £3.00,
   OAP/disabled free
&. ⇔ ✕

SCOTLAND

LOWLANDS

The Lowlands is a rich agricultural landscape of rolling hills, historic buildings and small villages with a picturesque coastline. Known as 'the home of golf', it has a great number of courses and attracts golfers from all over the world.

Country and woodland walks, forest, mountain and farm trails – there are an abundance to choose from. There are country parks, country gardens, shepherd centres, nature reserves, deer and wildlife parks, woodland exhibition centres, forest information centres, watermills, forest drives, fruit farms and herb nurseries. When weary from the outdoor pursuits take a look round the glass workshops and craft galleries or try some of the local malt whisky.

▶ *ABERFELDY* ◀

THE BIRKS OF ABERFELDY

Country walk

c/o Perth & Kinross District Council, Leisure and
  Recreation Dept, 3 High St, Perth PH1 5PH
☎ Perth (0738) 39911 ext 3617

*Pleasant 1½ mile walk, rising 150 metres, in
attractive woodland. Accessible from the
centre of Aberfeldy, its enchanting ravines
and waterfalls inspired Burns to dedicate a
poem to it.*

'The Birks of Aberfeldy' walk is off the A826 Crieff
  road, ¼ mile south of Aberfeldy
Open all hours
Free admission
& unsuitable for wheelchairs 🚌 🐴

CLUNY HOUSE GARDENS

Country garden

Cluny House, by Aberfeldy, Perthshire PH15 2JT
☎ Aberfeldy (0887) 20795

*Woodland garden with many specimen trees,
shrubs and rhododendrons. Large collections
of primulas, nomocharis, trilliums,
meconopsis and lilies. Most colourful in
spring and autumn.*

3½ miles outside Aberfeldy on the Weem–Strathay
  road
Open March–Oct 10.00am–6.00pm
Admission: adult £1.00, children under 16 free
& 🚌 advance notice required 🐴

GLENGOULANDIE DEER PARK

Deer and wildlife park

Glengoulandie, Foss, by Pitlochry, Perthshire PH15 6NL
☎ Kenmore (08873) 261

*Many excellent examples of red deer can be
seen in their natural environment. Also in
the park are highland cattle, goats, various
breeds of sheep, and many varieties of
wildfowl.*

8 miles from Aberfeldy on the B846 to Kinloch
  Rannoch
Open Easter–Sept 9.00am until 1 hour before sunset
Admission: car £3.50 or 70p for walkers
& 🚌 🐴

▶ *AYR* ◀

FORESTRY COMMISSION – LOCH BRADEN

Trout fishing

Dalmellington Rd, Straiton, nr Maybole, Ayrshire
  KA19 7NG
☎ Straiton (06557) 637

*Loch Bradan is situated in the wild,
magnificent scenery of the Galloway Forest
Park. Family groups welcome. Fly fishing
only in nearby Loch Skelloch (boat
available).*

Off the B7045 18 miles south of Ayr
Open March–Oct daily 8.00am–dusk
Admission: permit fishing prices adult £4.50, child £2.50.
  Weekly: adult £16.50, child £8.00
& 🚌 advance notice required 🐴

ROZELLE PARK NATURE TRAIL

Parkland estate

Parks and Recreation Dept, 30 Miller Rd, Ayr KA7 2AY
☎ Ayr (0292) 281511

*Museum and Maclaurin Art Gallery. The
nature trail embraces parkland, woodland
and ponds. It is an elementary introduction
to the plants and wildlife in a town park.*

Follow the B7024 from Ayr town centre, entrance
  to Rozelle Park approx 2 miles from town centre
  on left hand side
Open all year
Free admission
& 🚌 🐴

▶ *BALMACLELLAN* ◀

ANNE HUGHES POTTERY

Craft centre

Auchreoch, Balmaclellan, Kirkcudbrightshire DG7 3QB
☎ New Galloway (06442) 205

*Known for her unique flower plates, Anne
works in her old Galloway cottage. Variety
of colourful hand thrown domestic ware,
individual pierced plates and bowls, and
lustred porcelain.*

In the hills near Balmaclellan on the A712
Open May–Sept daily 10.00am–6.00pm or by
  appointment
Free admission
& access to shop, but no toilet facilities 🐴

THE GALLOWAY FOOTWEAR CO-OPERATIVE

Craft centre, workshop and shop

The Old School, Balmaclellan, Castle Douglas,
 Kirkcudbrightshire
☎ New Galloway (06442) 465/666

*Traditional British, Scandinavian and
French clogs; strap, buckle and lace-up
shoes; ankle and walking boots; sandals.
Made to order or from stock. Small museum
of footwear and clogmaking tools.*

13 miles north of Castle Douglas on the A713, turn
 right onto the A712. 1 mile on left, Balmaclellan
 village
Open May–Oct, Mon–Fri 2.00–5.00pm, other times by
 appointment
Admission: adult 50p, refundable with purchase
&. ⊞ appointment only, please park in village ⊁

TWEEDHOPE SHEEP DOGS

**Border collie & shepherd centre, farm trail and
farm visit**

Tweedhopefoot, Tweedsmuir, by Biggar, Lanarkshire
 ML12 6QS
☎ Tweedsmuir (08997) 267

*Visit the stars of 'One Man and His Dog'
working amidst rugged Border hills.
Experience the ancient craft of shepherding
and become aware of the extraordinary
relationship which exists between shepherd
and sheep dog. Light refreshments.*

On the A701 Moffat–Edinburgh road, 8 miles from
 Moffat, 15 miles from Biggar
Open Easter–Oct daily (except Saturdays), demonstrations
 11.00am, 2.00pm, 3.00pm. Other months and
 Saturdays by appointment
Admission: adult £1.50, child £1.00
&. it is possible to view sheepdog
demonstrations ⊞ ⊁

► *NORTH BERWICK* ◄

YELLOWCRAIG

Country walk

Leisure & Recreation Dept, Brunton Hall, Musselburgh
 EH21 6AE
☎ (031 665) 3711

*Yellowcraig is a coastal area beside the Forth
noted for its huge variety of seabirds and
plant life. Guided walks are available
throughout the summer led by experienced
rangers.*

Access road leads from the B1345
Open all year
Free admission
&. ⊞ ⊁

► *BONCHESTER BRIDGE* ◄

EASTER WEENS FARM

Cheese farm

Bonchester Bridge, nr Hawick, Roxburghshire
☎ Bonchester Bridge (045 086) 635

*Gourmet cheeses made daily from
unpasteurised milk from Jersey cows for sale
– self-service at the back door. Regret no
tours etc. due to hygiene risk.*

About ½ mile along the B6357 towards Jedburgh
Open April–Dec every day, self-service
&. ⊞ advance notice required ⊁

► *BIGGAR* ◄

GREENHILL COVENANTER'S HOUSE

17th century farmhouse

Biggar, Lanarkshire ML12 6DT
☎ Biggar (0899) 21050

On the A702, 28 miles south west of Edinburgh,
 12 miles from the A74/M74
Open April–Oct daily 2.00–5.00pm
Admission: adult 50p, child 30p, joint charge available
 with other local attractions
&. ⊞ parking nearby ⊁

► *CASTLE DOUGLAS* ◄

NORTH GLEN GALLERY

Glass workshop and gallery

Palnackie, Castle Douglas, Kirkcudbrightshire DG7 1PN
☎ Palnackie (055660) 200

*Glassblowing, advice on local walks,
mushrooms and other Natural History.
Telephone before travelling far.*

Approx 7 miles south of Castle Douglas just off the
 A710 coast road

Open 10.00am–6.00pm, 7 days a week during school
    holidays, Fri–Sun other times
Admission: adult 50p, child/OAP 10p (refunded with
    purchase)
 ⛽ advance notice required 🐎

► COLDINGHAM ◄

ST ABB'S HEAD

National nature reserve

Nature Reserve Centre in Northfield Farm steading
☎   Coldingham (089 07) 71443

*Managed jointly with the Scottish Wildlife
Trust. A spectacular headland of 192 acres,
with 300 ft cliffs. The most important
location for cliff-nesting seabirds in south
east Scotland. Exhibition.*

2 miles north of Coldingham, Berwickshire
Open all year. Parties by prior arrangement only

► COLDSTREAM ◄

THE HIRSEL

Country walks, craft workshops & museum

Coldstream, Berwickshire TD12 4LP
☎   Coldstream (0890) 2834

*At all seasons of the year The Hirsel can
provide interest and entertainment for every
member of the family – from peace and
beauty to the playground for the children.
Refreshments.*

Immediately west of Coldstream on the A697
    (Thistle sign at the lodge)
Open every day of the year, daylight hours
Admission: small charge for adults
 ⛽ 🐎

► COMRIE ◄

GLEN LEDNOCK CIRCULAR WALK

Country walk

c/o Perth & Kinross District Council, Leisure and
    Recreation Dept, 3 High St, Perth PH1 5PH
☎   Perth (0738) 39911 ext 3617

*A 4 mile walk through deciduous and
evergreen woodland, opening into attractive
countryside. The walk includes a short climb
to Lord Melville's monument which affords
excellent views. Waterfall.*

Car park off the A85 Crieff road, east end of
    Comrie
Open all hours
Free admission
  unsuitable for wheelchairs ⛽ 🐎

► CUPAR ◄

SCOTTISH DEER CENTRE

Deer centre

Cupar, Fife KY15 4NQ
☎   Letham (033781) 391

*Offering a unique hands-on experience of
majestic red deer and other species the
visitor centre, exhibition, films, nature
trails and Adventureland make a perfect
setting for family days out.*

On the A91 St Andrews road, 3 miles west of
    Cupar, 10 miles west of St Andrews
Open April–Oct daily 10.00am–5.00pm (extended opening
    June, July and August); Nov–March weekends & Bank
    Holidays, weekday group visits by appointment
Admission: adult £2.50, child (3–14 yrs) £1.50,
    concessions £2.00. Discounts available for pre-booked
    groups (1990 prices)
 ⛽ 🍽

► DUMFRIES ◄

ARBIGLAND ESTATE

Country garden and tea room

Kirkbean, Dumfries DG2 8BQ
☎   Kirkbean (038788) 283

*Rated outstanding in 'Managed Landscapes
of Scotland'. Gardens lead down to sandy
bay. The estate laid out by William Craik,
the agriculturalist (1703–1798), the gardens
by John Paul, father of John Paul Jones
founder of the American Navy.*

14 miles south west of Dumfries on the A710
    'Solway Coast Heritage Route' signposted from
    Kirkbean
Open for the grounds: May–Sept Tues, Thurs, Sun
    2.00–6.00pm. House & gardens: Whitsun week
Admission: adult £1.00, child 50p (1990 prices)
 ⛽ 🐎

► **DUNBAR** ◄

JOHN MUIR COUNTRY PARK

Country walk

Leisure & Recreation Dept, Brunton Hall, Mussselburgh
EH21 6AE
☎ (031 665) 3711

*John Muir country park was opened in 1976
and was named after the founder of the
American National Parks whose birthplace
can be visited in nearby Dunbar (video
presentation). Abundant flora and fauna and
a huge variety of birds. Guided walks.*

Take the A1, either Edinburgh or the south, then
along the A1087 approx 1 mile
Open all year
Free admission
& toilets open Easter–Sept 🚌 🅟

► **DUNS** ◄

ABBEY ST BATHANS TROUT FARM

Trout farm with woodland walks

Abbey St Bathans, Duns, Berwickshire
☎ Abbey St Bathans (03614) 242

*The estate lies in a beautiful, secluded valley.
Picnic area, tea room, potters at work,
gallery, woodland walks along riverside,
fresh and smoked trout for sale.*

Off the A1, 7 miles south west of Grantshouse, 21
miles from Berwick-upon-Tweed
Open Easter–Sept daily 11.00am–5.00pm
Free admission for car park, picnic area and walks. Trout
farm (feed for trout) 50p
& 🚌 advance notice required 🅟

► **EARLSTON** ◄

LEGERWOOD FARM TRAIL

Farm visit

c/o Borders Regional Council Ranger Service, Regional
HQ, Newtown St Boswells TD6 0SA
☎ St Boswells (0835) 23301 ext 433

*Easy walk around a working farm in the
Border countryside. Self-guide booklet 50p
from all local Tourist Information Centres or
from dispenser at farm (honesty box).
National Scenic area.*

1 mile east of the A68, 3 miles north of Earlston
Open June–Sept
Free parking
🅟

► **EDINBURGH** ◄

GORGIE CITY FARM

Outdoor community education

Gorgie Rd, Tynecastle Lane, Gorgie, Edinburgh EH11 2LA
☎ Edinburgh (031337) 4202

*Farm animals right in the middle of the city.
Cattle, sheep, pigs, hens, goats, ducks etc.
Visitor centre, 'Farm Kitchen' cafe,
craftwork, picnic and play area, vegetables
and crops on show.*

Adjacent to the A71 Gorgie road near the junction
with the A70, approx 2 miles west of Edinburgh
post office
Open all year daily 9.00am–4.30pm
Free admission, but donations welcome
& 🐕

► **FIFE** ◄

FIFE RANGER SERVICE

Country walk

Pitcairn Ranger Base, Glenrothes
☎ Glenrothes (0592) 741212

*Pitcairn is base for Fife Ranger Service in
the Lomond Hills. There are pleasant
footpaths and the rangers run a programme
of countryside walks and events. Please
phone to check details.*

Follow signposts from Coul roundabout on the
Leslie–Balfarg road, 2 miles north east of
Glenrothes centre
Pond, picnic area and walk to E. Lomond open at all
times. Pitcairn centre open when rangers are in
Free admission
& the walk is not suitable for wheelchairs 🅟

► **GARLIESTON** ◄

GALLOWAY HOUSE GARDENS

Country garden

Garlieston, Wigtownshire
☎ Garlieston (09886) 225

*Drifts of snowdrops and daffodils in spring
give way to all sorts of hybrid
rhododendrons. Masses of cherry blossom.
Camellias in the walled garden should be
seen in early spring.*

Take the A714 Newton–Stewart road, then the
   B7004
Open all year daily, dawn–dusk
Admission by donations in collection box
  🚫 🚃 🐕

▶ **GATEHOUSE OF FLEET** ◀

MURRAY FOREST INFORMATION CENTRE

Interpretative trail and forestry centre

Forestry Commission, 21 King St, Castle Douglas,
   DG7 1AA
☎   Castle Douglas (0556) 3626

*A 2 mile all weather trail through semi-
mature broadleaved forest. Impressive
displays of snowdrops and bluebells in
season. Opportunities to view a wide variety
of flora and fauna.*

Signposted from ¼ mile east of Gatehouse of Fleet
Open Jan–Dec 9.00am–5.00pm
Free admission
& 🐕

▶ **GIRVAN** ◀

BARGANY GARDENS

Country garden

Bargany Estate Office, Girvan, Ayrshire KA26 9RG
☎   Old Dailly (046 587) 249

*Woodland and rock garden centred on lily
pond surrounded by azaleas, snowdrops and
daffodils. Many species and hybrid
rhododendrons, fine trees and shrubs. At its
best mid April to mid June.*

Take the B734 from Girvan through Old Dailly
   about 1½ miles, entrance signposted on left
Open March–Oct daily 10.00am–7.00pm or sunset if
   earlier
Free admission, but there is a box for contributions
   towards the upkeep of the garden
& 🚃 advance notice required 🐕

▶ **GLENROTHES** ◀

BALGONIE CASTLE

Wildlife garden

By Markinch, Fife KY7 6HQ
☎   Glenrothes (0592) 750119

*17th century home of Sir Alexander Leslie,
Lord General of the Covenanting Army,
later created Earl of Leven. Garrisoned by
Rob Roy McGregor 1716. Wildlife garden
for educational purposes, picnic area.
Mediaeval banquets/dinners by candlelight.*

2 miles east of Glenrothes on the A911 then onto
   the B921. Central Fife
Open all year. Castle: 2.00–5.00pm, otherwise by
   appointment
Free admission to garden. Castle: adult £1.50, child 50p,
   OAP £1.00
& 🚃 🐕 4 deerhounds in residence

▶ **GOREBRIDGE** ◀

VOGRIE COUNTRY PARK

Country park

Vogrie House, by Gorebridge
☎   Gorebridge (0875) 21990

*250 acres. Information centre, signposted
paths, nature trails, adventure playground,
barbecue site, 9-hole golf course. Vogrie's
wildlife is very rich due to the diversity of
habitats which include woodlands, river
valleys and grasslands.*

Between Gorebridge on the A7 and Pathhead on the
   A68 and B6372, 12 miles south of Edinburgh
Open dawn until dusk every day
Free admission
& 🚃 🐕

▶ **HAWICK** ◀

CRAIK FOREST WALK AND PICNIC SITE

Walk, picnic site

c/o Forestry Commission, Borders Forest District,
   Ladylaw Centre, Bath St, Hawick, Roxburghshire
   TD9 7DP
☎   (0450) 77001

A gentle 3 mile walk through shady conifers and following the Aithouse burn brings the walker to the spectacular Wolfcleuch waterfall, returning to Craik car park by the varied policy wood. Picnic site. Car parking for 30 vehicles. Toilets.

On the A7, 2 miles south of Hawick take the B711 Roberton Road, just past Roberton village take left fork to Craik on unclassified road
Open Easter–Nov daily, 9.00am until dusk
Free admission
&. ⬛ 🐾

► *INGLISTON* ◄

SCOTTISH AGRICULTURAL MUSEUM

Agricultural museum

RHAS Showground, Ingliston, nr Edinburgh
☎ Edinburgh (031 333) 2674

Here visitors can learn how the social and economic life of Scotland's rural communities has evolved to create the countryside of today. Special exhibitions and audio-visual presentations.

Off the A8, near Edinburgh Airport
Open May–Sept Mon–Fri 10.00am–5.00pm; Sundays June–Sept
Free admission
&. ⬛ 🐾

► *JEDBURGH* ◄

THE WOODLAND VISITOR CENTRE

Woodland exhibition centre

Ancrum, Jedburgh, Roxburghshire TD8 6VQ
☎ Ancrum (08353) 306

The theme is 'wood, from seedling to furniture'. Giant games and puzzles to play, woodland walks, slide show, adventure play area, tea room with home baking, book and gift shop.

3½ miles north of Jedburgh near jct of the A68 and the B6400
Open times, please telephone for details
Admission: adult £1.75, child/OAP 90p, family ticket (2 adults and up to 4 children) £5.00, season tickets £5.00/£3.50/£11.00
&. ⬛ 🐾

► *KILMARNOCK* ◄

DEAN CASTLE COUNTRY PARK

Country park

Dean Rd, Kilmarnock, Ayrshire KA3 1RR
☎ Kilmarnock (0563) 22702

Nature trail, adventure playground, childrens corner, aviaries, riding school, picnic areas, visitor centre and tea room. Mediaeval castle with displays of armour, tapestries, musical instruments, and the life and works of Robert Burns.

Dean Road off Glasgow Road
Open for the country park: dawn–dusk. Castle and visitors centre: 12.00 noon–5.00pm all year (except Christmas and New Year)
Admission to the castle: non residents £1.00, children free. Country park free (1990 prices)
&. inside of castle not accessible to wheelchairs. Visitor centre (Dower House) tea room is accessible. There is a wheelchair available
⬛ advance notice required 🐾

► *KINROSS* ◄

VANE FARM

RSPB wildlife reserve

Kinross
☎ Kinross (0577) 62355

On south side of Loch Leven on the B9097 Glenrothes road, 2 miles east of the M90, jct 5
Open all times for the nature trail; nature centre and shop open daily 10.00am–5.00pm, centre closes at 4.00pm Jan–March, special facilities for schools
Admission: adult £1.00, child 50p, RSPB members free
&. ⬛ advance notice required 🐾

► *KIRKCUDBRIGHTSHIRE* ◄

THREAVE GARDENS

Country garden

Castle Douglas, Kirkcudbrightshire DG7 1RX
☎ Castle Douglas (0556) 2575

Wildfowl refuge with hides (Nov–March) for geese and ducks, ranger service.

1 mile west of town, signposts from the A75
Open April–Oct
Admission: adult £2.20, child/OAP £1.10. Party rates available
&. ⬛ 🐾

▶ LARGS ◀

KELBURN COUNTRY CENTRE

Country estate

Kelburn Estate, Fairlie, Ayrshire KA29 0BE
☎ Fairlie (0475) 568685

Adventure and assault courses, glen walks, gardens, pony trekking, craft workshop, museum and exhibition, shop, licensed cafe, ranger service, pets corner.

On the A78, 2 miles south of Largs
Open Easter–Oct 10.00am–6.00pm; Oct–Easter – park only
Admission: adult £2.00, accompanied child £1.00, Child/OAP/concession £1.40
&. ⟴ ⋔

▶ LAUDER ◀

THIRLESTANE CASTLE & BORDER COUNTRY LIFE EXHIBITIONS

Historic house

Thirlestane Castle, Lauder, Berwickshire TD2 6RU
☎ Lauder (05782) 430

Fine castle and historic home steeped in Scottish history. Magnificent 17th century ceilings, collection of historic toys, Border county life exhibitions. Tea room, gift shop, woodland walk and picnic area.

Castle entrance ½ mile from Lauder – follow signs on all main approach roads
Opening times 2.00–5.00pm, days vary month to month, please telephone for details
Admission: adult £3.00, child/OAP £2.50, family ticket £7.00, grounds only £1.00, booked parties £2.50
&. visitor route includes many stairs ⟴ ⋔

▶ LESLIE ◀

BALLINGALL FARM

Fruit farm

Ballingall, Leslie, Fife KY6 3HD
☎ Glenrothes (0592) 742963

1 mile north of Leslie on Falkland Hill road
Open July–Oct 10.00am–5.00pm
Free admission
&. ⟴ ⋔

▶ LEVEN ◀

LETHAM GLEN

Nature centre

Leven, Fife
☎ Leven (0333) 29231

Sunken garden with interesting plants, waterways through the park. Sheltered with large forest trees, firm pathways throughout, suitable for disabled. Interesting geology. Nature trail, tree rubbing trail, pets corner.

Within the town of Leven off the A915
Open daily all year. Nature centre: Oct–March 8.30am–3.30pm, April–Sept 7.30am–4.30pm (Sat & Sun 2.00–4.00pm all year)
&. no toilet facilities available for wheelchair users – to be remedied in the near future
⟴ advance notice required ⋔

SILVERBURN ESTATE

Country walks and trails

By Leven, Fife
☎ Leven (0333) 27568

Silverburn is a pleasure garden with interesting plants, with mini farm displaying old farm implements/animals. Sheltered with large forest trees, firm pathways suitable for disabled. Tree trail, tree rubbing trail, seashore trail, flax mill.

½ mile east of Leven off the A915
Open daily all year. Mini farm: Oct–March Mon–Fri 8.30am–3.30pm; April–Sept Sat & Sun 8.30am–4.30pm (All year 2.00–4.00pm)
Free admission
&. ⟴ ⋔

▶ LINLITHGOW ◀

BEECRAIGS DEER FARM

Deer farm

Beecraigs, Whitebaulks Visitor Centre, by Linlithgow, West Lothian
☎ Linlithgow (0506) 844516/8

Attractive deer farm in the Bathgate Hills, with public viewing walkway, and visitor centre with venison and souvenirs for sale. Also Beecraigs Country Park with fish farm, trim course, archery, climbing, orienteering etc.

Off the M9, 3 miles south of Linlithgow
Open all year. Guided walks by appointment
Free admission
&. ⛑ advance notice required ✖

► **LIVINGSTON** ◄

ALMOND VALLEY HERITAGE TRUST

18th century water-mill, countryside museum and childrens farm

Millfield, Livingston Village, Livingston, West Lothian
EH54 7AR
☎ Livingston (0506) 414957

A Heritage Centre containing the Scottish Shale Oil Museum, local history displays, and other exhibitions; plus a working farm steading with traditional livestock and a restored working 18th century watermill, conservation and nature study areas and picnic sites.

Approach via the A705 from either the M8 jct 4
(East Whitburn), the M8 jct 3 or the A899
(Livingston A71) – access off the B7015 (Mid
Calder) interchange on the A705, Livingston–
Whitburn road
Open all year
Admission charges to be decided
&. ⛑ ✖

► **LOCHGELLY** ◄

LOCHORE MEADOWS COUNTRY PARK (FIFE REGIONAL COUNCIL)

Country park and park centre

Crosshill, Lochgelly, Fife
☎ Ballingry (0592) 860086

Facilities include cafeteria, country walks, adventure play area, barbecues, golf course, brown trout fishery, watersports and horse riding.

At Crosshill on the B920 Lochgelly–Ballingry road.
Regular bus service from Dunfermline and
Lochgelly to Ballingry passes main entrance to
park
Open all year for country park. Park centre: Oct–March
9.00am–5.00pm April–Sept 9.00am–8.00pm
Free admission
&. ⛑ ✖

► **MAYBOLE** ◄

CULZEAN CASTLE AND COUNTRY PARK

Castle and country park

Nr Maybole, Ayrshire KA19 8LE
☎ Kirkoswald (06556) 269

The National Trust for Scotland's most popular property. 18th century Robert Adam clifftop castle surrounded by 560 acre estate declared Scotland's first country park in 1969. Coastline, gardens, ponds, deerpark, woodland walks, Ranger Service.

4 miles west of Maybole, 12 miles south of Ayr off
the A77
Country park open all year. Castle and park facilities 1
April–31 Oct 10.30am–5.30pm
Admission to Country park: pedestrians free, car £4.00,
minibus/caravan £6.00, coach £20.00. Castle: adult
£2.40, child/OAP £1.20. Special party rates, please
telephone for details. NTS/NT members free
&. ⛑ pre-booking essential ✖

► **MOFFAT** ◄

GREY MARE'S TAIL

Waterfall

Annandale & Eskdale, Dumfries & Galloway

Spectacular 200ft waterfall. Area rich in wild flowers and geological interest: herd of wild goats. NB: it is extremely dangerous to leave the paths. Ranger service July/August.

10 miles north east of Moffat on the A708
Open all year

► **MOTHERWELL** ◄

BARONS HAUGH

RSPB nature reserve

9 Wisteria Lane, Carluke ML8 5TB (warden)

Reserve has 4 bird hides, 265 acres of varying habitats, and a large car park. This area has a wealth of wildlife, chiefly on the wetlands, at all times of the year. Guided walks are available in the summer months.

1 mile south of Motherwell town centre with access
via Adele St opposite Motherwell civic centre,
then by lane leading off North Lodge Avenue

Open at all times
Free admission
 ♿ 🐴 advance notice required 🐾

▶   *NEW ABBEY*   ◀

MAINSRIDDLE POTTERY

Showroom, ceramic art for sale

The Tenements, Mainsriddle, nr Kirkbean, Dumfries
DG2 8AG
☎   Southwick (038778) 633

*Our studio pottery produces a range of
colourful ceramics in high-fired stoneware
and porcelain together with a small quantity
of hand-thrown domestic stoneware. We also
display original oil and watercolour
paintings.*

On the A710 Dumfries–Dalbeattie coast road
Open April–Oct 10.00am–6.00pm daily
Free admission
♿ there are no toilet facilities 🐴

NEW ABBEY CORN MILL

Renovated water-powered oatmeal mill

New Abbey, Dunfries-shire
☎   Edinburgh (031 244) 3101

*In New Abbey village, a carefully renovated
water-powered oatmeal mill won a Civic
Trust award in 1984. It is in full working
order and regular demonstrations are given.*

On the A710 coast road Dumfries–Dalbeattie
Open: 1 Oct–31 March Mon–Sat 9.30am–4.00pm, Sun
2.00–4.00pm, closed Thur pm and Fri in winter. 1
April–30 Sept Mon–Sat 9.30am–7.00pm, Sun 2.00–
7.00pm
Admission: adult £1.00, child/OAP 50p, discount for
groups
♿ 🐴 🐾

▶   *NEW GALLOWAY*   ◀

GALLOWAY DEER MUSEUM

Forestry centre

Clatteringshaws, New Galloway DG7 3GQ
☎   New Galloway (06442) 285

*The museum features the abundant animal
and bird life found in the Galloway Forest
Park. There are also historical artefacts and a
lifesize reconstruction of a Roman British
homestead.*

6 miles west of New Galloway on the A712
Open Easter–mid Oct daily 10.00am–5.00pm
Free admission
♿ 🐴 🍽

RAIDERS ROAD FOREST DRIVE

Forest drive

Forestry Commission, 21 King St, Castle Douglas,
Dumfries & Galloway DG7 1AA
☎   Castle Douglas (0556) 3626

*Forest drive 10 miles, car parks, 3 forest
walks, 1 path for disabled. Picnic, fish or
observe birdlife by Loch Stroan, try a forest
trail or let the children play in the safe rock
pools at the Otter Pool.*

North entrance/exit – 6 miles west of New Galloway
on the A712, south entrance/exit on the A762, 4
miles south of New Galloway
Open Easter–mid Oct daily 9.00am–8.00pm
Admission: £1.00 per car
♿ 🐾

▶   *NEWTON STEWART*   ◀

BRUCE'S STONE AND LOCH TROOL FOREST TRAIL

Country walk and forest trail

Glentrool, Bargrennan, Newton Stewart, Wigtownshire
☎   Newton Stewart (0671) 2420

*Excellent views from Bruce's Stone. Stout
footwear and sensible clothing necessary.*

From east take the A75 to Newton Stewart, turn
north onto A714 to Bargrennan and follow signs
to Loch Trool and Bruce's Stone. From north at
Girvan follow the A714 to Bargrennan, turn east
and follow signs as above
Open daily all year dawn–dusk
Free admission with accompanying leaflet available at
Caldons campsite or Forestry Commission offices
♿ 🐴 to within ½ mile of public car park 🐾

GALLOWAY FOREST PARK

Forest park

Dumfries & Galloway
☎   Newton Stewart (0671) 2420

*280 sq miles of mountain and forest.
2 campsites and seaonsonal lets available.
Coarse and game fishing visitor centre, deer
range and wild goat park.*

From the east take the A75 to Newton Stewart. From the north take the A714 from Girvan and follow Galloway Forest Park signs
Open March–Oct daily 9.00am until dusk
Free admission
&. ⬚ ⵏ

KIRROUGHTREE VISITOR CENTRE

Forestry centre

Daltamie, Stronord, Newton Stewart, Wigtownshire DG8 7BE
☎ Newton Stewart (0671) 2420

Audio-visual programme depicting use of conifers in Galloway Forest Park. Picnic areas and bird trail. Light refreshments.

3 miles east of Newton Stewart, turn north at Palnure village and follow 'Forest Centre' signs for 1 mile
Open all year daily dawn until dusk
Free admission
&. ⬚ ⵏ

MERRICK TRAIL

Mountain trail

Galloway Forest Park, Newton Stewart
☎ Newton Stewart (0671) 2420

Changes in weather conditions require great care. Follow the mountain and country code.

From the east take the A75 to Newton Stewart turn north onto the A714 to Bargrennan, follow signs to Loch Trool and Bruce's Stone
Open all year daily, dawn until dusk (except in inclement weather)
Free admission
&. ⬚ to within ½ mile of public car park ⵏ

RSPB NATURE RESERVE

Nature reserve and nature trail

Wood of Cree, Newton Stewart
☎ Newton Stewart (0671) 2861 (warden)

Probably the largest ancient broadleaved woodland remaining in south Scotland. 2 miles of nature trails follow cascading burns and offer fine views. Birds include redstart, pied flycatcher, woodcock, buzzard and great spotted woodpeckers.

4 miles north of Newton Stewart, through Minnigaff
Open all year daily
Free admission – donations welcome
&. ✕

STROAN BRIDGE FOREST TRAILS

Forest trails

Bargrennan, Newton Stewart, Dumfries and Galloway
☎ Newton Stewart (0671) 2420

Choice of 4 forest trails of varying lengths affording good views.

From the east take the A75 to Newton Stewart, turn north at Bargrennan then follow Caldons campsite signs at Glentrool village. From the north take the A714 from Girvan, turn left at Bargrennan and follow signs at Glentrool village
Open all year daily dawn until dusk
Free admission with accompanying leaflet available at Forestry Commission office
&. ⬚ ⵏ

TALNOTRY FOREST TRAIL

Forest trail

Queens Way, Newton Stewart
☎ Newton Stewart (0671) 2420

Good footwear and clothing necessary.

From the east take the A75 to jct A712 at Newton Stewart and turn north for 7 miles
Open daily all year
Free admission with accompanying leaflet obtainable from Talnotry campsite shop or Forestry Commission offices
&. ⵏ

▶ *PEEBLES* ◀

TWEEDDALE DISTRICT COUNCIL

Country park

Council Offices, Rosetta Rd, Peebles EH45 8HG
☎ Peebles (0721) 20153

Situated on the beautiful River Tweed. Numerous country and forest walks. Visit nearby St Ronan's Wells and Fitness Centre, or the Manor Valley National Site of Scientific Interest.

Take the A703 south of Edinburgh (23 miles), the A72 west of Glasgow (44 miles)
Open all year
Free admission
&. ⬚ ⵏ

► PRESTWICK ◄

MONKTONHILL FARM

Fruit farm

Monktonhill Farm, Prestwick, Ayrshire KA9 1UL
☎ Prestwick (0292) 74118/77114

Specialist fruits and vegetables, Britain's largest selection of strawberries. Friendly help always on hand.

North of Ayr on the B749 from Prestwick airport to Troon
Open June–Sept 10.00am–6.00pm, otherwise by appointment
Free admission
&. ▦ ✠

► ST ANDREWS ◄

CAMBO COUNTRY PARK

Country park

Kingsbarns, St Andrews, Fife KY16 8QD
☎ Crail (0333) 50810

Follow the coast road (A917) south of St Andrews for 6 miles. The park is on the coast side of the road between Kingsbarns and Crail
Open weekends March & April, daily May–Sept 10.00am–6.00pm
Admission: adult £1.70, child/OAP £1.00. Booked groups of 10+ 90p each
&. ▦ ✠

CRAIGTOUN COUNTRY PARK

Country park

St Andrews, Fife KY16 8NX
☎ St Andrews (0334) 73666

The park offers a wide range of facilities including Rio Grande railway, boats, crazy golf/putting, bouncy castle, bowling, glasshouses, aviaries, open air theatre, and its own Clydesdale horses. Restaurant/cafeteria.

2½ miles south west of St Andrews, signposted on the St Andrews–Pitscottie road
Open every day of the year. More facilities available during Easter–Sept
Admission: Easter–Sept only adult £1.25, child 2–5 60p, OAP 75p, students/UB40 (Mon–Fri) 75p
&. ✠

SEA LIFE CENTRE

Marine life attraction

The Scores, St Andrews, Fife
☎ (0334) 74786

Multi-level viewing of exciting sea creatures including seals and new British shark display and seal observatory. Displays, 'touch' pool, shop, restaurant and coffee shop.

On the sea front opposite the famous Royal and Ancient Golf Club
Open mid Feb–Dec daily 9.00am–6.00pm, restaurant until 5.30pm; July and Aug 9.00am–7.00pm, restaurant until 6.30pm
Admission: group discounts available, please telephone for details
&. ✠

► ST BOSWELLS ◄

THE FISHERMAN'S GALLERY

Art gallery

Benrig, St Boswells, Roxburghshire TD6 0EX
☎ (0835) 22485

Specializes in fishing and country prints, also fishing maps. Large range of postcards and greetings cards depicting wild and domestic birds and animals, fishing, shooting and golf.

Turn left 1 mile along the A699 from St Boswells to Kelso, signposted Benrig Cemetery 200 yards on right
Open all year Tues–Sat 2.30–5.30pm
Free admission
&. ▦ advance notice required ✠

► STENTON ◄

STENTON FRUIT FARM

Fruit farm

Ruchlaw Mains, Stenton, Dunbar, East Lothian EH42 1TD
☎ Stenton (03685) 321

Shop selling refreshments. Childrens playground, picnic area, toilets and farm walks.

315

Take the A1 to East Linton, then the road
  signposted Stenton/Garvald, follow fruit signs
Open July and August 10.00am–9.00pm for PYO fruit.
  24 hr information on crops available (03685) 321.
  School parties welcome with advance booking for farm
  visits year round (03685) 378
Free admission
⛄ 🚌 advance notice required 🐔

▶ ## STRANRAER ◀

CASTLE KENNEDY GARDENS

Country garden

Castle Kennedy, Stranraer, Wigtownshire DG9 8BX
☎ Stranraer (0776) 2024

*Many fine specimens of rhododendrons, trees
and shrubs helped by the North Atlantic
Drift. Designed around landscaped terraces
and mounds. Souvenir shop, light
refreshments available.*

On the A75, 3 miles east of Stranraer
Open April–Sept daily 10.00am–5.00pm
Admission: adult £1.80, child 50p, OAP £1.00, reductions
  for parties over 30
⛄ 🐔

▶ ## THORNHILL ◀

THE CRAFT CENTRE AT DRUMLANRIG CASTLE

Craft centre with 10 workshops

Thornhill, Dumfriesshire DG3 4AG
☎ (0848) 30129

*7 different types of business, each sells own
produce. Jewellery, stained glass, paintings,
textiles, leather, origami and pottery.*

Take the A76 to Thornhill, follow signposting for
  Drumlanrig Castle
Open May–Sept: May & June 1.30–5.00pm, July & Aug
  11.00am–5.00pm, Sun 2.00–6.00pm
Admission: adult £1.00, under 5s free (including
  admission to castle grounds)
⛄ 🚌 advance notice required 🍽

WOOD 'N' THINGS

Craft workshop and shop

Gravel Pit Cottage, Kirkland, Moniaive, Thornhill,
  Dumfriesshire DG3 4HB
☎ Moniaive (08482) 345

*Workshop specializes in wood turning and
wooden toys. Shop selling gifts hand made
in Scotland.*

Situated on the jct of the A702 Moniaive–Thornhill
  road and the B729 Moniaive–Dumfries road
Open all year: summer 10.00am–6.00pm; winter
  10.00am–4.00pm. Closed Tues mornings, also all day
  Thur except July and Aug
Free admission
⛄ assistance will be given, but no toilets for the
  disabled 🐔

▶ ## WHITHORN ◀

THE LOCAL HERB COMPANY

Herb nursery

Stonehouse Cottage, by Sorbie, Wigtownshire DG8 8AN
☎ Sorbie (098885) 249/303

*Small nursery in peaceful rural setting.
Over 100 varieties of quality herb plants
available. Also pot pourri and attractive,
original herbal products including bath
essence and body oil. Catalogue on request.*

Just off the B7052 between Sorbie and Whauphill,
  4 miles north of Whithorn
Open April–Sept, Thur–Sun 2.30–6.00pm or by
  appointment
Free admission
⛄ 🐔

► *WIGTOWN* ◄

BLADNOCH DISTILLERY

Malt whisky producer

Bladnoch, by Wigtown, Wigtownshire DG8 9AB
☎ Wigtown (09884) 2235, Fax 2341

1 mile south of Wigtown, 7 miles from Newton
   Stewart
Open Feb–Nov Mon–Fri, 10.00am–4.00pm, other times
   by appointment
Free admission
♿ ⛟ advance notice required ✖

CENTRAL HIGHLANDS

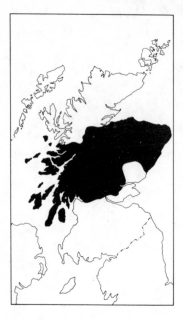

The Central Highlands encompasses both highland and lowland scenery. There are many sheltered glens on the west coast which is so warmed by the Gulf Stream that even sub-tropical plants grow. The Highlands are a refuge for many birds and animals no longer seen elsewhere in Britain – golden eagles, gannets, red deer, roe deer, pine martens and wildcats. This region is also famous for its lochs, game fishing rivers and its golf courses.

There are thousands of hectares of woodlands to explore, Sites of Special Scientific Interest, wildlife centres, heritage centres, a reindeer park, an otter haven, an oyster farm, highland wineries, whisky distilleries, speciality food centres and, for the craftsperson, stained glass, ceramics, weaving and spinning workshops.

► ABERFOYLE ◄

QUEEN ELIZABETH FOREST PARK

Forest park

c/o Aberfoyle Forest District, Stirling SK8 3UX
☎ (08772) 383

*20,000 hectares of woodlands with a full
range of recreational facilities: Loch Lomond
Oakwoods Forest Nature Reserve; Highland
Boundary Fault Trail, short circular
interpretive trail; visitor centre with shop,
cafe, picnic wing and audio-visual theatre;
Strathryre Forest Information Centre and
Achray Forest Drive.*

On the A81 Glasgow–Callender road
Open for park and forest cabins all year. Visitor centre,
drive and campsites Easter–end Oct
Admission: most facilities free, charge for Visitor Centre
car park, Achray Forest Drive £1.00
& full access to visitor centre, toilets
🚗 parking 🐕 except in visitor centre

► ABERLOUR ◄

TAMDHU DISTILLERY VISITOR CENTRE

Malt whisky distillery

Knockando, Aberlour, Banffshire IV35 7RP
☎ Carron (03406) 221

*See the total distilling process and a unique
collection of whiskies from the safety and
comfort of a viewing gallery. Sample a free
dram and visit the gift shop.*

On the B9102, 20 miles south of Elgin
Open Easter–May: Mon–Sat 10.00am–4.00pm; June–
Sept: 10.00am–4.00pm
Free admission
& not suitable for wheelchairs
🚗 advance notice required 🐕

► ACHARN BY KENMORE ◄

FALLS OF ACHARN BY KENMORE

Country walk

c/o Perth and Kinross District Council, Leisure and
Recreation Dept, 3 High St, Perth PH1 5JU
☎ Perth (0738) 39911 ext 3618

*A circular walk which includes Hermitage
Cave overlooking the Falls of Acharn. Good*

*views of Ben Lawyers to the mouth of Loch
Tay.*

Follow the Loch Tay south shore road to Acharn
village
Open all year
Free admission
& 🐕

► ALFORD ◄

HAUGHTON COUNTRY PARK

Interpretative centre

Alford, Aberdeenshire AB3 8NA
☎ Alford (09755) 62453

*Owned by Grampian Regional Council.
Ample recreational facilities including picnic
areas, way-faring, trim track, woodland and
riverside walks. Countryside Ranger Service.*

25 miles west of Aberdeen, on the A944
Open all year round
Free admission
& 🚗 🐕

KILDRUMMY CASTLE GARDENS TRUST

Castle gardens

Strathdon Rd, by Alford, Kildrummy AB3 8RA
☎ Kildrummy (09755) 71264/71277

*Specimen trees curtain the shrub and alpine
garden, sheltered in an ancient quarry.
Botanical interest, peaceful walks. Water
garden runs below the ruined castle-fortress
(not in the Trust). Play area, video room,
museum opened by request, plants for sale.*

On the A97, off the A944. Alford 10 miles, Huntly
17 miles, Strathdon 12 miles
Open 1 April–31 Oct daily 10.00am–5.00pm
Admission: adult £1.00, child 20p, teenagers 50p
(children must be accompanied). Car park free (1990
prices)
& 🚗 advance notice required 🐕

► AUCHTERARDER ◄

AUCHTERARDER HERITAGE CENTRE

Heritage centre

Glenruthven Mill, Abbey Rd, Auchterarder, Perthshire
PH3 1DP
☎ Auchterarder (0764) 62079

Scotland's story told by computerised special effects in converted weaving hall. Coffee and gift shop, mill shop, exhibitions and steam engine.

Open Easter–Oct daily 10.00am–5.00pm (July–Aug);
  2.00–5.00pm off season
Visitor centre: adult £1.50, accompanied children free
& ⊞ advance notice required ✕

► AVIEMORE ◄

GLENMORE FOREST PARK

Forest park, forest walks

Forestry Commission, Glenmore, Aviemore,
Inverness-shire PH2 1QU
☎ Cairngorm (047986) 271

This is an area of superb highland scenery with mountains, woodlands, lochs and rivers. Walking, fishing and water sports available, and skiing in season.

From Aviemore take the B970 for 2 miles to
  Coylumbridge, then road signposted 'Cairngorm'
  for approx 5 miles
Open at all times
Free admission
& ⊞ ✝

ROTHIEMURCHUS ESTATE

Country estate

Rothiemurchus Visitor Centre, by Aviemore,
  Inverness-shire PH22 1QH
☎ Aviemore (0479) 810858

Rothiemurchus includes part of the Cairngorms National Nature Reserve and 50 miles of footpaths. Guided walks and tours, fishing, clay shooting, educational programmes, corporate hospitality days can all be arranged.

From the A9, take the Aviemore turn off and follow
  the B9152 to the Cairngorms for ¼ mile
Open all year
Admission charges, please telephone for details
& ⊞ advance notice required ✝

► VILLAGE OF BALLINDALLOCH ◄

DISTILLERY

Malt whisky distillery

Ballindalloch, Banffshire, Scotland
☎ Ballindalloch (08072) 202

'Classic' malt whisky, including miniatures, on sale.

Take the B9137 near Bridge of Avon on the A95
  Grantown-on-Spey–Aberlour road
Open by appointment only
Free admission
& ⊞ advance notice required ✕

THE OLD MILL VISITOR CENTRE

Distillery

Tamnavulin-Glenlivet Distillery, Tomnavoulin,
  Ballindalloch, Banffshire
☎ Glenlivet (08073) 442

Situated on the River Livet from which the Glen takes its name. Visitors have a distillery tour, an audio-visual presentation and a tasting of either the Tamnavulin 10 year old malt or Glayva liquer. Picnic area on banks of the river.

South on the A95, then to Tomintoul on the A939
  and north east to Tomnavoulin on the B9008
Open March–Oct Mon–Fri 9.30am–4.30pm; Sun
  10.00am–4.00pm (June–Aug inc)
Free admission
& ⊞ ✝ but not on distillery tour

► BANCHORY ◄

CRATHES CASTLE, GARDEN AND ESTATE

Castle, country garden and estate

Crathes Castle, Banchory, Kincardineshire AB3 3QT
☎ Crathes (033 044) 525

Royal historic associations date from 1323 when the lands of Leys were granted to the Burnett family by King Robert the Bruce. Walled garden is a composite of 8 gardens. Yew hedges date from 1702. 6 trails.

3 miles east of Banchory and 15 miles west of
  Aberdeen

Open for castle, visitor centre, shop, licensed restaurant
and plant sales 13 April–28 Oct daily 11.00–6.00pm
(last tour of castle 5.15pm) Other times by prior
appointment only. Gardens and grounds open all year
daily 9.30am–sunset
Admission to grounds: adult £1.10, child 60p; castle,
garden and grounds: adult £3.00, child £1.50.
Pre-booked parties: adult £2.40, child £1.20
& incl car park. Wheelchairs available
🚌 advance notice required
🐕 dog trail available

► *BEAULY* ◄

CLUANIE DEER FARM PARK

Deer farm park

By Beauly, Inverness-shire IV4 7AE
☎ Inverness (0463) 782415

*Animals in a superb natural setting. Deer,
rare breeds of cows, sheep and pigs. Video
show and display; venison, books, crafts and
souvenirs for sale.*

4 miles west of Beauly on the A831 Glen Affric
road
Open mid May–mid Oct daily 10.00am–5.00pm
Admission: adult £2.00, child £1.50, OAP £1.75 (1990
prices)
& 🚌 advance notice required 🗙

► *BLAIR ATHOLL* ◄

FALLS OF BRUAR

Country walk

c/o Perth & Kinross District Council, Leisure and
Recreation Dept, 3 High St, Perth PH1 5PH
☎ Perth (0738) 3911 ext 3617

*The walk is 1 mile through forest woodland
viewing spectacular upper and lower falls. A
circular walk, it has many fine features.*

Off the A9(T) Perth–Inverness road, 3 miles west of
Blair Atholl
Open all hours
Free admission
& unsuitable for wheelchairs 🚌 🐕

► *BRODICK* ◄

BRODICK CASTLE GARDENS & COUNTRY PARK

Country park

Brodick, Isle of Arran, Scotland KA27 8HY
☎ Brodick (0770) 2202

Ferry sails from Ardrossan, Ayrshire (1 hour)
Open Easter–Oct (April and Oct: Mon, Wed, Sat only).
Gardens and country park 10.00am–5.00pm; castle
1.00–5.00pm
Admission: adult £2.40, child £1.20 (1990 prices)
& 🚌 🐕

► *CAIRNDOW* ◄

LOCH FYNE OYSTERS LTD

Sea food shop and restaurant

Oyster Bar & Sea Food Shop, Clachan Farm, Cairndow,
Argyll, PA26 9BH
☎ Cairndow (04996) 217/264

*The Oyster Bar serves only fresh produce
from its own oyster farm and smokehouse,
plus fish and game from the locality, locally
baked bread and Scottish cheeses.*

On the A83 Glasgow–Oban/Cambletown road, at the
head of Loch Fyne, approx 10 miles north of
Inveraray
Open all year 9.00am–9.00pm (except winter weekdays
9.00–6.00pm)
Free admission
& 🚌 advance notice required 🗙

► *CARRBRIDGE* ◄

LANDMARK HIGHLAND HERITAGE AND ADVENTURE PARK

Adventure park

Carrbridge, Inverness-shire, PH23 3AJ
☎ Carrbridge (047984) 613

*The Highlander show and exhibition tell the
story of man in the Highlands from the time
of the clans. In the woodland are the
adventure playground, nature trail, tree top
trail and forest nature centre. The Scottish
Forestry Park includes a 70 foot viewing
tower and working steam powered sawmill.*

6 miles north of Aviemore on the old A9
Open summer 9.30am–8.30pm; winter 9.30am–5.00pm
Admission: adult £2.95, child £1.75 (1990 prices)
 ♿ ᵫ free parking 🐕

Superb views from the top of the Knock on a good day.

Follow signs from the town centre
Open all year
Free admission
♿ 🐕

► **CRIEFF** ◄

DRUMMOND CASTLE GARDEN

Country garden

Estate Office, Muthill, Crieff, Perthshire PH5 2AA
☎ Muthill (076481) 257

Gardens originally laid out about 1630 by John Drummond, 2nd Earl of Perth. In about 1830, the parterre was Italianised. The most interesting piece of statuary is the sundial, designed and built by John Mylne, Master Mason to King Charles I.

On the A822, 2 miles south of Crieff
Open 1 May–31 Aug 2.00–6.00pm; Sept Wed & Sun
   only 2.00–6.00pm
Admission: adult £1.20, child/OAP 60p
♿ ᵫ advance notice required 🐕

GLENTURRET DISTILLERY LTD

Distillery

The Hosh, Crieff, Perthshire PH7 4HA
☎ Crieff (0764) 2424

Scotland's oldest highland malt distillery. Guided tours, free tasting, visitors heritage centre. Smugglers Restaurant, Pagoda Restaurant, extensive whisky and souvenir shop. A very popular attraction.

¼ mile to the right of the A85 Crieff–Comrie road, just outside Crieff
Open March–Dec, Mon–Sat 9.30am–5.30pm, last full
   tour 4.30pm
Admission: guided tour £1.25, heritage centre 50p,
VIP visit £4.75 (1990 prices)
♿ ᵫ advance notice required 🐕

THE KNOCK

Country walk

c/o Perth and Kinross District Council, Leisure and
   Recreation Dept, 3 High St, Perth PH1 5JU
☎ Perth (0738) 39911 ext 3618

► **CUMBERNAULD** ◄

PALACERIGG COUNTRY PARK

Country park, visitor centre

Cumbernauld, Dumbartonshire G67 3HU
☎ Cumbernauld (0236) 720047

700 acres of farm and forest with nature trails, picnic sites, rare breeds of farm animals and Northern European wildlife including bison and chamois, reindeer and red deer, wolves and lynx. Coffee shop; visitor centre exhibition; 18-hole golf course.

Follow signposts for Cumbernauld, then Palacerigg
   Country Park off the A80 Glasgow–Stirling road.
   Lies 2 miles south of Cumbernauld
Open daily for the country park. Visitor centre: daily
   (except Tues) 11.00am–6.00pm
Free admission to park and animal collection. Pony
   trekking: adult £3.50 per hour, child £ 2.50 per hour
♿ ᵫ 🗙

► **DALWHINNIE VILLAGE** ◄

DALWHINNIE DISTILLERY

Malt whisky distillery

Dalwhinnie, Inverness-shire
☎ Dalwhinnie (05282) 264

Dalwhinnie distillery was built in 1898 and is currently licenced to Jas. Buchanan & Co. Ltd., producers of the famous blend 'Black & White' Scotch Whisky. The 15 year old single malt bears the distillery name.

Distillery is just off the A9 Perth–Inverness road,
   follow Dalwhinnie signs from main road
Open April–Oct Mon–Fri 9.30am–4.00pm
Free admission
♿ ᵫ 🗙

► DOUNE ◄

DOUNE PONDS PONDS NATURE RESERVE & DOUNE TRAIL

Country walks

c/o Striling District Council, Dept of Leisure and
  Recreation, Beechwood House, Stirling FK8 2AD
☎ Stirling (0786) 79000

*Two ½ mile walks. Doune Ponds formerly a
gravel pit, now managed for water birds and
wild flowers; Doune Trail a level walk
through farmland and woodland.*

Trail leaflet from local Tourist Information Centres
Open at all times. Keys for observation hides available at
  Spar Grocers, 36 Main Street, Doune
Free admission
&. 1 hide adapted for wheelchairs 🚌 🏕

► DUFFTOWN ◄

THE GLENFIDDICH DISTILLERY

Malt distillery

William Grant & Sons Ltd, The Glenfiddich Distillery,
  Dufftown, Banffshire AB5 4DH
☎ DUFFTOWN (0340) 20373

*Audio-visual presentation in 6 languages;
guided tour. There is no charge for the visit,
and visitors receive a free dram. Groups over
12 please book in advance.*

½ mile north of Dufftown town centre on the A941
  Dufftown–Elgin road
Open all year except Christmas/New Year, weekdays
  9.30am–4.30pm. Also Easter–mid Oct Sat 9.30am–
  4.30pm, Sun 12.00–4.30pm. Please telephone for
  group bookings
Free admission
&. access to audio-visual and museum area, but not all
of the distillery
🚌 advance notice required 🏕

► DUNKELD ◄

THE HERMITAGE

Country park

Dunkeld, Perthshire
☎ Dunkeld (03502) 8641 Ranger

*Interesting mixed conifer and deciduous
woodlands with very tall Douglas Fir. 33
acres with picturesque folly built in 1758,
which is above the wooded gorge of the River
Braan. Ranger/naturalist service.*

1 mile west of Dunkeld, off the A9
Open all year
Free admission
&. 🚌 🏕

► ELLON ◄

HADDO COUNTRY PARK

Country park

Stable Block, Haddo Country Park, Tarves, Ellon,
  Aberdeenshire AB4 0EL
☎ Tarves (06515) 489

*Cared for by Grampian Regional Council,
the park consists of woodlands, a lake and
ponds, and is the home for a rich variety of
wildlife, including red squirrels and otters.*

Off the B999, 1 mile south of Tarves
Open all year dawn–dusk; visitor centre open May–Sept
  11.00am–6.00pm, limited opening at other times
Free admission
&. 🚌 🏕

► ELGIN ◄

OLD MILLS

Restored watermill

Oldmills Rd, Elgin IV30 1BX
☎ Elgin (0343) 545121/540698

*A peaceful rural haven minutes from the
town centre providing an enjoyable hour/half
day stop. Farm machinery display, short
nature trail and wooded turnery suitable for
all ages. Coffee bar and picnic area.*

Off the A96, at west end of Elgin
Open 1 May–30 Sept daily (except Mondays)
  9.00am–5.00pm
Admission: adult 50p, child 30p, school party 10p per
  head
&. 🚌 notice appreciated but not essential 🏕

▶ **FORRES** ◀

DARNAWAY FARM VISITOR CENTRE

Museum and country walk

Tearie, Darnaway, Forres, Moray
☎ (03094) 469

Milking herd and other animals; vintage tractors; woodland walks, picnic site; toilets.

2 miles west of Forres on the A96, turn south
  signposted 'Darnaway Farm Visitor Centre'
Open June–Sept
Admission: adult £1.20, child 60p
♿ 🚌 advance notice required ✝

▶ **FORT WILLIAM** ◀

GREAT GLEN FOODS LTD

Speciality food shop

Old Ferry Rd, North Ballachulish, Onich, Inverness-shire
  PH33 6RZ
☎ Onich (08553) 277

This famous speciality food shop offers one of the most extensive ranges of Scottish foods anywhere. 'Islay Tablet' confectionery is made on the premises, try a sample. Mail order available.

Off the A82, by Ballachulish bridge
Open March–Oct Mon–Sat 9.30am–5.30pm and Sundays
  in high season; Feb, Nov and Dec Mon–Sat
  10.00am–4.00pm only
Free admission
♿ 🚌 by appointment ✖

▶ **FRASERBURGH** ◀

CRIMONMOGATE FISHERY

Fishery

Crimonmogate, Lonmay, Fraserburgh, Aberdeenshire
  AB4 4UD
☎ Lonmay (0346) 32203

Fishing for good quality rainbow trout in a 6 acre lake set in a small country estate. Idyllic woodland setting within a nature reserve.

7 miles south of Fraserburgh, from the A952
  Fraserburgh–Peterhead road take the B9033
  towards St Combs, look out for fishery signs
Open all year 9.00am–10.00pm (or dusk if earlier)
Admission: £8.00 for 4 hours (limit 3 fish) or £12.00 all
  day (limit 4 fish); boats available at no extra charge
  but mainly jetty fishing
♿ please telephone for details
🚌 advance notice required ✝

THE GLENLIVET DISTILLERY VISITOR CENTRE

Distillery

Ballindallock, Banffshire
☎ Glenlivet (08073) 427

The first licensed distillery – founded in 1824.

Off the B9009 Balllindallock–Tomintoul road
Open Easter–Oct Mon–Sat 10.00am–4.00pm
Free admission
♿ 🚌 advance notice required ✖

▶ **GLENMORE** ◀

THE CAIRNGORM REINDEER CENTRE

Reindeer herd, exhibition and shop

Reindeer House, Glenmore, Aviemore, Inverness-shire
  PH22 1QU
☎ (04788) 228

Visits to the herd, exhibition and shop.

From Aviemore, take the A951 east to the
  Cairngorms, follow for 6 miles. Reindeer House
  is above the road on the left in Glenmore
Open all year. Daily visits to the herd Nov–March
  (weather permitting) 11.00am. Free exhibition and shop
  10.30am–5.30pm
Admission: adult £2.00, child (5–16) £1.00 . Party rates
  available
♿ visits not suitable for those in a wheelchair. Reindeer
centre accessible for disabled and there are always a
couple of reindeer at the centre 🚌 ✝

▶ **HUNTLY** ◀

THE OLD MANSE OF MARNOCH

Herb garden and cookery holidays

The Old Manse, Bridge of Marnoch, Huntly AB5 5RS
☎ Aberchirder (0466) 780873

Georgian country house set in 5 acres of gardens. Herbs compactly displayed in an Elizabethan knot garden. A wide variety of culinary, aromatic, medicinal and dye herbs. Plants are also available for sale.

On the B9117 less than 1 mile off the main Huntly–Banff A97 route
Open for the herb garden May–Oct 10.00am–5.00pm (Sun 1.00–5.00pm) Cookery courses by prior arrangement
Free admission to herb garden. Cookery courses by arrangement
&. no access to house for wheelchair disabled as all entrances have steps 🐴

INVERNESS

CRAIG PHADRIG FOREST WALK

Forest walk

Forestry Commission, Inverness Forest District, Smithtown, Inverness IV1 2NL
☎ Inverness (0463) 791575

A short walk on Craig Phadrig Hill. The path rises steeply through mixed woodland to a Bronze Age vitrified fort at the summit, with spectacular views of the surrounding countryside.

Leave Inverness by the A862, cross the Caledonian Canal then follow the signpost for Craig Phadrig. After 2 miles bear right signposted Upper Leachkin, Blackpark
Access at all times
Free admission
&. 🐴

CULLODEN FOREST WALK

Forest walk

Forestry Commission, Inverness Forest District, Smithtown, Inverness IV1 2NL
☎ Inverness (0463) 791575

A walk through a mixed forest. Places of interest include Tobar Na H'oige (well of youth), otherwise St Mary's Well or the Cloutie Well, the Lord Presidents Seat and Prisoners Stone.

From the A96, 2 miles east of Inverness take Smithtown, Culloden, Balloch distribution road for 1 mile, then road signposted Culloden Moor, Croy
Access at all times
Free admission
&. 🐴

ISLE OF ARRAN

ISLE OF ARRAN HERITAGE MUSEUM

Heritage museum

Rosaburn, Brodick, Isle of Arran KA27 8DP
☎ Brodick (0770) 2636

Group of old farm and croft buildings housing heritage museum. Also incorporates local heritage project in conjunction with local high school. Tea room, shop and picnic area.

By Caledonaian–Macbrayne ferry from Ardrossan
Open April–Oct 10.00am–5.00pm. Also on special Sundays
Admission: adult £1.00, child 50p, OAP 75p. Special group rates available (1990 prices)
&. 🚌 🐴

ISLE OF COLONSAY

ANDREW ABRAHAMS

Oyster farm/apiary

The Strand, Isle of Colonsay, Argyll PA61 7YR
☎ Colonsay (09512) 365

Colonsay oysters and Colonsay wildflower honey have gained a widespread reputation for high quality. An opportunity to experience them firsthand.

The Strand lies between Colonsay and Oronsay
Open all year
Free admission
&. ✗

KEMNAY

MORDON HERBS

Herb farm

Mill Farm, Aquithie, Kemnay, Inverurie, Aberdeenshire AB5 9NY
☎ Kemnay (0467) 43167

Large range of potted culinary and decorative herbs. Suppliers of fresh cut culinary herbs. Home grown dried flowers and selection of novelties for floral art.

Off the B993 to unclassified road to Kemnay Quarries where signposted
Open daily 9.00am–5.00pm
Free admission
& ⛟ advance notice required ⋔

▶ KINCRAIG ◀

ROCKWOOD PONDS PICNIC SITE AND FOREST WALK

Forest walk

Forestry Commission, Inshriach, Kincraig, by Kingussie, Inverness-shire
☎ Kincraig (05404) 223

High part of walk commands extensive views of Inshriach Forest and Strathspey. On ponds section woodland and aquatic wildlife may be seen. Picnic site.

Off the B970 at Lock Insh, 1 mile along Glenfeshie road
Open dawn–dusk all year
Free admission
& ⋔

▶ KIRKHILL ◀

HIGHLAND WINERIES

Winery

Moniack Castle, Kirkhill, Inverness
☎ (046 383) 283

Producers of country wines and liqueurs using traditional methods. Visitors see the production of wines and preserves in all stages. Optional guided tour (½ hour). Products may be bought or ordered and delivered.

7 miles from Inverness on the A862 Beauly road
Open daily throughout the year (except Sundays) 10.00am–5.00pm
⛟ ⋔

▶ LOCHEARNHEAD ◀

GLEN OGLE TRAIL

Country walk

c/o Stirling District Council, Dept of Leisure and Recreation, Beechwood House, Stirling FK8 2AD
☎ Stirling (0786) 79000 ext 72153

The sometimes steep walk follows both sides of a typical highland glen using the lines of the former Caledonian railway and military road, length approx 6 miles. Leaflet and route card from local Tourist Information Centres.

Off the A85, 200 yards north of jct of the A84 and the A85
Open all year
Free admission
⋔ except lambing season March–May

▶ LOCHGILPHEAD ◀

FORESTRY COMMISSION

Forest walks

Whitegates, Lochgilphead, Argyll
☎ Lochgilphead (0546) 2518

6 forest walks and several viewpoints with car parks and picnic areas in magnificent, mature forest beside scenic Loch Awe.

Take the B845 to Kilchrenan, then unclassified minor road to Dalavich, 16 miles south of Taynuilt
Open all year, daily
Free admission
⋔

▶ MARYCULTER ◀

STORYBOOK GLEN

Theme park

Maryculter, Aberdeen AB1 0AT
☎ Aberdeen (0224) 732941

Favourite nursery rhyme characters, flowers, trees, waterfalls and fairytale houses amidst 20 acres of spectacular scenery on Royal Deeside.

5 miles west of Aberdeen, on the B9077
Open March–Oct daily 10.00am–6.00pm; Nov–Feb Sat &
Sun only 11.00am–4.00pm
Admission: adult £1.75, OAP £1.00, child (2–14 years)
85p, under 2s free
 ♧ ⛶ ✱

► MILNGAVIE ◄

MUGDOCK COUNTRY PARK

Guided walk programme

Visitor Centre, Craigallian Rd, nr Milngavie, Glasgow
G62 8EL
☎ Glasgow (041) 956 6100

*500 acres of unspoilt countryside with
contrasting landscapes and a wealth of
wildlife – rich in history, with Mugdock and
Craigend castles. Guided walk programme.
Nature club practical conservation tasks and
events etc. on a regular basis.*

North off the A81, signposted from town. 4 car
parks around perimeter
Open all year – access to park at all times. Visitor centre
open 1.00–4.30pm
Free admission
♧ ⛶ ✱

► MINTLAW ◄

NORTH-EAST OF SCOTLAND AGRICULTURAL HERITAGE CENTRE

Country park

Aden Country Park, Mintlaw, by Peterhead, Banff and
Buchan, Grampian AB4 8LD
☎ Mintlaw (0771) 22857

*Set amidst Aden Country Park, the centre
presents the region's agricultural heritage by
use of displays, audio-visual programmes
and costume guides. Restaurant, ranger
service, wildlife centre, camp site and craft
shop.*

Off the A950, 1 mile west of Mintlaw
Open all year for country park. Heritage centre: May–Sept
daily 11.00am–5.00pm, April & Oct weekends only
12.00–5.00pm
Free admission
♧ ⛶ advance notice required ✱

► NEWTONMORE ◄

PATTACK FALLS FOREST WALK

Forest walk

Forestry Commission, Inshriach, Kincraig, by Kingussie,
Inverness-shire
☎ Kincraig (0504) 223

*This walk commands a fine panorama of
Strathmashie Forest, much of Badenoch and
views to the west. The walk starts from near
the falls.*

10 miles south of Newtonmore on the A86
Open all year dawn–dusk
Free admission
♧ ⛶ ✱

► OBAN ◄

OBAN DISTILLERY

Malt whisky distillery

Oban, Argyllshire
☎ Oban (0631) 64262

Distillery is on the A85 from the north and the
A816 from the south; it is just off George Street
in the town
Open Mon–Fri, 9.30am–5.00pm (last tour 4.15pm);
Saturdays Easter–Oct
Free admission
♧ toilet facilities
⛶ advance notice required ✱

SEA LIFE CENTRE

Marine life attraction

Barcaldine, Oban, Argyll PA37 1SE
☎ Ledaig (063 172) 386

*Multi-level viewing of marine creatures
including octopus and conger eels, feeding
displays. Daily talks explain the seal 'rear
and release' scheme – they can be viewed
from underwater or from a gallery. Picnic
area, gift shop, restaurant and coffee shop.*

Signposted on the A828, 10 miles north of Oban
Open mid Feb–Nov daily 9.00am–6.00pm (restaurant
until 5.30pm); July & Aug 9.00am–7.00pm, restaurant
until 6.30pm
Admission: group discounts available, please telephone
for details
♧ ⛶ ✱

▶ PERTH ◀

KINNOULL HILL

Country walk

c/o Perth and Kinross District Council, Leisure and
Recreation Dept, 3 High St, Perth PH1 5JU
☎ Perth (0738) 39911 ext 3618

*Well defined footpaths, superb views of
countryside and Tay estuary.*

From Perth cross the river Tay by Old Bridge, cross
Dundee Road and continue up Muirhall Road to
Quarry car park or Jubilee car park
Open all year
Free admission
& only from Jubilee car park 🚌 �",

QUARRYMILL WOODLAND PARK

Country walk and woodland park

Visitor Centre, Quarrymill Woodland Park, Isla Rd, Perth
PH2 HQ12
☎ Perth (0738) 33890

*Facilities include visitor centre, shop, paths,
seats, bridges, viewing points, barbecue,
picnic areas and a pond. There are approx 3
miles of pathway, $1^{1}/_{2}$ miles of which can be
used by disabled visitors.*

Off the A93 Blairgowrie road, 1 mile from north
side of Perth
Open all year for the park. Car park 9.00am–5.00pm or
7.00pm in spring/summer. Visitor centre Easter–Oct
9.00am–5.00pm weekdays, 10.00am–4.00pm weekends
Free admission
& emphasis on ease of access and facilities for
elderly and disabled visitors
🚌 advance notice required �"

▶ PITLOCHRY ◀

BLACK SPOUT WOOD

Country walk

c/o Perth and Kinross District Council, Leisure and
Recreation Dept, 3 High St, Perth PH1 5JU
☎ Perth (0738) 39911 ext 3618

*A viewing platform overlooking the 25 metre
Black Spout waterfall. A good stopping point
for short walks.*

Leave the A9(T) at Pitlochry jct, site signed ½ mile
on the right
Open all year
Free admission
& �"

BLAIR ATHOL DISTILLERY

Malt whisky distillery

Pitlochry, Perthshire
☎ Pitlochry (0796) 2234

*Guided tours give a detailed description of
the art of malt whisky making. Enjoy an
opportunity to browse in the shop and to
select from the wide range of whiskies offered
for sale.*

Just off the A9 trunk road north of Perth, the
distillery is clearly signposted
Open Mon–Sat 9.30am–4.30pm
Free admission
& disabled access is limited: shop, cafeteria and
reception areas. Disabled toilet.
🚌 advance notice required 🐾

GARRY – TUMMEL WALKS

Country walks and hydro power stations

c/o Perth & Kinross District Council, Leisure &
Recreation Dept, 3 High St, Perth PH1 5PH
☎ Perth (0738) 39911 ext 3618

*Loch Faskally makes a fitting centre piece to
this scenic area. The Garry – Tummel walks
are serviced by a variety of car parks thus
offering various starting points and lengths
of walks. Most car parks have large
information panel with information about
the walk.*

'Garry – Tummel walks' from Pitlochry north up
both sides of Loch Faskally and River Garry to
Killiecrankie
Open all year
Free admission
& reduced access for wheelchairs 🚌 �"

KILLIECRANKIE

Country walk

c/o The National Trust Information Centre, Killiecrankie,
Perthshire
☎ Pitlochry (0796) 3233

*Scene of the Battle of Killiecrankie in 1689.
54 acres of the Pass is in the Trust's care.
The wooded gorge, a famous beauty spot,
was admired by Queen Victoria. The
exhibition in the visitor centre features the
battle, natural history and Ranger services.*

Take the A9, 3 miles north of Pitlochry
Site open all year. Visitor centre, shop and snack bar
open 1 April–31 May and 1 Sept–28 Oct, daily
10.00am–5.00pm; 1 June–31 Aug, daily 9.30am–
6.00pm
Admission: adult 30p, child free
&. 🚌 🛉

LINN OF TUMMEL

Country walk

c/o The National Trust Information Centre, Killiecrankie,
Perthshire
☎ Pitlochry (0796) 3233

*Characteristic of the beauty of the Perthshire
Highlands, the Linn of Tummel comprises
47 acres by the banks of the Rivers Tummel
and Garry. Woodland walks. Ranger
naturalist.*

2½ miles north west of Pitlochry
Open at all times
Free admission
🚌 🛉

LOGAN BOTANIC GARDEN

Country garden

Port Logan, Wigtownshire DG9 9ND
☎ Ardwell (0776 86) 231

*A specialist garden of the Royal Botanic
Gardens, Edinburgh, with Australian tree
ferns and New Zealand cabbage palms.*

On the B7065, 14 miles south of Stranraer
Open 15 March–Oct 10.00am–6.00pm daily
Admission: adult £1.50, child 50p, OAP £1.00
&. 🚌 🛪

MUILEAN BHLAR ATHALL

Working watermill

John Ridley Projects Ltd, The Mill, Blair Atholl,
Perthshire PH18 5SH
☎ Blair Atholl (079681) 321

*Full working 17th century watermill where
flour and oatmeal are milled traditionally.
This produces a delicious wholesome smell,
which, together with the home baking is very
enticing for the visitor. Shop and tea room.*

Off the A9, 5 miles north of Pitlochry
Open Easter–Oct weekdays 10.00am–5.30pm, Sundays
12.00 noon–5.30pm
Admission: adult 75p, child 60p, car park free
&. 🚌 🛪

▶ *ROTHES* ◀

GLEN GRANT VISITOR CENTRE

Distillery

Glen Grant Distillery, Rothes, Morayshire
☎ Rothes (03403) 413

Please telephone for directions
Open April–Sept Mon–Fri 10.00am–4.00pm
Free admission
🚌 advance notice requried 🛪

▶ *TAYNUILT* ◀

BARGUILLEAN GARDENS

Country gardens

Glen Lonan, Taynuilt, Argyll PA35 1HY
☎ Taynuilt (08662) 333

*One of the largest collections of modern
hybrid rhododendrons in Scotland. The
garden covers 9 acres of woodland in a
beautiful natural setting with a spectacular
backdrop of water and mountains.*

Glen Lonan Road to the south, off the A85
Oban–Glasgow road. 8 miles due east of Oban
Open March–Oct daily 9.00am–5.00pm
Admission: 50p
&. not suitable for wheelchairs
🚌 advance notice required 🛪

▶ *TURRIFF* ◀

RUSSELL GURNEY WEAVERS

Country workshop with weaving and spinning

Brae Croft, Muiresk, Turriff, Aberdeenshire AB5 7HE
☎ Turriff (0888) 63544

*Country workshop at which weaving and
spinning demonstrations are given to those
interested. Also residential courses in these
crafts are available on a one to one basis.*

2½ miles from Turriff on the B9024 Turriff–Huntly
road. 600 yards off main road at end of a farm
road
Opan all year Mon–Sat 9.30am–5.30pm
Free admission
&. 🛪

Northern Highlands & Islands

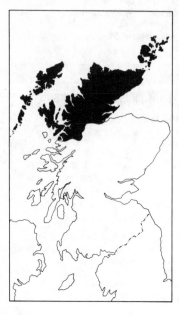

The Highlands and Islands of Scotland are wild and romantic with glens, sea lochs, and dramatic coastlines overlooked by imposing mountains.

Walk up to one of the highest waterfalls in Britain or climb and walk along any of the many country walks to see some of the breathtaking scenery of the region. There are woodland gardens and woodland walks, nature reserves, an otter haven, a herb nursery, an award-winning heritage centre and a croft museum to give the visitor an insight to life in the beautiful Highlands and Islands.

▶ *BALMACARA* ◀

BALMACARA ESTATE
Woodland garden

Lochalsh House, Balmacara IV40 8DN
☎ Balmacara (059 986) 207

Estate covers 5,616 acres – most of the Kyle/Plockton peninsula. Lochalsh woodland garden provides pleasant walks. Natural history display in Coach House.

On the A87, adjoining Kyle of Lochalsh
Open for woodland garden: all year, daily 9.00am–sunset.
   Information kiosk and coach house: 25 May–30 Sept,
   Mon–Sat 10.00am–1.00pm and 2.00–6.00pm, Sun
   2.00–6.00pm
Admission: adult 80p, child 40p (1990 prices)
& 🚍 🛉

BALMACARA WOODLAND WALKS
Woodland walks

Forestry Commission, The Square, Balmacara, by Kyle of
   Lochalsh, Highland IV40 8DN
☎ Balmacara (059986) 321

A walk through mature woodland with a considerable variety of species, while steep in parts the spectacular views of the mountains of Skye make it well worthwhile.

3 miles east of Kyle of Lochalsh on the A87
   Kyle–Invergarry road; walks start from the village
   square or campsite
Open all year
Free admission, leaflet 30p
& 🚍 🛉

▶ *BRAEMORE* ◀

CORRIESHALLOCH GORGE
National nature reserve

Braemore

Spectacular mile-long gorge, one of the finest examples in Britain of a box canyon, is 200ft deep. Farther downstream a viewing platform provides an excellent vantage point to see the Falls of Measach.

At Braemore, 12 miles south east of Ullapool, via
   the A835
Open all year
Free admission

▶ *CROMARTY* ◀

POYNTZFIELD
Herb nursery

Herb Nursery, Black Isle, by Dingwall, Ross & Cromarty,
   IV7 8LX
☎ Poyntzfield (03818) 352 (evenings)

Situated in an old walled garden, we have over 330 varieties on display and for sale. The plants originate from counties all over the world, and we include native Scottish herbs. Catalogue available (send 3 x 1st class stamps and s.a.e.)

5 miles west of Cromarty on the B9163 Shore road
Open March–Oct: Mon–Sat 1.00–5.00pm
Free admission – catalogue 60p
& 🚍 advance notice required 🛉

▶ *DUNBEATH* ◀

LAIDHAY CROFT MUSEUM
Museum

Laidhay, Dunbeath, Caithness KW6 6EH
☎ Caithness (059 33) 244

18th century rush thatched long house with cobble floored stable and byre attached. Outer cruck constructed barn. House furnished to the forties period. Implements and machinery on display.

1 mile north of Dunbeath on the A9
Open April–Sept daily 10.00am–6.00pm
Admission: adult 50p, child 20p
& byre floor with cobbled stones unsuitable for
disabled 🚍 🛉

▶ *GAIRLOCH* ◀

INVEREWE GARDEN
Country garden

Poolewe, W Ross
☎ Poolewe (044 586) 200

An 80 acre garden by the sea, sheltered by moorlands. Plants of interest at all seasons. Visitor centre and restaurant.

On the A832, 6 miles north of Gairloch
Open all year for the garden 9.30am–sunset
Admission: adult £2.20, child/OAP £1.10. Group rate
£1.80 (1990 prices)
  ♿ ☕ advance notice required ✕

GLENCOE AND DALNESS

Country walk

Lochaber
☎ Ballachulish (085 52) 307

*Some of the finest climbing and walking
country in the Highlands. Steeped in
history, the glen also has an abundance of
wildlife, including red deer, wildcat and
golden eagle. Ranger naturalist, shop, snack
bar, picnic area.*

On the A82 Glasgow–Fort William road
Open all year, daily. Visitor centre and snack bar open:
1 April–25 May and 10 Sept–21 Oct, daily 10.00am–
5.30pm; 26 May–9 Sept daily 9.30am–6.30pm
Admission: adult 30p, child 15p including parking (1990
prices)

▶   *HELMSDALE*   ◀

TIMESPAN

Heritage centre

Timespan Heritage Centre, Helmsdale, Sutherland
☎ Helmsdale (04312) 327

*Award-winning heritage centre, featuring
the dramatic story of the Highlands, with
life-size sets and sound effects, plus superb
audio-visual programme. Landscaped
riverside garden with outstanding collection
of rare and interesting plants.*

On the A9 Inverness–John O'Groats road
Open April–Oct Mon–Sat 10.00am–5.00pm, Sunday
2.00–5.00pm. Last admission 4.15pm
Admission: adult £1.90, child 90p, OAP £1.40, family
ticket (2 adults, 2 children) £5.00
  ♿ ☕ discount £1.00 per head ✕

▶   *KYLE OF LOCHALSH*   ◀

FALLS OF GLOMACH

Country walk

☎ Glenshiel (059 981) 219 Ranger

*One of the highest waterfalls in Britain,
370ft, set in a steep narrow cleft in remote
country. Best approach is from the
Dorusduain car park (Forestry Commission)
2½ miles off the north section of the loop in
the old A87. Path 5 miles: allow 5 hours for
round trip.*

18 miles east of Kyle of Lochalsh, off the A87
Open all year
Free admission

KINTAIL AND MORVICH

Country walk

Countryside Centre, Morvich Farm, Inverinale, Kyle,
Ross-shire IV40 8HQ
☎ Glenshiel (059 981) 354

*Magnificent stretch of West Highland
scenery. The 15,000 acres include the Five
Sisters of Kintail. Herds of red deer and wild
goats roam. Ranger naturalist.*

16 miles east of Kyle of Lochalsh, north of the A87
Open all year. Countryside Centre at Morvich (unmanned)
open 25 May–30 Sept Mon–Sat 10.00am–6.00pm,
Sun 2.00–6.00pm
Free admission

▶   *KYLERHEA SKYE*   ◀

KYLERHEA OTTER HAVEN

Wildlife interpretation and observation centre

Forestry Commission, The Square, Balmacara, by Kyle of
Lochalsh, Highland IV40 8DN
☎ Balmacara (059986) 321

*View otters in their natural sea/shore
habitat. A spacious hide enables visitors to
observe the abundant wildlife of this part of
Scotland. Binoculars are advisable.*

From the A850 Kyle Akin–Broadford road follow the
signposts, site is 5 miles from the turn off to
Kylerhea
Open Easter–Oct, and other times by arrangment
Free admission
  ♿ ✕

▶ *MUIR OF ORD* ◀

ORD DISTILLERY

Malt whisky distillery

Muir of Ord, Ross-shire
☎ Muir of Ord (0463) 870421

Distillery is by the A832 at Muir of Ord, 15 miles
west of Inverness
Open Mon–Fri 9.30am–4.30pm April–Oct (Nov–March by
arrangement)
Free admission
&. ⛟ ✕

TORRIDON

Country walks, museum

Ross & Cromarty
☎ Torridon (044 587) 221

*A 16,100 acre estate including some of
Scotland's finest mountain scenery. The
mountains, in addition to their scenic
splendour, hold much of interst to geologists
and naturalists. Ranger naturalist.*

9 miles south west of Kinlochewe, north of the
A896
Site and deer museum (unmanned) open all year, daily.
Countryside centre open 25 May–30 Sept Mon–Sat
10.00am–6.00pm, Sun 2.00–6.00pm
Admission: deer museum, adult 60p, child 30p.
Audio-visual display by donation
&. ⛟ 🐕 not on guided walk

WALES

CLWYD

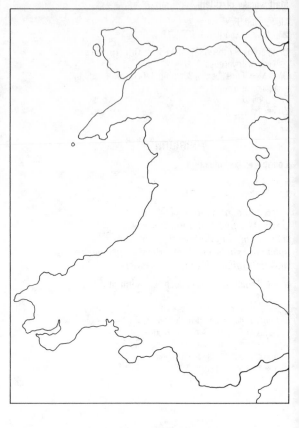

Clwyd contains some of the most spectacular scenery in Wales, high mountain ranges overlook the lush fields of the valleys of the Rivers Clwyd and Dee as they run down to the sea.

The Clwyd coastline runs in long, sandy stretches interspersed by occasional headlands. It has many popular resorts.

Take a country walk or follow an industrial heritage trail, visit one of the farm interpretation centres, take a glimpse of 17th century life at a watermill or tour round the various craft workshops, galleries and studios to enjoy the flavour of Clwyd.

▶ HOLYWELL ◀

ABBEY FARM MUSEUM

Country park, farm interpretation centre and farming museum

Greenfield Valley Heritage Park, Greenfield, Holywell, Clwyd CH8 7QB
☎ Holywell (0352) 714172

Once the cradle of the Industrial Revolution in Wales. Family groups and educational visits. Reservoirs, Basingwerk Abbey, woodlands, Abbey Farm Museum, farm buildings, machinery, animals, play park, audio-visual show.

Leave A55, signposted for Holywell. Also adjacent to the A548
Open Easter–Oct daily 10.00am–5.00pm
Admission: adult 75p, child/OAP 30p. Reduction for pre-booked groups
& ⊕ ⋔

▶ MOLD ◀

LOGGERHEADS COUNTRY PARK

Country walk, country park, countryside exhibition centre, water mill, picnic site, nature reserve, industrial heritage trail, education centre

Loggerheads, Mold, Clwyd CH7 5LH
☎ Llanferres (035 285) 586

The centre provides countryside information for the whole of Clwyd. Events are organised throughout the summer – telephone for details.

On the A494, 3 miles from Mold in the direction of Ruthin
Open all year. Information centre closed Christmas Day
Admission free
& ⊕ free parking ⋔

TRI THY CRAFT CENTRE

Craft centre, needlecraft shop and restaurant

Coed Talon, nr Mold, Clwyd CH7 4TU
☎ Pontyrbokin (0352) 771359

Set within 17th century Welsh farm buildings – browse through a collection of ideas for stitchers, buy crafts from our unique arcade, and sample Welsh hospitality from Mary's Tearoom.

Signposted off the Chester–Corwen road (A5104)
Needlecraft shop & restaurant open daily (except Mondays), Jan–23 Dec 10.30am–5.00pm, evenings by arrangement
Free admission
& ⊕ ⋔

▶ RUTHIN ◀

BOD PETRUAL WALKS, CLOCAENOG FOREST

Country walk and forestry centre

c/o Forestry Commission, Clawdd Newydd, Ruthin, Clwyd LL15 2NL
☎ Clawdd Newydd (08245) 208

2 forest walks and visitor interpretation centre adjacent to lakeside picnic area.

9 miles south west of Ruthin on the B5105
Open Easter–Sept 10.00am–5.00pm
Free admission
& there is a path with a gentle gradient ⊕ ⋔

RUTHIN CRAFT CENTRE

Craft centre

Park Rd, Ruthin, Clwyd LL15 1BB
☎ Ruthin (08242) 3992/4774/5675

Set at the foot of the Clwydian Range, a designated Area of Outstanding Beauty. The 13 independent craft studios surround an attractive landscaped courtyard. Galleries, exhibitions, shop, restaurant.

Take the Ruthin road from either Chester or Wrexham. When at Ruthin, follow road through to the ring road – craft centre is next to the roundabout
Open daily 10.00am–5.00pm
Free admission
& ⊕ advance notice required ⋔

▶ ST ASAPH ◀

FELIN-Y-GORS TROUT FISHERIES

Farm shop, farm visit, pick your own and speciality food producer

Bodelwyddan, Clwyd LL18 5UY
☎ St Asaph (0745) 584044

Fly fishing on 4 lakes, tuition by appointment. Visitors are most welcome to the fisheries and those wishing to view the farm may do so. Admission includes food to feed the trout, birds and other animals.

1½ miles from St Asaph on the A55 to the 'Marble Church' AA signs
Open all year (except Christmas/Boxing/New Year's Days) 8.30am–6.00pm
Admission: adult 40p, child 25p
& ▒ advance notice required ⋔

WREXHAM

THE PLASSEY CRAFT WORKSHOPS & BREWERY

Craft centre, nature trail

The Plassey, Eyton, Wrexham, Clwyd LL13 0SP
☎ Bangor-on-Dee (0978) 780277

Craft centre and mini-brewery, set in a unique award-winning Edwardian farm building with its Stables Coffee Shop serving home made fayre. The working craft units include stained glass, ceramics, antiques and a boutique. Nature trail.

Take the A483 towards Oswestry, south of Wrexham, turn left for Bangor-on-Dee onto the B5426. Entrance 2 miles on left
Open all year for the craft workshops, brewery by arrangement
Free admission
& ▒ advance notice required ⋔

TY MAWR COUNTRY PARK

Country park, country walk, farm trail, farm visit, farm interpretation centre

Cae Gwilym Lane, Cefn Mawr, nr Wrexham, Clwyd
☎ Wrexham (0978) 822780

Set in a river valley near Telford's aqueduct. Many varieties of farm animals can be found around the old sandstone barn/visitor centre.

Off the A483, between Wrexham and Oswestry
Open all year daily 9.00am–8.00pm (6.00pm in winter)
Free admission
& ▒ ⋔

DYFED

Dyfed's spectacular coastline is backed by sweeping moorlands rising to the higher Cambrian mountains in the north and east. A mixture of rich farmland, remote uplands and picturesque countryside, this is also a land full of ruined castles and romantic legends.

There are heritage parks, country and adventure parks, country and woodland walks, farm and nature trails and an industrial archaeological trail to follow. There are farms, farm museums, farm interpretation centres, craft centres, a woollen museum and other mills to visit. There are traditional cheeses, stoneground flours, local honeys and fresh-caught trout and salmon to sample. Coracles are still used to fish the salmon-rich rivers, as they have been since Roman times.

▶ ABERAERON ◀

ABERAERON VISITORS CENTRE

Visitors centre

The Quay, Aberaeron, Ceredigion, Dyfed SA46 0BT
☎ (0545) 570602

Provides information on the National Trust properties and activities in the area together with details on Ceredigion's Heritage Coast and coastal walks.

Open Easter–Oct daily
Free admission
&

HERITAGE COAST PROJECT

Heritage coast project

Planning Dept, Ceredigion District Council, County Hall, Aberaeron, Dyfed SA46 0AT
☎ Aberaeron (0545) 570881

The Project oversees the entire 50 mile coast of Ceredigion and has been instrumental in improving a series of coastal footpaths easily accessible from the A487 coast road. Responsible for a riverside walk with access for the disabled at Aberaeron.

On the A487
Open all year
Free admission
& riverside walk with access for the disabled at Aberaeron 🏃

▶ ABERYSTWYTH ◀

BWLCH NANT YR ARIAN VISITOR CENTRE

Visitor centre

Forest District Office, Llanafan, Aberystwyth, Dyfed SY23 4AY
☎ Crosswood (09743) 404

Tape/slide programme at Centre and start of forest walk and trail.

10 miles east of Aberystwyth on the A44. Near Ponterwyd
Open Easter–Sept daily 10.00am–5.00pm, July–Aug 10.00am–6.00pm
Educational parties or groups by arrangement only
Free admission to visitor centre, car parking 20p
& 🚌 🏃

YNYS–HIR

RSPB wildlife reserve

Furnace, Dyfed

Entrance off the A487 Aberystwyth–Machynlleth road in Furnace village
Open daily 9.00am–9.00pm or sunset
Admission: £2.50 non members – members free, guide 50p
& some provision is made for disabled visitors, please enquire for details
🚌 advance notice required 🏃

▶ BORTH ◀

BRYNLLYS (G & R A ROWLANDS)

Farm shop, farm interpretation centre, country walk, farm trail, farm visit & speciality food producer

Brynllys, Borth, Dyfed SY24 5LZ
☎ Borth (097 081) 489

Organic farm which holds the Soil Association's symbol for organic quality. Visitors can see how organic farming and nature conservation go hand in hand. Magnificent views of Dovey estuary, Cors Fochno and North Wales. Light refreshments.

Take the A487 Aberystwyth–Machynlleth road. Turn left to Borth on the B4353, village Dol-y-bont 1½ miles on right, through village first lane on left, signposted
Open April–Oct daily 10.00am–7.00pm
Free admission to families & individuals. Groups to book, fee £25.00 + VAT
& limited assistance available
🚌 advance notice required 🏃

▶ CAPEL-DEWI ◀

JOHN MORGAN & SON (SPINNERS & WEAVERS)

Craft centre (woollen mill)

Rock-Mills, Capel-Dewi, Llandysul, Dyfed SA44 4PH
☎ Llandysul (055 932) 2356

Water-powered woollen mill built in 1890 by great-grandfather of present operator.

400 yards off the B4459

Open Mon–Fri 8.30am–5.00pm, advisable to telephone for Nov–Feb visits

Free admission. Guided tours for groups: £1.00 each by prior arrangement

 ♿ toilet facilities are not suitable for the disabled

♿ advance notice required ♔ not inside mill

▶ **CENARTH** ◀

CENARTH MILL

17th century flour mill and coracle museum

Cenarth, Newcastle Emlyn, Dyfed SA38 9JL

☏ Newcastle Emlyn (0239) 710209

17th century mill in working order. A coracle maker can be seen, exhibition in mill.

On the A484 between Newcastle Emlyn and Cardigan on the River Teifi, Cenarth Falls

Open Easter–Oct 10.30am–5.30pm or by appointment

Free admission to mill but donations welcome for restoration

♿ ♿ advance notice required ⛌

▶ **CLYNDERWEN** ◀

PEMBROKESHIRE FISH FARMS

Farm shop and fish farm

Vicar's Mill, Llandissilio, Clynderwen, Dyfed

☏ Clynderwen (09916) 553

One of the few fishfarms where visitors are welcome to wander around and feed the fish or watch ongoing work. Good selection of fish and fish products in shop.

Off the A478, 4 miles north of Narberth, in village of Llandissilio, signposted

Open all year daily 10.00am–5.00pm

Admission: adult 50p, child/OAP 30p

♿ ♿ advance notice required ♔

▶ **CRYMYCH** ◀

P J & E M WHEELER

Farm interpretation centre, country walk, country park, country garden, farm trail, farm visit, nature reserve trail

Llywyngoras, Felindre, Crymych, Dyfed SA41 3XW

☏ Newport (0239) 820464

Old beef and corn farm, the corn fields now set with oak and beech plantings. Ancient woodland dropping down to the River Nevern.

First farm up river from the village of Nevern on the river Nevern. Leave Nevern on the B4582 towards Cardigan, ½ mile on right sign reads Llwyngoras

Open by arrangement

Free admission to members of Conservation Trusts, otherwise by arrangement with owner

♿ the trail is very muddy most of the year

♿ advance notice required ♔

▶ **DREFACH FELINDRE** ◀

MUSEUM OF THE WELSH WOOLLEN INDUSTRY

Woollen museum and craft workshops

Drefach Felindre, Llandysul, Dyfed SA44 5UP

☏ Llandysul (0559) 370929

Exhibition traces the conversion of fleece to fabric and the development of the industry in Wales. Workshops displaying hand made crafts, hand dyed yarns and hand made paper. Working water wheel, museum shop and cafe, picnic and play area.

4 miles east of Newcastle Emlyn, signposted off the A484 Carmarthen–Cardigan road

Open April–Sept Mon–Sat 10.00am–5.00pm, Oct–March Mon–Fri

Admission: adult £1.00, child 50p

♿ ♿ free car and coach park ♔

▶ **FISHGUARD** ◀

LLANGLOFFAN FARMHOUSE CHEESE CENTRE

Farm shop, farming museum, farm trail, farm visit, speciality food producer

Llangloffan, Castle Morris, Haverfordwest, Pembrokeshire, Dyfed SA62 5ET

☏ St Nicholas (034 85) 241

Visitors arriving at the farm between 10.00am and 12.30pm can watch the cheese-making process, see the original dairy and take the farm walk.

From Fishguard follow the A487 south westwards, after 5 miles turn left on to unclassified road towards Castle Morris for ½ mile, farm on right
Open for cheese-making 10.00am–12.30pm Mon, Wed, Thur, Sat in April and Oct; Mon–Sat in May, June, July, Aug & Sept: Farm shop open daily (except Sundays)
Admission: adult £1.25, child 75p, OAP £1.00 (1990 prices)
&. the cheese-making dairy can accommodate wheelchairs. Mirrors have been installed to enable disabled visitors to see the process. Toilets do not comply with the regulations
🚐 advance notice required ✸

▶ HAVERFORDWEST ◀

OAKWOOD PARK

Adventure and leisure park

Canaston Bridge, Narberth, Pembrokeshire, Dyfed SA67 8DE

Set in 80 acres of beautiful countryside. Rollercoaster, bobsleigh and waterfall rides, assault courses, go karts, boats, miniature trains, undercover playland, mini golf, orienteering, nature trails. Licensed restaurant, fast food outlets and shops.

Between Carmarthen and Haverfordwest, signposted off the A40
Open Easter–end Sept daily from 10.00am. Restricted opening in Oct
All inclusive entry price
&. 🚐 advance notice required, car park free
✸ free kennel provided

SCOLTON MANOR HERITAGE PARK

Country park, countryside centre, museum, railway exhibits

Spittal, Haverfordwest, Dyfed SA62 5QL
☎ Clarbeston (043782) 457, museum 328

Craft demonstrations and guided walks throughout the summer. Nature trails, play area and countryside centre. 1840 manor house includes Victorian and Edwardian period fittings. The railway area includes an 1878 saddle tank locomotive.

On the B4329 Haverfordwest–Cardigan road, 5½ miles north of Haverfordwest
Country park open all year except Christmas and Boxing day. Easter–Sept 10.00am–7.00pm, Oct–Easter 10.00am–4.30pm. Museum open daily except Mondays May–Sept 10.00am–4.30pm

Admission: Country park: free admission, there may be a charge when an event is being staged. Museum: adult 50p, child free, OAP/unemployed 25p, reduction for parties
&. &. 🚐 advance notice required ✸

SKOMER ISLAND NATIONAL NATURE RESERVE

Seabird nature reserve

Marloes, Haverfordwest, Dyfed SA62 3BL

Largest seabird colonies in southern Britain, many rare birds late May/Aug–Sept

From Haverfordwest take the B4327 to Dale, after 9½ miles (over Mullock bridge) take right hand turn to Marloes. Through village and head for Martins Haven
Open April (Easter if earlier) to end Sept daily (closed Mon except Bank Holidays). Boats leave 10.00am–12.00 noon, return from 3.00pm
Admission: landing fee: adult £3.00, child £1.00; boat: adult £4.00, child £2.00
&. steep cliff steps
🚐 advance notice required ✸

TREGWYNT WOOLLEN MILL

Working woollen mill and craft centre

Letterston, Haverfordwest, Dyfed SA62 5UX
☎ St Nicholas (03485) 225

Experience one of the traditions of Wales. Woollens from this family owned mill can now be found worldwide, but you can still purchase its quality products direct from the mill. Small cafe open Easter–Nov.

Off the A487, 4 miles south of Fishguard, 9 miles north of St Davids
Open all year: mill Mon–Fri 9.00am–5.00pm; shop Mon–Sat 9.00am–5.00pm
Free admission
&. 🚐 ✸

▶ LAMPETER ◀

FELIN NEWYDD – THE MILL AT CRUGYBAR

Working watermill producing stoneground wholemeal flour, nature reserve

Felin Newydd, Crugybar, Llanwrda, Dyfed SA19 8UE
☎ Pumsaint (05585) 375

One of the last, and most authentic, of Welsh watermills. Comprehensive tours demonstrate flour production and reveal 260 years of the mill's fascinating history using visible evidence within the building. Tea room selling local arts and crafts.

Midway between Lampeter and Llanwrda on the A482, at the junction with the B4302 from Llandeilo
Open Easter–Oct (except Mondays, unless a Bank Holiday) 10.00am–6.00pm
Admission: adult £1.50, child £1.00 (1990 prices)
 ♧ 🚑 advance notice required ✿

► LLANDEILO ◄

CRUG-LAS FARM

Craft teaching and source of materials and equipment, country walk within National Park

Bethlehem, Llandeilo, Dyfed SA19 9DT
☎ Llandeilo (0558) 823367

Handspinning, textile design and fleeces. Superb photographic location and important SSSI. Within Brecon Beacons National Park.

Using touring map, approach via Llandeilo, Ffairfach, Bethlehem. In village take signposted route to 'Garn Goch' Ancient Monument. End of access road is Crug-las Farm.
Open by appointment. Easter–end October
♧ 🐔

GELLI AUR COUNTRY PARK

Country park and country walks

Golden Grove, Llandeilo, Dyfed SA32 8LR
☎ Dryslwyn (05584) 885

The country park offers access to 90 acres of wooded parkland surrounding a magnificent mansion, completed in 1832 as the country seat for the Earls of Cawdor. Programme of events, craft demonstrations and guided walks throughout the summer. Deer park, play area, arboretum and visitor centre.

3 miles south west of Llandeilo and signposted along various routes. Entrance is just a short distance off the B4300 or the A476
Open all year (except Christmas Day and Boxing Day), Easter–Sept 10.00am–7.00pm; Oct–Easter 10.00am–5.00pm
Free admission, there may be a charge when an event is being staged
♧ 🚑 advance notice required 🐔

► LLANDYSUL ◄

TEIFI FARMHOUSE CHEESE

Farm shop, speciality food producer

Glynhynod, Ffostrasol, Llandysul, Dyfed SA44 5JY
☎ Rhydlewis (023975) 528

Home of Teifi Farmhouse Cheese, traditionally made using a recipe over 400 years old.

Off the A486 at Bwlch-y-Groes, 5 miles north of Llandysul signposted 'Farm Cheese Shop'
Open all year daily 9.00am–6.00pm; cheese-making demonstrations 9.30am–12.00 noon
Admission for cheese-making demonstrations: adult £1.25, child 75p
♧ 🚑 🐔

► LLANRHYSTUD ◄

'TURNING WORMS' AND ORGANIC SUPPLIES

Organic garden shop

Perthi Yard, Llanrhystud, Dyfed SY23 5EH
☎ Nebo (097 46) 240

Organic garden centre for retail sales of our own composts plus a full range of organic bedding, herb and vegetable plants, shrubs etc. Demonstration patch.

Take the B4337 Lampeter/Llanrhystud road, 1 mile from Llanrhystud take the road from Blaenpennal, go 1 mile
Open: April–Sept Mon–Sat 9.00am–5.30pm including Bank Holidays
Free admission
♧ 🚑 advance notice required 🐔

► LLANYBYDDER ◄

TEIFI VALLEY FISH

Farm shop and trout farm with catch your own facilities, picnic area and feed the fish

Ty Mawr, Llanybydder, Dyfed SA40 9RE
☎ Llanybydder (0570) 480789

2 angling lakes, bait or fly, tackle and tuition available. Fish caught charged at £1.78 per lb. Locally caught salmon and sea trout for sale in season; caravan club 5 van licence.

2 miles from Llanybydder on the B4337 to
   Llansawel
Open daily, dawn until dusk
Free admission
 ♾ ⛟ 🐀

► *LLAWHADEN* ◄

RIDGEWAY POTTERY AND HONEY FARM

Pottery, honey farm – speciality food producer

Rock Cottage, Llawhaden, nr Narberth, Dyfed SA67 8HL
☏   Llawhaden (09914) 268

*Handmade stoneware varies from breadbins
to modelled animals. During summer Raku
firings can be attended and comb honey is
available.*

Turn north off the A40 to Llawhaden Castle. The
   pottery is signposted second turning on left
Open May–Sept daily 10.00am–5.30pm, irregular hours
   outside season
Free admission to pottery showroom and workshop,
   charge for apiary visits, £5.00 minimum – apiary visits
   depend on weather and season (bookings only)
♿ there is a ramp entrance to the showroom, but no
toilet facilities
♾ advance notice required 🐀

► *NEWCASTLE EMLYN* ◄

CAWS CENARTH – WELSH TRADITIONAL CHEESE

**Country walk, farm shop and speciality food
producer**

Fferm Glyneithinog, Pontseli, Boncath, Dyfed SA37 0LH
☏   Newcastle Emlyn (0239) 710432

*Visitors can watch and converse with
cheesemaker by 2 way microphone system
from a special viewing gallery. The award
winning Cenarth cheese is suitable for
vegetarians.*

In Newcastle Emlyn enquire for swimming pool.
   Continue up the hill to first crossroads at
   Penrherber post office, turn right, first left then
   right. Continue for ¼ mile to farm entrance on
   left hand side
Open all year. Cheese-making most weekday mornings
   (please check), farmshop – if we are in we are open
Free admission (Oxfam collecting box)
♿ it is possible to watch the cheese-making from inside
the cheese room porch at ground level
♾ advance notice required 🐀

► *PEMBROKE* ◄

HERBERTS MOOR OPEN FARM AND NATURE TRAIL

**National park, farming museum, farm trail and
farm visit**

Herberts Moor, Lamphey, Pembroke, Dyfed SA71 5JY

*Working family dairy farm with nature trail
through old unspoilt woodland with named
flowers and trees. Close contact with farm
animals with opportunity to view milking.
Refreshments available; camp site.*

On the B4584 Freshwater East road, 3 miles south
   east of Pembroke
Open May–Sept daily 10.00am–6.00pm
Admission: adult £1.40, child/OAP 70p
♾ advance notice required 🐀

Step off the earth for a while...

Where can a narrowboat 'fly' at over 300 feet?
What are the seven Wonders of the Waterways?
How do you get a place on a sea training vessel?
How easy is it to learn to drive a canal cruiser?

Why keep your feet on the ground when there's a water-based activity to suit you?
A new FREE leaflet, produced by the British Marine Industries Federation and the National
Tourist Boards, will give you all the answers - whether you are interested in inland
waterways, yacht charter, sailing schools, powerboating, waterskiing, canoeing, surfing,
diving, sea training, learning courses... With hints and tips, ideas for holidays and short
breaks, a round-up of what's available, plus a handy reference guide to such things
as classic craft, sail marks, types of boat.

For your FREE leaflet, send off the coupon, or write to Holidays Afloat Offer,
Harrington Dock, Liverpool X, L70 1AX.

Please send me your FREE leaflet on holidays afloat

Name: ————————————————————————————

Address: ——————————————————————————

————————————————————————————————

Post Code: ——————————————————————————

Send to: Holidays Afloat Offer, Harrington Dock, Liverpool X, L70 1AX.

MID GLAMORGAN

Mid Glamorgan includes the valleys of the Rhondda that stretch down from the edge of the Brecon Beacons; Caerphilly, famous for the crumbly cheese of the same name and its thirteenth century castle, the largest in Wales; and the coast around Porthcawl which has fine beaches and resorts. Despite its coal mining associations the rolling landscape of Mid Glamorgan has much to offer including the new character of the old mining valleys and many fine views of the Brecon Beacons.

There is a nature reserve that provides a wintering ground for wildfowl, an interpretative centre and a country walk to give the visitor a glimpse of the country delights Mid Glamorgan can offer.

▶ *PORTHCAWL* ◀

KENFIG NATIONAL NATURE RESERVE

Country walk and nature reserve, interpretative centre

Ton Kenfig, Pyle, Mid Glamorgan CF33 4PT
☎ Kenfig Hill (0656) 743386

A nature reserve rising to 50 feet above sea level with over 600 species of flowering plant. Wintering ground for wildfowl, and a stop-over for passage migrants as well as breeding birds; 21 species of dragonfly. Warden is Steve Moon.

Off the B4283, 2 miles north west of Porthcawl. Access off M4 at jct 35 or 37
Open all year 2.00–5.00pm at weekends, telephone for weekday times
Free admission
& 🚐 advance notice required 🐾

SOUTH GLAMORGAN

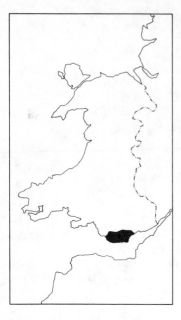

South Glamorgan has a coastline with many fine beaches backed by the beautiful landscapes of the Vale of Glamorgan that runs for twenty miles west of Cardiff, a seaport city and the capital of Wales.

There are country walks including guided walks through areas that range from wild countryside to formal town parks, they are led by experts in different fields; nature reserves with wild flower meadows; woodland gardens; historic sites; picnic areas and an open air folk museum that includes farming and historic buildings.

► CARDIFF ◄

BUTE PARK (TAFF VALLEY)

Country walk, ornamental areas and picnic areas

c/o Director of Leisure and Amenities, Cardiff City
Council, King George V Drive, Cardiff, South
Glamorgan CF4 4EP

☎ Cardiff (0222) 751235 ext 4540

*Bute Park contains some fine mature
woodlands, 2 herbaceous borders and a
newly created arboretum adjacent to Cardiff
Castle. There is also the remains of a
Dominican Priory and Gorsedd Stone Circle.*

Cycleway/heritage trail linking Cardiff Castle and
Castle Coch, Tongwynlais
Open all year during daylight hours (closes ½ hr before
sunset)
Free admission
👤 🚌 advance notice required 🐂

GLAMORGANSHIRE CANAL LOCAL NATURE RESERVE

Local nature reserve, including picnic areas

c/o Director of Leisure and Amenities, Cardiff City
Council, King George V Drive, Heath Park, Cardiff,
South Glamorgan CF4 4EP

☎ Cardiff (0222) 751235 ext 4540

*Wooded hillslopes, attractive meadows and
former canal which contains many rare
unusual aquatic flora and fauna. The area is
served by a Wardens Centre and
Conservation Centre.*

Off the M4 at Coryton interchange, direction
Whitchurch, at roundabout just before town turn
down Velindre Road. ½ mile to Forest Farm
Road, 1 mile down this road to T junction, turn
right
Open all year
Free admission
👤 a large proportion of the reserve is accessible to
riders, however there are no public toilet facilities
🚌 advance notice required 🐂

GUIDED WALKS PROGRAMME

Country walk, guided walks programme

c/o Leisure and Amenities Dept, Cardiff City Council,
King George V Drive, Heath Park, Cardiff, South
Glamorgan CF4 4EP

☎ Cardiff (0222) 751235 ext 4540

*The walks arranged throughout the year are
led by experts in natural history,
archaeology, horticulture and local history.
The areas covered range from wild
countryside with views across Cardiff Bay to
formal town parks.*

Various sites, please apply to above address for a
leaflet
Open times, please enquire for details
Admission charges, please enquire for details
👤 some walks have facilities
🚌 advance notice required 🐂

HOWARDIAN NATURE RESERVE, ROATH

Local nature reserve

c/o Director of Leisure and Amenities, Cardiff City
Council, King George V Drive, Heath Park, Cardiff,
South Glamorgan CF4 4EP

☎ Cardiff (0222) 751235 ext 4540

*This newly created nature reserve provides a
wide variety of features which include marsh
areas, woodlands, wild flower meadows and
extensive newly planted areas.*

Please telephone for directions
Open all year
Free admission
👤 🐂

PARC CEFN ONN

Woodland garden

Cherry Orchard Rd, Lisvane, Cardiff, South Glamorgan
☎ Cardiff (0222) 751089

*Over 200 acres of ornamental gardens and
woodland walks. It is particularly attractive
between April/June when azaleas,
rhododendrons and camelias are in full
bloom. Interesting tree collection.*

6 miles north of Cardiff city centre adjacent to
Lisvane, Thornhill
Open all year during normal daylight hours (closes ½ hr
before sunset)
Free admission
👤 most of the garden is accessible to wheelchairs,
assistance would be required on steep sections 🚌 🐂

WELSH NATIONAL FOLK MUSEUM

Open air national folk museum including farming and historic buildings

St Fagans, Cardiff, South Glamorgan CF5 6XB
☎ Cardiff (0222) 569441

Set in 100 acres of parkland, an elegant castle, re-erected farmhouses, humble cottages and work buildings reflect the domestic, cultural and social life of Wales. Permanent displays.

Off the M4, jct 33, follow signposts
Open Easter–Oct daily 10.00am–5.00pm, closed Sunday Nov–March
Admission: adult £3.00, child £1.50, OAP £2.25, family ticket £7.50, party reductions, free parking
&. wheelchairs available 🚌 🍴

WEST GLAMORGAN

West Glamorgan encompasses Swansea, a major port, Port Talbot, a highly industrialised area, the almost unspoilt Gower peninsula and the Vale of Neath, where young trees grow out of the cleared and reclaimed former industrial sites – an interesting mixture of landscapes.

There are industrial museums featuring collieries, mining and miners. There are historic buildings, country parks and water cascades, deer and rare breeds to see and enjoy, country walks and forest trails to follow.

▶ *NEATH* ◀

CEFN COED COLLIERY MUSEUM

Industrial museum in countryside

Crynant, Neath, West Glamorgan
☎ Crynant (0639) 750556

The museum is located in the surface buildings of the disused Cefn Coed Colliery. It features a simulated mining gallery and a preserved colliery winding engine driven by electricity. Picnic areas and forest trails nearby.

Adjoins the A4109, 4 miles north east of Neath
Open April–Sept daily 10.30am–6.00pm, Oct–March daily
  10.30am–4.00pm (except Christmas Day/New Year's
  Day)
Admission: adult £1.00, child/OAP 60p
& ⇔ advance notice required ⋔

GNOLL GROUNDS

Country park

Off Cimla Road, Neath, West Glamorgan
☎ Neath (0639) 641121

A naturally wooded deciduous and coniferous area with waymarked paths, taking in views of the nearby reservoir, the highly attractive water 'cascades' and the distant Swansea Bay and Gower Peninsula.

Take the B4287 from Neath to Pontrhydyfen.
  Entrance signposted ¼ mile along Cimla Road or
  take B4434 from Neath to Tonna. Signpost to
  Moss House seen on right hand side
Open all year, during daylight hours
Free admission
& please telephone to discuss arrangements for disabled
visitors
⇔ advance notice required ⋔

The park is on the A4107, 6 miles north east of
  Port Talbot, exit 40 of the M4
Open all year for the country park walks, Welsh Miners'
  Museum & countryside centre: April–Oct daily
  10.30am–6.00pm, Nov–Mar Sat & Sun only
  10.30am–5.00pm
Admission to museum: adult 50p, child 15p, (1990
  prices), car park 20p
& ⇔ ⋔

MARGAM PARK

Country park and country walk

Margam, Port Talbot, West Glamorgan SA13 2TJ
☎ Port Talbot (0639) 881635

Historic buildings, 800 acres of parkland with many waymarked walks, fun activities, ornamental gardens, iron age hill fort, deer and rare breeds, maze, putting, boating, pony trekking and nursery rhyme village.

Approx ½ mile from jct 38 of the M4 on the A48
  Margam–Pyle road, 5 miles east of Port Talbot
Open daily 29 March–30 Sept 10.00am–7.00pm, last
  admission 4.00pm, 1 Oct–28 March Wed–Sun
  10.00am–5.00pm, last admission 3.00pm (limited
  facilities open in winter)
Admission: Summer; all classes £2.50 family ticket £6.50;
  Winter; adult £1.10, child/OAP 55p, under 5s free,
  special party rates
& ⇔ special rates if pre-booked ⋔

▶ *PORT TALBOT* ◀

AFAN ARGOED COUNTRY PARK & WELSH MINERS' MUSEUM

Country park, country walk, forestry centre, cycle hire centre and Welsh Miners' Museum

Cynonville, nr Port Talbot, West Glamorgan SA13 3HG
☎ Cymmer (0639) 850564

Camping site, Landrover forest tours.

GWENT

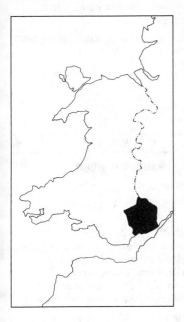

Gwent's quiet pastoral countryside stretches from the beautiful wooded Wye valley in the east to the dramatic Brecon Beacons in the west. Picturesque roads follow the Usk river valley, its waters offer excellent salmon fishing. This border country has several historic and fortified towns and castles – a reflection of its turbulent past.

Country parks and nature reserves are open to the visitor to explore. They offer acres of ancient woodland or excellent bird-watching opportunities. There are castles and museums and countryside centres as well as an award-winning rural life museum to visit.

▶ ABERGAVENNY ◀

ABERGAVENNY CASTLE & MUSEUM

Local history museum with rural life and craft displays

The Castle, Castle Street, Abergavenny, Gwent NP7 5EE
☎ Abergavenny (0873) 4282

Regular events and temporary exhibitions throughout the year.

Off the A40 from Monmouth to Brecon and the A465 to Hay-on-Wye
Open March–Oct: Mon–Sat 11.00am–1.00pm, 2.00–5.00pm, Sun 2.00–5.00pm. Nov–Feb: Mon–Sat 11.00am–1.00pm, 2.00–4.00pm. Closed Sunday
Admission: adult 75p, child/OAP/pre-booked groups 35p, residents of Monmouth borough & educational groups free
🚲 we try to be as flexible and helpful as possible
🚌 advance notice required 🐕

CASTLE MEADOWS

Country park and country walk

Tudor St, Abergavenny, Gwent

On the southern outskirts of town, close to Llanfoist Bridge. Parking available at Tudor Street and Castle Street
Open all year
Free admission
🚲 🚌 🐕

CLYDACH GORGE WALKS

Country walk and picnic area

c/o Blaenau Gwent Borough Council, Municipal Offices, Civic Centre, Ebbw Vale, Gwent NP3 6XB
☎ Ebbw Vale (0495) 350555

Discover the area where countryside and industrial heritage combine to offer walks at Clydach Gorge, Gilwern and Nantyglo, also places to eat and stay whilst exploring. Home of Garden Festival Wales 1992.

Off the A465, 6 miles west of Abergavenny
Open all year
Free admission
🚲 🚌 🐕

WERNDDU FARM

Farm shop and pick your own

Old Ross Rd, Abergavenny, Gwent NP7 8NG
☎ Abergavenny (0873) 5289

Beautiful setting with views of Usk Valley and Brecon Beacons. Strawberries and many other soft fruits and vegetables may be picked. Refreshments; pay phone; golf driving range.

1½ miles east of town on the B4521 (off the A465)
Open June–Sept 10.00am–7.00pm
Free admission
🚲 🚌 🐕

▶ CAERWENT ◀

HARDWICK WOOD

Nature reserve

c/o Gwent Wildlife Trust, 16 White Swan Court, Monmouth, Gwent NP5 3NY
☎ Monmouth (0600) 5501

Nature reserve consisting of a remnant of a mixed deciduous woodland with a rich ground flora of lime-loving plants. Many of the plants have disappeared, but various orchids and other flowers may still be found.

Off Highmoor Hill, Caerwent: enter woodland on Forestry Commission track by telephone box and turn right almost immediately onto a footpath, and, where the path forks, turn right again. The reserve, which is only half a hectare, lies alongside the track and continues to edge of the wood
Open all year
Free admission
🚲 🐕

▶ CALDICOT ◀

CALDICOT CASTLE AND COUNTRY PARK

Castle and country park

The Castle Keeper/Country Park Warden, Caldicot, nr Chepstow, Gwent
☎ (0291) 420241/430241

A popular country park surrounding the mediaeval Caldicot Castle. Archaeological excavation until 1992 of a fascinating Bronze Age site within the park. Toilets, including disabled; caravan rally site; personal stereo guides for castle.

7 miles west of Severn Bridge, off the A48 or the
B4245
Park open all year. Castle open March–Oct. Bronze
Age Excavation open May–Sept, Sun–Fri
Free admission to park; admission to castle: adults £1.00,
child/OAP 50p
    ♿ 🚌 ♞

▶ **CROSS KEYS** ◀

SIRHOWY VALLEY COUNTRY PARK

Country walk and country park

Full Moon Visitor Centre, Cross Keys, Gwent
☎ Ynysddu (0495) 270991

*A 1,000 acre Country Park of well wooded
hillside and attractive river banks in the
lower Sirhowy Valley; one of the historic and
beautiful Gwent valleys. The usual outdoor
activities are supplemented by an annual
events programme.*

6 miles north of Newport – follow the A467 from
jct 28 on the M4
Open all year
Free admission to the country park
♿ 🚌 advance notice required ♞

▶ **CWMBRAN** ◀

FIVE LOCKS CANAL

Nature reserve

c/o Gwent Wildlife Trust, 16 White Swan Court,
Monmouth, Gwent NP5 3NY
☎ Monmouth (0600) 5501

*Nature reserve consists of overhanging
alders providing perches for kingfishers and
much frequented in winter by flocks of tits,
siskins and redpolls. The slow-moving water
in the canal provides an important habitat
for aquatic plants and invertebrates.*

The reserve begins at Five Locks at Pontnewydd,
north of Cwmbran, and continues for about ½
mile to Bevan's Bridge just south of Sebastopol
Open all year
Free admission
♿ ♞

▶ **CWMFELINFACH** ◀

YNYS HYWEL COUNTRYSIDE CENTRE

**Farm trail, farm visit, farm interpretation centre
and country walk**

Cwmfelinfach, Cross Keys, Gwent NP1 7JX
☎ Blackwood (0495) 200113

*A traditional 120 acre hill farm being
restored with field boundaries and laid out to
1846 tithe map. The Longhouse is being
extended for residential and conference/study
accommodation.*

1 mile south of the village of Cwmfelinfach on the
A4048. M4 exit 28 to the A467 then the A4048
Open all year for walks and accommodation, weekends
for afternoon teas during the summer
Free admission
♿ 🚌 advance notice required ♞

▶ **EBBW VALE** ◀

CWM MERDDOG

Nature reserve

c/o Gwent Wildlife Trust, 16 White Swan Court,
Monmouth, Gwent NP5 3NY
☎ Monmouth (0600) 5501

*Wood of approx 55 acres, mature beech, oak,
some alder wood and scrub, interesting flora
alongside the Nant Merddog and nesting
birds include redstarts and pied flycatchers.
Nature trail leaflet available from Trust
offices.*

Off the A4064 south of Ebbw Vale, to the east of
Cwm Cemetery
Open all year
Free admission
♿ ♞

▶ **MONMOUTH** ◀

DIXTON EMBANKMENT

Nature reserve

c/o Gwent Wildlife Trust, 16 White Swan Court,
Monmouth, Gwent NP5 3NY
☎ Monmouth (0600) 5501

*Nature reserve consists of 1 acre with a
diversity of lime-loving plants, especially bee
orchids. Rich insect life such as white-legged
dragonflies and butterflies.*

South of the A40, 1 mile north east of Monmouth.
Follow riverside footpath from Dixton church
Open all year
Free admission
♿ ♞

PENALLT OLD CHURCH WOOD

Nature reserve

c/o Gwent Wildlife Trust, 16 White Swan Court,
Monmouth, Gwent NP5 3NY
☎ Monmouth (0600) 5501

*Nature reserve consists of 10 acres of
deciduous woodland on a steep slope above
the River Wye. Spring flowers include wild
daffodil and moschatel; birds include a nest
box colony of pied flycatchers and
sparrowhawk.*

Take the B4293 Trellech road from Monmouth; turn
left near the top of Lydart Hill for Penallt. Bear
left again and after about 1 mile turn left
following the signs to the old church. The wood
lies on the slope between the road leading to the
church and the road dropping down from it
Open all year
Free admission
& 🛪

PRISK WOOD

Nature reserve

c/o Gwent Wildlife Trust, 16 White Swan Court,
Monmouth, Gwent NP5 3NY
☎ Monmouth (0600) 5501

*Nature reserve consists of a diversity of trees
and shrubs including ash, wych-elm, cherry
and small leaved lime. Birds include
flycatchers, sparrowhawk and woodcock.*

From Monmouth take the B4293 south, after 2
miles bear left to Penallt. Straight over
crossroads at Penallt village; park ¾ mile down
the lane where an area of woodland meets the
road on the right
Open all year
Free admission
& 🛪

STRAWBERRY COTTAGE WOOD

Nature reserve

c/o Gwent Wildlife Trust, 16 White Swan Court,
Monmouth, Gwent NP5 3NY
☎ Monmouth (0600) 5501

*Nature reserve consisting of 16 acres of
wood, mostly of sessile oak with hazel.
Voluntary warden: Jerry Lewis, tel
Abergavenny (0873) 5091.*

3 miles north of Abergavenny on the A465. Take
the Llanthony road from Llanvihangel Crucorney
for 2 miles, parking near the Stanton Forest coal
pit road. 100 yards back is a footbridge across
the Honddu; cross the field beyond and turn left
through the gate by Strawberry Cottage
Open all year
Free admission
& 🛪

► ◄ **NEWPORT**

CWMCARN FOREST DRIVE AND VISITOR CENTRE

Country walk and forestry centre

Forestry Commission, Wentwood, Llanvaches, Newport,
Gwent NP6 3AZ
☎ Cwmcarn (0633) 400205

*High in the Ebbw Forest overlooking the
Bristol Channel and surrounding
countryside. Forest walks, childrens play
area, picnic places, barbecue hearths.*

8 miles north of jct 28 off the M4 on the A467 to
Cross Keys – follow the highway signs
Open Good Friday–31 Oct 11.00am–7.00pm
Admission: car £2, minibus from £6, coach £20 –
(advance booking/payment less 20% for these prices).
'Scenic Super Saver' multi visit ticket £6
& 🚌 🛪

TREDEGAR HOUSE & PARK

**Craft centre, country walk, farm trail, country
garden and historic house**

Newport, Gwent NP1 9YW
☎ Newport (0633) 815880

*Visitors may relax in the historic parkland,
with the option to tour the house and formal
walled garden. Country park and home farm
trail leaflets available at 25p each.*

2 miles west of Newport, signposted from the A48
and M4 jct 28
Open for the country park daily, dawn until dusk; house
and facilities Easter–Sept, Wed–Sun, Public Holidays
and weekends in Oct
Admission to house and gardens £2.70/£1.70; gardens
only £1.00; carriage rides £1.00/50p
& wheelchairs available. If visiting house, please
give advance notice so that ramps can be sited 🚌 🛪

► **OAKDALE** ◄

PEN-Y-FAN POND COUNTRY PARK

Country park

Oakdale, Blackwood, Gwent

☎ Blackwood (0495) 214753

Attractive country park centred on a 14 acre pond, once a feeder pond serving the Monmouthshire Canal. Walking, bird watching and panoramic views. Picnic area, footpaths, model-boat sailing, refreshments, toilets and footpaths for disabled.

Signposted from the B4251 Blackwood–Crumlin road
Open all year
Free admission
&

► **PETERSTONE** ◄

PETERSTONE WENTLOOGE

Nature reserve

c/o Gwent Wildlife Trust, 16 White Swan Court, Monmouth, Gwent NP5 3NY

☎ Monmouth (0600) 5501

Peterstone is the most important estuarine nature reserve in Gwent. Wildfowl include shoveller, and shelduck, dunlin and some locally rare species such as little ringed plover, avocet and ruff. Voluntary warden: Dr Al Venables, tel Cardiff (0222) 756697.

From Peterstone (on the B4239) take the public footpath which runs beside the church down to the sea wall
Open all year
Free admission
& ⴕ

► **RAGLAN** ◄

WILLIAMS FRUIT

Farm shop, pick your own and picnic area

Great Tyrmynach, Raglan, Gwent NP5 2JP

☎ Raglan (0291) 690470

Small cheerful PYO giving a warm welcome. All vegetables and fruit are produced on the farm and picked daily for the farm shop.

Take the Old Abergavenny road from Raglan (signposted Clytha). Turn left into farm immediately after the 'Crickle Creek' public house
Open approx mid June–mid Aug daily 9.30am–7.00pm
Free admission
& ⴳ ⴕ

► **REDWICK** ◄

GOLDCLIFF NATURE RESERVE

Nature reserve

c/o Gwent Wildlife Trust, 16 White Swan Court, Monmouth, Gwent NP5 3NY

☎ Monmouth (0600) 5501

Reserve is a feeding ground for a variety of birds such as passage and winter waders, invertebrate life and the saltmarsh at Magor Pill supports several locally rare plants. Voluntary warden: Derek Upton, tel Caldicot (0291) 420137.

Off the M4 at jct 23, follow signs to Llanwern Steel works, then Whitson and Goldcliff. 2 miles beyond steel works is small chapel on corner, park here and follow footpath to Goldcliff
Open all year
Free admission
& ⴕ

► **TREDEGAR** ◄

BRYN BACH PARK

Country park with visitor centre

Merthyr Rd, Tredegar, Gwent NP2 3AY

☎ Tredegar (0495) 711816

500 acres of reclaimed opencast mine land, lake with fishing, windsurfing and waterski-ing. Visitor centre with Wales Tourist Board information centre. Video and display facilities; picnic and barbecue areas.

Off the A465 Heads of Valleys road follow directions from Tredegar or Rhymney roundabouts
Open all year 9.00am–dusk. Accommodation available for supervised groups of up to 18 people by prior arrangement
Free admission – charges for events
& ⴳ ⴕ

► *TRELLECH* ◄

CLEDDON SHOOTS

Nature reserve

c/o Gwent Wildlife Trust, 16 White Swan Court,
Monmouth, Gwent NP5 3NY
☎ Monmouth (0600) 5501

*Consists of about 20 acres of ancient
semi-natural woodland on the very steep
slopes of the Wye Valley. The shoots are a
series of waterfalls.*

From Trellech, take the Llandogo road past Cleddon
Bog and down a narrow lane on the left to
Cleddon. There is a small parking area at the top
of the reserve
Open all year
Free admission
占 ★

► *USK* ◄

GWENT RURAL LIFE MUSEUM

Farming museum

The Malt Barn, New Market St, Usk, Gwent NP5 1AU
☎ Usk (02913) 3777

Award winning private collection.

In centre of Usk, signposted from Bridge Street.
Usk is approached from M4 (jct 25) via the
B4596, or (jct 24) via the A449, or from the
A472
Open April–Sept Mon–Fri 10.00am–5.00pm; weekends
2.00–5.00pm. Oct–March, please telephone Museum
for opening times
Admission: please telephone for details
占 ▄▄▄ advance notice required ★

PRIORY WOOD

Nature reserve

c/o Gwent Wildlife Trust, 16 White Swan Court,
Monmouth, Gwent NP5 3NY
☎ Monmouth (0600) 5501

*Varied broad leaved woodland, with an
abundance of cherry trees. Nesting birds
include pied flycatchers and occasionally
hawfinches.*

From the Chain Bridge (on the A471, 4 miles north
of Usk) take the Bettws Newydd road, the
reserve is ½ mile along on the right
Open all year
Free admission
占 ★

GWYNEDD

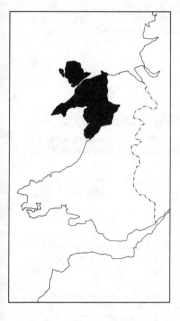

Gwynedd incorporates craggy mountains with hill farms and glens in the south, rugged shores along the Llŷn Peninsula, the island of Anglesey and the wild mountains of the Snowdonia National Park within its boundaries. The Talylyn narrow gauge railway at Tywyn once transported slate, now it carries people to enjoy the views and the ride.

Visit one of the working farms, meet the farm animals, including goats, and their young. Try the local produce at one of the farm shops before taking a country walk. There are slate works to visit, a copper mine to explore, a pottery and a woollen mill for the craft enthusiast.

► **AMLWCH** ◄

EARTHSONG DAIRY GOATS

Farm shop, country park, farm trail, farm visit and speciality food and drink producer

Nebo, Amlwch, Anglesey, Gwynedd LL68 9NH
☎ Holyhead (0407) 830413

Small herd of pedigree dairy goats kept free-range on natural old pasture, magnificent views over the sea to North Wales mountain range, coast and the Great Orme.

Situated on top of Eilian mountain off the A5025, 2 miles from Amlwch
Open most days 10.00am–8.00pm – please telephone for appointment
Free admission
&. easy access to farmyard, but farm buildings and toilet facilities unsuitable ✘

► **BEDDGELERT – SNOWDONIA** ◄

SYGUN COPPER MINE, TY-HEN

Mine tours

Beddgelert, nr Caernarfon, Gwynedd LL55 4NE
☎ Beddgelert (076686) 595

Set in the heart of Snowdonia, this Prince of Wales award winning attraction offers unforgettable underground audio-visual tours, preserving the past for the future.

1 mile from Beddgelert on the A498 towards Capel Curig
Open March–Oct daily 10.00am–5.15pm (last tour), please enquire for winter opening times
Admission: adult £2.50, child £1.40, OAP £1.95, group rates available (1990 prices)
&. toilets and park of the area suitable for disabled
🚌 ✝

GLYNLLIFON PARK

Country park

c/o Gwynedd County Council, County Officer, Caernarfon, Gwynedd LL55 1SH
☎ Caernarfon (0286) 4121 ext 2386 / manager 830222

Country park featuring country walk, historic country garden and sculpture, workshops, visitor centre and tea room.

Main entrance on the A499, 5 miles south of Caernarfon
Open Spring Bank Holiday–end Sept 10.00am–5.00pm, grounds open all year
Admission: 50p per person, car park charge 30p
&. there is a path approx 1½ miles long suitable for wheelchairs, toilet facilities 🚌 ✝

► **CAERNARFON** ◄

PADARN COUNTRY PARK

Country park, craft centre, woodland walk, water sport activities, industrial archaeological trail, snack bar

c/o Gwynedd County Planning Dept, Gwynedd County Council, County Offices, Caernarfon, Gwynedd LL55 1SH
☎ Caernarfon (0286) 4121 ext 2386

Signposts to Padarn County Park on Llanberis bypass (A4086), 6 miles east of Caernarfon
Open all year for park. Other facilities open April–Oct
Free admission, charges for Welsh Slate Museum and Llanberis Lake railway
&. there is vehicular access for disabled visitors to Quarry Hospital and viewing point in main car park information point by arrangement 🚌 ✝

► **DOLGELLAU** ◄

COED Y BRENIN FOREST PARK AND VISITOR CENTRE

Forest trails, walks, nature reserve, wildlife hide, childrens play area, shop, cafe

Forestry Commission, Maesgwm, Ganllwyd, Dolgellau, Gwynedd LL40 2HY
☎ Dolgellau (0341) 422 289

The visitor centre with is interpretive displays should be the starting point of your visit. Picnic areas with barbeques, childrens play area, shop, cafe. Mountain biking, interpretive displays and sign making unit.

Take the A470 Dolgellau–Blaenau Ffestiniog road. 8 miles north of Dolgellau, turn left at sign to Visitor Centre
Open Easter–Oct, 10.00am–5.00pm, Nov–Easter by prior arrangement
Free admission
&. 🚌 ✝

► DWYRAN ◄

BRYNTIRION OPEN FARM

Working farm, farm trail and farm visit

Dwyran, Anglesey, Gwynedd LL61 6BQ
☎ Brynsiencyn (0248) 430232

A real working farm: meet the farmer, watch our activites, see a wide range of farm animals and their young (newly hatched chicks, multi-coloured pigs). Fish the pools or try organic produce.

Just off the A4080 on the outskirts of Dwyran,
   3 miles from Brynsiencyn
Open June–Sept 10.30am–5.30pm
Admission: adult £1.50, child £1.00
&. ᗿ advance notice required ✕

► GROESLON ◄

INIGO JONES & CO LTD

Tour of slate works, historical lettercutting and calligraphy exhibition, demonstrations, craft showroom and cafe

Tudor Slate Works, Groeslon, Gwynedd
☎ Llanwnda (0286) 830242

Slateworks established in 1861, where craftsmen can be seen at work. Self-guided tour includes illustrated booklet, a video on how the slate is mined at Aberllefenni, taped commentary around factory as well as lettercutting and calligraphy exhibition, where visitors can have a go at engraving.

The works are situated on the main A487
   Caernarfon–Porthmadog road, 6 miles from
   Caernarfon between the villages of Groeslon and
   Pen-y-Groes
Open all year, Easter–Sept: Mon–Fri 9.00am–4.30pm, Sat
   & Sun 10.00am–4.30pm; last self-guided tour 4.00pm.
   Oct–Easter daily, Mon–Fri 9.00am–4.30pm, Sat
   9.00am–12.00 noon
Admission: adult £1.50, child/OAP £1.00, discounts for
   group booking
&. ᗿ ᛏ

► HOLYHEAD ◄

FARMLIFE

Farm shop, craft centre, farm interpretation centre, country walk, farming museum, farm trail and farm visit

Bodowyr Farm, Bodedern, Holyhead, Anglesey, Gwynedd
☎ Valley (0407) 741171

Refreshments available in the cafeteria.

Off the A5, 8 miles south east of Holyhead
Open all year (except 25, 26 Dec & Jan) 10.00am–
   5.00pm (dusk in summer), parties by appointment
Admission: adult £1.50, child/OAP 75p, family ticket
   £5.00, party prices on application (1990 prices)
&. ᗿ ✕ free kennels available

► LLANDUDNO ◄

GREAT ORME COUNTRY PARK & NATURE RESERVE

Country park

c/o Department of Tourism and Amenities, Aberconwy
   Borough Council, Chapel St, Llandudno, Gwynedd
   LL30 2UY
☎ Llandudno (0492) 874151

This limestone headland is designated a Heritage Coast and SSSI in recognition of the outstanding landscape quality and wildlife interest. Access is by car, foot, tramway or cable car.

The site lies north west of Llandudno and
   dominates the town. Access via the A546
Open all year; visitor centre 9.30am–5.00pm April–Sept
Free admission
&. ᛏ

►LLANSANFFRAID GLAN CONWY◄

FELIN ISAF 17TH CENTURY WATERMILL

17th century watermill museum and crafts

Llansanffraid Glan Conwy, Gwynedd LL28 5TE
☎ Aberconwy (0492) 580646

A fascinating glimpse of 17th century life. Things to touch, places to explore – a good wet weather visit. Winner of the Prince of Wales award, Civic Trust award and the Times conservation award. School visit specialists.

On the A470 between Llandudno and Colwyn Bay,
   follow signs for Bodnant Garden
Open all year daily 10.00am–dusk
Admission: adult £1.25, child/disabled 75p
&. there is a ramp into mill for wheelchair access, all
level paths, special drive in for disabled to drive up to
mill direct ᗿ ✕

▶ **MENAI BRIDGE** ◀

PILI PALAS – BUTTERFLY PALACE

Butterfly farm, shop and cafe, reptile house and pets corner

Ffordd Penmyndd, Porthaethwy, Ynys Môn, Gwynedd
LL59 5RP
☎ Menai Bridge (0248) 712474

Butterfly palace with over 400 free flying butterflies. Bird house with a walk through aviary. Mini beast corner with scorpions, African snails and locusts. Snake house with pythons and corn snakes. Teas and refreshments.

Off the B5025 near Fourcrosses roundabout, take
the B5420 to Llangefni, ¼ mile down the road
Open Easter–Oct 10.00am–5.30pm
Admission: adult £2.20, child £1.20, OAP £1.75
&. ⇔ ⋇ in the butterfly house

▶ **PORTHMADOG** ◀

PORTHMADOG POTTERY

Pottery

Y Felin, Snowdon St, Porthmadog, Gwynedd
☎ Porthmadog (0766) 512137

See a production pottery at work, have a go at making your own pot or painting a plate. Best and Seconds shop, pottery pantry cafe and picnic garden.

From town centre 250 yards down Snowdon Street
(opposite Woolworths); from the main car park
50 yards from the one way exit, follow signs
Open Easter–Oct Mon–Fri 9.00am–5.30pm
Admission: 25p; child under 14 yrs free, activity £1.50
each (1990 prices)
&. assistance available with wheelchairs and we have
special needs groups ⇔ ⋇

▶ **PWLLHELI** ◀

RHOSFAWR NURSERIES

Farm shop, nursery, country garden, country walk and speciality organic food producer

Rhosfawr Nurseries, Y-Ffôr, Pwllheli, Gwynedd LL53 6YA
☎ Pwllheli (0766) 810545

Campsite and bed and breakfast also.

Off the B4354, 5 miles north of Pwllheli
Open all year
Free admission
&. ⋇

▶ **TREFRIW** ◀

TREFRIW WOOLLEN MILLS LTD

Woollen mill and shop

Trefriw, Gwynedd LL27 0NQ
☎ Llanrwst (0492) 640462

Woollen mill where bedspreads and tweeds are manufactured from the raw wool. Visitors can tour the mill and see the weaving and the hydro-electric turbines. Shop and cafe.

On the B5106 Conwy–Betws-y-Coed road in centre
of village, car park opposite mill
Mill open all year except Bank Holidays, 3rd Mon in Oct,
2 weeks over Christmas. Shop and weaving open as
above plus Sat 10.00am–4.00pm, Sun 2.00–5.00pm
Spring Bank Holiday–end Aug
Free admission, except for school parties which must be
pre-booked
&. ⇔ ⋇

▶ **TYWYN** ◀

PENTRE BACH

Farm shop and speciality food producer

Pentre Bach, Llwyngwril, Gwynedd LL37 2JU
☎ Fairbourne (0341) 250294

Pleased to take visitors round organically run walled garden and poly tunnel when not busy. Self catering holidays offered, bed & breakfast. Free-range hen and duck eggs, home-made preserves.

8 miles north of Tywyn, entrance is on the A493
coast road, in the centre of Llwyngwril, near the
primary school
Open daily during daylight hours all year; Oct–March,
preferably by appointment please
Free admission
&. there is a cottage available with a disabled toilet for
use if unoccupied. Please telephone in advance ⋇

POWYS

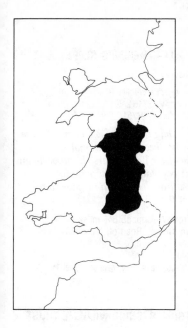

Powys with its mountains and deserted moorland, hill farms and forestry is extremely rich in wildlife and historical associations. The landscape appears totally uninhabited in places, it is wonderful walking and touring country either on foot, by horse or by mountain bike.

You can follow Offa's dyke or a trail around one of the many wildlife and nature reserves where you might see red kites, peregrines or merlins. There are country parks and farms to visit, interpretation centres where you can watch sheep shearing and spinning, educational reserves and opportunities for a good day's fishing.

▶ KNIGHTON ◀

OFFA'S DYKE CENTRE

Country walk, interpretation centre

West St, Knighton, Powys LD7 1EW
☎ Knighton (0547) 528783

The Offa's Dyke Association is a charitable body promoting and protecting the Offa's Dyke path. The centre provides information, sells guides and maps, also has an interpreting exhibition.

200 yards from town centre, in West St, off the A488
Open April–Oct daily, Nov–March weekdays 9.00am–5.30pm
No admission charge, but donations towards our work are invited. Membership invited
&. ㅎ advance notice required ⅋

▶ LLANDRINDOD WELLS ◀

BAILEY EINON NATURE RESERVE

Country walk and nature trail

c/o Radnorshire Wildlife Trust, 1 Gwalia Annexe, Ithon Rd, Llandrindod Wells, Powys LD1 6AS
☎ Llandrindod Wells (0597) 823298

Bailey Einon is a mixed woodland set on the banks of the River Ithon with a full complement of woodbirds. ¾ mile nature trail leading to circular country walk. Iron Age fort and picnic area nearby.

Approx 2 miles east of Llandrindod Wells along unclassified road (Cefnllys Lane)
Open all year
Free admission
&. ⅋

▶ NEWTOWN ◀

GLASLYN RESERVE

Nature reserve

c/o Montgomeryshire Wildlife Trust, 8 Severn Square, Newtown, Powys SY16 2AG
☎ Newtown (0686) 24751

535 acres of heather moorland and mountains with red kite, peregrine, merlin, buzzard and many other birds of moorland and bog. A leaflet is available at the reserve.

Between Machynlleth and Llanidloes, car park signposted off the road with lakeside nature trail
Open all year
Free admission
⅋

LLANMEREWIG GLEBE

Wildlife reserve

c/o Montgomeryshire Wildlife Trust, 8 Severn Square, Newtown, Powys SY16 2AG
☎ Newtown (0686) 24751

An ancient hay meadow once owned by the church, it has been in traditional management for many years. It supports an important population of the now rare meadow saffron – an autumn flowering member of the lily family.

10 miles from Welshpool, 8½ miles from Newtown, Church Road off the A483
Open all year
Free admission
&. access across fields only, gate and stile ⅋

MONTGOMERYSHIRE WILDLIFE TRUST

Wildlife Trust office

8 Severn Square, Newtown, Powys SY16 2AG
☎ Newtown (0686) 24751

Manages several reserves, telephone for their details. The headquarters of this wildlife charity is in the heart of Newtown and Montgomeryshire.

At one end of Severn St, close to town centre
Open 9.00am–5.00pm Mon–Fri (except Bank Holidays)
Free admission
⅋

NETTESHEIM FISH FARM

Farm shop and trout fishery

Lake Mochdre, Newtown, Powys SY16 4JN
☎ Newtown (0686) 625623

Off the A489, 4 miles south of Newtown, or off the A483, signposted 'Country Lane' to Mochdre, approx 3 miles to farm
Open daily 10.00am–6.00pm, fishery until sunset
Admission to fishery: day ticket £14.00, half day £7.50; walkabouts and picnics 50p per adult
&. ⅋

POWYS

ROUNDTON HILL RESERVE

Nature reserve

c/o Montgomeryshire Wildlife Trust, 8 Severn Square,
Newtown, Powys SY16 2AG
☎ Newtown (0686) 24751

A 90 acre reserve of ancient grassland on an old volcano. There are 2 nature trails around the hill – one level and one steep. A leaflet is available at the reserve.

Near Churchstoke, car park signposted from the A489
Open all year
Free admission
🏇

ZEST FOODS

Speciality food producer

No 4 St Giles Technology Park, Pool Road, Newtown,
Powys SY16 3AZ
☎ Newtown (0686) 622058

Zest Foods is a 5 year old company specializing in herb sauces – using the latest processing equipment. Zest's Pesto Basil Sauce is sold in Fortnum & Mason and all over the Uk in delis and wholefood shops.

Please telephone for directions
Open times, please telephone for details
Admission charges, please telephone for details
♿ ✗

► RHAYADER ◄

ELAN VALLEY VISITOR CENTRE

Interpretation centre covering the Elan Valley dams and estate

Elan Valley, Rhayader, Powys LD5 5HP
☎ Rhayader (0597) 810880/810898

The centre houses an exhibition of local history and wildlife, an audio-visual programme, cafe and information office from which to explore the magnificent 70 square miles of the Elan Estate.

3 miles west of Rhayader, off the B4518
Open Easter–Oct daily 10.00am–6.00pm
Free admission, but visitors are asked to contribute 50p per car (£2 per coach) towards cost of all visitors facilities
♿ 🚌 🏇

GIGRIN FARM & NATURE TRAIL

Farm trail, farm visit, fishing and bird watching

Rhayader, Powys LD6 5BL
☎ Rhayader (0597) 810243

Approx 2 mile trail amongst farm animals, with superb views. Conservation area comprising bird reserve, wild flowers, labelled trees, duck, fish and frog ponds. Play and picnic site and indoor straw jump.

½ mile south of Rhayader, off the A470
Open Easter–Oct daily 10.00am–5.00pm, other times by appointment
Admission: adult £1.00, child 50p
♿ 🚌 advance notice required 🏇

THE WELSH SHEEPTACULAR

Farm interpretation centre

Elan Valley Visitor Centre, Elan Valley, Rhayader, Powys

Unique opportunity to see 20 different sheep breeds of Wales live on stage. Sheep shearing, wool spinning and a sheepdog display.

Signposted from Builth Wells
Open May–Sept daily, shows 1.00pm, 2.30pm and 4.00pm
Admission: adult £1.50, child £1.00, families £4.00
♿ 🚌 🏇

► WELSHPOOL ◄

SEVERN FARM POND

Urban educational reserve

c/o Montgomeryshire Wildlife Trust, 8 Severn Square,
Newtown, Powys SY16 2AG
☎ Newtown (0686) 24751

A small pool and wetland created as a borrow pit when the nearby railway was constructed 100 years ago. The pool has been rejuvenated in the last few years. Many water and marsh birds can be seen including ruddy duck, reed bunting and mute swan.

Between Severn Farm Industrial Estate and railway
Open daily including weekends & Bank Holidays
Free admission
♿ there is a specially adapted bird hide and wide paths, but no toilet facilities
🚌 advance notice required 🏇

▶ *YSTRADGYNLAIS* ◀

CRAIG-Y-NOS COUNTRY PARK

Country park

Pen-y-cae, Swansea Valley, Powys SA9 1GL
☎ Abercrave (0639) 730395

Over 40 acres of cool woodland, peaceful riverside walks and lush meadows. The Victorian Pavilion forms part of the 'pleasure grounds' of opera singer Adelina Patti.

Leave town by the A4067 northwards, country park is about 6 miles north, on east of road

Open all year 10.00am–dusk. All groups must be booked in advance

Free admission, parking 30p–£1.00 depending on length of stay, coaches £5.00

& toilet and wheelchair available ⚲

INDEX

T

Tea Rooms/Shop:
Meads Farm Golf Range and Family Activity Centre, Cornwall, 39; Treworgie Barton Trails, Cornwall, 40; Melbourne Hall, Derbys, 65; Moorhouse Farm Cream Teas, Devon, 71; Mangerton Mill, Dorset, 87; The Master Makers, Kent, 144; Sarre Windmill, Kent, 144; Cedar Farm Gallery, Lancs, 157; Halsted House Farm Shop and Tea Room, Leics, 161; Jack O'Lantern, Lincs, 165; Waterperry Gardens, Oxon, 201; Staffordshire Peak Arts Centre, Staffs, 223; Essington Fruit Farm, Staffs, 223; Craft at the Suffolk Barn, Suffolk, 226; Corn Craft, Suffolk, 228; Somerleyton Hall, Suffolk, 230; Heaven Farm Country Tours, Sussex, 247; Abbots Harbor, Yorks, 289; Castle Espie Centre, NI, 299; Arbigland Estate, Scottish Lowlands, 307; Pili Palas – Butterfly Palace, Gwynedd, 359.

V

Vineyard:
Westbury Vineyard, Winery and Fishery, Berks, 12; The Thames Valley Vineyard, Berks, 13; Chilford Hundred Vineyard, Cambs, 21; Polmassick Vineyard, Cornwall, 45; Whitmoor House Vineyard, Devon, 73; Chudleigh Vineyard (Organic), Devon, 74; Manstree Vineyard, Devon, 74; Loddiswell Vineyard and Winery, Devon, 77; Highfield Vineyards, Devon, 83; New Hall Vineyards, Essex, 103; St Annes Vineyard, Glos, 115; Lymington Vineyard, Hants, 125; The Mean Valley Vineyard, Hants, 128; Frithsden, Herts, 136; Biddenden Vineyards, Kent, 143; Elham Valley Vineyards, Kent, 143; Staple Vineyards, Kent, 144; St Nicholas of Ash Vineyard and Winery, Kent, 144; Three Corners Vineyard, Kent, 145; Chiddingstone Vineyards Ltd, Kent, 146; Bearsted Vineyard, Kent, 147; Mt Ephraim Gardens, Kent, 147; Headcorn Vineyard and Flower Nursery, Kent, 148; Kent Garden Country Wines, Kent, 149; Syndale Valley Vineyards, Kent, 150; Harbourne Vineyard, Kent, 151; Penshurst Vineyard, Kent, 151; Elmham Park, Norfolk, 172; Pulham Vineyards Ltd, Norfolk, 173; W R B Foster and Partners, Norfolk, 175; Chiltern Valley Wines, Oxon, 199; Moorlynch Vineyard, Somerset, 208; Castle Cary Vineyard, Somerset, 209; Whatley Vineyard and Herb Garden, Somerset, 211; Avalon Vineyard, Somerset, 213; Pilton Manor Vineyard, Somerset, 213; Wootton Vineyard, Somerset, 214;

Brympton D'Evercy, Somerset, 216; Gifford's Hall, Suffolk, 226; Cavendish Manor Vineyards, Suffolk, 228; Bruisyard Vineyard and Winery, Herb and Water Gardens, Suffolk, 230; Boyton Vineyard, Suffolk, 231; Godstone Vineyards, Surrey, 238; Chilsdown Vineyard, Sussex, 243; Carr Taylor Vineyards, Sussex, 247; Flexerne Vineyard, Sussex, 251; Nutbourne Manor Vineyard, Sussex, 251; Sedlescombe Vineyard, Sussex, 252; Steyning Vineyard, Sussex, 253; Halfpenny Green Vineyards, W Midlands, 265; Elms Cross Vineyard, Wilts, 268; Fonthill Vineyard, Wilts, 271; Astley Vineyards, Worcs, 277; Barton Manor Vineyard and Gardens, Isle of Wight, 295; Adgestone Vineyards Ltd, Isle of Wight, 296; Morton Manor, Isle of Wight, 296.

Visitor Centre:
North Cornwall Heritage Coast Service, Cornwall, 40; Priests Mill, Cumbria, 52; Grizedale Forest Park, Cumbria, 54; Lake District National Park Visitor Centre, Cumbria, 61; High Peak Junction Workshops, Derbys, 65; Middleton Top Engine House and Visitor Centre, Derbys, 67; Thorndon Country Park, Essex, 103; Weald Country Park, Essex, 103; New Forest Museum and Visitor Centre, Hants, 126; Northumberland National Park Visitor Centre, Northumberland, 185; Kielder Castle Visitor Centre, Northumberland, 187; Northumberland National Park Visitor Centre, Ingram, Northumberland, 188; Lake Vyrnwy, Shrops, 203; Willow and Wetlands Visitor Centre, Somerset, 214; The Taunton Cider Mill and Morses Place, Somerset, 216; Lowestoft Fishing Industry, Suffolk, 230; Buchan Country Park, Sussex, 244; Beachy Head Countryside Centre, Sussex, 245; Hartshill Hayes Country Park, W Midlands, 266; Bracken Hall Countryside Centre, Yorks, 281; Dalby Forest Drive and Visitor Centre, Yorks, 286; Kelburn Country Centre, Scottish Lowlands, 311; Placerigg Country Park, C Highlands, 322; Aberaeron Visitors Centre, Dyfed, 338; Bwlch Nant Yr Arian Visitor Centre, Dyfed, 338; Bryn Bach Park, Gwent, 355.

W

Walks, Canal:
Macclesfield Canal, Cheshire, 27; North Cornwall Tourism Development Unit, Cornwall, 42; Grand Western Canal, Devon, 83.

SPORTING BREAKS

A guide to help you combine your favourite sport with a weekend break or short holiday for all the family

- 61 courses around Britain and Northern Ireland
- sports and leisure pursuits around the courses
- places to visit in each area
- location maps and a colour atlas

£9.95 from all major bookshops

GOLF

FAMILY LEISURE GUIDES

SPORTING BREAKS

A guide to help you combine your favourite sport with a weekend break for all the family

- over 130 golf courses
- sports and leisure pursuits around the courses
- places to visit in each area
- location maps and a colour atlas

£9.95 from all major bookshops

HORSE·RACING

FAMILY LEISURE GUIDES

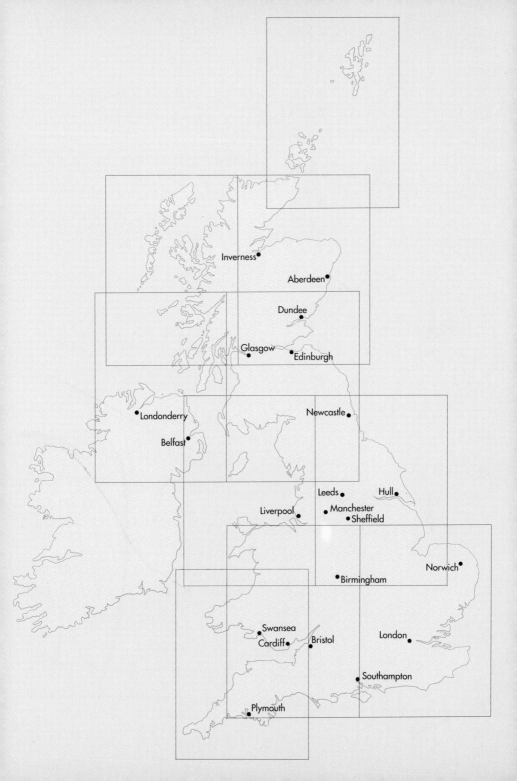

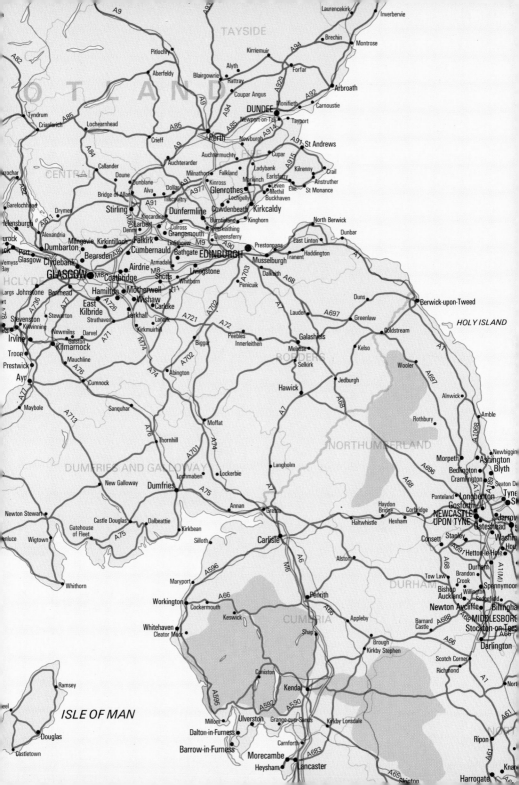

SHETLAND
ISLANDS

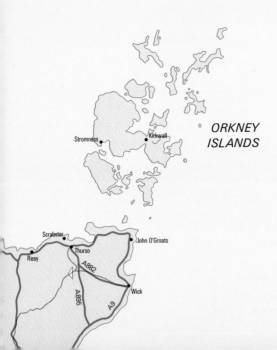

ORKNEY
ISLANDS